Nora Pulliam 1971

NOBEL PRIZE LIBRARY

———

CAMUS

CHURCHILL

Nobel Prize Library

PUBLISHED UNDER THE SPONSORSHIP OF THE
NOBEL FOUNDATION & THE SWEDISH ACADEMY

Albert Camus

Winston Churchill

ALEXIS GREGORY, *New York*, AND
CRM PUBLISHING, *Del Mar, California*

CONTENTS

Albert Camus

1957

"For his important literary production,
which with clearsighted earnestness
illuminates the problems of the human
conscience in our times"

Illustrated by **PHILIPPE FELLMER**

PRESENTATION ADDRESS

By ANDERS ÖSTERLING

PERMANENT SECRETARY
OF THE SWEDISH ACADEMY

FRENCH LITERATURE is no longer linked geographically to the frontiers of France in Europe. In many respects it reminds one of a garden plant, noble and irreplaceable, which when cultivated outside its territory still retains its distinctive character, although tradition and variation alternately influence it. The Nobel laureate for this year, Albert Camus, is an example of this evolution. Born in a small town in eastern Algeria, he has returned to this North African milieu to find the source of all the determining influences that have marked his childhood and youth. Even today the man Camus is aware of this great French overseas territory, and the writer in him is often pleased to recall this fact.

From a quasi-proletarian origin, Camus found it necessary to get ahead in life on his own; a poverty-stricken student, he worked at all sorts of jobs to meet his needs. It was an arduous schooling, but one which in the diversity of its teaching was certainly not useless to the realist he was to become. In the course of his years of study, which he spent at the University of Algiers, he belonged to a circle of intellectuals who later came to play an important role in the North African Resistance. His first books were published by a local publishing house in Algiers, but at the age of twenty-five he reached France as a journalist and soon came to make his reputation in the metropolis as a writer of the first rank, prematurely tempered by the harsh, feverish atmosphere of the war years.

Even in his first writings Camus reveals a spiritual attitude that was born of the sharp contradictions within him between the awareness of earthly life and the gripping consciousness of the reality of death. This is more than the typical Mediterranean fatalism whose origin is the certainty

[3]

that the sunny splendor of the world is only a fugitive moment bound to be blotted out by the shades. Camus represents also the philosophical movement called Existentialism, which characterizes man's situation in the universe by denying it all personal significance, seeing in it only absurdity. The term "absurd" occurs often in Camus' writings, so that one may call it a *leitmotif* in his work, developed in all its logical moral consequences on the levels of freedom, responsibility, and the anguish that derives from it.

The Greek myth of Sisyphus, who eternally rolls his rock to the mountain top from which it perpetually rolls down again, becomes in one of Camus' essays a laconic symbol of human life. But Sisyphus, as Camus interprets him, is happy in the depth of his soul, for the attempt alone satisfies him. For Camus, the essential thing is no longer to know whether life is worth living but *how* one must live it, with the share of sufferings it entails.

This short presentation does not permit me to dwell longer on Camus' always fascinating intellectual development. It is more worthwhile to refer to the works in which, using an art with complete classical purity of style and intense concentration, he has embodied these problems in such fashion that characters and action make his ideas live before us, without commentary by the author. This is what makes *L'Étranger* [*The Stranger*] (1942) famous. The main character, an employee of a government department, kills an Arab following a chain of absurd events; then, indifferent to his fate, he hears himself condemned to death. At the last moment, however, he pulls himself together and emerges from a passivity bordering on torpor. In *La Peste* [*The Plague*] (1947), a symbolic novel of greater scope, the main characters are Doctor Rieux and his assistant, who heroically combat the plague that has descended on a North African town. In its calm and exact objectivity, this convincingly realistic narrative reflects experiences of life during the Resistance, and Camus extols the revolt which the conquering evil arouses in the heart of the intensely resigned and disillusioned man.

Quite recently Camus has given us the very remarkable story-monologue, *La Chute* [*The Fall*] (1956), a work exhibiting the same mastery of the art of storytelling. A French lawyer, who examines his conscience in a sailors' bar in Amsterdam, draws his own portrait, a mirror in which his contemporaries can equally recognize themselves. In these pages one can see Tartuffe shake hands with the Misanthrope in the name of that science of the human heart in which classical France excelled. The mordant irony, employed by an aggressive author obsessed with truth, becomes a weapon against universal hypocrisy. One may wonder, of course, where Camus is heading by his insistence on a Kierkegaardian sense of guilt whose bottomless abyss is omnipresent, for one always has the feeling that the author has reached a turning point in his development.

Personally Camus has moved far beyond nihilism. His serious, austere meditations on the duty of restoring without respite that which has been ravaged, and of making justice possible in an unjust world, rather make him a humanist who has not forgotten the worship of Greek proportion and beauty as they were once revealed to him in the dazzling summer light on the Mediterranean shore at Tipasa.

Active and highly creative, Camus is in the center of interest in the literary world, even outside of France. Inspired by an authentic moral engagement, he devotes himself with all his being to the great fundamental questions of life, and certainly this aspiration corresponds to the idealistic end for which the Nobel Prize was established. Behind his incessant affirmation of the absurdity of the human condition is no sterile negativism. This view of things is supplemented in him by a powerful imperative, a "nevertheless," an appeal to the will which incites to revolt against absurdity and which, for that reason, creates a value.

ACCEPTANCE SPEECH

By ALBERT CAMUS

In RECEIVING THE DISTINCTION with which your free Academy has so generously honored me, my gratitude has been profound, particularly when I consider the extent to which this recompense has surpassed my personal merits. Every man, and for stronger reasons, every artist, wants to be recognized. So do I. But I have not been able to learn of your decision without comparing its repercussions to what I really am. A man almost young, rich only in his doubts and with his work still in progress, accustomed to living in the solitude of work or in the retreats of friendship: how would he not feel a kind of panic at hearing the decree that transports him all of a sudden, alone and reduced to himself, to the center of a glaring light? And with what feelings could he accept this honor at a time when other writers in Europe, among them the very greatest, are condemned to silence, and even at a time when the country of his birth is going through unending misery?

I felt that shock and inner turmoil. In order to regain peace I have had, in short, to come to terms with a too generous fortune. And since I cannot live up to it by merely resting on my achievement, I have found nothing to support me but what has supported me through all my life, even in the most contrary circumstances: the idea that I have of my art and of the role of the writer. Let me only tell you, in a spirit of gratitude and friendship, as simply as I can, what this idea is.

For myself, I cannot live without my art. But I have never placed it above everything. If, on the other hand, I need it, it is because it cannot be separated from my fellow men, and it allows me to live, such as I am, on one level with them. It is a means of stirring the greatest number of people by offering them a privileged picture of common joys and sufferings. It obliges the artist not to keep himself apart; it subjects him to the most humble and the most universal truth. And often he who has chosen the fate of the artist because he felt himself to be different soon realizes that he can maintain neither his art nor his difference unless he admits that he is like the others. The artist forges himself to the others, midway between the beauty he cannot do without and the community he cannot tear himself away from. That is why true artists scorn nothing: they are obliged to understand rather than to judge. And if they have to take sides in this world, they can perhaps side only with that society in which, according to Nietzsche's great words, not the judge but the creator will rule, whether he be a worker or an intellectual.

By the same token, the writer's role is not free from difficult duties. By definition he cannot put himself today in the service of those who make history; he is at the service of those who suffer it. Otherwise, he will be alone and deprived of his art. Not all the armies of tyranny with their millions of men will free him from his isolation, even and particularly if he falls into step with them. But the silence of an unknown prisoner, abandoned to humiliations at the other end of the world, is enough to draw the writer out of his exile, at least whenever, in the midst of the privileges of freedom, he manages not to forget that silence, and to transmit it in order to make it resound by means of his art.

None of us is great enough for such a task. But in all circumstances of life, in obscurity or temporary fame, cast in the irons of tyranny or for a time free to express himself, the writer can win the heart of a living community that will justify him, on the one condition that he will accept to the limit of his abilities the two tasks that constitute the greatness of his craft: the service of truth and the service of liberty. Because his task is to unite the greatest possible number of people, his art must not compromise with lies and servitude which, wherever they rule, breed solitude. Whatever our personal weaknesses may be, the nobility of our craft will always be rooted in two commitments, difficult to maintain: the refusal to lie about what one knows and the resistance to oppression.

For more than twenty years of an insane history, hopelessly lost like all the men of my generation in the convulsions of time, I have been supported by one thing: by the hidden feeling that to write today was an honor because this activity was a commitment—and a commitment not only to write. Specifically, in view of my powers and my state of being, it was a commitment to bear, together with all those who were living through the same history, the misery and the hope we shared. These men, who were born at the beginning of the First World War, who were twenty when Hitler came to power and the first revolutionary trials were beginning, who were then confronted as a completion of their education with the Spanish Civil War, the Second World War, the world of concentration camps, a Europe of torture and prisons—these men must today rear their sons and create their works in a world threatened by nuclear destruction. Nobody, I think, can ask them to be optimists. And I even think that we should understand—without ceasing to fight it—the error of those who in an excess of despair have asserted their right to dishonor and have rushed into the nihilism of the era. But the fact remains that most of us, in my country and in Europe, have refused this nihilism and have engaged upon a quest for legitimacy. They have had to forge for themselves an art of living in times of catastrophe in order to be born a second time and to fight openly against the instinct of death at work in our history.

Each generation doubtless feels called upon to reform the world. Mine knows that it will not reform it, but its task is perhaps even greater. It consists in preventing the world from destroying itself. Heir to a corrupt history, in which are mingled fallen revolutions, technology gone mad, dead gods, and worn-out ideologies, where mediocre powers can destroy all yet no longer know how to convince, where intelligence has debased itself to become the servent of hatred and oppression, this generation starting from its own negations has had to re-establish, both within and without, a little of that which constitutes the dignity of life and death. In a world threatened by disintegration, in which our grand inquisitors run the risk of establishing forever the kingdom of death, it knows that it should, in an insane race against the clock, restore among the nations a peace that is not servitude, reconcile anew labor and culture, and remake with all men the Ark of the Covenant. It is not certain that this generation will ever be able to accomplish this immense task, but already it is rising everywhere in the world to the double challenge of truth and liberty and, if necessary, knows how to die for it without hate. Wherever it is found, it deserves to be saluted and encouraged, particularly where it is sacrificing itself. In any event, certain of your complete approval, it is to this generation that I should like to pass on the honor that you have just given me.

At the same time, after having outlined the nobility of the writer's craft, I should have put him in his proper place. He has no other claims but those which he shares with his comrades in arms: vulnerable but obstinate, unjust but impassioned for justice, doing his work without shame or pride in view of everybody, not ceasing to be divided between sorrow and beauty, and devoted finally to drawing from his double existence the creations that he obstinately tries to erect in the destructive movement of history. Who after all this can expect from him complete solutions and high morals? Truth is mysterious, elusive, always to be conquered. Liberty is dangerous, as hard to live with as it is elating. We must march toward these two goals, painfully but resolutely, certain in advance of our failings on so long a road. What writer would from now on in good conscience dare set himself up as a preacher of virtue? For myself, I must state once more that I am not of this kind. I have never been able to renounce the light, the pleasure of being, and the freedom in which I grew up. But although this nostalgia explains many of my errors and my faults, it has doubtless helped me toward a better understanding of my craft. It is helping me still to support unquestioningly all those silent men who sustain the life made for them in the world only through memory of the return of brief and free happiness.

Thus reduced to what I really am, to my limits and debts as well as to my difficult creed, I feel freer, in concluding, to comment upon the extent and the generosity of the honor you have just bestowed upon me, freer also to tell you that I would receive it as an homage rendered to all those who, sharing in the same fight, have not received any privilege, but have on the contrary known misery and persecution. It remains for me to thank you from the bottom of my heart and to make before you publicly, as a personal sign of my gratitude, the same and ancient promise of faithfulness which every true artist repeats to himself in silence every day.

THE PLAGUE

By ALBERT CAMUS

It is as reasonable to represent one kind of imprisonment by another, as it is to represent anything that really exists by that which exists not.

DANIEL DEFOE

THE PLAGUE

By ALBERT CAMUS

Translated from the French by Stuart Gilbert

PART I

The unusual events described in this chronicle occurred in 194- at Oran. Everyone agreed that, considering their somewhat extraordinary character, they were out of place there. For its ordinariness is what strikes one first about the town of Oran, which is merely a large French port on the Algerian coast, headquarters of the Prefect of a French Department.

The town itself, let us admit, is ugly. It has a smug, placid air and you need time to discover what it is that makes it different from so many business centers in other parts of the world. How to conjure up a picture, for instance, of a town without pigeons, without any trees or gardens, where you never hear the beat of wings or the rustle of leaves—a thoroughly negative place, in short? The seasons are discriminated only in the sky. All that tells you of spring's coming is the feel of the air, or the baskets of flowers brought in from the suburbs by peddlers; it's a spring cried in the marketplaces. During the summer the sun bakes the houses bone-dry, sprinkles our walls with grayish dust, and you have no option but to survive those days of fire indoors, behind closed shutters. In autumn, on the other hand, we have deluges of mud. Only winter brings really pleasant weather.

Perhaps the easiest way of making a town's acquaintance is to ascertain how the people in it work, how they love, and how they die. In our little town (is this, one wonders, an effect of the climate?) all three are done on much the same lines, with the same feverish yet casual air. The truth is that everyone is bored, and devotes himself to cultivating habits. Our citizens work hard, but solely with the object of getting rich. Their chief interest is in commerce, and their chief aim in life is, as they call it, "doing business." Naturally they don't eschew such simpler pleasures as love-making, sea-bathing, going to the pictures. But, very sensibly, they reserve these pastimes for Saturday afternoons and Sundays and employ the rest of the week in making money, as much as possible. In the evening, on leaving the office, they forgather, at an hour that never varies, in the cafés, stroll the same boulevard, or take the air on their balconies. The passions of the young are violent and short-lived; the vices of older men seldom range beyond an addiction to bowling, to banquets and "socials," or clubs where large sums change hands on the fall of a card.

It will be said, no doubt, that these

[13]

habits are not peculiar to our town; really all our contemporaries are much the same. Certainly nothing is commoner nowadays than to see people working from morn till night and then proceeding to fritter away at card-tables, in cafés and in small-talk what time is left for living. Nevertheless there still exist towns and countries where people have now and then an inkling of something different. In general, it doesn't change their lives. Still, they have had an intimation, and that's so much to the good. Oran, however, seems to be a town without intimations; in other words, completely modern. Hence I see no need to dwell on the manner of loving in our town. The men and women consume one another rapidly in what is called "the act of love," or else settle down to a mild habit of conjugality. We seldom find a mean between these extremes. That, too, is not exceptional. At Oran, as elsewhere, for lack of time and thinking, people have to love one another without knowing much about it.

What is more exceptional in our town is the difficulty one may experience there in dying. "Difficulty," perhaps, is not the right word; "discomfort" would come nearer. Being ill is never agreeable, but there are towns that stand by you, so to speak, when you are sick; in which you can, after a fashion, let yourself go. An invalid needs small attentions, he likes to have something to rely on, and that's natural enough. But at Oran the violent extremes of temperature, the exigencies of business, the uninspiring surroundings, the sudden nightfalls, and the very nature of its pleasures call for good health. An invalid feels out of it there. Think what it must be for a dying man, trapped behind hundreds of walls all sizzling with heat, while the whole population, sitting in cafés or hanging on the telephone, is discussing shipments, bills of lading, discounts! It will then be obvious what discomfort attends death, even modern death, when it waylays you under such conditions in a dry place.

These somewhat haphazard observations may give a fair idea of what our town is like. However, we must not exaggerate. Really, all that was to be conveyed was the banality of the town's appearance and of life in it. But you can get through the days there without trouble, once you have formed habits. And since habits are precisely what our town encourages, all is for the best. Viewed from this angle, its life is not particularly exciting; that must be admitted. But, at least, social unrest is quite unknown among us. And our frank-spoken, amiable, and industrious citizens have always inspired a reasonable esteem in visitors. Treeless, glamourless, soulless, the town of Oran ends by seeming restful and, after a while, you go complacently to sleep there.

It is only fair to add that Oran is grafted on to a unique landscape, in the center of a bare plateau, ringed with luminous hills and above a perfectly shaped bay. All we may regret is the town's being so disposed that it turns its back on the bay, with the result that it's impossible to see the sea, you always have to go to look for it.

Such being the normal life of Oran, it will be easily understood that our fellow citizens had not the faintest reason to apprehend the incidents that took place in the spring of the year in question and were (as we subsequently realized) premonitory signs of the grave events we are to chronicle. To some, these events will seem quite natural; to others, all but incredible. But, obviously, a narrator cannot take account of these differences of outlook. His business is only to say: "This is what happened," when he knows that it actually did happen, that it closely affected the life of a whole populace, and that there are thousands of eyewitnesses who can appraise in their hearts the truth of what he writes.

In any case the narrator (whose identity will be made known in due course) would have little claim to competence for a task like this, had not chance put him in the way of gathering much information, and had he not been, by the force of things, closely involved in all that he proposes to narrate. This is his justification for playing the part of a historian. Naturally, a historian, even an amateur, always has data, personal or at second hand, to guide him. The present narrator has three kinds of data: first, what he saw himself; secondly, the accounts of other eyewitnesses (thanks to the part he played, he was enabled to learn their personal impressions from all those figuring in this chronicle); and, lastly, documents that subsequently came into his hands. He proposes to draw on these records whenever this seems desirable, and to employ them as he thinks best. He also proposes . . .

But perhaps the time has come to drop preliminaries and cautionary remarks and to launch into the narrative proper. The account of the first days needs giving in some detail.

When leaving his surgery on the morning of April 16, Dr. Bernard Rieux felt something soft under his foot. It was a dead rat lying in the middle of the landing. On the spur of the moment he kicked it to one side and, without giving it a further thought, continued on his way downstairs. Only when he was stepping out into the street did it occur to him that a dead rat had no business to be on his landing, and he turned back to ask the concierge of the building to see to its removal. It was not until he noticed old M. Michel's reaction to the news that he realized the peculiar nature of his discovery. Personally, he had thought the presence of the dead rat rather odd, no more than that; the concierge, however, was genuinely outraged. On one point he was categorical: "There weren't no rats here." In vain the doctor assured him that there *was* a rat, presumably dead, on the second-floor landing; M. Michel's conviction wasn't to be shaken. There "weren't no rats in the building," he repeated, so someone must have brought this one from outside. Some youngster trying to be funny, most likely.

That evening, when Dr. Rieux was standing in the entrance, feeling for the latch-key in his pocket before starting up the stairs to his apartment, he saw a big rat coming toward him from the dark end of the passage. It moved uncertainly, and its fur was sopping wet. The animal stopped and seemed to be trying to get its balance, moved forward again toward the doctor, halted again, then spun round on itself with a little squeal and fell on its side. Its mouth was slightly open and blood was spurting from it. After gazing at it for a moment, the doctor went upstairs.

He wasn't thinking about the rat. That glimpse of spurting blood had switched his thoughts back to something that had been on his mind all day. His wife, who had been ill for a year now, was due to leave next day for a sanatorium in the mountains. He found her lying down in the bedroom, resting, as he had asked her to do, in view of the exhausting journey before her. She gave him a smile.

"Do you know, I'm feeling ever so much better!" she said.

The doctor gazed down at the face that turned toward him in the glow of the bedside lamp. His wife was thirty, and the long illness had left its mark on her face. Yet the thought that came to Rieux's mind as he gazed at her was: "How young she looks, almost like a little girl!" But perhaps that was because of the smile, which effaced all else.

"Now try to sleep," he counseled. "The nurse is coming at eleven, you know, and you have to catch the midday train."

He kissed the slightly moist forehead. The smile escorted him to the door.

Next day, April 17, at eight o'clock the concierge buttonholed the doctor as he was going out. Some young scallywags, he said, had dumped three dead rats in the hall. They'd obviously been caught in traps with very strong springs, as they were bleeding profusely. The concierge had lingered in the doorway for quite a while, holding the rats by their legs and keeping a sharp eye on the passers-by, on the off chance that the miscreants would give themselves away by grinning or by some facetious remark. His watch had been in vain.

"But I'll nab 'em all right," said M. Michel hopefully.

Much puzzled, Rieux decided to begin his round in the outskirts of the town, where his poorer patients lived. The scavenging in these districts was done late in the morning and, as he drove his car along the straight, dusty streets, he cast glances at the garbage cans aligned along the edge of the sidewalk. In one street alone the doctor counted as many as a dozen rats deposited on the vegetable and other refuse in the cans.

He found his first patient, an asthma case of long standing, in bed, in a room that served as both dining-room and bedroom and overlooked the street. The invalid was an old Spaniard with a hard, rugged face. Placed on the coverlet in front of him were two pots containing dried peas. When the doctor entered, the old man was sitting up, bending his neck back, gasping and wheezing in his efforts to recover his breath. His wife brought a bowl of water.

"Well, doctor," he said, while the in-

jection was being made, "they're coming out, have you noticed?"

"The rats, he means," his wife explained. "The man next door found three."

"They're coming out, you can see them in all the trash cans. It's hunger!"

Rieux soon discovered that the rats were the great topic of conversation in that part of the town. After his round of visits he drove home.

"There's a telegram for you, sir, upstairs," M. Michel informed him.

The doctor asked him if he'd seen any more rats.

"No," the concierge replied, "there ain't been any more. I'm keeping a sharp lookout, you know. Those youngsters wouldn't dare when I'm around."

The telegram informed Rieux that his mother would be arriving next day. She was going to keep house for her son during his wife's absence. When the doctor entered his apartment he found the nurse already there. He looked at his wife. She was in a tailor-made suit, and he noticed that she had used rouge. He smiled to her.

"That's splendid," he said. "You're looking very nice."

A few minutes later he was seeing her into the sleeping-car. She glanced round the compartment.

"It's too expensive for us really, isn't it?"

"It had to be done," Rieux replied.

"What's this story about rats that's going round?"

"I can't explain it. It certainly is queer, but it'll pass."

Then hurriedly he begged her to forgive him; he felt he should have looked after her better, he'd been most remiss. When she shook her head, as if to make him stop, he added: "Anyhow, once you're back everything will be better. We'll make a fresh start."

"That's it!" Her eyes were sparkling. "Let's make a fresh start."

But then she turned her head and seemed to be gazing through the car window at the people on the platform, jostling one another in their haste. The hissing of the locomotive reached their ears. Gently he called his wife's first name; when she looked round he saw her face wet with tears.

"Don't," he murmured.

Behind the tears the smile returned, a little tense. She drew a deep breath.

"Now off you go! Everything will be all right."

He took her in his arms, then stepped back on the platform. Now he could only see her smile through the window.

"Please, dear," he said, "take great care of yourself."

But she could not hear him.

As he was leaving the platform, near the exit he met M. Othon, the police magistrate, holding his small boy by the hand. The doctor asked him if he was going away.

Tall and dark, M. Othon had something of the air of what used to be called a man of the world, and something of an undertaker's assistant.

"No," the magistrate replied, "I've come to meet Madame Othon, who's been to present her respects to my family."

The engine whistled.

"These rats, now—" the magistrate began.

Rieux made a brief movement in the direction of the train, then turned back toward the exit.

"The rats?" he said. "It's nothing."

The only impression of that moment which, afterwards, he could recall was the passing of a railroadman with a box full of dead rats under his arm.

Early in the afternoon of that day, when his consultations were beginning, a young man called on Rieux. The doctor gathered that he had called before, in the morning, and was a journalist by profession. His name was Raymond Rambert. Short, square-shouldered, with a determined-looking face and keen, intelligent eyes, he gave the impression of someone who could keep his end up in any circumstances. He wore a sports type of clothes. He came straight to the point. His newspaper, one of the leading Paris dailies, had commissioned him to make a report on the living-conditions prevailing among the Arab population, and especially on the sanitary conditions.

Rieux replied that these conditions were not good. But, before he said any more, he wanted to know if the journalist would be allowed to tell the truth.

"Certainly," Rambert replied.

"I mean," Rieux explained, "would you be allowed to publish an unqualified condemnation of the present state of things?"

"Unqualified? Well, no, I couldn't go that far. But surely things aren't quite so bad as that?"

"No," Rieux said quietly, they weren't so bad as that. He had put the question solely to find out if Rambert could or couldn't state the facts without paltering with the truth. "I've no use for statements in which something is kept back," he added. "That is why I shall not furnish information in support of yours."

The journalist smiled. "You talk the language of Saint-Just."

Without raising his voice Rieux said he knew nothing about that. The language he used was that of a man who was sick and tired of the world he lived in— though he had much liking for his fellow men—and had resolved, for his part, to have no truck with injustice and compromises with the truth.

His shoulders hunched, Rambert gazed at the doctor for some moments without speaking. Then, "I think I understand you," he said, getting up from his chair.

The doctor accompanied him to the door.

"It's good of you to take it like that," he said.

"Yes, yes, I understand," Rambert repeated, with what seemed a hint of impatience in his voice. "Sorry to have troubled you."

When shaking hands with him, Rieux suggested that if he was out for curious stories for his paper, he might say something about the extraordinary number of dead rats that were being found in the town just now.

"Ah!" Rambert exclaimed. "That certainly interests me."

On his way out at five for another round of visits, the doctor passed on the stairway a stocky, youngish man, with a big, deeply furrowed face and bushy eyebrows. He had met him once or twice in the top-floor apartment, which was occupied by some male Spanish dancers. Puffing a cigarette, Jean Tarrou was gazing down at the convulsions of a rat dying on the step in front of him. He looked up, and his gray eyes remained fixed on the doctor for some moments; then, after wishing him good day, he remarked that it was rather odd, the way all these rats were coming out of their holes to die.

"Very odd," Rieux agreed, "and it ends by getting on one's nerves."

"In a way, doctor, only in a way. We've not seen anything of the sort before, that's all. Personally I find it interesting, yes, definitely interesting."

Tarrou ran his fingers through his hair to brush it off his forehead, looked again at the rat, which had now stopped moving, then smiled toward Rieux.

"But really, doctor, it's the concierge's headache, isn't it?"

As it so happened, the concierge was the next person Rieux encountered. He was leaning against the wall beside the street door; he was looking tired and his normally rubicund face had lost its color.

"Yes, I know," the old man told Rieux, who had informed him of the latest casualty among the rats. "I keep finding 'em by twos and threes. But it's the same thing in the other houses in the street."

He seemed depressed and worried, and was scratching his neck absentmindedly. Rieux asked him how he felt. The concierge wouldn't go so far as to say he was feeling ill. Still he wasn't quite up to the mark. In his opinion it was just due to worry; these damned rats had given him "a shock, like." It would be a relief when they stopped coming out and dying all over the place.

Next morning—it was April 18—when the doctor was bringing back his mother from the station, he found M. Michel looking still more out of sorts. The stairway from the cellar to the attics was strewn with dead rats, ten or a dozen of them. The garbage cans of all the houses in the street were full of rats.

The doctor's mother took it quite calmly.

"It's like that sometimes," she said vaguely. She was a small woman with silver hair and dark, gentle eyes. "I'm so glad to be with you again, Bernard," she added. "The rats can't change *that*, anyhow."

He nodded. It was a fact that everything seemed easy when she was there.

However, he rang up the Municipal Office. He knew the man in charge of the department concerned with the extermination of vermin and he asked him if he'd heard about all the rats that were coming out to die in the open. Yes, Mercier knew all about it; in fact, fifty rats had been found in his offices, which were near the wharves. To tell the truth, he was rather perturbed; did the doctor think it meant anything serious? Rieux couldn't give a definite opinion, but he thought the sanitary service should take action of some kind.

Mercier agreed. "And, if you think it's really worth the trouble, I'll get an order issued as well."

"It certainly is worth the trouble," Rieux replied.

His charwoman had just told him that several hundred dead rats had been collected in the big facotry where her husband worked.

It was about this time that our townsfolk began to show signs of uneasiness. For, from April 18 onwards, quantities of dead or dying rats were found in factories and warehouses. In some cases the animals were killed to put an end to their agony. From the outer suburbs to the center of the town, in all the byways where the doctor's duties took him, in every thoroughfare, rats were piled up in garbage cans or lying in long lines in the gutters. The evening papers that day took up the matter and inquired whether or not the city fathers were going to take steps, and what emergency measures were contemplated, to abate this particularly disgusting nuisance. Actually the municipality had not contemplated doing anything at all, but now a meeting was convened to discuss the situation. An order was transmitted to the sanitary service to collect the dead rats at daybreak every morning. When the rats had been collected, two municipal trucks were to take them to be burned in the town incinerator.

But the situation worsened in the following days. There were more and more dead vermin in the streets, and the collectors had bigger truckloads every morning. On the fourth day the rats began to come out and die in batches. From basements, cellars, and sewers they emerged in long wavering files into the light of day, swayed helplessly, then did a sort of pirouette and fell dead at the feet of the horrified onlookers. At night, in passages and alleys, their shrill little death-cries could be clearly heard. In the mornings the bodies were found lining the gutters, each with a gout of blood, like a red flower, on its tapering muzzle; some were bloated and already beginning to rot, others rigid, with their whiskers still erect. Even in the busy heart of the town you found them piled in little heaps on landings and in backyards. Some stole forth to die singly in the halls of public offices, in school playgrounds, and even on café terraces. Our townsfolk were amazed to find such busy centers as the Place d'Armes, the boulevards, and the promenade along the waterfront, dotted with repulsive little corpses. After the daily clean-up of the town, which took place at sunrise, there was a brief respite; then gradually the rats began to appear again in numbers that went on increasing throughout the day. People out at night would often feel underfoot the squelchy roundness of a still warm body. It was as if the earth on which our houses stood were being purged of its secreted humors; thrusting up to the surface the abscesses and pus-clots that had been forming in its entrails. You must picture the consternation of our little town, hitherto so tranquil, and now, out of the blue, shaken to its core, like a quite healthy man who all of a sudden feels his temperature shoot up and the blood seething like wildfire in his veins.

Things went so far that the Ransdoc Information Bureau (inquiries on all subjects promptly and accurately answered), which ran a free-information talk on the radio, by way of publicity, began its talk by announcing that no less than 6,231 rats had been collected and burned in a single day, April 25. Giving as it did an ampler and more precise view of the scene daily enacted before our eyes, this amazing figure administered a jolt to the public nerves. Hitherto people had merely grumbled at a stupid, rather obnoxious visitation; they now realized that this strange phenomenon, whose scope could not be measured and whose origins escaped detection, had something vaguely menacing about it. Only the old Spaniard whom Dr. Rieux was treating for asthma went on rubbing his hands and chuckling: "They're coming out, they're coming out," with senile glee.

On April 28, when the Ransdoc Bureau announced that 8,000 rats had been collected, a wave of something like panic swept the town. There was a demand for drastic measures, the authorities were accused of slackness, and people who had houses on the coast spoke of moving there, early in the year though it was. But next day the bureau informed them that the phenomenon had abruptly ended and the sanitary service had collected only a trifling number of rats. Everyone breathed more freely.

It was, however, on this same day, at noon, that Dr. Rieux, when parking his car in front of the apartment house where he lived, noticed the concierge coming toward him from the end of the street. He was dragging himself along, his head bent, arms and legs curiously splayed out, with the jerky movements of a clockwork doll. The old man was leaning on the arm of a priest whom the doctor knew. It was Father Paneloux, a learned and militant Jesuit, whom he had met occasionally and who was very highly thought of in our town, even in circles quite indifferent to religion. Rieux waited for the two men to draw up to him. M. Michel's eyes were fever-bright and he was breathing wheezily. The old man explained that, feeling "a bit off color," he had gone out to take the air. But he had started feeling pains in all

sorts of places—in his neck, armpits, and groin—and had been obliged to turn back and ask Father Paneloux to give him an arm.

"It's just swellings," he said. "I must have strained myself somehow."

Leaning out of the window of the car, the doctor ran his hand over the base of Michel's neck; a hard lump, like a knot in wood, had formed there.

"Go to bed at once, and take your temperature. I'll come to see you this afternoon."

When the old man had gone, Rieux asked Father Paneloux what he made of this queer business about the rats.

"Oh, I suppose it's an epidemic they've been having." The Father's eyes were smiling behind his big round glasses.

After lunch, while Rieux was reading for the second time the telegram his wife had sent him from the sanatorium, announcing her arrival, the phone rang. It was one of his former patients, a clerk in the Municipal Office, ringing him up. He had suffered for a long time from a constriction of the aorta, and, as he was poor, Rieux had charged no fee.

"Thanks, doctor, for remembering me. But this time it's somebody else. The man next door has had an accident. Please come at once." He sounded out of breath.

Rieux thought quickly; yes, he could see the concierge afterwards. A few minutes later he was entering a small house in the rue Faidherbe, on the outskirts of the town. Halfway up the drafty, foul-smelling stairs, he saw Joseph Grand, the clerk, hurrying down to meet him. He was a man of about fifty years of age, tall and drooping, with narrow shoulders, thin limbs, and a yellowish mustache.

"He looks better now," he told Rieux, "but I really thought his number was up." He blew his nose vigorously.

On the top floor, the third, Rieux noticed something scrawled in red chalk on a door on the left: *Come in, I've hanged myself.*

They entered the room. A rope dangled from a hanging lamp above a chair lying on its side. The dining-room table had been pushed into a corner. But the rope hung empty.

"I got him down just in time." Grand seemed always to have trouble in finding his words, though he expressed himself in the simplest possible way. "I was going out and I heard a noise. When I saw that writing on the door, I thought it was a— a prank. Only, then I heard a funny sort of groan; it made my blood run cold, as they say." He scratched his head. "That must be a painful way of—of doing it, I should think. Naturally I went in."

Grand had opened a door and they were standing on the threshold of a bright but scantily furnished bedroom. There was a brass bedstead against one of the walls, and a plump little man was lying there, breathing heavily. He gazed at them with bloodshot eyes. Rieux stopped short. In the intervals of the man's breathing he seemed to hear the little squeals of rats. But he couldn't see anything moving in the corners of the room. Then he went to the bedside. Evidently the man had not fallen from a sufficient height, or very suddenly, for the collar-bone had held. Naturally there was some asphyxia. An X-ray photograph would be needed. Meanwhile the doctor gave him a camphor injection and assured him he would be all right in a few days.

"Thanks, doctor," the man mumbled.

When Rieux asked Grand if he had notified the police, he hung his head.

"Well, as a matter of fact, I haven't. The first thing, I thought, was to—"

"Quite so," Rieux cut in. "I'll see to it."

But the invalid made a fretful gesture and sat up in bed. He felt much better, he explained; really it wasn't worth the trouble.

"Don't feel alarmed," Rieux said. "It's little more than a formality. Anyhow, I have to report this to the police."

"Oh!" The man slumped back on the bed and started sobbing weakly.

Grand, who had been twiddling his mustache while they were speaking, went up to the bed.

"Come, Monsieur Cottard," he said. "Try to understand. People could say the doctor was to blame, if you took it into your head to have another shot at it."

Cottard assured him tearfully that there wasn't the least risk of that; he'd had a sort of crazy fit, but it had passed and all he wanted now was to be left in peace. Rieux was writing a prescription.

"Very well," he said. "We'll say no more about it for the present. I'll come and see you again in a day or two. But don't do anything silly."

On the landing he told Grand that he was obliged to make a report, but would ask the police inspector to hold up the inquiry for a couple of days.

"But somebody should watch Cottard tonight," he added. "Has he any relations?"

"Not that I know of. But I can very well stay with him. I can't say I really know him, but one's got to help a neighbor, hasn't one?"

As he walked down the stairs Rieux caught himself glancing into the darker corners, and he asked Grand if the rats had quite disappeared in his part of the town.

Grand had no idea. True, he'd heard some talk about rats, but he never paid much attention to gossip like that. "I've other things to think about," he added.

Rieux, who was in a hurry to get away, was already shaking his hand. There was a letter to write to his wife, and he wanted to see the concierge first.

News-vendors were shouting the latest news—that the rats had disappeared. But Rieux found his patient leaning over the edge of the bed, one hand pressed to his belly and the other to his neck, vomiting pinkish bile into a slop-pail. After retching for some moments, the man lay back again, gasping. His temperature was 103, the ganglia of his neck and limbs were swollen, and two black patches were developing on his thighs. He now complained of internal pains.

"It's like fire," he whimpered. "The bastard's burning me inside."

He could hardly get the words through his fever-crusted lips and he gazed at the doctor with bulging eyes that his headache had suffused with tears. His wife cast an anxious look at Rieux, who said nothing.

"Please, doctor," she said, "what is it?"

"It might be—almost anything. There's nothing definite as yet. Keep him on a light diet and give him plenty to drink."

The sick man had been complaining of a raging thirst.

On returning to his apartment Rieux rang up his colleague Richard, one of the leading practitioners in the town.

"No," Richard said, "I can't say I've noticed anything exceptional."

"No cases of fever with local inflammation?"

"Wait a bit! I have two cases with inflamed ganglia."

"Abnormally so?"

"Well," Richard said, "that depends on what you mean by 'normal.'"

Anyhow, that night the porter was running a temperature of 104 and in delirium, always babbling about "them rats." Rieux tried a fixation abscess. When he felt the sting of the turpentine, the old man yelled: "The bastards!"

The ganglia had become still larger and felt like lumps of solid fibrous matter embedded in the flesh. Mme Michel had completely broken down.

"Sit up with him," the doctor said, "and call me if necessary."

Next day, April 30, the sky was blue and slightly misty. A warm, gentle breeze was blowing, bringing with it a smell of flowers from the outlying suburbs. The morning noises of the streets sounded louder, gayer than usual. For everyone in our little town this day brought the promise of a new lease of life, now that the shadow of fear under which they had been living for a week had lifted. Rieux, too, was in an optimistic mood when he went down to see the concierge; he had been cheered up by a letter from his wife that had come with the first mail.

Old M. Michel's temperature had gone down to 99 and, though he still looked very weak, he was smiling.

"He's better, doctor, isn't he?" his wife inquired.

"Well, it's a bit too early to say."

At noon the sick man's temperature shot up abruptly to 104, he was in constant delirium and had started vomiting again. The ganglia in the neck were painful to the touch, and the old man seemed to be straining to hold his head as far as possible from his body. His wife sat at the foot of the bed, her hands on the counterpane, gently clasping his feet. She gazed at Rieux imploringly.

"Listen," he said, "we'll have to move him to a hospital and try a special treatment. I'll ring up for the ambulance."

Two hours later the doctor and Mme Michel were in the ambulance bending over the sick man. Rambling words were issuing from the gaping mouth, thickly coated now with sores. He kept on repeating: "Them rats! Them damned rats!" His face had gone livid, a grayish green, his lips were bloodless, his breath came in sudden gasps. His limbs spread out by the ganglia, embedded in the berth as if he were trying to bury himself in it or a voice from the depths of the earth were summoning him below, the unhappy man seemed to be stifling under some unseen pressure. His wife was sobbing.

"Isn't there any hope left, doctor?"

"He's dead," said Rieux.

Michel's death marked, one might say, the end of the first period, that of bewildering portents, and the beginning of another, relatively more trying, in which the perplexity of the early days gradually gave place to panic. Reviewing that first phase in the light of subsequent events, our townsfolk realized that they had never dreamed it possible that our little town should be chosen out for the scene of such grotesque happenings as the wholesale death of rats in broad daylight or the decease of concierges through exotic maladies. In this respect they were wrong, and their views obviously called for revision. Still, if things had gone thus far and no farther, force of habit would doubtless have gained the day, as usual. But other members of our community, not all menials or poor people, were to follow the path down which M. Michel had led the way. And it was then that fear, and with fear serious reflection, began.

However, before entering on a detailed account of the next phase, the narrator proposes to give the opinion of another witness on the period that has been described. Jean Tarrou, whose acquaintance we have already made at the beginning of this narrative, had come to Oran some weeks before and was staying in a big hotel in the center of the town. Apparently he had private means and was not engaged in business. But though he gradually became a familiar figure in our midst, no one knew where he hailed from or what had brought him to Oran. He was often to be seen in public and at the beginning of spring was seen on one or other of the beaches almost every day; obviously he was fond of swimming. Good-humored, always ready with a smile, he seemed an addict of all normal pleasures without being their slave. In fact, the only habit he was known to have was that of cultivating the society of the Spanish dancers and musicians who abound in our town.

His notebooks comprise a sort of chronicle of those strange early days we all lived through. But an unusual type of chronicle, since the writer seems to make a point of understatement, and at first sight we might almost imagine that Tarrou had a habit of observing events and people through the wrong end of a telescope. In those chaotic times he set himself to recording the history of what the normal historian passes over. Obviously we may deplore this curious kink in his character and suspect in him a lack of proper feeling. All the same, it is undeniable that these notebooks, which form a sort of discursive diary, supply the chronicler of the period with a host of seemingly-trivial details which yet have their importance, and whose very oddity should be enough to prevent the reader from passing hasty judgment on this singular man.

The earliest entries made by Jean Tarrou synchronize with his coming to Oran. From the outset they reveal a paradoxical satisfaction at the discovery of a town so intrinsically ugly. We find in them a minute description of the two bronze lions adorning the Municipal Office, and appropriate comments on the lack of trees, the hideousness of the houses, and the absurd lay-out of the town. Tarrou sprinkles his descriptions with bits of conversation overheard in streetcars and in the streets, never adding a comment on them except—this comes somewhat later—in the report of a dialogue concerning a man named Camps. It was a chat between two streetcar conductors.

"You knew Camps, didn't you?" asked one of them.

"Camps? A tall chap with a black mustache?"

"That's him. A switchman."

"Ah yes, I remember now."

"Well, he's dead."

"Oh? When did he die?"

"After that business about the rats."

"You don't say so! What did he die of?"

"I couldn't say exactly. Some kind of fever. Of course, he never was what you might call fit. He got abscesses under the arms, and they did him in, it seems."

"Still, he didn't look that different from other people."

"I wouldn't say that. He had a weak chest and he used to play the trombone in the town band. It's hard on the lungs, blowing a trombone."

"Ah, if you've got weak lungs, it don't do you any good, blowing down a big instrument like that."

After jotting down this dialogue Tarrou went on to speculate why Camps had joined a band when it was so clearly inadvisable, and what obscure motive had led him to risk his life for the sake of parading the streets on Sunday mornings.

We gather that Tarrou was agreeably impressed by a little scene that took place daily on the balcony of a house facing his window. His room at the hotel looked on to a small side street and there were always several cats sleeping in the shadow of the walls. Every day, soon after lunch, at a time when most people stayed indoors, enjoying a siesta, a dapper little old man stepped out on the balcony on the other side of the street. He had a soldierly bearing, very erect, and affected a military style of dressing;

his snow-white hair was always brushed to perfect smoothness. Leaning over the balcony he would call: "Pussy! Pussy!" in a voice at once haughty and endearing. The cats blinked up at him with sleep-pale eyes, but made no move as yet. He then proceeded to tear some paper into scraps and let them fall into the street; interested by the fluttering shower of white butterflies, the cats came forward, lifting tentative paws toward the last scraps of paper. Then, taking careful aim, the old man would spit vigorously at the cats and, whenever a liquid missile hit the quarry, would beam with delight.

Lastly, Tarrou seemed to have been quite fascinated by the commercial character of the town, whose aspect, activities, and even pleasures all seemed to be dictated by considerations of business. This idiosyncrasy—the term he uses in his diary—was warmly approved of by Tarrou; indeed, one of his appreciative comments ends on the exclamation: "At last!"

These are the only passages in which our visitor's record, at this period, strikes a seemingly personal note. Its significance and the earnestness behind it might escape the reader on a casual perusal. For example, after describing how the discovery of a dead rat led the hotel cashier to make an error in his bill, Tarrou added: *"Query:* How contrive not to waste one's time? *Answer:* By being fully aware of it all the while. *Ways in which this can be done:* By spending one's days on an uneasy chair in a dentist's waiting-room; by remaining on one's balcony all a Sunday afternoon; by listening to lectures in a language one doesn't know; by traveling by the longest and least-convenient train routes, and of course standing all the way; by lining up at the box-office of theaters and then not buying a seat; and so forth."

Then, immediately following these eccentricities of thought and expression, we come on a detailed description of the streetcar service in the town, the structure of the cars, their indeterminate color, their unvarying dirtiness—and he concludes his observations with a "Very odd," which explains nothing.

So much by way of introduction to Tarrou's comments on the phenomenon of the rats.

"The little old fellow opposite is quite disconsolate today. There are no more no question of their eating the dead rats. strewn about the street may have excited their hunting instinct; anyhow, they all have vanished. To my thinking, there's no question of their eating the dead rats. Mine, I remember, turned up their noses at dead things. All the same, they're probably busy hunting in the cellars— hence the old boy's plight. His hair isn't as well brushed as usual, and he looks less alert, less military. You can see he is worried. After a few moments he went back into the room. But first he spat once—on emptiness.

"In town today a streetcar was stopped because a dead rat had been found in it. (*Query:* How did it get there?) Two or three women promptly alighted. The rat was thrown out. The car went on.

"The night watchman at the hotel, a level-headed man, assured me that all these rats meant trouble coming. 'When the rats leave a ship . . .' I replied that this held good for ships, but for towns it hadn't yet been demonstrated. But he stuck to his point. I asked what sort of 'trouble' we might expect. That he couldn't say; disasters always come out of the blue. But he wouldn't be surprised if there were an earthquake brewing. I admitted that was possible, and then he asked if the prospect didn't alarm me.

" 'The only thing I'm interested in,' I told him, 'is acquiring peace of mind.'

"He understood me perfectly.

"I find a family that has its meals in this hotel quite interesting. The father is a tall, thin man, always dressed in black and wearing a starched collar. The top of his head is bald, with two tufts of gray hair on each side. His small, beady eyes, narrow nose, and hard, straight mouth make him look like a well-brought-up owl. He is always first at the door of the restaurant, stands aside to let his wife—a tiny woman, like a black mouse—go in, and then comes in himself with a small boy and girl, dressed like performing poodles, at his heels. When they are at the table he remains standing till his wife is seated and only then the two poodles can perch themselves on their chairs. He uses no terms of endearment to his family, addresses politely spiteful remarks to his wife, and bluntly tells the kids what he thinks of them.

" 'Nicole, you're behaving quite disgracefully.'

"The little girl is on the brink of tears —which is as it should be.

"This morning the small boy was all excitement about the rats, and started saying something on the subject.

" 'Philippe, one doesn't talk of rats at table. For the future I forbid you to use the word.'

" 'Your father's right,' approved the mouse.

"The two poodles buried their noses in their plates, and the owl acknowledged thanks by a curt, perfunctory nod.

"This excellent example notwithstanding, everybody in town is talking about the rats, and the local newspaper has taken a hand. The town-topics column, usually very varied, is now devoted exclusively to a campaign against the local authorities. 'Are our city fathers aware that the decaying bodies of these rodents constitute a grave danger to the population?' The manager of the hotel can talk of nothing else. But he has a personal grievance, too; that dead rats should be found in the elevator of a three-star hotel seems to him the end of all things. To console him, I said: 'But, you know, everybody's in the same boat.'

" 'That's just it,' he replied. 'Now we're like everybody else.'

"He was the first to tell me about the outbreak of this queer kind of fever which is causing much alarm. One of his chambermaids has got it.

" 'But I feel sure it's not contagious,' he hastened to assure me.

"I told him it was all the same to me.

" 'Ah, I understand, sir. You're like me, you're a fatalist.'

"I had said nothing of the kind and, what's more, am not a fatalist. I told him so. . . ."

From this point onwards Tarrou's entries deal in some detail with the curious fever that was causing much anxiety among the public. When noting that the little old man, now that the rats had ceased appearing, had regained his cats and was studiously perfecting his shooting, Tarrou adds that a dozen or so cases of this fever were known to have occurred, and most had ended fatally.

For the light it may throw on the narrative that follows, Tarrou's description of Dr. Rieux may be suitably inserted here. So far as the narrator can judge, it is fairly accurate.

"Looks about thirty-five. Moderate height. Broad shoulders. Almost rectangular face. Dark, steady eyes, but prominent jaws. A biggish, well-modeled nose. Black hair, cropped very close. A curving mouth with thick, usually tightset lips. With his tanned skin, the black down on his hands and arms, the dark but becoming suits he always wears, he reminds one of a Sicilian peasant.

"He walks quickly. When crossing a street, he steps off the sidewalk without changing his pace, but two out of three times make a little hop when he steps on to the sidewalk on the other side. He is absentminded and, when driving his car, often leaves his side-signals on after he has turned a corner. Always bareheaded. Looks knowledgeable."

Tarrou's figures were correct. Dr. Rieux was only too well aware of the serious turn things had taken. After seeing to the isolation of the concierge's body, he had rung up Richard and asked what he made of these inguinal-fever cases.

"I can make nothing of them," Richard confessed. "There have been two deaths, one in forty-eight hours, the other in three days. And the second patient showed all the signs of convalescence when I visited him on the second day."

"Please let me know if you have other cases," Rieux said.

He rang up some other colleagues. As a result of these inquiries he gathered that there had been some twenty cases of the same type within the last few days. Almost all had ended fatally. He then advised Richard, who was chairman of the local Medical Association, to have any fresh cases put into isolation wards.

"Sorry," Richard said, "but I can't do anything about it. An order to that effect can be issued only by the Prefect. Anyhow, what grounds have you for supposing there's danger of contagion?"

"No definite grounds. But the symptoms are definitely alarming."

Richard, however, repeated that "such measures were outside his province." The most he could do was to put the matter up to the Prefect.

But while these talks were going on, the weather changed for the worse. On the day following old Michel's death the sky clouded up and there were brief torrential downpours, each of which was followed by some hours of muggy heat. The aspect of the sea, too, changed; its dark-blue translucency had gone and, under the lowering sky, it had steely or

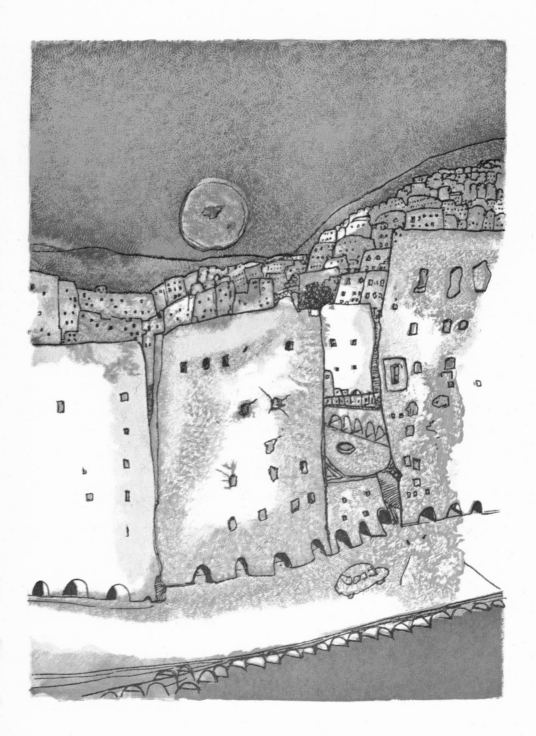

silvery glints that hurt the eyes to look at. The damp heat of the spring made everyone long for the coming of the dry, clean summer heat. On the town, humped snailwise on its plateau and shut off almost everywhere from the sea, a mood of listlessness descended. Hemmed in by lines and lines of whitewashed walls, walking between rows of dusty shops, or riding in the dingy yellow streetcars, you felt, as it were, trapped by the climate. This, however, was not the case with Rieux's old Spanish patient, who welcomed this weather with enthusiasm.

"It cooks you," he said. "Just the thing for asthma."

Certainly it "cooked you," but exactly like a fever. Indeed, the whole town was running a temperature; such anyhow was the impression Dr. Rieux could not shake off as he drove to the rue Faidherbe for the inquiry into Cottard's attempted suicide. That this impression was unreasonable he knew, and he attributed it to nervous exhaustion; he had certainly his full share of worries just at present. In fact, it was high time to put the brakes on and try to get his nerves into some sort of order.

On reaching his destination he found that the police inspector hadn't turned up yet. Grand, who met him on the landing, suggested they should wait in his place, leaving the door open. The municipal clerk had two rooms, both very sparsely furnished. The only objects to catch the eye were a bookshelf on which lay two or three dictionaries, and a small blackboard on which one could just read two half-obliterated words: "flowery avenues."

Grand announced that Cottard had had a good night. But he'd waked up this morning with pains in his head and feeling very low. Grand, too, looked tired and overwrought; he kept pacing up and down the room, opening and closing a portfolio crammed with sheets of manuscript that lay on the table.

Meanwhile, however, he informed the doctor that he really knew very little about Cottard, but believed him to have private means in a small way. Cottard was a queer bird. For a long while their relations went no farther than wishing each other good-day when they met on the stairs.

"I've only had two conversations with him. Some days ago I upset a box of colored chalks I was bringing home, on the landing. They were red and blue chalks. Just then Cottard came out of his room and he helped me pick them up. He asked me what I wanted colored chalks for."

Grand had then explained to him that he was trying to brush up his Latin. He'd learned it at school, of course, but his memories had grown blurred.

"You see, doctor, I've been told that a knowledge of Latin gives one a better understanding of the real meanings of French words."

So he wrote Latin words on his blackboard, then copied out again in blue chalk the part of each word that changed in conjugation or declension, and in red chalk the part of the word that never varied.

"I'm not sure if Cottard followed this very clearly, but he seemed interested and asked me for a red chalk. That rather surprised me, but after all—Of course I couldn't guess the use he'd put it to."

Rieux asked what was the subject of their second conversation. But just then the inspector came, accompanied by a clerk, and said he wished to begin by hearing Grand's statement. The doctor noticed that Grand, when referring to Cottard, always called him "the unfortunate man," and at one moment used even the expression "his grim resolve." When discussing the possible motives for the attempted suicide, Grand showed an almost finical anxiety over his choice of words. Finally he elected for the expression "a secret grief." The inspector asked if there had been anything in Cottard's manner that suggested what he called his "intent to felo-de-se."

"He knocked at my door yesterday," Grand said, "and asked me for a match. I gave him a box. He said he was sorry to disturb me but that, as we were neighbors, he hoped I wouldn't mind. He assured me he'd bring back my box, but I told him to keep it."

The inspector asked Grand if he'd noticed anything queer about Cottard.

"What struck me as queer was that he always seemed to want to start a conversation. But he should have seen I was busy with my work." Grand turned to Rieux and added rather shyly: "Some private work."

The inspector now said that he must see the invalid and hear what he had to say. Rieux thought it would be wiser to prepare Cottard for the visit. When he entered the bedroom he found Cottard, who was wearing a gray flannel nightshirt, sitting up in bed and gazing at the door with a scared expression on his face.

"It's the police, isn't it?"

"Yes," Rieux said, "but don't get flustered. There are only some formalities to be gone through, and then you'll be left in peace."

Cottard replied that all this was quite needless, to his thinking, and anyhow he didn't like the police.

Rieux showed some irritation.

"I don't love them either. It's only a matter of answering a few questions as briefly and correctly as you can, and then you'll be through with it."

Cottard said nothing and Rieux began to move to the door. He had hardly taken a step when the little man called him back and, as soon as he was at the bedside, gripped his hands.

"They can't be rough with an invalid, a man who's hanged himself, can they, doctor?"

Rieux gazed down at him for a moment, then assured him that there was no question of anything like that, and in any case he was here to protect his patient. This seemed to relieve Cottard, and Rieux went out to get the inspector.

After Grand's deposition had been read out, Cottard was asked to state the exact motive of his act. He merely replied, without looking at the police officer, that "a secret grief" described it well enough. The inspector then asked him peremptorily if he intended to "have another go at it." Showing more animation, Cottard said certainly not, his one wish was to be left in peace.

"Allow me to point out, my man," the police officer rejoined with asperity, "that just now it's you who're troubling the peace of others." Rieux signed to him not to continue, and he left it at that.

"A good hour wasted!" the inspector sighed when the door closed behind them. "As you can guess, we've other things to think about, what with this fever everybody's talking of."

He then asked the doctor if there was any serious danger to the town; Rieux answered that he couldn't say.

"It must be the weather," the police officer decided. "That's what it is."

No doubt it was the weather. As the day wore on, everything grew sticky to the touch, and Rieux felt his anxiety increasing after each visit. That evening a neighbor of his old patient in the suburbs started vomiting, pressing his hand to his groin, and running a high fever accompanied by delirium. The ganglia were much bigger than M. Michel's. One of them was beginning to suppurate, and presently split open like an overripe fruit. On returning to his apartment, Rieux rang up the medical-stores depot for the district. In his professional diary for the day the only entry was: "Negative reply."

Already he was receiving calls for similar cases from various parts of the town. Obviously the abscesses had to be lanced. Two crisscross strokes, and the ganglion disgorged a mixture of blood and pus. Their limbs stretched out as far as they could manage, the sick men went on bleeding. Dark patches appeared on their legs and stomachs; sometimes a ganglion would stop suppurating, then suddenly swell again. Usually the sick man died, in a stench of corruption.

The local press, so lavish of news about the rats, now had nothing to say. For rats died in the street; men in their homes. And newspapers are concerned only with the street. Meanwhile, government and municipal officials were putting their heads together. So long as each individual doctor had come across only two or three cases, no one had thought of taking action. But it was merely a matter of adding up the figures and, once this had been done, the total was startling. In a very few days the number of cases had risen by leaps and bounds, and it became evident to all observers of this strange malady that a real epidemic had set in. This was the state of affairs when Castel, one of Rieux's colleagues and a much older man than he, came to see him.

"Naturally," he said to Rieux, "you know what it is."

"I'm waiting for the result of the post-mortems."

"Well, *I* know. And I don't need any post-mortems. I was in China for a good part of my career, and I saw some cases in Paris twenty years ago. Only no one dared to call them by their name on that occasion. The usual taboo, of course; the public mustn't be alarmed, that wouldn't do at all. And then, as one of my colleagues said, 'It's unthinkable. Everyone knows it's ceased to appear in western Europe.' Yes, everyone knew that—except the dead men. Come now, Rieux, you know as well as I do what it is."

Rieux pondered. He was looking out of the window of his surgery, at the tall cliff that closed the half-circle of the bay on the far horizon. Though blue, the sky had a dull sheen that was softening as the light declined.

"Yes, Castel," he replied. "It's hardly credible. But everything points to its being plague."

Castel got up and began walking toward the door.

"You know," the old doctor said, "what they're going to tell us? That it vanished from temperate countries long ago."

" 'Vanished'? What does that word really mean?" Rieux shrugged his shoulders.

"Yes. And don't forget. Just under twenty years ago, in Paris too."

"Right. Let's hope it won't prove any worse this time than it did then. But really it's incredible."

The word "plague" had just been uttered for the first time. At this stage of the narrative, with Dr. Bernard Rieux standing at his window, the narrator may, perhaps, be allowed to justify the doctor's uncertainty and surprise—since, with very slight differences, his reaction was the same as that of the great majority of our townsfolk. Everybody knows that pestilences have a way of recurring in the world; yet somehow we find it hard to believe in ones that crash down on our heads from a blue sky. There have been as many plagues as wars in history; yet always plagues and wars take people equally by surprise.

In fact, like our fellow citizens, Rieux was caught off his guard, and we should understand his hesitations in the light of this fact; and similarly understand how he was torn between conflicting fears and confidence. When a war breaks out, people say: "It's too stupid; it can't last long." But though a war may well be "too stupid," that doesn't prevent its lasting. Stupidity has a knack of getting its way; as we should see if we were not always so much wrapped up in ourselves.

In this respect our townsfolk were like everybody else, wrapped up in themselves; in other words they were humanists: they disbelieved in pestilences. A pestilence isn't a thing made to man's measure; therefore we tell ourselves that pestilence is a mere bogy of the mind, a bad dream that will pass away. But it doesn't always pass away and, from one bad dream to another, it is men who pass away, and the humanists first of all, because they haven't taken their precautions. Our townsfolk were not more to blame than others; they forgot to be modest, that was all, and thought that everything still was possible for them; which presupposed that pestilences were impossible. They went on doing business, arranged for journeys, and formed views. How should they have given a thought to anything like plague, which rules out any future, cancels journeys, silences the exchange of views? They fancied themselves free, and no one will ever be free so long as there are pestilences.

Indeed, even after Dr. Rieux had admitted in his friend's company that a handful of persons, scattered about the town, had without warning died of plague, the danger still remained fantastically unreal. For the simple reason that, when a man is a doctor, he comes to have his own ideas of physical suffering, and to acquire somewhat more imagination than the average. Looking from his window at the town, outwardly quite unchanged, the doctor felt little more than a faint qualm for the future, a vague unease.

He tried to recall what he had read about the disease. Figures floated across his memory, and he recalled that some thirty or so great plagues known to history had accounted for nearly a hundred million deaths. But what are a hundred million deaths? When one has served in a war, one hardly knows what a dead man is, after a while. And since a dead man has no substance unless one has actually seen him dead, a hundred million corpses broadcast through history are no more than a puff of smoke in the imagination. The doctor remembered the plague at Constantinople that, according to Procopius, caused ten thousand deaths in a single day. Ten thousand dead made about five times the audience in a biggish cinema. Yes, that was how it should be done. You should collect the people at the exits of five picture-houses, you should lead them to a city square and make them die in heaps if you wanted to get a clear notion of what it means. Then at least you could add some familiar faces to the anonymous mass. But naturally that was impossible to put into practice; moreover, what man knows ten thousand faces? In any case the figures of those old historians, like Procopius, weren't to be relied on; that was common knowledge. Seventy years ago, at Canton, forty thousand rats died of plague before the disease spread to the inhabitants. But, again, in the Canton epidemic there was no reliable way of counting up the rats. A very rough estimate was all that could be made, with, obviously, a wide margin for error. "Let's see," the doctor murmured to himself, "supposing the length of a rat to be ten inches, forty thousand rats placed end to end would make a line of . . ."

He pulled himself up sharply. He was letting his imagination play pranks—the last thing wanted just now. A few cases, he told himself, don't make an epidemic; they merely call for serious precautions. He must fix his mind, first of all, on the observed facts: stupor and extreme prostration, buboes, intense thirst, delirium, dark blotches on the body, internal dilatation, and, in conclusion . . . In conclusion, some words came back to the doctor's mind; aptly enough, the concluding sentence of the description of the symptoms given in his medical handbook: "The pulse becomes fluttering, dicrotic, and intermittent, and death ensues as the result of the slightest movement." Yes, in conclusion, the patient's life hung on a thread, and three people out of four (he remembered the exact figures) were too impatient not to make the very slight movement that snapped the thread.

The doctor was still looking out of the window. Beyond it lay the tranquil radiance of a cool spring sky; inside the room a word was echoing still, the word "plague." A word that conjured up in the doctor's mind not only what science chose to put into it, but a whole series of fantastic possibilities utterly out of keeping with that gray and yellow town under his eyes, from which were rising the sounds of mild activity characteristic of the hour; a drone rather than a bustling, the noises of a happy town, in short, if it's possible to be at once so dull and happy. A tranquillity so casual and thoughtless seemed almost effortlessly to give the lie to those old pictures of the plague: Athens, a charnel-house reeking to heaven and deserted even by the birds; Chinese towns cluttered up with victims silent in their agony; the convicts at Marseille piling rotting corpses into pits; the building of the Great Wall in Provence to fend off the furious plague-wind; the damp, putrefying pallets stuck to the mud floor at the Constantinople lazarhouse, where the patients were hauled up from their beds with hooks; the carnival of masked doctors at the Black Death; men and women copulating in the cemeteries of Milan; cartloads of dead bodies rumbling through London's ghoulhaunted darkness—nights and days filled always, everywhere, with the eternal cry of human pain. No, all those horrors were not near enough as yet even to ruffle the equanimity of that spring afternoon. The clang of an unseen streetcar came through the window, briskly refuting cruelty and pain. Only the sea, murmurous behind the dingy checkerboard of houses, told of the unrest, the precariousness, of all things in this world. And, gazing in the direction of the bay, Dr. Rieux called to mind the plague-fires of which Lucretius tells, which the Athenians kindled on the seashore. The dead were brought there after nightfall, but there was not room enough, and the living fought one another with torches for a space where to lay those who had been dear to them; for they had rather engage in bloody conflicts than abandon their dead to the waves. A picture rose before him of the red glow of the pyres mirrored on a wine-dark, slumbrous sea, battling torches whirling sparks across the darkness, and thick, fetid smoke rising toward the watchful sky. Yes, it was not beyond the bounds of possibility. . . .

But these extravagant forebodings dwindled in the light of reason. True, the word "plague" had been uttered; true, at this very moment one or two victims were being seized and laid low by the disease. Still, that could stop, or be stopped. It was only a matter of lucidly recognizing what had to be recognized; of dispelling extraneous shadows and doing what needed to be done. Then the plague would come to an end, because it was unthinkable, or, rather, because one thought of it on misleading lines. If, as was most likely, it died out, all would be well. If not, one would know it anyhow for what it was and what steps should be taken for coping with and finally overcoming it.

The doctor opened the window, and at once the noises of the town grew louder.

The brief, intermittent sibilance of a machine-saw came from a near-by workshop. Rieux pulled himself together. There lay certitude; there, in the daily round. All the rest hung on mere threads and trivial contingencies; you couldn't waste your time on it. The thing was to do your job as it should be done.

The doctor's musings had reached this point when the visit of Joseph Grand was announced. Grand's duties as clerk in the Municipal Office were varied, and he was sometimes employed in the statistical department on compiling the figures of births, marriages, and deaths. Thus it had fallen to him to add up the number of deaths during the last few days, and, being of an obliging disposition, he had volunteered to bring a copy of the latest figures to the doctor.

Grand, who was waving a sheet of paper, was accompanied by his neighbor, Cottard.

"The figures are going up, doctor. Eleven deaths in forty-eight hours."

Rieux shook hands with Cottard and asked him how he was feeling. Grand put in a word explaining that Cottard was bent on thanking the doctor and apologizing for the trouble he had given. But Rieux was gazing frowningly at the figures on the sheet of paper.

"Well," he said, "perhaps we'd better make up our minds to call this disease by its name. So far we've been only shilly-shallying. Look here, I'm off to the laboratory; like to come with me?"

"Quite so, quite so," Grand said as he went down the stairs at the doctor's heels. "I, too, believe in calling things by their name. But what's the name in this case?"

"That I shan't say, and anyhow you wouldn't gain anything by knowing."

"You see," Grand smiled. "It's not so easy after all!"

They started off toward the Place d'Armes. Cottard still kept silent. The streets were beginning to fill up. The brief dusk of our town was already giving place to night, and the first stars glimmered above the still clearly marked horizon. A few moments later all the street-lamps went on, dimming the sky, and the voices in the street seemed to rise a tone.

"Excuse me," Grand said at the corner of the Place d'Armes, "but I must catch my car now. My evenings are sacred. As we say in my part of the world: 'Never put off to tomorrow—' "

Rieux had already noticed Grand's trick of professing to quote some turn of speech from "his part of the world" (he hailed from Montélimar), and following up with some such hackneyed expression as "lost in dreams," or "pretty as a picture."

"That's so," Cottard put in. "You can never budge him from his den after dinner."

Rieux asked Grand if he was doing extra work for the municipality. Grand said no, he was working on his own account.

"Really?" Rieux said, to keep the conversation going. "And are you getting on well with it?"

"Considering I've been at it for years, it would be surprising if I wasn't. Though in one sense there hasn't been much progress."

"May one know"—the doctor halted—"what it is that you're engaged on?"

Grand put a hand up to his hat and tugged it down upon his big, protruding ears, then murmured some half-inaudible remark from which Rieux seemed to gather that Grand's work was connected with "the growth of a personality." Then he turned rather hastily and a moment later was hurrying, with short, quick steps, under the fig trees lining the boulevard de la Marne.

When they were at the laboratory gate, Cottard told the doctor that he would greatly like to see him and ask his advice about something. Rieux, who was fingering in his pocket the sheet of paper with the figures on it, said he'd better call during his consulting-hours; then, changing his mind, told him he would be in his part of the town next day and would drop in to see him at the end of the afternoon.

On leaving Cottard the doctor noticed that he was thinking of Grand, trying to picture him in the midst of an outbreak of plague—not an outbreak like the present one, which would probably not prove serious, but like one of the great visitations of the past. "He's the kind of man who always escapes in such cases." Rieux remembered having read somewhere that the plague spared weak constitutions and chose its victims chiefly among the robust. Still thinking of Grand, he decided that he was something of a "mystery man" in his small way.

True, at first sight, Grand manifested both the outward signs and typical manner of a humble employee in the local administration. Tall and thin, he seemed lost in the garments that he always chose a size too large, under the illusion that they would wear longer. Though he still had most of the teeth in his lower jaw, all the upper ones were gone, with the result that when he smiled, raising his upper lip—the lower scarcely moved—his mouth looked like a small black hole let into his face. Also he had the walk of a shy young priest, sidling along walls and slipping mouselike into doorways, and he exuded a faint odor of smoke and basement rooms; in short, he had all the attributes of insignificance. Indeed, it cost an effort to picture him otherwise than bent over a desk, studiously revising the tariff of the town baths or gathering for a junior secretary the materials of a report on the new garbage-collection tax. Even before you knew what his employment was, you had a feeling that he'd been brought into the world for the sole purpose of performing the discreet but needful duties of a temporary assistant municipal clerk on a salary of sixty-two francs, thirty centimes a day.

This was, in fact, the entry that he made each month in the staff register at the Municipal Office, in the column *Post in Which Employed*. When twenty-two years previously—after obtaining a matriculation certificate beyond which, for lack of money, he was unable to progress—he was given this temporary post, he had been led to expect, or so he said, speedy "confirmation" in it. It was only a mattter of proving his ability to cope with the delicate problems raised by the administration of our city. Once confirmed, they had assured him, he couldn't fail to be promoted to a grade that would enable him to live quite comfortably. Ambition, certainly, was not the spur that activated Joseph Grand; that he would swear to, wryly smiling. All he desired was the prospect of a life suitably insured on the material side by honest work, enabling him to devote his leisure to his hobbies. If he'd accepted the post offered him, it was from honorable motives and, if he might say so, loyalty to an ideal.

But this "temporary" state of things had gone on and on, the cost of living rose by leaps and bounds, and Grand's pay, in spite of some statutory rises, was still a mere pittance. He had confided this to Rieux, but nobody else seemed aware of his position. And here lies Grand's originality, or anyhow an indication of it. He could certainly have brought to official notice, if not his rights—of which he wasn't sure—at least the promises given him. But, for one thing, the departmental head who had made them had been dead for some time and, furthermore, Grand no longer remembered their exact terms. And lastly—this was the real trouble—Joseph Grand couldn't find his words.

This peculiarity, as Rieux had noticed, was really the key to the personality of our worthy fellow citizen. And this it was which always prevented him from writing the mildly protesting letter he had in mind, or taking the steps the situation called for. According to him, he felt a particular aversion from talking about his "rights"—the word was one that gave him pause—and likewise from mentioning a "promise"—which would have implied that he was claiming his due and thus bespoken an audacity incompatible with the humble post he filled. On the other hand, he refused to use expressions such as "your kindness," "gratitude," or even "solicit," which, to his thinking, were incompatible with his personal dignity. Thus, owing to his inability to find the right words, he had gone on performing his obscure, ill-paid duties until a somewhat advanced age. Also—this, anyhow, was what he told Dr. Rieux—he had come, after long experience, to realize that he could always count on living within his means; all he had to do was to scale down his needs to his income. Thus he confirmed the wisdom of an opinion often voiced by our mayor, a business magnate of the town, when he insisted vehemently that in the last analysis (he emphasized this choice expression, which indeed clinched his argument) there was no reason to believe that anyone had ever died of hunger in the town. In any case, the austere, not to say ascetic life of Joseph Grand was, in the last analysis, a guarantee against any anxiety in this respect. He went on looking for his words.

In a certain sense it might well be said that his was an exemplary life. He was one of those rare people, rare in our town as elsewhere, who have the courage of their good feelings. What little he told of his personal life vouched for acts of kindness and a capacity for affection that no one in our times dares own to. Without a blush he confessed to dearly loving his nephews and sister, his only surviving near relation, whom he went to France to visit every other year. He admitted that the thought of his parents, whom he lost when he was very young, often gave him a pang. He did not conceal the fact that he had a special affection for a church bell in his part of the town which started pealing very melodiously at about five every afternoon. Yet to express such emotions, simple as they were, the least word cost him a terrible effort. And this difficulty in finding his words had come to be the bane of his life. "Oh, doctor," he would exclaim, "how I'd like to learn to express myself!" He brought the subject up each time he met Rieux.

That evening, as he watched Grand's receding form, it flashed on the doctor what it was that Grand was trying to convey; he was evidently writing a book or something of the sort. And quaintly enough, as he made his way to the laboratory, this thought reassured him. He realized how absurd it was, but he simply couldn't believe that a pestilence on the great scale could befall a town where people like Grand were to be found, obscure functionaries cultivating harmless eccentricities. To be precise, he couldn't picture such eccentricities existing in a plague-stricken community, and he concluded that the chances were all against the plague's making any headway among our fellow citizens.

Next day, by dint of a persistence that many thought ill-advised, Rieux persuaded the authorities to convene a health committee at the Prefect's office.

"People in town are getting nervous,

that's a fact," Dr. Richard admitted. "And of course all sorts of wild rumors are going round. The Prefect said to me, 'Take prompt action if you like, but don't attract attention.' He personally is convinced that it's a false alarm."

Rieux gave Castel a lift to the Prefect's office.

"Do you know," Castel said when they were in the car, "that we haven't a gram of serum in the whole district?"

"I know. I rang up the depot. The director seemed quite startled. It'll have to be sent from Paris."

"Let's hope they're quick about it."

"I sent a wire yesterday," Rieux said.

The Prefect greeted them amiably enough, but one could see his nerves were on edge.

"Let's make a start, gentlemen," he said. "Need I review the situation?"

Richard thought that wasn't necessary. He and his colleagues were acquainted with the facts. The only question was what measures should be adopted.

"The question," old Castel cut in almost rudely, "is to know whether it's plague or not."

Two or three of the doctors present protested. The others seemed to hesitate. The Prefect gave a start and hurriedly glanced toward the door to make sure it had prevented this outrageous remark from being overheard in the corridor. Richard said that in his opinion the great thing was not to take an alarmist view. All that could be said at present was that we had to deal with a special type of fever, with inguinal complications; in medical science, as in daily life, it was unwise to jump to conclusions. Old Castel, who was placidly chewing his draggled yellow mustache, raised his pale, bright eyes and gazed at Rieux. Then, after sweeping the other members of the committee with a friendly glance, he said that he knew quite well that it was plague and, needless to say, he also knew that, were this to be officially admitted, the authorities would be compelled to take very drastic steps. This was, of course, the explanation of his colleagues' reluctance to face the facts and, if it would ease their minds, he was quite prepared to say it wasn't plague. The Prefect seemed ruffled and remarked that, in any case, this line of argument seemed to him unsound.

"The important thing," Castel replied, "isn't the soundness or otherwise of the argument, but for it to make you think."

Rieux, who had said nothing so far, was asked for his opinion.

"We are dealing," he said, "with a fever of a typhoidal nature, accompanied by vomiting and buboes. I have incised these buboes and had the pus analyzed; our laboratory analyst believes he has identified the plague bacillus. But I am bound to add that there are specific modifications that don't quite tally with the classical description of the plague bacillus."

Richard pointed out that this justified a policy of wait-and-see; anyhow, it would be wise to await the statistical report on the series of analyses that had been going on for several days.

"When a microbe," Rieux said, "after a short intermission can quadruple in three days' time the volume of the spleen, can swell the mesenteric ganglia to the size of an orange and give them the consistency of gruel, a policy of wait-and-see is, to say the least of it, unwise. The foci of infection are steadily extending. Judging by the rapidity with which the disease is spreading, it may well, unless we can stop it, kill off half the town before two months are out. That being so, it has small importance whether you call it plague or some rare kind of fever. The important thing is to prevent its killing off half the population of this town."

Richard said it was a mistake to paint too gloomy a picture, and, moreover, the disease hadn't been proved to be contagious; indeed, relatives of his patients, living under the same roof, had escaped it.

"But others have died," Rieux observed. "And obviously contagion is never absolute; otherwise you'd have a constant mathematical progression and the death-rate would rocket up catastrophically. It's not a question of painting too black a picture. It's a question of taking precautions."

Richard, however, summing up the situation as he saw it, pointed out that, if the epidemic did not cease spontaneously, it would be necessary to apply the rigorous prophylactic measures laid down in the Code. And, to do this, it would be necessary to admit officially that plague had broken out. But of this there was no absolute certainty; therefore any hasty action was to be deprecated.

Rieux stuck to his guns. "The point isn't whether the measures provided for in the Code are rigorous, but whether they are needful to prevent the death of half the population. All the rest is a matter of administrative action, and I needn't remind you that our constitution has provided for such emergencies by empowering prefects to issue the necessary orders."

"Quite true," the Prefect assented, "but I shall need your professional declaration that the epidemic is one of plague."

"If we don't make that declaration," Rieux said, "there's a risk that half the population may be wiped out."

Richard cut in with some impatience.

"The truth is that our colleague is convinced it's plague; his description of the syndrome proved it."

Rieux replied that he had not described a "syndrome," but merely what he'd seen with his own eyes. And what he'd seen was buboes, and high fever accompanied by delirium, ending fatally within forty-eight hours. Could Dr.

Richard take the responsibility of declaring that the epidemic would die out without the imposition of rigorous prophylactic measures?

Richard hesitated, then fixed his eyes on Rieux.

"Please answer me quite frankly. Are you absolutely convinced it's plague?"

"You're stating the problem wrongly. It's not a question of the term I use; it's a question of time."

"Your view, I take it," the Prefect put in, "is this. Even if it isn't plague, the prophylactic measures enjoined by law for coping with a state of plague should be put into force immediately?"

"If you insist on my having a 'view,' that conveys it accurately enough."

The doctors confabulated. Richard was their spokesman:

"It comes to this. We are to take the responsibility of acting as though the epidemic were plague."

This way of putting it met with general approval.

"It doesn't matter to me," Rieux said, "how you phrase it. My point is that we should not act as if there were no likelihood that half the population would be wiped out; for then it would be."

Followed by scowls and protestations, Rieux left the committee-room. Some minutes later, as he was driving down a back street redolent of fried fish and urine, a woman screaming in agony, her groin dripping blood, stretched out her arms toward him.

On the day after the committee meeting the fever notched another small advance. It even found its way into the papers, but discreetly; only a few brief references to it were made. On the following day, however, Rieux observed that small official notices had been just put up about the town, though in places where they would not attract much attention. It was hard to find in these notices any indication that the authorities were facing the situation squarely. The measures enjoined were far from Draconian and one had the feeling that many concessions had been made to a desire not to alarm the public. The instructions began with a bald statement that a few cases of a malignant fever had been reported in Oran; it was not possible as yet to say if this fever was contagious. The symptoms were not so marked as to be really perturbing and the authorities felt sure they could rely on the townspeople to treat the situation with composure. None the less, guided by a spirit of prudence that all would appreciate, the Prefect was putting into force some precautionary measures. If these measures were carefully studied and properly applied, they would obviate any risk of an epidemic. This being so, the Prefect felt no doubt that everybody in his jurisdiction would wholeheartedly second his personal efforts.

The notice outlined the general program that the authorities had drawn up. It included a systematic extermination of the rat population by injecting poison gas into the sewers, and a strict supervision of the water-supply. The townspeople were advised to practice extreme cleanliness, and any who found fleas on their persons were directed to call at the municipal dispensaries. Also heads of households were ordered promptly to report any fever case diagnosed by their doctors and to permit the isolation of sick members of their families in special wards at the hospital. These wards, it was explained, were equipped to provide patients with immediate treatment and ensure the maximum prospect of recovery. Some supplementary regulations enjoined compulsory disinfection of the sickroom and of the vehicle in which the patient traveled. For the rest, the Prefect confined himself to advising all who had

been in contact with the patient to consult the sanitary inspector and strictly to follow his advice.

Dr. Rieux swung round brusquely from the poster and started back to his surgery. Grand, who was awaiting him there, raised his arms dramatically when the doctor entered.

"Yes," Rieux said, "I know. The figures are rising."

On the previous day ten deaths had been reported. The doctor told Grand that he might be seeing him in the evening, as he had promised to visit Cottard.

"An excellent idea," Grand said. "You'll do him good. As a matter of fact, I find him greatly changed."

"In what way?"

"He's become amiable."

"Wasn't he amiable before?"

Grand seemed at a loss. He couldn't say that Cottard used to be unamiable; the term wouldn't have been correct. But Cottard was a silent, secretive man, with something about him that made Grand think of a wild boar. His bedroom, meals at a cheap restaurant, some rather mysterious comings and goings—these were the sum of Cottard's days. He described himself as a traveling salesman in wines and spirits. Now and then he was visited by two or three men, presumably customers. Sometimes in the evening he would go to a movie across the way. In this connection Grand mentioned a detail he had noticed—that Cottard seemed to have a preference for gangster films. But the thing that had struck him most about the man was his aloofness, not to say his mistrust of everyone he met.

And now, so Grand said, there had been a complete change.

"I don't quite know how to put it, but I must say I've an impression that he is trying to make himself agreeable to all and sundry, to be in everybody's good books. Nowadays he often talks to me, he suggests we should go out together, and I can't bring myself to refuse. What's more, he interests me, and of course I saved his life."

Since his attempt at suicide Cottard had had no more visitors. In the streets, in shops, he was always trying to strike up friendships. To the grocer he was all affability; no one could take more pains than he to show his interest in the tobacconist's gossip.

"This particular tobacconist—it's a woman, by the way," Grand explained, "is a holy terror. I told Cottard so, but he replied that I was prejudiced and she had plenty of good points, only one had to find them out."

On two or three occasions Cottard had invited Grand to come with him to the luxury restaurants and cafés of the town, which he had recently taken to patronizing.

"There's a pleasant atmosphere in them," he explained, "and then one's in good company."

Grand noticed that the staff made much of Cottard and he soon discovered why, when he saw the lavish tips his companion gave. The traveling salesman seemed greatly to appreciate the amiability shown him in return for his largesse. One day when the head waiter had escorted him to the door and helped him into his overcoat, Cottard said to Grand:

"He's a nice fellow, and he'd make a good witness."

"A witness? I don't follow."

Cottard hesitated before answering.

"Well, he could say I'm not really a bad kind of man."

But his humor had its ups and downs. One day when the grocer had shown less affability, he came home in a tearing rage.

"He's siding with the others, the swine!"

"With what others?"

"The whole damned lot of them."

Grand had personally witnessed an odd scene that took place at the tobacconist's. An animated conversation was in progress and the woman behind the counter started airing her views about a murder case that had created some stir in Algiers. A young commercial employee had killed an Algerian on a beach.

"I always say," the woman began, "if they clapped all that scum in jail, decent folks could breathe more freely."

She was too much startled by Cottard's reaction—he dashed out of the shop without a word of excuse—to continue. Grand and the woman gazed after him, dumbfounded.

Subsequently Grand reported to the doctor other changes in Cottard's character. Cottard had always professed very liberal ideas, as his pet dictum on economic questions, "Big fish eat little fish," implied. But now the only Oran newspaper he bought was the conservative organ, and one could hardly help suspecting that he made a point of reading it in public places. Somewhat of the same order was a request he made to Grand shortly before he left his sick-bed; Grand mentioned he was going to the post office and Cottard asked him to be kind enough to dispatch a money order for a hundred francs to a sister living at a distance, mentioning that he sent her this sum every month. Then, just when Grand was leaving the room, he called him back.

"No, send her two hundred francs. That'll be a nice surprise for her. She believes I never give her a thought. But actually I'm devoted to her."

Not long after this he made some curious remarks to Grand in the course of conversation. He had badgered Grand into telling him about the somewhat mysterious "private work" to which Grand gave his evenings.

"I know!" Cottard exclaimed. "You're writing a book, aren't you?"

"Something of the kind. But it's not so simple as that."

"Ah!" Cottard sighed. "I only wish I had a knack for writing."

When Grand showed his surprise, Cottard explained with some embarrassment that being a literary man must make things easier in lots of ways.

"Why?" Grand asked.

"Why, because an author has more rights than ordinary people, as everybody knows. People will stand much more from him."

"It looks," said Rieux to Grand on the morning when the official notices were posted, "as if this business of the rats had addled his brain, as it has done for so many other people. That's all it is. Or perhaps he's scared of the 'fever.' "

"I doubt it, doctor. If you want to know my opinion, he—"

He paused; with a machine-gun rattle from its exhaust the "deratization" van was clattering by. Rieux kept silent until it was possible to make himself audible, then asked, without much interest, what Grand's opinion was.

"He's a man with something pretty serious on his conscience," Grand said gravely.

The doctor shrugged his shoulders. As the inspector had said, he'd other fish to fry.

That afternoon Rieux had another talk with Castel. The serum had not yet come.

"In any case," Rieux said, "I wonder if it will be much use. This bacillus is such a queer one."

"There," Castel said, "I don't agree with you. These little brutes always have an air of originality. But, at bottom, it's always the same thing."

"That's *your* theory, anyhow. Actually, of course, we know next to nothing on the subject."

"I grant you, it's only my theory. Still, in a sense, that goes for everybody."

Throughout the day the doctor was conscious that the slightly dazed feeling that came over him whenever he thought about the plague was growing more pronounced. Finally he realized that he was afraid! On two occasions he entered crowded cafés. Like Cottard he felt a need for friendly contacts, human warmth. A stupid instinct, Rieux told himself; still, it served to remind him that he'd promised to visit the traveling salesman.

Cottard was standing beside the dining-table when the doctor entered his room that evening. A detective story lay open on the tablecloth. But the night was closing in and it would have been difficult to read in the growing darkness. Most likely Cottard had been sitting musing in the twilight until he heard the ring at his door. Rieux asked how he was feeling. Cottard sat down and replied rather grumpily that he was feeling tolerably well, adding that he'd feel still better if only he could be sure of being left in peace. Rieux remarked that one couldn't always be alone.

"That's not what I meant. I was thinking of people who take an interest in you only to make trouble for you." When Rieux said nothing, he went on: "Mind you, that's not my case. Only I've been reading that detective story. It's about a poor devil who's arrested one fine morning, all of a sudden. People had been taking an interest in him and he knew nothing about it. They were talking about him in offices, entering his name on card indexes. Now, do you think that's fair? Do you think people have a right to treat a man like that?"

"Well," Rieux said, "that depends. In one sense I agree, nobody has the right. But all that's beside the mark. What's important is for you to go out a bit. It's a mistake staying indoors too much."

Cottard seemed vexed and said that on the contrary he was always going out, and, if need arose, all the people in the street could vouch for him. What's more, he knew lots of people in other parts of the town.

"Do you know Monsieur Rigaud, the architect? He's a friend of mine."

The room was in almost complete darkness. Outside, the street was growing noisier and a sort of murmur of relief greeted the moment when all the street-lamps lit up, all together. Rieux went out on the balcony, and Cottard followed him. From the outlying districts—as happens every evening in our town—a gentle breeze wafted a murmur of voices, smells of roasting meat, a gay, perfumed tide of freedom sounding on its way, as the streets filled up with noisy young people released from shops and offices. Nightfall, with its deep, remote baying of unseen ships, the rumor rising from the sea, and the happy tumult of the crowd—that first hour of darkness which in the past had always had a special charm for Rieux—seemed today charged with menace, because of all he knew.

"How about turning on the lights?" he suggested when they went back into the room.

After this had been done, the little man gazed at him, blinking his eyes.

"Tell me, doctor. Suppose I fell ill, would you put me in your ward at the hospital?"

"Why not?"

Cottard then inquired if it ever happened that a person in a hospital or a nursing home was arrested. Rieux said it had been known to happen, but all depended on the invalid's condition.

"You know, doctor," Cottard said, "I've confidence in you." Then he asked the doctor if he'd be kind enough to give him a lift, as he was going into town.

In the center of the town the streets were already growing less crowded and the lights fewer. Children were playing in front of the doorways. At Cottard's request the doctor stopped his car beside one of the groups of children. They were playing hopscotch and making a great deal of noise. One of them, a boy with sleek, neatly parted hair and a grubby face, stared hard at Rieux with bright, bold eyes. The doctor looked away. Standing on the sidewalk Cottard shook his head. He then said in a hoarse, rather labored voice, casting uneasy glances over his shoulder:

"Everybody's talking about an epidemic. Is there anything in it, doctor?"

"People always talk," Rieux replied. "That's only to be expected."

"You're right. And if we have ten deaths they'll think it's the end of the world. But it's not that we need here."

The engine was ticking over. Rieux had his hand on the lever. But he was looking again at the boy who was still watching him with an oddly grave intentness. Suddenly, unexpectedly, the child smiled, showing all his teeth.

"Yes? And what do we need here?" Rieux asked, returning the child's smile.

Abruptly Cottard gripped the door of the car and, as he turned to go, almost shouted in a rageful, passionate voice:

"An earthquake! A big one!"

There was no earthquake, and the whole of the following day was spent, so far as Rieux was concerned, in long drives to every corner of the town, in parleyings with the families of the sick and arguments with the invalids themselves. Never had Rieux known his profession to weigh on him so heavily. Hitherto his patients had helped to lighten his task; they gladly put themselves into his hands. For the first time the doctor felt they were keeping aloof, wrapping themselves up in their malady with a sort of bemused hostility. It was a struggle to which he wasn't yet accustomed. And when, at ten that evening, he parked his car outside the home of his old asthma patient—his last visit of the day—it was an effort for Rieux to drag himself from his seat. For some moments he lingered, gazing up the dark street, watching the stars appear and disappear in the blackness of the sky.

When Rieux entered the room, the old man was sitting up in bed, at his usual occupation, counting out dried peas from one pan to another. On seeing his visitor he looked up, beaming with delight.

"Well, doctor? It's cholera, isn't it?"

"Where on earth did you get that idea from?"

"It's in the paper, and the radio said it, too."

"No, it's not cholera."

"Anyhow," the old man chuckled excitedly, "the big bugs are laying it on thick. Got the jitters, haven't they?"

"Don't you believe a word of it," the doctor said.

He had examined the old man and now was sitting in the middle of the dingy little dining-room. Yes, despite what he had said, he was afraid. He knew that in this suburb alone eight or ten unhappy people, cowering over their buboes, would be awaiting his visit next morning. In only two or three cases had incision of the buboes caused any improvement. For most of them it would mean going to the hospital, and he knew how poor people feel about hospitals. "I don't want them trying their experiments on him," had said the wife of one of his patients. But he wouldn't be experimented on; he would die, that was all. That the regulations now in force were inadequate was lamentably clear. As for the "specially equipped" wards, he knew what they amounted to: two outbuildings from which the other patients had been hastily evacuated, whose windows had been hermetically sealed, and round which a sanitary cordon had been set. The only hope was that the outbreak would die a natural death; it certainly wouldn't be arrested by the measures the authorities had so far devised.

Nevertheless, that night the official communiqué was still optimistic. On the following day Ransdoc announced that the rules laid down by the local administration had won general approval and already thirty sick persons had reported. Castel rang up Rieux.

"How many beds are there in the special wards?"

"Eighty."

"Surely there are far more than thirty cases in the town?"

"Don't forget there are two sorts of cases: those who take fright, and those—they're the majority—who don't have time to do so."

"I see. Are they checking up on the burials?"

"No. I told Richard over the phone that energetic measures were needed, not just words; we'd got to set up a real barrier against the disease, otherwise we might just as well do nothing."

"Yes? And what did he say?"

"Nothing doing. He hadn't the powers. In my opinion, it's going to get worse."

That was so. Within three days both wards were full. According to Richard, there was talk of requisitioning a school and opening an auxiliary hospital. Meanwhile Rieux continued incising buboes and waiting for the anti-plague serum. Castel went back to his old books and spent long hours in the public library.

"Those rats died of plague," was his conclusion, "or of something extremely like it. And they've loosed on the town tens of thousands of fleas, which will spread the infection in geometrical progression unless it's checked in time."

Rieux said nothing.

About this time the weather appeared set fair, and the sun had drawn up the last puddles left by the recent rain. There was a serene blue sky flooded with golden light each morning, with sometimes a drone of planes in the rising heat—all seemed well with the world. And yet within four days the fever had made four startling strides: sixteen deaths, twenty-four, twenty-eight, and thirty-two. On the fourth day the opening of the auxiliary hospital in the premises of a primary school was officially announced. The local population, who so far had made a point of masking their anxiety by facetious comments, now seemed tongue-tied and went their ways with gloomy faces.

Rieux decided to ring up the Prefect. "The regulations don't go anywhere near far enough."

"Yes," the Prefect replied. "I've seen the statistics and, as you say, they're most perturbing."

"They're more than perturbing; they're conclusive."

"I'll ask government for orders."

When Rieux next met Castel, the Prefect's remark was still rankling.

"Orders!" he said scornfully. "When what's needed is imagination."

"Any news of the serum?"

"It'll come this week."

The Prefect sent instructions to Rieux, through Richard, asking him to draw up a minute to be transmitted for orders to the central administration of the colony. Rieux included in it a clinical diagnosis and statistics of the epidemic. On that day forty deaths were reported. The Prefect took the responsibility, as he put it, of tightening up the new regulations. Compulsory declaration of all cases of fever and their isolation were to be strictly enforced. The residences of sick people were to be shut up and disinfected; persons living in the same house were to go into quarantine; burials were to be supervised by the local authorities —in a manner which will be described later on. Next day the serum arrived by plane. There was enough for immediate requirements, but not enough if the epidemic were to spread. In reply to his telegram Rieux was informed that the emergency reserve stock was exhausted, but that a new supply was in preparation.

Meanwhile, from all the outlying districts, spring was making its progress into the town. Thousands of roses wilted in the flower-vendors' baskets in the market-places and along the streets, and the air was heavy with their cloying perfume. Outwardly, indeed, this spring was like any other. The streetcars were always packed at the rush hours, empty and untidy during the rest of the day. Tarrou watched the little old man, and the little old man spat on the cats. Grand hurried home every evening to his mysterious literary activities. Cottard went his usual desultory ways, and M. Othon, the magistrate, continued to parade his menagerie. The old Spaniard decanted his dried peas from pan to pan, and sometimes you encountered Rambert, the journalist, looking interested as ever in all he saw. In the evening the usual crowd thronged the streets and the lines lengthened outside the picture-houses. Moreover, the epidemic seemed to be on the wane; on some days only ten or so deaths were notified. Then, all of a sudden, the figure shot up again, vertically. On the day when the death-roll touched thirty, Dr. Rieux read an official telegram that the Prefect had just handed him, remarking: "So they've got alarmed at last." The telegram ran: *Proclaim a state of plague stop close the town.*

PART II

From now on, it can be said that plague was the concern of all of us. Hitherto, surprised as he may have been by the strange things happening around him, each individual citizen had gone about his business as usual, so far as this was possible. And no doubt he would have continued doing so. But once the town gates were shut, every one of us realized that all, the narrator included, were, so to speak, in the same boat, and each would have to adapt himself to the new conditions of life. Thus, for example, a feeling normally as individual as the ache of separation from those one loves suddenly became a feeling in which all shared alike and—together with fear—the greatest affliction of the long period of exile that lay ahead.

One of the most striking consequences of the closing of the gates was, in fact, this sudden deprivation befalling people who were completely unprepared for it. Mothers and children, lovers, husbands and wives, who had a few days previously taken it for granted that their parting would be a short one, who had kissed one another good-by on the platform and exchanged a few trivial remarks, sure as they were of seeing one another again after a few days or, at most, a few weeks, duped by our blind human faith in the near future and little if at all diverted from their normal interests by this leave-taking—all these people found themselves, without the least warning, hopelessly cut off, prevented from seeing one another again, or even communicating with one another. For actually the closing of the gates took place some hours before the official order was made known to the public, and, naturally enough, it was impossible to take individual cases of hardship into account. It might indeed be said that the first effect of this brutal visitation was to compel our townspeople to act as if they had no feelings as individuals. During the first part of the day on which the prohibition to leave the town came into force the Prefect's office was besieged by a crowd of applicants advancing pleas of equal cogency but equally impossible to take into consideration. Indeed, it needed several days for us to realize that we were completely cornered; that words like "special arrangements," "favor," and "priority" had lost all effective meaning.

Even the small satisfaction of writing letters was denied us. It came to this: not only had the town ceased to be in touch with the rest of the world by normal means of communication, but also—according to a second notification—all correspondence was forbidden, to obviate the risk of letters' carrying infection outside the town. In the early days a favored few managed to persuade the sentries at the gates to allow them to get messages through to the outside world. But that was only at the beginning of the epidemic, when the sentries found it natural to obey their feelings of humanity. Later on, when these same sentries had had the gravity of the situation drummed into them, they flatly refused to take responsibilities whose possible after-effects they could not foresee. At first, telephone calls to other towns were allowed, but this led to such crowding of the telephone booths and delays on the lines that for some days they also were prohibited, and thereafter limited to what were called "urgent cases," such as deaths, marriages, and births. So we had to fall back on telegrams. People linked together by friendship, affection, or physical love found themselves reduced to hunting for tokens of their past communion within the compass of a ten-word telegram. And since, in practice, the phrases one can use in a telegram are quickly exhausted, long lives passed side by side, or passionate yearnings, soon declined to the exchange of such trite formulas as: "Am well. Always thinking of you. Love."

Some few of us, however, persisted in writing letters and gave much time to hatching plans for corresponding with the outside world; but almost always these plans came to nothing. Even on the rare occasions when they succeeded, we could not know this, since we received no answer. For weeks on end we were reduced to starting the same letter over and over again recopying the same scraps of news and the same personal appeals, with the result that after a certain time the living words, into which we had as it were transfused our hearts' blood, were drained of any meaning. Thereafter we went on copying them mechanically, trying, through the dead phrases, to convey some notion of our ordeal. And in the long run, to these sterile, reiterated monologues, these futile colloquies with a blank wall, even the banal formulas of a telegram came to seem preferable.

Also, after some days—when it was clear that no one had the least hope of being able to leave our town—inquiries began to be made whether the return of people who had gone away before the outbreak would be permitted. After some days' consideration of the matter the authorities replied affirmatively. They pointed out, however, that in no case would persons who returned be allowed to leave the town again; once here, they would have to stay, whatever happened. Some families—actually very few—refused to take the position seriously and in their eagerness to have the absent members of the family with them again, cast prudence to the winds and wired to them to take this opportunity of returning. But very soon those who were prisoners of the plague realized the terrible danger to which this would expose their relatives, and sadly resigned themselves to their absence. At the height of the epidemic we saw only one case in which natural emotions overcame the fear of death in a particularly painful form. It was not, as might be expected, the case of two young people, whose passion made them yearn for each other's nearness at whatever cost of pain. The two were old Dr. Castel and his wife, and they had been married for very many years. Mme Castel had gone on a visit to a neighboring town some days before the epidemic started. They weren't one of those exemplary married couples of the Darby-and-Joan pattern;

on the contrary, the narrator has grounds for saying that, in all probability, neither partner felt quite sure the marriage was all that could have been desired. But this ruthless, protracted separation enabled them to realize that they could not live apart, and in the sudden glow of this discovery the risk of plague seemed insignificant.

That was an exception. For most people it was obvious that the separation must last until the end of the epidemic. And for every one of us the ruling emotion of his life—which he had imagined he knew through and through (the people of Oran, as has been said, have simple passions)—took on a new aspect. Husbands who had had complete faith in their wives found, to their surprise, that they were jealous; and lovers had the same experience. Men who had pictured themselves as Don Juans became models of fidelity. Sons who had lived beside their mothers hardly giving them a glance fell to picturing with poignant regret each wrinkle in the absent face that memory cast upon the screen. This drastic, clean-cut deprivation and our complete ignorance of what the future held in store had taken us unawares; we were unable to react against the mute appeal of presences, still so near and already so far, which haunted us day-long. In fact, our suffering was twofold; our own to start with, and then the imagined suffering of the absent one, son, mother, wife, or mistress.

Under other circumstances our towns-folk would probably have found an outlet in increased activity, a more sociable life. But the plague forced inactivity on them, limiting their movements to the same dull round inside the town, and throwing them, day after day, on the illusive solace of their memories. For in their aimless walks they kept on coming back to the same streets and usually, owing to the smallness of the town, these were streets in which, in happier days, they had walked with those who now were absent.

Thus the first thing that plague brought to our town was exile. And the narrator is convinced that he can set down here, as holding good for all, the feeling he personally had and to which many of his friends confessed. It was undoubtedly the feeling of exile—that sensation of a void within which never left us, that irrational longing to hark back to the past or else to speed up the march of time, and those keen shafts of memory that stung like fire. Sometimes we toyed with our imagination, composing ourselves to wait for a ring at the bell announcing somebody's return, or for the sound of a familiar footstep on the stairs; but, though we might deliberately stay at home at the hour when a traveler coming by the evening train would normally have arrived, and though we might contrive to forget for the moment that no trains were running, that game of make-believe, for obvious reasons, could not last. Always a moment came when we had to face the fact that no trains were coming in. And then we realized that the separation was destined to continue, we had no choice but to come to terms with the days ahead. In short, we returned to our prison-house, we had nothing left us but the past, and even if some were tempted to live in the future, they had speedily to abandon the idea—anyhow, as soon as could be—once they felt the wounds that the imagination inflicts on those who yield themselves to it.

It is noteworthy that our townspeople very quickly desisted, even in public, from a habit one might have expected them to form—that of trying to figure out the probable duration of their exile. The reason was this: when the most pessimistic had fixed it at, say, six months; when they had drunk in advance the dregs of bitterness of those six black

months, and painfully screwed up their courage to the sticking-place, straining all their remaining energy to endure valiantly the long ordeal of all those weeks and days—when they had done this, some friend they met, an article in a newspaper, a vague suspicion, or a flash of foresight would suggest that, after all, there was no reason why the epidemic shouldn't last more than six months; why not a year, or even more?

At such moments the collapse of their courage, willpower, and endurance was so abrupt that they felt they could never drag themselves out of the pit of despond into which they had fallen. Therefore they forced themselves never to think about the problematic day of escape, to cease looking to the future, and always to keep, so to speak, their eyes fixed on the ground at their feet. But, naturally enough, this prudence, this habit of feinting with their predicament and refusing to put up a fight, was ill rewarded. For, while averting that revulsion which they found so unbearable, they also deprived themselves of those redeeming moments, frequent enough when all is told, when by conjuring up pictures of a reunion to be, they could forget about the plague. Thus, in a middle course between these heights and depths, they drifted through life rather than lived, the prey of aimless days and sterile memories, like wandering shadows that could have acquired substance only by consenting to root themselves in the solid earth of their distress.

Thus, too, they came to know the incorrigible sorrow of all prisoners and exiles, which is to live in company with a memory that serves no purpose. Even the past, of which they thought incessantly, had a savor only of regret. For they would have wished to add to it all that they regretted having left undone, while they might yet have done it, with the man or woman whose return they now awaited; just as in all the activities, even the relatively happy ones, of their life as prisoners they kept vainly trying to include the absent one. And thus there was always something missing in their lives. Hostile to the past, impatient of the present, and cheated of the future, we were much like those whom men's justice, or hatred, forces to live behind prison bars. Thus the only way of escaping from that intolerable leisure was to set the trains running again in one's imagination and in filling the silence with the fancied tinkle of a doorbell, in practice obstinately mute.

Still, if it was an exile, it was, for most of us, exile in one's own home. And though the narrator experienced only the common form of exile, he cannot forget the case of those who, like Rambert the journalist and a good many others, had to endure an aggravated deprivation, since, being travelers caught by the plague and forced to stay where they were, they were cut off both from the person with whom they wanted to be and from their homes as well. In the general exile they were the most exiled; since while time gave rise for them, as for us all, to the suffering appropriate to it, there was also for them the space factor; they were obsessed by it and at every moment knocked their heads against the walls of this huge and alien lazar-house secluding them from their lost homes. These were the people, no doubt, whom one often saw wandering forlornly in the dusty town at all hours of the day, silently invoking nightfalls known to them alone and the daysprings of their happier land. And they fed their despondency with fleeting intimations, messages as disconcerting as a flight of swallows, a dew-fall at sundown, or those queer glints the sun sometimes dapples on empty streets. As for that outside world, which can always offer an escape from everything, they shut their eyes to it, bent

as they were on cherishing the all-too-real phantoms of their imagination and conjuring up with all their might pictures of a land where a special play of light, two or three hills, a favorite tree, a woman's smile, composed for them a world that nothing could replace.

To come at last, and more specifically, to the case of parted lovers, who present the greatest interest and of whom the narrator is, perhaps, better qualified to speak—their minds were the prey of different emotions, notably remorse. For their present position enabled them to take stock of their feelings with a sort of feverish objectivity. And, in these conditions, it was rare for them not to detect their own shortcomings. What first brought these home to them was the trouble they experienced in summoning up any clear picture of what the absent one was doing. They came to deplore their ignorance of the way in which that person used to spend his or her days, and reproached themselves for having troubled too little about this in the past, and for having affected to think that, for a lover, the occupations of the loved one when they are not together could be a matter of indifference and not a source of joy. Once this had been brought home to them, they could retrace the course of their love and see where it had fallen short. In normal times all of us know, whether consciously or not, that there is no love which can't be bettered; nevertheless, we reconcile ourselves more or less easily to the fact that ours has never risen above the average. But memory is less disposed to compromise. And, in a very definite way, this misfortune which had come from outside and befallen a whole town did more than inflict on us an unmerited distress with which we might well be indignant. It also incited us to create our own suffering and thus to accept frustration as a natural state. This was one of the tricks the pestilence had of diverting attention and confounding issues.

Thus each of us had to be content to live only for the day, alone under the vast indifference of the sky. This sense of being abandoned, which might in time have given characters a finer temper, began, however, by sapping them to the point of futility. For instance, some of our fellow citizens became subject to a curious kind of servitude, which put them at the mercy of the sun and the rain. Looking at them, you had an impression that for the first time in their lives they were becoming, as some would say, weather-conscious. A burst of sunshine was enough to make them seem delighted with the world, while rainy days gave a dark cast to their faces and their mood. A few weeks before, they had been free of this absurd subservience to the weather, because they had not to face life alone; the person they were living with held, to some extent, the foreground of their little world. But from now on it was different; they seemed at the mercy of the sky's caprices—in other words, suffered and hoped irrationally.

Moreover, in this extremity of solitude none could count on any help from his neighbor; each had to bear the load of his troubles alone. If, by some chance, one of us tried to unburden himself or to say something about his feelings, the reply he got, whatever it might be, usually wounded him. And then it dawned on him that he and the man with him weren't talking about the same thing. For while he himself spoke from the depths of long days of brooding upon his personal distress, and the image he had tried to impart had been slowly shaped and proved in the fires of passion and regret, this meant nothing to the man to whom he was speaking, who pictured a conventional emotion, a grief that is traded on the market-place, mass-produced. Whether friendly or hostile, the reply always missed fire, and the attempt to communicate had to be given up. This was true of those at least for whom silence was unbearable, and since the others could not find the truly expressive word, they resigned themselves to using the current coin of language, the commonplaces of plain narrative, of anecdote, and of their daily paper. So in these cases, too, even the sincerest grief had to make do with the set phrases of ordinary conversation. Only on these terms could the prisoners of the plague ensure the sympathy of their concierge and the interest of their hearers.

Nevertheless—and this point is most important—however bitter their distress and however heavy their hearts, for all their emptiness, it can be truly said of these exiles that in the early period of the plague they could account themselves privileged. For at the precise moment when the residents of the town began to panic, their thoughts were wholly fixed on the person whom they longed to meet again. The egoism of love made them immune to the general distress and, if they thought of the plague, it was only in so far as it might threaten to make their separation eternal. Thus in the very heart of the epidemic they maintained a saving indifference, which one was tempted to take for composure. Their despair saved them from panic, thus their misfortune had a good side. For instance, if it happened that one of them was carried off by the disease, it was almost always without his having had time to realize it. Snatched suddenly from his long, silent communion with a wraith of memory, he was plunged straightway into the densest silence of all. He'd had no time for anything.

While our townspeople were trying to come to terms with their sudden isolation, the plague was posting sentries at the gates and turning away ships bound for Oran. No vehicle had entered the town since the gates were closed. From that day onwards one had the impression that all cars were moving in circles. The harbor, too, presented a strange appearance to those who looked down on it from the top of the boulevards. The commercial activity that hitherto made it one of the chief ports on the coast had ceased abruptly. Only a few ships, detained in quarantine, were anchored in the bay. But the gaunt, idle cranes on the wharves, tip-carts lying on their sides, neglected heaps of sacks and barrels—all testified that commerce, too, had died of plague.

In spite of such unusual sights our townsfolk apparently found it hard to grasp what was happening to them. There were feelings all could share, such as fear and separation, but personal interests, too, continued to occupy the foreground of their thoughts. Nobody as yet had really acknowledged to himself what the disease connoted. Most people were chiefly aware of what ruffled the normal tenor of their lives or affected their interests. They were worried and irritated—but these are not feelings with which to confront plague. Their first reaction, for instance, was to abuse the authorities. The Prefect's riposte to criticisms echoed by the press—Could not the regulations be modified and made less stringent?—was somewhat unexpected. Hitherto neither the newspapers nor the Ransdoc Information Bureau had been given any official statistics relating to the epidemic. Now the Prefect supplied them daily to the bureau, with the request that they should be broadcast once a week.

In this, too, the reaction of the public was slower than might have been expected. Thus the bare statement that three hundred and two deaths had taken place in the third week of plague failed to strike their imagination. For one thing, all the three hundred and two deaths might not have been due to plague. Also, no one in the town had any idea of the average weekly death-rate in ordinary times. The population of the town was about two hundred thousand. There was no knowing if the present death-rate were really so abnormal. This is, in fact, the kind of statistics that nobody ever troubles much about—notwithstanding that its interest is obvious. The public lacked, in short, standards of comparison. It was only as time passed and the steady rise in the death-rate could not be ignored that public opinion became alive to the truth. For in the fifth week there were three hundred and twenty-one deaths, and three hundred and forty-five in the sixth. These figures, anyhow, spoke for themselves. Yet they were still not sensational enough to prevent our townsfolk, perturbed though they were, from persisting in the idea that what was happening was a sort of accident, disagreeable enough, but certainly of a temporary order.

So they went on strolling about the town as usual and sitting at the tables on café terraces. Generally speaking, they did not lack courage, bandied more jokes than lamentations, and made a show of accepting cheerfully unpleasantnesses that obviously could be only passing. In short, they kept up appearances. However, toward the end of the month, about the time of the Week of Prayer which will be described later on, there were more serious developments, altering the whole aspect of the town. To begin with, the Prefect took measures controlling the traffic and the food-supply. Gasoline was rationed and restrictions were placed on the sale of foodstuffs. Reductions were ordered in the use of electricity. Only necessaries were brought by road or air to Oran. Thus the traffic thinned out progressively until hardly any private cars were on the roads; luxury shops closed overnight, and others began to put up *"Sold Out"* notices, while crowds of buyers stood waiting at their doors.

Oran assumed a novel appearance. You saw more pedestrians, and in the slack hours numbers of people, reduced to idleness because shops and a good many offices were closed, crowded the streets and cafés. For the present they were not unemployed; merely on holiday. So it was that on fine days, toward three in the afternoon, Oran brought to mind a city where public rejoicings are in progress, shops are shut, and traffic is stopped to give a merry-making populace the freedom of the streets.

Naturally the picture-houses benefited by the situation and made money hand over fist. They had one difficulty, however—to provide a change of program, since the circulation of films in the region had been suspended. After a fortnight the various cinemas were obliged to exchange films and, after a further lapse of time, to show always the same program. In spite of this their takings did not fall off.

The cafés, thanks to the big stocks accumulated in a town where the wine-and-liquor trade holds pride of place, were equally able to cater for their patrons. And, to tell the truth, there was much heavy drinking. One of the cafés had the brilliant idea of putting up a slogan: "The best protection against infection is a bottle of good wine," which confirmed an already prevalent opinion that alcohol is a safeguard against infectious disease. Every night, toward two a.m., quite a number of drunken men, ejected from the cafés, staggered down the streets, vociferating optimism.

Yet all these changes were, in one sense, so fantastic and had been made so precipitately that it wasn't easy to regard them as likely to have any permanence. With the result that we went on focusing our attention on our personal feelings.

When leaving the hospital two days after the gates were closed, Dr. Rieux met Cottard in the street. The little man was beaming with satisfaction. Rieux congratulated him on his appearance.

"Yes," Cottard said, "I'm feeling very fit. Never was fitter in my life. But tell me, doctor. This blasted plague, what about it? Getting to look mighty serious, isn't it?" When the doctor nodded, he continued exuberantly: "And there's no reason for it to stop now. This town's going to be in an unholy mess, by the look of things."

They walked a little way together. Cottard told the story of a grocer in his street who had laid by masses of canned provisions with the idea of selling them later on at a big profit. When the ambulance men came to fetch him he had several dozen cans of meat under his bed. "He died in the hospital. There's no money in plague, that's sure." Cottard was a mine of stories of this kind, true or false, about the epidemic. One of them was about a man with all the symptoms and running a high fever who dashed out into the street, flung himself on the first woman he met, and embraced her, yelling that he'd "got it."

"Good for him!" was Cottard's comment. But his next remark seemed to belie his gleeful exclamation. "Anyhow, we'll all be nuts before long, unless I'm much mistaken."

It was on the afternoon of the same day that Grand at last unburdened himself to Rieux. Noticing Mme Rieux's photograph on the desk, he looked at the doctor inquiringly. Rieux told him that his wife was under treatment in a sanatorium some distance from the town. "In one way," Grand said, "that's lucky."

The doctor agreed that it was lucky in a sense; but, he added, the great thing was that his wife should recover.

"Yes," Grand said, "I understand."

And then, for the first time since Rieux had made his acquaintance, he became quite voluble. Though he still had trouble over his words he succeeded nearly always in finding them; indeed, it was as if for years he'd been thinking over what he now said.

When in his teens, he had married a very young girl, one of a poor family living near by. It was, in fact, in order to marry that he'd abandoned his studies and taken up his present job. Neither he nor Jeanne ever stirred from their part of the town. In his courting days he used to go to see her at her home, and the family were inclined to make fun of her bashful, silent admirer. Her father was a railroad-man. When off duty, he spent most of the time seated in a corner beside the window gazing meditatively at the passers-by, his enormous hands splayed out on his thighs. His wife was always busy with domestic duties, in which Jeanne gave her a hand. Jeanne was so tiny that it always made Grand nervous to see her crossing a street, the vehicles bearing down on her looked so gigantic. Then one day shortly before Christmas they went out for a short walk together and stopped to admire a gaily decorated shop-window. After gazing ecstatically at it for some moments, Jeanne turned to him. "Oh, isn't it lovely!" He squeezed her wrist. It was thus that the marriage had come about.

The rest of the story, to Grand's think-ing, was very simple. The common lot of married couples. You get married, you go on loving a bit longer, you work. And you work so hard that it makes you forget to love. As the head of the office where Grand was employed hadn't kept his promise, Jeanne, too, had to work

outside. At this point a little imagination was needed to grasp what Grand was trying to convey. Owing largely to fatigue, he gradually lost grip of himself, had less and less to say, and failed to keep alive the feeling in his wife that she was loved. An overworked husband, pov-erty, the gradual loss of hope in a better future, silent evenings at home—what chance had any passion of surviving such conditions? Probably Jeanne had suffered. And yet she'd stayed; of course one may often suffer a long time without knowing it. Thus years went by. Then, one day, she left him. Naturally she hadn't gone alone. "I was very fond of you, but now I'm so tired. I'm not happy to go, but one needn't be happy to make another start." That, more or less, was what she'd said in her letter.

Grand, too, had suffered. And he, too, might—as Rieux pointed out—have made a fresh start. But no, he had lost faith. Only, he couldn't stop thinking about her. What he'd have liked to do was to write her a letter justifying himself.

"But it's not easy," he told Rieux. "I've been thinking it over for years. While we loved each other we didn't need words to make ourselves understood. But people don't love forever. A time came when I should have found the words to keep her with me—only I couldn't." Grand pro-duced from his pocket something that looked like a checked napkin and blew his nose noisily. Then he wiped his mus-tache. Rieux gazed at him in silence. "Forgive me, doctor," Grand added hastily, "but—how shall I put it?—I feel you're to be trusted. That's why I can talk to you about these things. And then, you see, I get all worked up."

Obviously Grand's thoughts were leagues away from the plague.

That evening Rieux sent a telegram to his wife telling her that the town was closed, that she must go on taking great care of herself, and that she was in his thoughts.

One evening when he was leaving the hospital—it was about three weeks after the closing of the gates—Rieux found a young man waiting for him in the street.

"You remember me, don't you?"

Rieux believed he did, but couldn't quite place him.

"I called on you just before this trouble started," the young man said, "for information about the living-conditions in the Arab quarter. My name is Raymond Rambert."

"Ah yes, of course. Well, you've now the makings of a good story for your paper."

Rambert, who gave the impression of being much less self-assured than he had seemed on the first occasion when they met, said it wasn't that he'd come about. He wanted to know if the doctor would kindly give him some help.

"I must apologize," he continued, "but really I don't know a soul here, and the local representative of my paper is a complete dud."

Rieux said he had to go to a dispensary in the center of the town and suggested they should walk there together. Their way lay through the narrow streets of the Negro district. Evening was coming on, but the town, once so noisy at this hour, was strangely still. The only sounds were some bugle-calls echoing through the air, still golden with the end of daylight; the army, anyhow, was making a show of carrying on as usual. Meanwhile, as they walked down the steep little streets flanked by blue, mauve, and saffron-yellow walls, Rambert talked incessantly, as if his nerves were out of hand.

He had left his wife in Paris, he said. Well, she wasn't actually his wife, but it came to the same thing. The moment the town was put into quarantine he had sent her a wire. His impression then was that this state of things was quite temporary, and all he'd tried to do was to get a letter through to her. But the post-office officials had vetoed this, his colleagues of the local press said they could do nothing for him, and a clerk in the Prefect's office had laughed in his face. It was only after waiting in line for a couple of hours that he had managed to get a telegram accepted: *All goes well. Hope to see you soon.*

But next morning, when he woke up, it had dawned on him that, after all, there was absolutely no knowing how long this business was going to last. So he'd decided to leave the town at once. Being able, thanks to his professional status, to pull some strings, he had secured an interview with a high official in the Prefect's office. He had explained that his presence in Oran was purely accidental, he had no connection with the town and no reasons for staying in it; that being so, he surely was entitled to leave, even if, once outside the town, he had to undergo a spell of quarantine. The official told him he quite appreciated his position, but no exceptions could be made. He would, however, see if anything could be done, though he could hold out little hope of a quick decision, as the authorities were taking a very serious view of the situation.

"But, confound it," Rambert exclaimed, "I don't belong here!"

"Quite so. Anyhow, let's hope the epidemic will soon be over." Finally, he had tried to console Rambert by pointing out that, as a journalist, he had an excellent subject to his hand in Oran; indeed, when one came to think of it, no event, however disagreeable in some ways, but had its bright side. Whereat Rambert had shrugged his shoulders petulantly and walked out.

They had come to the center of the town.

"It's so damn silly, doctor, isn't it? The truth is I wasn't brought into the world to write newspaper articles. But it's quite likely I was brought into the world to live with a woman. That's reasonable enough, isn't it?"

Rieux replied cautiously that there might be something in what he said.

The central boulevards were not so crowded as usual. The few people about were hurrying to distant homes. Not a smile was to be seen on any face. Rieux guessed that this was a result of the latest Ransdoc announcement. After twenty-four hours our townspeople would begin to hope again. But on the days when they were announced, the statistics were too fresh in everybody's memory.

"The truth," Rambert remarked abruptly, "is that she and I have been together only a short time, and we suit each other perfectly." When Rieux said nothing, he continued: "I can see I'm boring you. Sorry. All I wanted to know was whether you couldn't possibly give me a certificate stating that I haven't got this damned disease. It might make things easier, I think."

Rieux nodded. A small boy had just run against his legs and fallen; he set him on his feet again. Walking on, they came to the Place d'Armes. Gray with dust, the palms and fig trees drooped despondently around a statue of the Republic, which too was coated with grime and dust. They stopped beside the statue. Rieux stamped his feet on the flagstones to shake off the coat of white dust that had gathered on them. His hat pushed slightly back, his shirt-collar gaping under a loosely knotted tie, his cheeks ill-shaven, the journalist had the sulky, stubborn look of a young man who feels himself deeply injured.

"Please don't doubt I understand you," Rieux said, "but you must see your argu-ment doesn't hold water. I can't give you that certificate because I don't know whether you have the disease or not, and even if I did, how could I certify that between the moment of leaving my con-sulting-room and your arrival at the Pre-fect's office you wouldn't be infected? And even if I did—"

"And even if you did—?"

"Even if I gave you a certificate, it wouldn't help."

"Why not?"

"Because there are thousands of people placed as you are in this town, and there can't be any question of allow-ing them to leave it."

"Even supposing they haven't got plague?"

"That's not a sufficient reason. Oh, I know it's an absurd situation, but we're all involved in it, and we've got to accept it as it is."

"But I don't belong here."

"Unfortunately, from now on you'll belong here, like everybody else."

Rambert raised his voice a little.

"But, damn it, doctor, can't you see it's a matter of common human feeling? Or don't you realize what this sort of separation means to people who are fond of each other?"

Rieux was silent for a moment, then said he understood it perfectly. He wished nothing better than that Rambert should be allowed to return to his wife and that all who loved one another and were parted should come together again. Only the law was the law, plague had broken out, and he could only do what had to be done.

"No," Rambert said bitterly, "you can't understand. You're using the lan-guage of reason, not of the heart; you live in a world of abstractions."

The doctor glanced up at the statue of the Republic, then said he did not know if he was using the language of reason, but he knew he was using the language of the facts as everybody could see them —which wasn't necessarily the same thing.

The journalist tugged at his tie to straighten it.

"So, I take it, I can't count on help from you. Very good. But"—his tone was challenging—"leave this town I shall."

The doctor repeated that he quite understood, but all that was none of his business.

"Excuse me, but it *is* your business." Rambert raised his voice again. "I approached you because I'd been told you played a large part in drawing up the orders that have been issued. So I thought that in one case anyhow you could unmake what you'd helped to make. But you don't care; you never gave a thought to anybody, you didn't take the case of people who are separated into account."

Rieux admitted this was true up to a point; he'd preferred not to take such cases into account.

"Ah, I see now!" Rambert exclaimed. "You'll soon be talking about the interests of the general public. But public welfare is merely the sum total of the private welfares of each of us."

The doctor seemed abruptly to come out of a dream.

"Oh, come!" he said. "There's that, but there's much more to it than that. It doesn't do to rush to conclusions, you know. But you've no reason to feel angered. I assure you that if you find a way out of your quandary, I shall be extremely pleased. Only, there are things that my official position debars me from doing."

Rambert tossed his head petulantly.

"Yes, yes, I was wrong to show annoyance. And I've taken up too much of your time already."

Rieux asked him to let him know how he got on with his project, and not to bear him a grudge for not having been more amenable. He was sure, he added, that there was some common ground on which they could meet. Rambert looked perplexed.

Then, "Yes," he said after a short silence, "I rather think so, too—in spite of myself, and of all you've just been saying." He paused. "Still, I can't agree with you."

Pulling down his hat over his eyes, he walked quickly away. Rieux saw him enter the hotel where Tarrou was staying.

After a moment the doctor gave a slight nod, as if approving of some thought that had crossed his mind. Yes, the journalist was right in refusing to be balked of happiness. But was he right in reproaching him, Rieux, with living in a world of abstractions? Could that term "abstraction" really apply to these days he spent in his hospital while the plague was battening on the town, raising its death-toll to five hundred victims a week? Yes, an element of abstraction, of a divorce from reality, entered into such calamities. Still when abstraction sets to killing you, you've got to get busy with it. And so much Rieux knew: that this wasn't the easiest course. Running this auxiliary hospital, for instance, of which he was in charge—there were now three such hospitals—was no light task.

He had had an anteroom, leading into his surgery, installed, equipped for dealing with patients on arrival. The floor had been excavated and replaced by a shallow lake of water and cresylic acid, in the center of which was a sort of island made of bricks. The patient was carried to the island, rapidly undressed, and his clothes dropped into the disinfectant water. After being washed, dried, and dressed in one of the coarse hospital nightshirts, he was taken to Rieux for examination, then carried to one of the wards. This hospital, a requisitioned schoolhouse, now contained five hundred beds, almost all of which were occupied. After the reception of the patients, which he personally supervised, Rieux injected serum, lanced buboes, checked the statistics again, and returned for his afternoon consultations. Only when night was setting in did he start on his round of visits, and he never got home till a very late hour. On the previous night his mother, when handing him a telegram from his wife, had remarked that his hands were shaking.

"Yes," he said. "But it's only a matter of sticking to it, and my nerves will steady down, you'll see."

He had a robust constitution and, as yet, wasn't really tired. Still his visits, for one thing, were beginning to put a great strain on his endurance. Once the epidemic was diagnosed, the patient had to be evacuated forthwith. Then indeed began "abstraction" and a tussle with the family, who knew they would not see the sick man again until he was dead or cured. "Have some pity, doctor!" It was Mme Loret, mother of the chambermaid at Tarrou's hotel, who made the appeal. An unnecessary appeal; of course he had pity. But what purpose could it serve? He *had* to telephone, and soon the ambulance could be heard clanging down the street. (At first the neighbors used to open windows and watch. Later they promptly shut them.) Then came a second phase of conflict, tears and pleadings—abstraction, in a word. In those fever-hot, nerve-ridden sickrooms crazy scenes took place. But the issue was always the same. The patient was removed. Then Rieux, too, could leave.

In the early days he had merely telephoned, then rushed off to see other patients, without waiting for the ambulance. But no sooner was he gone than the family locked and barred their doors, preferring contact with the plague to a parting whose issue they now knew only too well. There followed objurgations, screams, batterings on the door, action by the police, and later armed force; the patient was taken by storm. Thus during the first few weeks Rieux was compelled to stay with the patient till the ambulance came. Later, when each doctor was accompanied by a volunteer police officer, Rieux could hurry away to the next patient.

But, to begin with, every evening was like that evening when he was called in for Mme Loret's daughter. He was shown into a small apartment decorated with fans and artificial flowers. The mother greeted him with a faltering smile.

"Oh, I do hope it's not the fever everyone's talking about."

Lifting the coverlet and chemise, he gazed in silence at the red blotches on the girl's thighs and stomach, the swollen ganglia. After one glance the mother broke into shrill, uncontrollable cries of grief. And every evening mothers wailed thus, with a distraught abstraction, as their eyes fell on those fatal stigmata on limbs and bellies; every evening hands gripped Rieux's arms, there was a rush of useless words, promises, and tears; every evening the nearing tocsin of the ambulance provoked scenes as vain as every form of grief. Rieux had nothing to look forward to but a long sequence of such scenes, renewed again and again. Yes, plague, like abstraction, was monotonous; perhaps only one factor changed, and that was Rieux himself. Standing at the foot of the statue of the Republic that evening, he felt it; all he was conscious of was a bleak indifference steadily gaining on him as he gazed at the door of the hotel Rambert had just entered.

After these wearing weeks, after all those nightfalls when the townsfolk poured into the streets to roam them aimlessly, Rieux had learned that he need no longer steel himself against pity. One grows out of pity when it's useless. And in this feeling that his heart had slowly closed in on itself, the doctor found a solace, his only solace, for the almost unendurable burden of his days. This, he knew, would make his task easier, and therefore he was glad of it. When he came home at two in the morning and his mother was shocked at the blank look he gave her, she was deploring precisely the sole alleviation Rieux could then experience. To fight abstraction you must have something of it in your own make-up. But how could Rambert be expected to grasp that? Abstraction for him was all that stood in the way of his happiness. Indeed, Rieux had to admit the journalist was right, in one sense. But he knew, too, that abstraction sometimes proves itself stronger than happiness; and then, if only then, it has to be taken into account. And this was what was going to happen to Rambert, as the doctor was to learn when, much later, Rambert told him more about himself. Thus he was enabled to follow, and on a different plane, the dreary struggle in progress between each man's happiness and the abstractions of the plague—which constituted the whole life of our town over a long period of time.

But where some saw abstraction others saw the truth. The first month of the plague ended gloomily, with a violent recrudescence of the epidemic and a dramatic sermon preached by Father Paneloux, the Jesuit priest who had given an arm to old Michel when he was tottering home at the start of his illness. Father Paneloux had already made his mark with frequent contributions to the Oran Geographical Society; these dealt chiefly with ancient inscriptions, on which he was an authority. But he had also reached a wider, non-specialist public with a series of lectures on present-day individualism. In these he had shown himself a stalwart champion of Christian doctrine at its most precise and purest, equally remote from modern laxity and the obscurantism of the past. On these occasions he had not shrunk from trouncing his hearers with some vigorous home-truths. Hence his local celebrity.

Toward the end of the month the ecclesiastical authorities in our town resolved to do battle against the plague with the weapons appropriate to them, and organized a Week of Prayer. These manifestations of public piety were to be concluded on Sunday by a High Mass celebrated under the auspices of St. Roch, the plague-stricken saint, and Father Paneloux was asked to preach the sermon. For a fortnight he desisted from the research work on St. Augustine and the African Church that had won for him a high place in his Order. A man of a passionate, fiery temperament, he flung himself wholeheartedly into the task assigned him. The sermon was a topic of conversation long before it was delivered and, in its way, it marks an important date in the history of the period.

There were large attendances at the services of the Week of Prayer. It must not, however, be assumed that in normal times the townsfolk of Oran are particularly devout. On Sunday mornings, for instance, sea-bathing competes seriously with churchgoing. Nor must it be thought that they had seen a great light and had a sudden change of heart. But, for one thing, now that the town was closed and the harbor out of bounds, there was no question of bathing; moreover, they were in a quite exceptional frame of mind and, though in their heart of hearts they were far from recognizing the enormity of what had come on them, they couldn't help feeling, for obvious reasons, that decidedly something had changed. Nevertheless, many continued hoping that the epidemic would soon die out and they and their families be spared. Thus they felt under no obligation to make any change in their habits as yet. Plague was for them an unwelcome visitant, bound to take its leave one day as unexpectedly as it had come. Alarmed, but far from desperate, they hadn't yet reached the phase when plague would seem to them the very tissue of their existence; when they forgot the lives that until now it had been given them to lead. In short, they were waiting for the turn of events. With regard to religion—as to many other problems—plague had induced in them a curious frame of mind, as remote from indifference as from fervor; the best name to give it, perhaps, might be "objectivity." Most of those who took part in the Week of Prayer would have echoed a remark made by one of the churchgoers in Dr. Rieux's hearing: "Anyhow, it can't do any harm." Even Tarrou, after recording in his notebook that in such cases the Chinese fall to playing tambourines before the Genius of Plague, observed that there was no means of telling whether, in practice, tambourines proved more efficacious than prophylactic measures. He merely added that, to decide the point, we should need first to ascertain if a Genius of Plague actually existed, and our ignorance on this point nullified any opinions we might form.

In any case the Cathedral was practically always full of worshippers throughout the Week of Prayer. For the first two or three days many stayed outside, under the palms and pomegranate trees in the garden in front of the porch, and listened from a distance to the swelling tide of prayers and invocations whose backwash filled the neighboring streets. But once an example had been given, they began to enter the Cathedral and join timidly in the responses. And on the Sunday of the sermon a huge congregation filled the nave, overflowing on to the steps and precincts. The sky had clouded up on the previous day, and now it was raining heavily. Those in the open unfurled umbrellas. The air inside the Cathedral was heavy with fumes of incense and the smell of wet clothes when Father Paneloux stepped into the pulpit.

He was a stockily built man, of medium height. When he leaned on the edge of the pulpit, grasping the woodwork with his big hands, all one saw was a black, massive torso and, above it, two rosy cheeks overhung by steel-rimmed spectacles. He had a powerful, rather emotional delivery, which carried to a great distance, and when he launched at the congregation his opening phrase in clear, emphatic tones: "Calamity has come on you, my brethren, and, my brethren, you deserved it," there was a flutter that extended to the crowd massed in the rain outside the porch.

In strict logic what came next did not seem to follow from this dramatic opening. Only as the sermon proceeded did it become apparent to the congregation that, by a skillful oratorical device, Father Paneloux had launched at them, like a fisticuff, the gist of his whole discourse. After launching it he went on at once to quote a text from Exodus relating to the plague of Egypt, and said: "The first time this scourge appears in history, it was wielded to strike down the enemies of God. Pharaoh set himself up against the divine will, and the plague beat him to his knees. Thus from the dawn of recorded history the scourge of God has humbled the proud of heart and laid low those who hardened themselves against Him. Ponder this well, my friends, and fall on your knees."

The downpour had increased in violence, and these words, striking through a silence intensified by the drumming of raindrops on the chancel windows, carried such conviction that, after a momentary hesitation, some of the worshippers

slipped forward from their seats on to
their knees. Others felt it right to follow
their example, and the movement gradually spread until presently everyone was
kneeling, from end to end of the cathedral. No sound, except an occasional
creak of chairs, accompanied the movement. Then Paneloux drew himself up to
his full height, took a deep breath, and
continued his sermon in a voice that
gathered strength as it proceeded.

"If today the plague is in your midst,
that is because the hour has struck for
taking thought. The just man need have
no fear, but the evildoer has good cause
to tremble. For plague is the flail of God
and the world His threshing-floor, and
implacably He will thresh out His harvest
until the wheat is separated from the
chaff. There will be more chaff than
wheat, few chosen of the many called.
Yet this calamity was not willed by God.
Too long this world of ours has connived
at evil, too long has it counted on the
divine mercy, on God's forgiveness. Re-
pentance was enough, men thought;
nothing was forbidden. Everyone felt
comfortably assured; when the day came,
he would surely turn from his sins and
repent. Pending that day, the easiest
course was to surrender all along the
line; divine compassion would do the
rest. For a long while God gazed down
on this town with eyes of compassion;
but He grew weary of waiting, His eternal hope was too long deferred, and now
He has turned His face away from us.
And so, God's light withdrawn, we walk
in darkness, in the thick darkness of this
plague."

Someone in the congregation gave a
little snort, like that of a restive horse.
After a short silence the preacher continued in a lower tone.

"We read in the *Golden Legend* that in
the time of King Umberto Italy was
swept by plague and its greatest ravages
took place in Rome and Pavia. So dread-

ful were these that the living hardly
sufficed to bury the dead. And a good
angel was made visible to human eyes,
giving his orders to an evil angel who
bore a great hunting-spear, and bidding
him strike the houses; and as many
strokes as he dealt a house, so many dead
were carried out of it."

Here Paneloux stretched forth his two
short arms toward the open porch, as if
pointing to something behind the tum-
bling curtain of the rain.

"My brothers," he cried, "that fatal
hunt is up, and harrying our streets
today. See him there, that angel of the
pestilence, comely as Lucifer, shining
like Evil's very self! He is hovering above
your roofs with his great spear in his
right hand, poised to strike, while his left
hand is stretched toward one or other of
your houses. Maybe at this very moment
his finger is pointing to your door, the
red spear crashing on its panels, and even
now the plague is entering your home
and settling down in your bedroom to
await your return. Patient and watchful,
ineluctable as the order of the scheme of
things, it bides its time. No earthly
power, nay, not even—mark me well—
the vaunted might of human science can
avail you to avert that hand once it is
stretched toward you. And winnowed
like corn on the blood-stained threshing-
floor of suffering, you will be cast away
with the chaff."

At this point the Father reverted with
heightened eloquence to the symbol of
the flail. He bade his hearers picture a
huge wooden bar whirling above the
town, striking at random, swinging up
again in a shower of drops of blood, and
spreading carnage and suffering on earth,
"for the seed-time that shall prepare the
harvest of the truth."

At the end of his long phrase Father
Paneloux paused; his hair was straggling
over his forehead, his body shaken by
tremors that his hands communicated to

the pulpit. When he spoke again, his voice was lower, but vibrant with accusation.

"Yes, the hour has come for serious thought. You fondly imagined it was enough to visit God on Sundays, and thus you could make free of your weekdays. You believed some brief formalities, some bendings of the knee, would recompense Him well enough for your criminal indifference. But God is not mocked. These brief encounters could not sate the fierce hunger of His love. He wished to see you longer and more often; that is His manner of loving and, indeed, it is the only manner of loving. And this is why, wearied of waiting for you to come to Him, He loosed on you this visitation; as He has visited all the cities that offended against Him since the dawn of history. Now you are learning your lesson, the lesson that was learned by Cain and his offspring, by the people of Sodom and Gomorrah, by Job and Pharaoh, by all that hardened their hearts against Him. And like them you have been beholding mankind and all creation with new eyes, since the gates of this city closed on you and on the pestilence. Now, at last, you know the hour has struck to bend your thoughts to first and last things."

A wet wind was sweeping up the nave, making the candle-flames bend and flicker. The pungency of burning wax, coughs, a stifled sneeze, rose toward Father Paneloux, who, reverting to his exordium with a subtlety that was much appreciated, went on in a calm, almost matter-of-fact voice: "Many of you are wondering, I know, what I am leading up to. I wish to lead you to the truth and teach you to rejoice, yes, rejoice—in spite of all that I have been telling you. For the time is past when a helping hand or mere words of good advice could set you on the right path. Today the truth is a command. It is a red spear sternly pointing to the narrow path, the one way of salvation. And thus, my brothers, at last it is revealed to you, the divine compassion which has ordained good and evil in everything; wrath and pity; the plague and your salvation. This same pestilence which is slaying you works for your good and points your path.

"Many centuries ago the Christians of Abyssinia saw in the plague a sure and God-sent means of winning eternal life. Those who were not yet stricken wrapped round them sheets in which men had died of plague, so as to make sure of their death. I grant you such a frenzied quest of salvation was not to be commended. It shows an overhaste—indeed, a presumptuousness, which we can but deplore. No man should seek to force God's hand or to hurry on the appointed hour, and from a practice that aims at speeding up the order of events which God has ordained unalterably from all time, it is but a step to heresy. Yet we can learn a salutary lesson from the zeal, excessive though it was, of those Abyssinian Christians. Much of it is alien to our more enlightened spirits, and yet it gives us a glimpse of that radiant eternal light which glows, a small still flame, in the dark core of human suffering. And this light, too, illuminates the shadowed paths that lead towards deliverance. It reveals the will of God in action, unfailingly transforming evil into good. And once again today it is leading us through the dark valley of fears and groans towards the holy silence, the wellspring of all life. This, my friends, is the vast consolation I would hold out to you, so that when you leave this house of God you will carry away with you not only words of wrath, but a message, too, of comfort for your hearts."

Everyone supposed that the sermon had ended. Outside, the rain had ceased and watery sunshine was yellowing the Cathedral square. Vague sounds of

voices came from the streets, and a low hum of traffic, the speech of an awakening town. Discreetly, with a subdued rustling, the congregation gathered together their belongings. However, the Father had a few more words to say. He told them that after having made it clear that this plague came from God for the punishment of their sins, he would not have recourse, in concluding, to an eloquence that, considering the tragic nature of the occasion, would be out of keeping. He hoped and believed that all of them now saw their position in its true light. But, before leaving the pulpit, he would like to tell them of something he had been reading in an old chronicle of the Black Death at Marseille. In it Mathieu Marais, the chronicler, laments his lot; he says he has been cast into hell to languish without succor and without hope. Well, Mathieu Marais was blind! Never more intensely than today had he, Father Paneloux, felt the immanence of divine succor and Christian hope granted to all alike. He hoped against hope that, despite all the horrors of these dark days, despite the groans of men and women in agony, our fellow citizens would offer up to heaven that one prayer which is truly Christian, a prayer of love. And God would see to the rest.

It is hard to say if this sermon had any effect on our townsfolk. M. Othon, the magistrate, assured Dr. Rieux that he had found the preacher's arguments "absolutely irrefutable." But not everyone took so unqualified a view. To some the sermon simply brought home the fact that they had been sentenced, for an unknown crime, to an indeterminate period of punishment. And while a good many people adapted themselves to confinement and carried on their humdrum lives as before, there were others who rebelled and whose one idea now was to break loose from the prison-house.

At first the fact of being cut off from the outside world was accepted with a more or less good grace, much as people would have put up with any other temporary inconvenience that interfered with only a few of their habits. But, now they had abruptly become aware that they were undergoing a sort of incarceration under that blue dome of sky, already beginning to sizzle in the fires of summer, they had a vague sensation that their whole lives were threatened by the present turn of events, and in the evening, when the cooler air revived their energy, this feeling of being locked in like criminals prompted them sometimes to foolhardy acts.

It is noteworthy—this may or may not have been due to mere coincidence—that this Sunday of the sermon marked the beginning of something like a widespread panic in the town, and it took so deep a hold as to lead one to suspect that only now had the true nature of their situation dawned on our townspeople. Seen from this angle, the atmosphere of the town was somewhat changed. But, actually, it was a problem whether the change was in the atmosphere or in their hearts.

A few days after the sermon, when Rieux, on his way to one of the outlying districts of the town, was discussing the change with Grand, he collided in the darkness with a man who was standing in the middle of the pavement swaying from side to side without trying to advance. At the same moment the street-lamps, which were being lit later and later in the evening, went on suddenly, and a lamp just behind Rieux and his companion threw its light full on the man's face. His eyes were shut and he was laughing soundlessly. Big drops of sweat were rolling down the face convulsed with silent merriment.

"A lunatic at large," Grand observed.

Rieux took his arm and was shepherding him on when he noticed that Grand was trembling violently.

"If things go on as they are going," Rieux remarked, "the whole town will be a madhouse." He felt exhausted, his throat was parched. "Let's have a drink."

They turned into a small café. The only light came from a lamp over the bar, the heavy air had a curious reddish tinge, and for no apparent reason everyone was speaking in undertones.

To the doctor's surprise Grand asked for a small glass of straight liquor, which he drank off at a gulp. "Fiery stuff!" he observed; then, a moment later, suggested making a move.

Out in the street it seemed to Rieux that the night was full of whispers. Somewhere in the black depths above the street-lamps there was a low soughing that brought to his mind that unseen flail threshing incessantly the languid air of which Paneloux had spoken.

"Happily, happily," Grand muttered, then paused.

Rieux asked him what he had been going to say.

"Happily, I've my work."

"Ah yes," Rieux said. "That's something, anyhow." Then so as not to hear that eerie whistling in the air, he asked Grand if he was getting good results.

"Well, yes, I think I'm making headway."

"Have you much more to do?"

Grand began to show an animation unlike his usual self, and his voice took ardor from the liquor he had drunk.

"I don't know. But that's not the point, doctor; yes, I can assure you that's not the point."

It was too dark to see clearly, but Rieux had the impression that he was waving his arms. He seemed to be working himself up to say something, and when he spoke, the words came with a rush.

"What I really want, doctor, is this. On the day when the manuscript reaches the publisher, I want him to stand up—after he's read it through, of course—and say to his staff: 'Gentlemen, hats off!'"

Rieux was dumbfounded, and, to add to his amazement, he saw, or seemed to see, the man beside him making as if to take off his hat with a sweeping gesture, bringing his hand to his head, then holding his arm out straight in front of him. That queer whistling overhead seemed to gather force.

"So you see," Grand added, "it's got to be flawless."

Though he knew little of the literary world, Rieux had a suspicion that things didn't happen in it quite so picturesquely—that, for instance, publishers do not keep their hats on in their offices. But, of course, one never can tell, and Rieux preferred to hold his peace. Try as he might to shut his ears to it, he still was listening to that eerie sound above, the whispering of the plague. They had reached the part of the town where Grand lived and, as it was on a slight eminence, they felt the cool night breeze fanning their cheeks and at the same time carrying away from them the noises of the town.

Grand went on talking, but Rieux failed to follow all the worthy man was saying. All he gathered was that the work he was engaged on ran to a great many pages, and he was at almost excruciating pains to bring it to perfection. "Evenings, whole weeks, spent on one word, just think! Sometimes on a mere conjunction!"

Grand stopped abruptly and seized the doctor by a button of his coat. The words came stumbling out of his almost toothless mouth.

"I'd like you to understand, doctor. I grant you it's easy enough to choose between a 'but' and an 'and.' It's a bit more difficult to decide between 'and' and 'then.' But definitely the hardest thing may be to know whether one should put an 'and' or leave it out."

"Yes," Rieux said, "I see your point."

He started walking again. Grand looked abashed, then stepped forward and drew level.

"Sorry," he said awkwardly. "I don't know what's come over me this evening."

Rieux patted his shoulder encouragingly, saying he'd been much interested in what Grand had said and would like to help him. This seemed to reassure Grand, and when they reached his place he suggested, after some slight hesitation, that the doctor should come in for a moment. Rieux agreed.

They entered the dining-room and Grand gave him a chair beside a table strewn with sheets of paper covered with writing in a microscopic hand, crisscrossed with corrections.

"Yes, that's it," he said in answer to the doctor's questioning glance. "But won't you drink something? I've some wine."

Rieux declined. He was bending over the manuscript.

"No, don't look," Grand said. "It's my opening phrase, and it's giving trouble, no end of trouble."

He too was gazing at the sheets of paper on the table, and his hand seemed irresistibly drawn to one of them. Finally he picked it up and held it to the shadeless electric bulb so that the light shone through. The paper shook in his hand and Rieux noticed that his forehead was moist with sweat.

"Sit down," he said, "and read it to me."

"Yes." There was a timid gratitude in Grand's eyes and smile. "I think I'd like you to hear it."

He waited for a while, still gazing at the writing, then sat down. Meanwhile Rieux was listening to the curious buzzing sound that was rising from the streets as if in answer to the soughings of the plague. At that moment he had a preternaturally vivid awareness of the town stretched out below, a victim world secluded and apart, and of the groans of agony stifled in its darkness. Then, pitched low but clear, Grand's voice came to his ears.

"One fine morning in the month of May an elegant young horsewoman might have been seen riding a handsome sorrel mare along the flowery avenues of the Bois de Boulogne."

Silence returned, and with it the vague murmur of the prostrate town. Grand had put down the sheet and was still staring at it. After a while he looked up.

"What do you think of it?"

Rieux replied that this opening phrase had whetted his curiosity; he'd like to hear what followed. Whereat Grand told him he'd got it all wrong. He seemed excited and slapped the papers on the table with the flat of his hand.

"That's only a rough draft. Once I've succeeded in rendering perfectly the picture in my mind's eye, once my words have the exact tempo of this ride—the horse is trotting, one-two-three, one-two-three, see what I mean?—the rest will come more easily and, what's even more important, the illusion will be such that from the very first words it will be possible to say: 'Hats off!' "

But before that, he admitted, there was lots of hard work to be done. He'd never dream of handing that sentence to the printer in its present form. For though it sometimes satisfied him, he was fully aware it didn't quite hit the mark as yet, and also that to some extent it had a facility of tone approximating, remotely perhaps, but recognizably, to the commonplace. That was more or less what he was saying when they heard the sound of people running in the street below the window. Rieux stood up.

"Just wait and see what I make of it,"

Grand said, and, glancing toward the window, added: "When all this is over."

But then the sound of hurried footsteps came again. Rieux was already halfway down the stairs, and when he stepped out into the street two men brushed past him. They seemed to be on their way to one of the town gates. In fact, what with the heat and the plague, some of our fellow citizens were losing their heads; there had already been some scenes of violence and nightly attempts were made to elude the sentries and escape to the outside world.

Others, too, Rambert for example, were trying to escape from this atmosphere of growing panic, but with more skill and persistence, if not with greater success. For a while Rambert had gone on struggling with officialdom. If he was to be believed, he had always thought that perseverance would win through, inevitably, and, as he pointed out, resourcefulness in emergency was up his street, in a manner of speaking. So he plodded away, calling on all sorts of officials and others whose influence would have had weight in normal conditions. But, as things were, such influence was unavailing. For the most part they were men with well-defined and sound ideas on everything concerning exports, banking, the fruit or wine trade; men of proved ability in handling problems relating to insurance, the interpretation of ill-drawn contracts, and the like; of high qualifications and evident good intentions. That, in fact, was what struck one most—the excellence of their intentions. But as regards plague their competence was practically nil.

However, whenever opportunity arose, Rambert had tackled each of them and pleaded his cause. The gist of his argument was always the same: that he was a stranger to our town and, that being so, his case deserved special consideration. Mostly the men he talked to conceded this point readily enough. But usually they added that a good number of other people were in a like case, and thus his position was not so exceptional as he seemed to suppose. To this Rambert could reply that this did not affect the substance of his argument in any way. He was then told that it did affect the position, already difficult, of the authorities, who were against showing any favoritism and thus running the risk of creating what, with obvious repugnance, they called "a precedent."

In conversation with Dr. Rieux, Rambert classified the people whom he had approached in various categories. Those who used the arguments mentioned above he called the sticklers. Besides these there were the consolers, who assured him that the present state of things couldn't possibly last and, when asked for definite suggestions, fobbed him off by telling him he was making too much fuss about a passing inconvenience. Then there were the very important persons who asked the visitor to leave a brief note of his case and informed him they would decide on it in due course; the triflers, who offered him billeting warrants or gave the addresses of lodgings; the red-tape merchants, who made him fill up a form and promptly interred it in a file; overworked officials, who raised their arms to heaven, and much-harassed officials who simply looked away, and, finally, the traditionalists—these were by far the greatest number—who referred Rambert to another office or recommended some new method of approach.

These fruitless interviews had thoroughly worn out the journalist; on the credit side he had obtained much insight into the inner workings of a municipal office and a Prefect's headquarters, by dint of sitting for hours on imitation-leather sofas, confronted by posters urging him to invest in savings bonds exempt from income-tax, or to enlist in the colonial army; and by dint of entering offices where human faces were as blank as the filing-cabinets and the dusty records on the shelves behind them. The only thing gained by all this expenditure of energy, Rambert told Rieux with a hint of bitterness, was that it served to keep his mind off his predicament. In fact, the rapid progress of the plague practically escaped his notice. Also, it made the days pass more quickly and, given the situation in which the whole town was placed, it might be said that every day lived through brought everyone, provided he survived, twenty-four hours nearer the end of his ordeal. Rieux could but admit the truth of this reasoning, but to his mind its truth was of rather too general an order.

At one moment Rambert had a gleam of hope. A form was sent him from the Prefect's office with instructions that he was to fill in carefully all the blanks. It included questions concerning his identity, his family, his present and former sources of income; in fact, he was to give what is known as a *curriculum vitæ*. He got an impression that inquiries were on foot with a view to drawing up a list of persons who might be instructed to leave the town and return to their homes. Some vague information gleaned from an employee in one of the offices confirmed this impression. But on going further into the matter and finally discovering the office from which the form had emanated, he was told that this information was being collected with a view to certain contingencies.

"What contingencies?" he asked.

He then learned that the contingency was the possibility of his falling ill and dying of plague; the data supplied would enable the authorities to notify his family and also to decide if the hospital expenses should be borne by the municipality or if, in due course, they could be recovered from his relatives. On the face of it this implied that he was not completely cut off from the woman who was awaiting his return, since the powers that be were obviously giving heed to both of them. But that was no consolation. The really remarkable thing, and Rambert was greatly struck by this, was the way in which, in the very midst of catastrophe, offices could go on functioning serenely and take initiatives of no immediate relevance, and often unknown to the highest authority, purely and simply because they had been created originally for this purpose.

The next phase was at once the easiest and the hardest for Rambert. It was a period of sheer lethargy. He had gone the round of offices, taken every step that could be taken, and realized that for the present all avenues of that kind were closed to him. So now he drifted aimlessly from café to café. In the mornings he would sit on the terrace of one of them and read a newspaper in the hope of finding some indication that the epidemic was on the wane. He would gaze at the faces of the passers-by, often turning away disgustedly from their look of unrelieved gloom, and after reading for the nth time the shopsigns on the other side of the street, the advertisements of popular drinks that were no longer procurable, would rise and walk again at random in the yellow streets. Thus he killed time till nightfall, moving about the town and stopping now and then at a café or restaurant. One evening Rieux noticed him hovering round the door of a café, unable to make up his mind to enter. At last he decided to go in and sat down at a table at the back of the room. It was the time when, acting under orders, café-proprietors deferred as long as possible turning on their lights. Gray dusk was seeping into the room, the pink of sunset glowed in the wall mirrors, and the marble-topped tables glimmered white in the gathering darkness. Seated in the empty café, Rambert looked pathetically lost, a mere shade among the shadows, and Rieux guessed this was the hour when he felt most derelict. It was, indeed, the hour of day when all the prisoners of the town realized their dereliction and each was thinking that something, no matter what, must be done to hasten their deliverance. Rieux turned hurriedly away.

Rambert also spent a certain amount of time at the railroad station. No one was allowed on the platforms. But the waiting-rooms, which could be entered from outside, remained open and, being cool and dark, were often patronized by beggars on very hot days. Rambert spent much time studying the timetables, reading the prohibitions against spitting, and the passengers' regulations. After that he sat down in a corner. An old cast-iron stove, which had been stone-cold for months, rose like a sort of landmark in the middle of the room, surrounded by figure-of-eight patterns on the floor, the traceries of long-past sprinklings. Posters on the walls gaily invited tourists to a carefree holiday at Cannes or Bandol. And in his corner Rambert savored that bitter sense of freedom which comes of total deprivation. The evocations which at that time he found most poignant were—anyhow according to what he told Rieux—those of Paris. There rose before his eyes, unsummoned, vistas of old stones and riverbanks, the pigeons of the Palais-Royal, the Gare du Nord, quiet old streets round the Pantheon, and many another scene of the city he'd never known he loved so much, and these mental pictures killed all desire for any form of action. Rieux felt fairly sure he was identifying these scenes with memories of his love. And when one day Rambert told him that he liked waking up at four in the morning and thinking of his beloved Paris, the doctor guessed easily enough, basing this on his own experience, that that was his favorite time for conjuring up pictures of the woman from whom he now was parted. This was, indeed, the hour when he could feel surest she was wholly his. Till four in the morning one is seldom doing anything and at that hour, even if the night has been a night of betrayal, one is asleep. Yes, everyone sleeps at that hour, and this is reassuring, since the great longing of an unquiet heart is to possess constantly and consciously the loved one, or, failing that, to be able to plunge the loved one, when a time of absence intervenes, into a dreamless sleep timed to last unbroken until the day they meet again.

Shortly after Father Paneloux's sermon the hot weather set in with a vengeance. On the day following the unseasonable downpour of that Sunday, summer blazed out above the housetops. First a strong, scorching wind blew steadily for a whole day, drying up the walls. And then the sun took charge, incessant waves of heat and light swept the town daylong, and but for arcaded streets and the interiors of houses, everything lay naked to the dazzling impact of the light. The sun stalked our townsfolk along every byway, into every nook; and when they paused, it struck.

Since this first onslaught of the heat synchronized with a startling increase in the number of victims—there were now nearly seven hundred deaths a week—a mood of profound discouragement settled on the town. In the suburbs little was left of the wonted animation between the long flat streets and the terraced houses; ordinarily people living in these districts used to spend the best part of the day on their doorsteps, but now every door was shut, nobody was to be seen, even the venetian blinds stayed down, and there was no knowing if it was the heat or the plague that they were trying to shut out. In some houses groans could be heard. At first, when that happened, people often gathered outside and listened, prompted by curiosity or compassion. But under the prolonged strain it seemed that hearts had toughened; people lived beside those groans or walked past them as though they had become the normal speech of men.

As a result of the fighting at the gates, in the course of which the police had had to use their revolvers, a spirit of lawlessness was abroad. Some had certainly been wounded in these brushes with the police, but in the town, where, owing to the combined influences of heat and terror, everything was exaggerated, there was talk of deaths. One thing, anyhow, was certain; discontent was on the increase and, fearing worse to come, the local officials debated lengthily on the measures to be taken if the populace, goaded to frenzy by the epidemic, got completely out of hand. The newspapers published new regulations reiterating the orders against attempting to leave the town and warning those who infringed them that they were liable to long terms of imprisonment.

A system of patrols was instituted and often in the empty, sweltering streets, heralded by a clatter of horse hoofs on the cobbles, a detachment of mounted police would make its way between the parallel lines of close-shut windows. Now and again a gunshot was heard; the special brigade recently detailed to destroy cats and dogs, as possible carriers of infection, was at work. And these whipcrack sounds startling the silence increased the nervous tension already existing in the town.

For in the heat and stillness, and for the troubled hearts of our townsfolk, anything, even the least sound, had a heightened significance. The varying aspects of the sky, the very smells rising from the soil that mark each change of season, were taken notice of for the first time. Everyone realized with dismay that hot weather would favor the epidemic, and it was clear that summer was setting in. The cries of swifts in the evening air above the housetops were growing shriller. And the sky, too, had lost the spaciousness of those June twilights when our horizons seem infinitely remote. In the markets the flowers no longer came in buds; they were already in full bloom, and after the morning's marketing the dusty pavements were littered with trampled petals. It was plain to see that spring had spent itself, lavished its ardor on the myriads of flowers that were bursting everywhere into bloom, and now was being crushed out by the twofold onslaught of heat and plague. For our fellow citizens that summer sky, and the streets thick in dust, gray as their present lives, had the same ominous import as the hundred deaths now weighing daily on the town. That incessant sunlight and those bright hours associated with siesta or with holidays no longer invited, as in the past, to frolics and flirtation on the beaches. Now they rang hollow in the silence of the closed town, they had lost the golden spell of happier summers. Plague had killed all colors, vetoed pleasure.

That, indeed, was one of the great changes brought by the epidemic. Hitherto all of us welcomed summer in with pleasant anticipation. The town was open to the sea and its young folk made free of the beaches. But this summer, for all its nearness, the sea was out of bounds; young limbs had no longer the run of its delights. What could we do under these conditions? It is Tarrou once again who paints the most faithful picture of our life in those days. Needless to say, he outlines the progress of the plague and he, too, notes that a new phase of the epidemic was ushered in when the radio announced no longer weekly totals, but ninety-two, a hundred and seven, and a hundred and thirty deaths in a day. "The newspapers and the authorities are playing ball with the plague. They fancy they're scoring off it because a hundred and thirty is a smaller figure than nine hundred and ten." He also records such striking or moving incidents of the epidemic as came under his notice; that, for instance, of the woman in a lonely street who abruptly opened a shuttered window just above his head and gave two loud shrieks before closing the shutters again on the dark interior of a bedroom. But he also noted that peppermint lozenges had vanished from the drugstores, because there was a popular belief that when sucking them you were proof against contagion.

He went on watching his pet specimen on the opposite balcony. It seemed that tragedy had come to the ancient small-game hunter as well. One morning there had been gunshots in the street and, as Tarrou put it, "some gobs of lead" had killed off most of the cats and scared away the others; anyhow they were no longer about. That day the little old man went on to his balcony at the usual hour, showed some surprise, and, leaning on the rail, closely scanned the corners of the street. Then he settled down to wait, fretfully tapping the balustrade with his right hand. After staying there for some time he tore up a few sheets of paper, went back into his room, and came out again. After another longish wait he retreated again into the room, slamming the french windows behind him. He followed the same procedure daily during the rest of the week, and the sadness and bewilderment on the old face deepened as the days went by. On the eighth day Tarrou waited in vain for his appearance; the windows stayed resolutely closed on all too comprehensible distress. This entry ends with Tarrou's summing up. "It is forbidden to spit on cats in plague-time."

In another context Tarrou notes that, on coming home in the evenings, he invariably saw the night watchman pacing the hall, like a sentry on his beat. The man never failed to remind everyone he met that he'd foreseen what was happening. Tarrou agreed that he'd predicted a disaster, but reminded him that the event predicted by him was an earthquake. To which the old fellow replied: "Ah, if only it had been an earthquake! A good bad shock, and there you are! You count the dead and living, and that's an end of it. But this here damned disease—even them who haven't got it can't think of anything else."

The manager of the hotel was equally downhearted. In the early days travelers, unable to leave the town, had kept on their rooms. But one by one, seeing that the epidemic showed no sign of abating, they moved out to stay with friends. And the same cause that had led to all the rooms' being occupied now kept them empty, since there were no newcomers to the town. Tarrou was one of the very few remaining guests, and the manager never lost an opportunity of informing him that, were he not reluctant to put these gentlemen to inconvenience, he would have closed the hotel long ago. He often asked Tarrou to say how long he thought the epidemic would last. "They say," Tarrou informed him, "that cold weather stamps out diseases of this type." The manager looked aghast. "But, my dear sir, it's never really cold in these parts. And, anyhow, that would mean it's going to last many months more." Moreover, he was sure that for a long while to come travelers would give the town a wide berth. This epidemic spelt the ruin of the tourist trade, in fact.

After a short absence M. Othon, the

owlish paterfamilias, made a reappearance in the restaurant, but accompanied only by the two "performing poodles," his offspring. On inquiry it came out that Mme Othon was in quarantine; she had been nursing her mother, who had succumbed to plague.

"I don't like it a bit," the manager told Tarrou. "Quarantine or not, she's under suspicion, which means that they are, too."

Tarrou pointed out that, if it came to that, everyone was "under suspicion." But the manager had his own ideas and was not to be shaken out of them.

"No, sir. You and I, we're not under suspicion. But they certainly are."

However, M. Othon was impervious to such considerations and would not let the plague change his habits. He entered the restaurant with his wonted dignity, sat down in front of his children, and addressed to them at intervals the same nicely worded, unamiable remarks. Only the small boy looked somewhat different; dressed in black like his sister, a little more shrunken than before, he now seemed a miniature replica of his father. The night watchman, who had no liking for M. Othon, had said of him to Tarrou:

"That fine gentleman will pass out with his clothes on. All dressed up and ready to go. So he won't need no laying-out."

Tarrou has some comments on the sermon preached by Paneloux: "I can understand that type of fervor and find it not displeasing. At the beginning of a pestilence and when it ends, there's always a propensity for rhetoric. In the first case, habits have not yet been lost; in the second, they're returning. It is in the thick of a calamity that one gets hardened to the truth—in other words, to silence. So let's wait."

Tarrou also records that he had a long talk with Dr. Rieux; all he remembered was that it had "good results." In this connection he notes the color of Mme Rieux's, the doctor's mother's, eyes, a limpid brown, and makes the odd observation that a gaze revealing so much goodness of heart would always triumph over plague.

He has also a good deal to say about Rieux's asthma patient. He went with the doctor to see him, immediately after their conversation. The old man greeted Tarrou with a chuckle and rubbed his hands cheerfully. He was sitting up in bed with the usual two pans of dried peas in front of him. "Ah, here's another of 'em!" he exclaimed when he saw Tarrou. "It's a topsy-turvy world all right, more doctors than patients. Because it's mowing them down, ain't it, more and more. That priest's right; we were asking for it." Next day Tarrou came to see him without warning.

From Tarrou's notes we gather that the old man, a drygoods dealer by occupation, decided at the age of fifty that he'd done enough work for a lifetime. He took to his bed and never left it again— but not because of his asthma, which would not have prevented his getting about. A small fixed income had seen him through to his present age, seventy-five, and the years had not damped his cheerfulness. He couldn't bear the sight of a watch, and indeed there wasn't one in the whole house. "Watches," he said, "are silly gadgets, and dear at that." He worked out the time—that is to say, the time for meals—with his two saucepans, one of which was always full of peas when he woke in the morning. He filled the other, pea by pea, at a constant, carefully regulated speed. Thus time for him was reckoned by these pans and he could take his bearings in it at any moment of the day. "Every fifteen pans," he said, "it's feeding-time. What could be simpler?"

If his wife was to be trusted, he had

given signs of his vocation at a very early age. Nothing, in fact, had ever interested him; his work, friendship, cafés, music, women, outings—to all he was indifferent. He had never left his home town except once when he had been called to Algiers for family affairs, and even then he had alighted from the train at the first station after Oran, incapable of continuing the adventure. He took the first train back.

To Tarrou, who had shown surprise at the secluded life he led, he had given the following explanation, more or less. According to religion, the first half of a man's life is an upgrade; the second goes downhill. On the descending days he has no claim, they may be snatched from him at any moment; thus he can do nothing with them and the best thing, precisely, is to do nothing with them. He obviously had no compunction about contradicting himself, for a few minutes later he told Tarrou that God did not exist, since otherwise there would be no need for priests. But, from some observations which followed, Tarrou realized that the old fellow's philosophy was closely involved with the irritation caused by the house-to-house collections in aid of charities, which took place almost incessantly in that part of the town. What completed the picture of the old man was a desire he expressed several times, and which seemed deeply rooted: the desire to die at a very advanced age.

"Is he a saint?" Tarrou asked himself, and answered: "Yes, if saintliness is an aggregate of habits."

Meanwhile Tarrou was compiling a longish description of a day in the plague-stricken town; it was to give a full and accurate picture of the life of our fellow citizens during that summer. "Nobody laughs," Tarrou observes, "except the drunks, and they laugh too much." After which he embarks on his description.

"At daybreak light breaths of air fan the still empty streets. At this hour, between the night's victims and the death-agonies of the coming day, it is as if for a while plague stays its hand and takes breath. All shops are shut. But on some a notice: *Closed owing to plague,* shows that when the others open presently, these will not. Still half-asleep, the newsboys do not yet cry the news but, lounging at street corners, offer their wares to the lamp-posts, with the vague gestures of sleepwalkers. Soon, awakened by the early streetcars, they will fan out through the town, holding at arm's length sheets on which the word *PLAGUE* looms large. Will there be a plague autumn? Professor B. says: 'No.' Toll of the 94th day of plague: 124 deaths.

"In spite of the growing shortage of paper, which has compelled some dailies to reduce their pages, a new paper has been launched: the *Plague Chronicle,* which sets out 'to inform our townspeople, with scrupulous veracity, of the daily progress or recession of the disease; to supply them with the most authoritative opinions available as to its future course; to offer the hospitality of its columns to all, in whatever walk of life, who wish to join in combating the epidemic; to keep up the morale of the populace; to publish the latest orders issued by the authorities; and to centralize the efforts of all who desire to give active and wholehearted help in the present emergency.' Actually this newspaper very soon came to devote its columns to advertisements of new, 'infallible' antidotes against plague.

"Toward six in the morning all these papers are being sold to the lines that begin to form outside the shops over an hour before they open; then to the passengers alighting from the streetcars coming in, packed to capacity, from the suburbs. The cars are now the only means of transport, and they have much difficulty in progressing, what with people standing on the running-boards and hanging in clusters from the hand-rails. A queer thing is how the passengers all try to keep their backs turned to their neighbors, twisting themselves into grotesque attitudes in the attempt—the idea being, of course, to avoid contagion. At every stop a cataract of men and women is disgorged, each in haste to put a safe distance between himself or herself and the rest.

"When the first cars have gone by, the town gradually wakes up, early cafés open their doors, and you see an array of cards on the counter: *No Coffee, Bring Your Own Sugar,* and the like. Next the shops open and the streets grow livelier. And meanwhile the light is swelling and the sky, even at this early hour, beginning to grow leaden-hued with heat. This is the time when those who have nothing to do venture out on the boulevards. Most of them seem determined to counteract the plague by a lavish display of luxury. Daily, about eleven, you see a sort of dress parade of youths and girls, who make you realize the frantic desire for life that thrives in the heart of every great calamity. If the epidemic spreads, morals too will broaden, and we may see again the saturnalia of Milan, men and women dancing round the graves.

"At noon, in a flash, all the restaurants fill up. Very quickly small groups of people unable to find a seat form at the doors. Because of the intense heat the sky is losing its brightness. Under big awnings the aspirants to food wait their turn, aligned along the curbs of streets gaping and sizzling in the fires of noon. The reason for the restaurants' being so crowded is that they solve for many the feeding problem. But they do nothing to allay the fear of contagion. Many of the customers spend several minutes methodically wiping their plates. Not long ago some restaurants put up notices: *Our plates, knives, and forks guaranteed sterilized.*

But gradually they discontinued publicity of this order, since their customers came in any case. People, moreover, spend very freely. Choice wines, or wines alleged to be such, the costliest extras—a mood of reckless extravagance is setting in. It seems that there was something like a panic in a restaurant because a customer suddenly felt ill, went very white, and staggered precipitately to the door.

"Toward two o'clock the town slowly empties, it is the time when silence, sunlight, dust, and plague have the streets to themselves. Wave after wave of heat flows over the frontage of the tall gray houses during these long, languid hours. Thus the afternoon wears on, slowly merging into an evening that settles down like a red winding-sheet on the serried tumult of the town. At the start of the great heat, for some unascertained reason, the evenings found the streets almost empty. But now the least ripple of cooler air brings an easing of the strain, if not a flutter of hope. Then all stream out into the open, drug themselves with talking, start arguing or love-making, and in the last glow of sunset the town, freighted with lovers two by two and loud with voices, drifts like a helmless ship into the throbbing darkness. In vain a zealous evangelist with a felt hat and flowing tie threads his way through the crowd, crying without cease: 'God is great and good. Come unto Him.' On the contrary, they all make haste toward some trivial objective that seems of more immediate interest than God.

"In the early days, when they thought this epidemic was much like other epidemics, religion held its ground. But once these people realized their instant peril, they gave their thoughts to pleasure. And all the hideous fears that stamp their faces in the daytime are transformed in the fiery, dusty nightfall into a sort of hectic exaltation, an unkempt freedom fevering their blood.

"And I, too, I'm no different. But what matter? Death means nothing to men like me. It's the event that proves them right."

It was Tarrou who had asked Rieux for the interview he refers to in his diary. On that evening, as it happened, just before Tarrou arrived, the doctor had gazed for some moments at his mother, who was sitting very still in a corner of the dining-room. Once her household tasks were over, she spent most of her time in that chair. Her hands folded in her lap, she sat there waiting. Rieux wasn't even sure it was for him she waited. However, something always changed in his mother's face when he came in. The silent resignation that a laborious life had given it seemed to light up with a sudden glow. Then she returned to her tranquillity. That evening she was gazing out of the window at the now empty street. The street lighting had been reduced by two thirds, and only at long intervals a lamp cast flickering gleams through the thick darkness of the town.

"Will they keep to the reduced lighting as long as the plague lasts?" Mme Rieux asked.

"I expect so."

"Let's hope it doesn't last till winter. It would be terribly depressing."

"Yes," Rieux said.

He saw his mother's gaze settle on his forehead. He knew that the worry and overwork of the last few days had scored their traces there.

"Didn't things go well today?" his mother asked.

"Oh, much as usual."

As usual! That was to say the new consignment of serum sent from Paris seemed less effective than the first, and the death-rate was rising. It was still impossible to administer prophylactic inoculations elsewhere than in families already attacked; if its use was to be generalized, very large quantities of the vaccine would have been needed. Most of the buboes refused to burst—it was as if they underwent a seasonal hardening—and the victims suffered horribly. During the last twenty-four hours there had been two cases of a new form of the epidemic; the plague was becoming pneumonic. On this very day, in the course of a meeting, the much-harassed doctors had pressed the Prefect—the unfortunate man seemed quite at his wits' end—to issue new regulations to prevent contagion being carried from mouth to mouth, as happens in pneumonic plague. The Prefect had done as they wished, but as usual they were groping, more or less, in the dark.

Looking at his mother, he felt an uprush of a half-forgotten emotion, the love of his boyhood, at the sight of her soft brown gaze intent on him.

"Don't you ever feel alarmed, Mother?"

"Oh, at my age there isn't much left to fear."

"The days are very long, and just now I'm hardly ever at home."

"I don't mind waiting, if I know you're going to come back. And when you aren't here, I think of what you're doing. Have you any news?"

"Yes, if I'm to believe the last telegram, everything's going as well as could be expected. But I know she says that to prevent my worrying."

The doorbell rang. The doctor gave his mother a smile and went to open the door. In the dim light on the landing Tarrou looked like a big gray bear. Rieux gave his visitor a seat facing his desk, while he himself remained standing behind the desk chair. Between them was the only light in the room, a desk lamp.

Tarrou came straight to the point. "I

know," he said, "that I can talk to you quite frankly."

Rieux nodded.

"In a fortnight, or a month at most," Tarrou continued, "you'll serve no purpose here. Things will have got out of hand."

"I agree."

"The sanitary department is inefficient—understaffed, for one thing—and you're worked off your feet."

Rieux admitted this was so.

"Well," Tarrou said, "I've heard that the authorities are thinking of a sort of conscription of the population, and all men in good health will be required to help in fighting the plague."

"Your information was correct. But the authorities are in none too good odor as it is, and the Prefect can't make up his mind."

"If he daren't risk compulsion, why not call for voluntary help?"

"It's been done. The response was poor."

"It was done through official channels, and half-heartedly. What they're short on is imagination. Officialdom can never cope with something really catastrophic. And the remedial measures they think up are hardly adequate for a common cold. If we let them carry on like this they'll soon be dead, and so shall we."

"That's more than likely," Rieux said. "I should tell you, however, that they're thinking of using the prisoners in the jails for what we call the 'heavy work.'"

"I'd rather free men were employed."

"So would I. But might I ask why you feel like that?"

"I loathe men's being condemned to death."

Rieux looked Tarrou in the eyes.

"So—what?" he asked.

"It's this I have to say. I've drawn up a plan for voluntary groups of helpers. Get me empowered to try out my plan, and then let's sidetrack officialdom. In any case the authorities have their hands more than full already. I have friends in many walks of life; they'll form a nucleus to start from. And, of course, I'll take part in it myself."

"I need hardly tell you," Rieux replied, "that I accept your suggestion most gladly. One can't have too many helpers, especially in a job like mine under present conditions. I'll undertake to get your plan approved by the authorities. Anyhow, they've no choice. But—" Rieux pondered. "But I take it you know that work of this kind may prove fatal to the worker. And I feel I should ask you this; have you weighed the dangers?"

Tarrou's gray eyes met the doctor's gaze serenely.

"What did you think of Paneloux's sermon, doctor?"

The question was asked in a quite ordinary tone, and Rieux answered in the same tone.

"I've seen too much of hospitals to relish any idea of collective punishment. But, as you know, Christians sometimes say that sort of thing without really thinking it. They're better than they seem."

"However, you think, like Paneloux, that the plague has its good side; it opens men's eyes and forces them to take thought?"

The doctor tossed his head impatiently.

"So does every ill that flesh is heir to. What's true of all the evils in the world is true of plague as well. It helps men to rise above themselves. All the same, when you see the misery it brings, you'd need to be a madman, or a coward, or stone blind, to give in tamely to the plague."

Rieux had hardly raised his voice at all; but Tarrou made a slight gesture as if to calm him. He was smiling.

"Yes." Rieux shrugged his shoulders. "But you haven't answered my question

[71]

yet. Have you weighed the consequences?"

Tarrou squared his shoulders against the back of the chair, then moved his head forward into the light.

"Do you believe in God, doctor?"

Again the question was put in an ordinary tone. But this time Rieux took longer to find his answer.

"No—but what does that really mean? I'm fumbling in the dark, struggling to make something out. But I've long ceased finding that original."

"Isn't that it—the gulf between Paneloux and you?"

"I doubt it. Paneloux is a man of learning, a scholar. He hasn't come in contact with death; that's why he can speak with such assurance of the truth— with a capital T. But every country priest who visits his parishioners and has heard a man gasping for breath on his deathbed thinks as I do. He'd try to relieve human suffering before trying to point out its excellence." Rieux stood up; his face was now in shadow. "Let's drop the subject," he said, "as you won't answer."

Tarrou remained seated in his chair; he was smiling again.

"Suppose I answer with a question."

The doctor now smiled, too.

"You like being mysterious, don't you? Yes, fire away."

"My question's this," said Tarrou. "Why do you yourself show such devotion, considering you don't believe in God? I suspect your answer may help me to mine."

His face still in shadow, Rieux said that he'd already answered: that if he believed in an all-powerful God he would cease curing the sick and leave that to Him. But no one in the world believed in a God of that sort; no, not even Paneloux, who believed that he believed in such a God. And this was proved by the fact that no one ever threw himself on providence completely. Anyhow, in this respect Rieux believed himself to be on the right road—in fighting against creation as he found it.

"Ah," Tarrou remarked. "So that's the idea you have of your profession?"

"More or less." The doctor came back into the light.

Tarrou made a faint whistling noise with his lips, and the doctor gazed at him.

"Yes, you're thinking it calls for pride to feel that way. But I assure you I've no more than the pride that's needed to keep me going. I have no idea what's awaiting me, or what will happen when all this ends. For the moment I know this; there are sick people and they need curing. Later on, perhaps, they'll think things over; and so shall I. But what's wanted now is to make them well. I defend them as best I can, that's all."

"Against whom?"

Rieux turned to the window. A shadow-line on the horizon told of the presence of the sea. He was conscious only of his exhaustion, and at the same time was struggling against a sudden, irrational impulse to unburden himself a little more to his companion; an eccentric, perhaps, but who, he guessed, was one of his own kind.

"I haven't a notion, Tarrou; I assure you I haven't a notion. When I entered this profession, I did it 'abstractedly,' so to speak; because I had a desire for it, because it meant a career like another, one that young men often aspire to. Perhaps, too, because it was particularly difficult for a workman's son, like myself. And then I had to see people die. Do you know that there are some who *refuse* to die? Have you ever heard a woman scream 'Never!' with her last gasp? Well, I have. And then I saw that I could never get hardened to it. I was young then, and I was outraged by the whole scheme of things, or so I thought. Subsequently I grew more modest. Only, I've never man-

aged to get used to seeing people die.
That's all I know. Yet after all—"

Rieux fell silent and sat down. He felt
his mouth dry.

"After all—?" Tarrou prompted softly.

"After all," the doctor repeated, then
hesitated again, fixing his eyes on Tarrou,
"it's something that a man of your sort
can understand most likely, but, since the
order of the world is shaped by death,
mightn't it be better for God if we refuse
to believe in Him and struggle with all
our might against death, without raising
our eyes toward the heaven where He sits
in silence."

Tarrou nodded.

"Yes. But your victories will never be
lasting; that's all."

Rieux's face darkened.

"Yes, I know that. But it's no reason
for giving up the struggle."

"No reason, I agree. Only, I now can
picture what this plague must mean for
you."

"Yes. A never ending defeat."

Tarrou stared at the doctor for a moment, then turned and tramped heavily
toward the door. Rieux followed him and
was almost at his side when Tarrou, who
was staring at the floor, suddenly said:

"Who taught you all this, doctor?"

The reply came promptly:

"Suffering."

Rieux opened the door of his surgery
and told Tarrou that he, too, was going
out; he had a patient to visit in the suburbs. Tarrou suggested they should go
together and he agreed. In the hall they
encountered Mme Rieux, and the doctor
introduced Tarrou to her.

"A friend of mine," he said.

"Indeed," said Mme Rieux, "I'm very
pleased to make your acquaintance."

When she left them Tarrou turned to
gaze after her. On the landing the doctor
pressed a switch to turn on the lights
along the stairs. But the stairs remained
in darkness. Possibly some new light-

saving order had come into force. Really,
however, there was no knowing; for
some time past, in the streets no less than
in private houses, everything had been
going out of order. It might be only that
the concierge, like nearly everyone in the
town, was ceasing to bother about his
duties. The doctor had no time to follow
up his thoughts: Tarrou's voice came
from behind him.

"Just one word more, doctor, even if it
sounds to you a bit nonsensical. You are
perfectly right."

The doctor merely gave a little shrug,
unseen in the darkness.

"To tell the truth, all that's outside my
range. But you—what do *you* know
about it?"

"Ah," Tarrou replied quite coolly,
"I've little left to learn."

Rieux paused and, behind him, Tarrou's foot slipped on a step. He steadied
himself by gripping the doctor's shoulder.

"Do you really imagine you know
everything about life?"

The answer came through the darkness
in the same cool, confident tone.

"Yes."

Once in the street, they realized it
must be quite late, eleven perhaps. All
was silence in the town, except for some
vague rustlings. An ambulance bell
clanged faintly in the distance. They
stepped into the car and Rieux started
the engine.

"You must come to the hospital tomorrow," he said, "for an injection. But,
before embarking on this adventure,
you'd better know your chances of coming out of it alive; they're one in three."

"That sort of reckoning doesn't hold
water; you know it, doctor, as well as I.
A hundred years ago plague wiped out
the entire population of a town in Persia,
with one exception. And the sole survivor
was precisely the man whose job it was
to wash the dead bodies, and who carried
on throughout the epidemic."

"He pulled off his one-in-three chance, that's all." Rieux had lowered his voice. "But you're right; we know next to nothing on the subject."

They were entering the suburbs. The headlights lit up empty streets. The car stopped. Standing in front of it, Rieux asked Tarrou if he'd like to come in. Tarrou said: "Yes." A glimmer of light from the sky lit up their faces. Suddenly Rieux gave a short laugh, and there was much friendliness in it.

"Out with it, Tarrou! What on earth prompted you to take a hand in this?"

"I don't know. My code of morals, perhaps."

"Your code of morals? What code?"

"Comprehension."

Tarrou turned toward the house and Rieux did not see his face again until they were in the old asthma patient's room.

Next day Tarrou set to work and enrolled a first team of workers, soon to be followed by many others.

However, it is not the narrator's intention to ascribe to these sanitary groups more importance than their due. Doubtless today many of our fellow citizens are apt to yield to the temptation of exaggerating the services they rendered. But the narrator is inclined to think that by attributing overimportance to praiseworthy actions one may, by implication, be paying indirect but potent homage to the worst side of human nature. For this attitude implies that such actions shine out as rare exceptions, while callousness and apathy are the general rule. The narrator does not share that view. The evil that is in the world always comes of ignorance, and good intentions may do as much harm as malevolence, if they lack understanding. On the whole, men are more good than bad; that, however, isn't the real point. But they are more or less ignorant, and it is this that we call vice or virtue; the most incorrigible vice being that of an ignorance that fancies it knows everything and therefore claims for itself the right to kill. The soul of the murderer is blind; and there can be no true goodness nor true love without the utmost clear-sightedness.

Hence the sanitary groups, whose creation was entirely Tarrou's work, should be considered with objectivity as well as with approval. And this is why the narrator declines to vaunt in overglowing terms a courage and a devotion to which he attributes only a relative and reasonable importance. But he will continue being the chronicler of the troubled, rebellious hearts of our townspeople under the impact of the plague.

Those who enrolled in the "sanitary squads," as they were called, had, indeed, no such great merit in doing as they did, since they knew it was the only thing to do, and the unthinkable thing would then have been not to have brought themselves to do it. These groups enabled our townsfolk to come to grips with the disease and convinced them that, now that plague was among us, it was up to them to do whatever could be done to fight it. Since plague became in this way some men's duty, it revealed itself as what it really was; that is, the concern of all.

So far, so good. But we do not congratulate a schoolmaster on teaching that two and two make four, though we may, perhaps, congratulate him on having chosen his laudable vocation. Let us then say it was praiseworthy that Tarrou and so many others should have elected to prove that two and two make four rather than the contrary; but let us add that this good will of theirs was one that is shared by the schoolmaster and by all who have the same feelings as the schoolmaster, and, be it said to the credit of mankind, they are more numerous than one would think—such, anyhow, is the narrator's conviction. Needless to say, he can see quite clearly a point that could be made against him, which is that these men were risking their lives. But again and again there comes a time in history when the man who dares to say that two and two make four is punished with death. The schoolteacher is well aware of this. And the question is not one of knowing what punishment or reward attends the making of this calculation. The question is that of knowing whether two and two do make four. For those of our towns-folk who risked their lives in this pre-dicament the issue was whether or not plague was in their midst and whether or not they must fight against it.

Many fledgling moralists in those days were going about our town proclaiming there was nothing to be done about it and we should bow to the inevitable. And Tarrou, Rieux, and their friends might give one answer or another, but its con-clusion was always the same, their certi-tude that a fight must be put up, in this way or that, and there must be no bow-ing down. The essential thing was to save the greatest possible number of persons from dying and being doomed to unend-ing separation. And to do this there was only one resource: to fight the plague. There was nothing admirable about this attitude; it was merely logical.

Thus it was only natural that old Dr. Castel should plod away with unshaken confidence, never sparing himself, at making anti-plague serum on the spot with the makeshift equipment at his dis-posal. Rieux shared his hope that a vac-cine made with cultures of the bacilli obtained locally would take effect more actively than serum coming from outside, since the local bacillus differed slightly from the normal plague bacillus as de-fined in textbooks of tropical diseases. And Castel expected to have his first

supply ready within a surprisingly short period.

That, too, is why it was natural that Grand, who had nothing of the hero about him, should now be acting as a sort of general secretary to the sanitary squads. A certain number of the groups organized by Tarrou were working in the congested areas of the town, with a view to improving the sanitary conditions there. Their duties were to see that houses were kept in a proper hygienic state and to list attics and cellars that had not been disinfected by the official sani-tary service. Other teams of volunteers accompanied the doctors on their house-to-house visits, saw to the evacuation of infected persons, and subsequently, owing to the shortage of drivers, even drove the vehicles conveying sick persons and dead bodies. All this involved the upkeep of registers and statistics, and Grand under-took the task.

From this angle, the narrator holds that, more than Rieux or Tarrou, Grand was the true embodiment of the quiet courage that inspired the sanitary groups. He had said yes without a moment's hesitation and with the large-heartedness that was a second nature with him. All he had asked was to be allotted light duties: he was too old for anything else. He could give his time from six to eight every evening. When Rieux thanked him with some warmth, he seemed surprised. "Why, that's not difficult! Plague is here and we've got to make a stand, that's obvious. Ah, I only wish everything were as simple!" And he went back to his phrase. Sometimes in the evening, when he had filed his reports and worked out his statistics, Grand and Rieux would have a chat. Soon they formed the habit of including Tarrou in their talks and Grand unburdened himself with increas-ingly apparent pleasure to his two com-panions. They began to take a genuine interest in the laborious literary task to which he was applying himself while plague raged around him. Indeed, they, too, found in it a relaxation of the strain.

"How's your young lady on horseback progressing?" Tarrou would ask. And invariably Grand would answer with a wry smile: "Trotting along, trotting along!" One evening Grand announced that he had definitely discarded the adjective "elegant" for his horsewoman. From now on it was replaced by "slim." "That's more concrete," he explained. Soon after, he read out to his two friends the new version of the sentence:

" 'One fine morning in May a slim young horsewoman might have been seen riding a handsome sorrel mare along the flowery avenues of the Bois de Boulogne.'

"Don't you agree with me one sees her better that way? And I've put 'one fine morning in May' because 'in the month of May' tended rather to drag out the trot, if you see what I mean."

Next he showed some anxiety about the adjective "handsome." In his opinion it didn't convey enough, and he set to looking for an epithet that would promptly and clearly "photograph" the superb animal he saw with his mind's eye. "Plump" wouldn't do; though concrete enough, it sounded perhaps a little disparaging, also a shade vulgar. "Beautifully groomed" had tempted him for a moment, but it was cumbrous and made the rhythm limp somewhat. Then one evening he announced triumphantly that he had got it: "A black sorrel mare." To his thinking, he explained, "black" conveyed a hint of elegance and opulence.

"It won't do," Rieux said.

"Why not?"

"Because 'sorrel' doesn't mean a breed of horse; it's a color."

"What color?"

"Well—er—a color that, anyhow, isn't black."

Grand seemed greatly troubled.

"Thank you," he said warmly. "How fortunate you're here to help me! But you see how difficult it is."

"How about 'glossy'?" Tarrou suggested.

Grand gazed at him meditatively, then "Yes!" he exclaimed. "That's good." And slowly his lips parted in a smile.

Some days later he confessed that the word "flowery" was bothering him considerably. As the only towns he knew were Oran and Montélimar, he sometimes asked his friends to tell him about the avenues of the Bois de Boulogne, what sort of flowers grew in them and how they were disposed. Actually neither Rieux nor Tarrou had ever gathered the impression that those avenues were "flowery," but Grand's conviction on the subject shook their confidence in their memories. He was amazed at their uncertainty. "It's only artists who know how to use their eyes," was his conclusion. But one evening the doctor found him in a state of much excitement. For "flowery" he had substituted "flower-strewn." He was rubbing his hands. "At last one can see them, smell them! Hats off, gentlemen!" Triumphantly he read out the sentence:

"One fine morning in May a slim young horsewoman might have been seen riding a glossy sorrel mare along the flower-strewn avenues of the Bois de Boulogne."

But, spoken aloud, the numerous "s" sounds had a disagreeable effect and Grand stumbled over them, lisping here and there. He sat down, crestfallen; then he asked the doctor if he might go. Some hard thinking lay ahead of him.

It was about this time, as was subsequently learned, that he began to display signs of absentmindedness in the office. A serious view was taken of these lapses of attention, as the municipality not only was working at high pressure with a reduced staff, but was constantly having new duties thrust upon it. His department suffered, and his chief took him severely to task, pointing out that he was paid to do certain work and was failing to do it as it should be done. "I am told that you are acting as a voluntary helper in the sanitary groups. You do this out of office hours, so it's no concern of mine. But the best way of making yourself useful in a terrible time like this is to do your work well. Otherwise all the rest is useless."

"He's right," Grand said to Rieux.

"Yes, he's right," the doctor agreed.

"But I can't steady my thoughts; it's the end of my phrase that's worrying me, I don't seem able to sort it out."

The plethora of sibilants in the sentence still offended his ear, but he saw no way of amending them without using what were, to his mind, inferior synonyms. And that "flower-strewn" which had rejoiced him when he first lit on it now seemed unsatisfactory. How could one say the flowers were "strewn" when presumably they had been planted along the avenues, or else grew there naturally? On some evenings, indeed, he looked more tired than Rieux.

Yes, this unavailing quest which never left his mind had worn him out; none the less, he went on adding up the figures and compiling the statistics needed for the sanitary groups. Patiently every evening he brought his totals up to date, illustrated them with graphs, and racked his brains to present his data in the most exact, clearest form. Quite often he went to see Rieux at one of the hospitals and asked to be given a table in an office or the dispensary. He would settle down at it with his papers, exactly as he settled down at his desk in the Municipal Office, and wave each completed sheet to dry the ink in the warm air, noisome with disinfectants and the disease itself. At these times he made honest efforts not to think about his "horsewoman," and concentrate on what he had to do.

Yes, if it is a fact that people like to have examples given them, men of the type they call heroic, and if it is absolutely necessary that this narrative should include a "hero," the narrator commends to his readers, with, to his thinking, perfect justice, this insignificant and obscure hero who had to his credit only a little goodness of heart and a seemingly absurd ideal. This will render to the truth its due, to the addition of two and two its sum of four, and to heroism the secondary place that rightly falls to it, just after, never before, the noble claim of happiness. It will also give this chronicle its character, which is intended to be that of a narrative made with good feelings— that is to say, feelings that are neither demonstrably bad nor overcharged with emotion in the ugly manner of a stageplay.

Such at least was Dr. Rieux's opinion when he read in newspapers or heard on the radio the messages and encouragement the outer world transmitted to the plague-ridden populace. Besides the comforts sent by air or overland, compassionate or admiring comments were lavished on the henceforth isolated town, by way of newspaper articles or broadcast talks. And invariably their epical or prize-speech verbiage jarred on the doctor. Needless to say, he knew the sympathy was genuine enough. But it could be expressed only in the conventional language with which men try to express what unites them with mankind in general; a vocabulary quite unsuited, for example, to Grand's small daily effort, and incapable of describing what Grand stood for under plague conditions.

Sometimes at midnight, in the great silence of the sleep-bound town, the doctor turned on his radio before going to bed for the few hours' sleep he allowed himself. And from the ends of the earth, across thousands of miles of land and sea, kindly, well-meaning speakers tried to voice their fellow-feeling, and indeed did so, but at the same time proved the utter incapacity of every man truly to share in suffering that he cannot see. "Oran! Oran!" In vain the call rang over oceans, in vain Rieux listened hopefully; always the tide of eloquence began to flow, bringing home still more the unbridgeable gulf that lay between Grand and the speaker. "Oran, we're with you!" they called emotionally. But not, the doctor told himself, to love or to die together—"and that's the only way. They're too remote."

❁

And, as it so happens, what has yet to be recorded before coming to the culmination, during the period when the plague was gathering all its forces to fling them at the town and lay it waste, is the long, heartrendingly monotonous struggle put up by some obstinate people like Rambert to recover their lost happiness and to balk the plague of that part of themselves which they were ready to defend in the last ditch. This was their way of resisting the bondage closing in upon them, and while their resistance lacked the active virtues of the other, it had (to the narrator's thinking) its point, and moreover it bore witness, even in its futility and incoherences, to a salutary pride.

Rambert fought to prevent the plague from besting him. Once assured that there was no way of getting out of the town by lawful methods, he decided, as he told Rieux, to have recourse to others. He began by sounding café waiters. A waiter usually knows much of what's going on behind the scenes. But the first he spoke to knew only of the very heavy penalties imposed on such attempts at evasion. In one of the cafés he visited he was actually taken for a stoolpigeon and

curtly sent about his business. It was not until he happened to meet Cottard at Rieux's place that he made a little headway. On that day he and Rieux had been talking again about his unsuccessful efforts to interest the authorities in his case, and Cottard heard the tail end of the conversation.

Some days later Cottard met him in the street and greeted him with the hail-fellow-well-met manner that he now used on all occasions.

"Hello, Rambert! Still no luck?"

"None whatever."

"It's no good counting on the red-tape merchants. They couldn't understand if they tried."

"I know that, and I'm trying to find some other way. But it's damned difficult."

"Yes," Cottard replied. "It certainly is."

He, however, knew a way to go about it, and he explained to Rambert, who was much surprised to learn this, that for some time past he had been going the rounds of the cafés, had made a number of acquaintances, and had learned of the existence of an "organization" handling this sort of business. The truth was that Cottard, who had been beginning to live above his means, was now involved in smuggling ventures concerned with rationed goods. Selling contraband cigarettes and inferior liquor at steadily rising prices, he was on the way to building up a small fortune.

"Are you quite sure of this?" Rambert asked.

"Quite. I had a proposal of the sort made to me the other day."

"But you didn't accept it."

"Oh, come, there's no need to be suspicious." Cottard's tone was genial. "I didn't accept it because, personally, I've no wish to leave. I have my reasons." After a short silence he added: "You don't ask me what my reasons are, I notice."

"I take it," Rambert replied, "that they're none of my business."

"That's so, in a way, of course. But from another angle—Well, let's put it like this: I've been feeling much more at ease here since plague settled in."

Rambert made no comment. Then he asked:

"And how does one approach this organization, as you call it?"

"Ah," Cottard replied, "that's none too easy. Come with me."

It was four in the afternoon. The town was warming up to boiling-point under a sultry sky. Nobody was about, all shops were shuttered. Cottard and Rambert walked some distance without speaking, under the arcades. This was an hour of the day when the plague lay low, so to speak; the silence, the extinction of all color and movement, might have been due as much to the fierce sunlight as to the epidemic, and there was no telling if the air was heavy with menace or merely with dust and heat. You had to look closely and take thought to realize that plague was here. For it betrayed its presence only by negative signs. Thus Cottard, who had affinities with it, drew Rambert's attention to the absence of the dogs that in normal times would have been seen sprawling in the shadow of the doorways, panting, trying to find a non-existent patch of coolness.

They went along the boulevard des Palmiers, crossed the Place d'Armes, and then turned down toward the docks. On the left was a café painted green, with a wide awning of coarse yellow canvas projecting over the sidewalk. Cottard and Rambert wiped their brows on entering. There were some small iron tables, also painted green, and folding chairs. The room was empty, the air humming with flies; in a yellow cage on the bar a parrot squatted on its perch, all its feathers drooping. Some old pictures of military scenes, covered with grime and cobwebs, adorned the walls. On the tables, including that at which Rambert was sitting, bird-droppings were drying, and he was puzzled whence they came until, after some wing-flappings, a handsome cock came hopping out of his retreat in a dark corner.

Just then the heat seemed to rise several degrees more. Cottard took off his coat and banged on the table-top. A very small man wearing a long blue apron that came nearly to his neck emerged from a doorway at the back, shouted a greeting to Cottard, and, vigorously kicking the cock out of his way, came up to the table. Raising his voice to drown the cock's indignant cacklings, he asked what the gentlemen would like. Cottard ordered white wine and asked: "Where's Garcia?" The dwarf replied that he'd not shown up at the café for several days.

"Think he'll come this evening?"

"Well, I ain't in his secrets—but you know when he usually comes, don't you?"

"Yes. Really, it's nothing very urgent; I only want him to know this friend of mine."

The barkeeper rubbed his moist hands on the front of his apron.

"Ah, so this gentleman's in business too?"

"Yes," Cottard said.

The little man made a snuffling noise.

"All right. Come back this evening. I'll send the kid to warn him."

After they had left, Rambert asked what the business in question might be.

"Why, smuggling, of course. They get the stuff in past the sentries at the gates. There's plenty money in it."

"I see." Rambert paused for a moment, then asked: "And, I take it, they've friends in court?"

"You've said it!"

In the evening the awning was rolled up, the parrot squawking in its cage, and the small tables were surrounded by men in their shirt-sleeves. When Cottard entered, one man, with a white shirt gaping on a brick-red chest and a straw hat planted well back on his head, rose to his feet. He had a sun-tanned face, regular features, small black eyes, very white teeth, and two or three rings on his fingers. He looked about thirty.

"Hi!" he said to Cottard, ignoring Rambert. "Let's have one at the bar."

They drank three rounds in silence. "How about a stroll?" Garcia suggested.

They walked toward the harbor. Garcia asked what he was wanted to do. Cottard explained that it wasn't really for a deal that he wanted to introduce his friend, M. Rambert, but only for what he called a "get-away." Puffing at his cigarette, Garcia walked straight ahead. He asked some questions, always referring to Rambert as "he" and appearing not to notice his presence.

"Why does he want to go?"

"His wife is in France."

"Ah!" After a short pause he added: "What's his job?"

"He's a journalist."

"Is he, now? Journalists have long tongues."

"I told you he's a friend of mine," Cottard replied.

They walked on in silence until they were near the wharves, which were now railed off. Then they turned in the direction of a small tavern from which came a smell of fried sardines.

"In any case," Garcia said finally, "it's not up my alley. Raoul's your man. And I'll have to get in touch with him. It's none too easy."

"That so?" Cottard sounded interested. "He's lying low, is he?"

Garcia made no answer. At the door of the tavern he halted and for the first time addressed Rambert directly.

"The day after tomorrow, at eleven, at the corner of the customs barracks in the upper town." He made as if to go, then seemed to have an afterthought. "It's going to cost something, you know." He made the observation in a quite casual tone.

Rambert nodded. "Naturally."

On the way back the journalist thanked Cottard.

"Don't mention it, old chap. I'm only too glad to help you. And then, you're a journalist, I dare say you'll put in a word for me one day or another."

Two days later Rambert and Cottard climbed the wide shadeless street leading to the upper part of the town. The barracks occupied by the customs officers had been partly transformed into a hospital, and a number of people were standing outside the main entrance, some of them hoping to be allowed to visit a patient—a futile hope, since such visits were strictly prohibited—and others to glean some news of an invalid, news that in the course of an hour would have ceased to count. For these reasons there were always a number of people and a certain amount of movement at this spot, a fact that probably accounted for its choice by Garcia for his meeting with Rambert.

"It puzzles me," Cottard remarked, "why you're so keen on going. Really, what's happening here is extremely interesting."

"Not to me," Rambert replied.

"Well, yes, one's running some risks, I grant you. All the same, when you come to think of it, one ran quite as much risk in the old days crossing a busy street."

Just then Rieux's car drew up level with them. Tarrou was at the wheel, and Rieux seemed half-asleep. He roused himself to make the introductions.

"We know each other," Tarrou said.

"We're at the same hotel." He then offered to drive Rambert back to the center.

"No, thanks. We've an appointment here."

Rieux looked hard at Rambert.

"Yes," Rambert said.

"What's that?" Cottard sounded surprised. "The doctor knows about it?"

"There's the magistrate." Tarrou gave Cottard a warning glance.

Cottard's look changed. M. Othon was striding down the street toward them, briskly, yet with dignity. He took off his hat as he came up with them.

"Good morning, Monsieur Othon," said Tarrou.

The magistrate returned the greeting of the men in the car and, turning to Rambert and Cottard, who were in the background, gave them a quiet nod. Tarrou introduced Cottard and the journalist. The magistrate gazed at the sky for a moment, sighed, and remarked that these were indeed sad times.

"I've been told, Monsieur Tarrou," he continued, "that you are helping to enforce the prophylactic measures. I need hardly say how commendable that is, a fine example. Do you think, Dr. Rieux, that the epidemic will get worse?"

Rieux replied that one could only hope it wouldn't, and the magistrate replied that one must never lose hope, the ways of Providence were inscrutable.

Tarrou asked if his work had increased as the result of present conditions.

"Quite the contrary. Criminal cases of what we call the first instance are growing rarer. In fact, almost my only work just now is holding inquiries into more serious breaches of the new regulations. Our ordinary laws have never been so well respected."

"That's because, by contrast, they necessarily appear good ones," Tarrou observed.

The magistrate, who seemed unable to take his gaze off the sky, abruptly dropped his mildly meditative air and stared at Tarrou.

"What does that matter? It's not the law that counts, it's the sentence. And that is something we must all accept."

"That fellow," said Tarrou when the magistrate was out of hearing, "is Enemy Number One."

He pressed the starter.

Some minutes later Rambert and Cottard saw Garcia approaching. Without making any sign of recognition he came straight up to them and, by way of greeting, said: "You'll have to wait a bit."

There was complete silence in the crowd around them, most of whom were women. Nearly all were carrying parcels; they had the vain hope of somehow smuggling these in to their sick relatives, and the even crazier idea that the latter could eat the food they'd brought. The gate was guarded by armed sentries, and now and then an eerie cry resounded in the courtyard between the barrack rooms and the entrance. Whenever this happened, anxious eyes turned toward the sick-wards.

The three men were watching the scene when a brisk "Good morning" from behind them made them swing round. In spite of the heat Raoul was wearing a well-cut dark suit and a felt hat with rolled-up brim. He was tall and strongly built, his face rather pale. Hardly moving his lips, he said quickly and clearly:

"Let's walk down to the center. You, Garcia, needn't come."

Garcia lit a cigarette and remained there while they walked away. Placing himself between Rambert and Cottard, Raoul set the pace, a fast one.

"Garcia's explained the situation," he said. "We can fix it. But I must warn you it'll cost you a cool ten thousand."

Rambert said he agreed to these terms.

"Lunch with me tomorrow at the Spanish restaurant near the docks."

Rambert said: "Right," and Raoul shook his hand, smiling for the first time. After he had gone, Cottard said he wouldn't be able to come to lunch next day, as he had an engagement, but anyhow Rambert didn't need him any more.

When next day Rambert entered the Spanish restaurant, everyone turned and stared at him. The dark, cellarlike room, below the level of the small yellow street, was patronized only by men, mostly Spaniards, judging by their looks. Raoul was sitting at a table at the back of the room. Once he had beckoned to the journalist and Rambert started to go toward him, the curiosity left the faces of the others and they bent over their plates again. Raoul had beside him a tall, thin, ill-shaven man, with enormously wide shoulders, an equine face, and thinning hair. His shirt-sleeves were rolled up, displaying long, skinny arms covered with black hair. When Rambert was introduced he gave three slow nods. His own name, however, was not announced and Raoul, when referring to him, always said "our friend."

"Our friend here thinks he may be able to help you. He is going—" Raoul broke off, as the waitress had just come to take Rambert's order. "He is going to put you in touch with two of our friends who will introduce you to some sentries whom we've squared. But that doesn't mean you can start right away. You'll have to leave it to the sentries to decide on the best moment. The simplest thing will be for you to stay some nights with one of them; his home is quite near the gate. The first thing is for our friend here to give you the contacts needed; then when everything's set, you'll settle with him for the expenses."

Again the "friend" slowly moved his equine head up and down, without ceasing to munch the tomato and pimento salad he was shoveling into his mouth. After which he began to speak, with a slight Spanish accent. He asked Rambert to meet him, the next day but one, at eight in the morning, in the Cathedral porch.

"Another two days' wait," Rambert observed.

"It ain't so easy as all that, you see," Raoul said. "Them boys take some finding."

Horse-face nodded slow approval once more. Some time was spent looking for a subject of conversation. The problem was solved easily enough when Rambert discovered that horse-face was an ardent football-player. He, too, had been very keen on soccer. They discussed the French championship, the merits of professional English teams, and the technique of passing. By the end of the meal horse-face was in high good humor, was calling Rambert "old boy," and trying to convince him that the most sporting position by far on the football field was that of center half. "You see, old boy, it's the center half that does the placing. And that's the whole art of the game, isn't it?" Rambert was inclined to agree, though he, personally, had always played center forward. The discussion proceeded peacefully until a radio was turned on and, after at first emitting a series of sentimental songs, broke into the announcement that there had been a hundred and thirty-seven plague deaths on the previous day. No one present betrayed the least emotion. Horse-face merely shrugged and stood up. Raoul and Rambert followed his example.

As they were going out, the center half shook Rambert's hand vigorously. "My name's Gonzales," he said.

To Rambert the next two days seemed endless. He looked up Rieux and described to him the latest developments, then accompanied the doctor on one of his calls. He took leave of him on the doorstep of a house where a patient, suspected to have plague, was awaiting him. There was a sound of footsteps and voices in the hall; the family were being warned of the doctor's visit.

"I hope Tarrou will be on time," Rieux murmured. He looked worn out.

"Is the epidemic getting out of hand?" Rambert asked.

Rieux said it wasn't that; indeed, the death-graph was rising less steeply. Only they lacked adequate means of coping with the disease.

"We're short of equipment. In all the armies of the world a shortage of equipment is usually compensated for by man-power. But we're short of man-power, too."

"Haven't doctors and trained assistants been sent from other towns?"

"Yes," Rieux said. "Ten doctors and a hundred helpers. That sounds a lot, no doubt. But it's barely enough to cope with the present state of affairs. And it will be quite inadequate if things get worse."

Rambert, who had been listening to the sounds within the house, turned to Rieux with a friendly smile.

"Yes," he said, "you'd better make haste to win your battle." Then a shadow crossed his face. "You know," he added in a low tone: "it's not because of *that* I'm leaving."

Rieux replied that he knew it very well, but Rambert went on to say:

"I don't think I'm a coward—not as a rule, anyhow. And I've had opportunities of putting it to the test. Only there are some thoughts I simply cannot endure."

The doctor looked him in the eyes.

"You'll see her again," he said.

"Maybe. But I just can't stomach the thought that it may last on and on, and all the time she'll be growing older. At thirty one's beginning to age, and one's got to squeeze all one can out of life. But I doubt if you can understand."

Rieux was replying that he thought he could, when Tarrou came up, obviously much excited.

"I've just asked Paneloux to join us."

"Well?" asked the doctor.

"He thought it over, then said yes."

"That's good," the doctor said. "I'm glad to know he's better than his sermon."

"Most people are like that," Tarrou replied. "It's only a matter of giving them the chance." He smiled and winked at Rieux. "That's my job in life—giving people chances."

"Excuse me," Rambert said, "I've got to be off."

On Thursday, the day of the appointment, Rambert entered the Cathedral porch at five minutes to eight. The air was still relatively cool. Small fleecy clouds, which presently the sun would swallow at a gulp, were drifting across the sky. A faint smell of moisture rose from the lawns, parched though they were. Still masked by the eastward houses, the sun was warming up Joan of Arc's helmet only, and it made a solitary patch of brightness in the Cathedral square. A clock struck eight. Rambert took some steps in the empty porch. From inside came a low sound of intoning voices, together with stale wafts of incense and dank air. Then the voices ceased. Ten small black forms came out of the building and hastened away toward the center of the town. Rambert grew impatient. Other black forms climbed the steps and entered the porch. He was about to light a cigarette when it struck him that smoking might be frowned on here.

At eight fifteen the organ began to play, very softly. Rambert entered. At first he could see nothing in the dim light of the aisle; after a moment he made out in the nave the small black forms that had preceded him. They were all grouped in a corner, in front of a makeshift altar on which stood a statue of St. Roch, carved in haste by one of our local sculptors. Kneeling, they looked even smaller than before, blobs of clotted darkness hardly more opaque than the gray, smoky haze in which they seemed to float. Above them the organ was playing endless variations.

When Rambert stepped out of the Cathedral, he saw Gonzales already going down the steps on his way back to the town.

"I thought you'd cleared off, old boy," he said to the journalist. "Considering how late it is."

He proceeded to explain that he'd gone to meet his friends at the place agreed on—which was quite near by—at ten to eight, the time they'd fixed, and waited twenty minutes without seeing them.

"Something must have held them up. There's lots of snags, you know, in our line of business."

He suggested another meeting at the same time on the following day, beside the war memorial. Rambert sighed and pushed his hat back on his head.

"Don't take it so hard," Gonzales laughed. "Why, think of all the swerves and runs and passes you got to make to score a goal."

"Quite so," Rambert agreed. "But the game lasts only an hour and a half."

The war memorial at Oran stands at the one place where one has a glimpse of the sea, a sort of esplanade following for a short distance the brow of the cliff overlooking the harbor. Next day, being again the first to arrive at the meeting-place, Rambert whiled away the time reading the list of names of those who had died for their country. Some minutes later two men strolled up, gave him a casual glance, then, resting their elbows on the parapet of the esplanade, gazed down intently at the empty, lifeless harbor. Both wore short-sleeved jerseys and blue trousers, and were of much the same height. The journalist moved away and, seated on a stone bench, studied their appearance at leisure. They were obviously youngsters, not more than twenty. Just then he saw Gonzales coming up.

"Those are our friends," he said, after apologizing for being late. Then he led Rambert to the two youths, whom he introduced as Marcel and Louis. They looked so much alike that Rambert had no doubt they were brothers.

"Right," said Gonzales. "Now you know each other, you can get down to business."

Marcel, or Louis, said that their turn of guard duty began in two days and lasted a week; they'd have to watch out for the night when there was the best chance of bringing it off. The trouble was that there were two other sentries, regular soldiers, besides themselves, at the west gate. These two men had better be kept out of the business; one couldn't depend on them, and anyhow it would pile up expenses unnecessarily. Some evenings, however, these two sentries spent several hours in the back room of a near-by bar. Marcel, or Louis, said that the best thing Rambert could do would be to stay at their place, which was only a few minutes' walk from the gate, and wait till one of them came to tell him the coast was clear. It should then be quite easy for him to "make his get-away." But there was no time to lose; there had been talk about setting up duplicate sentry posts a little farther out.

Rambert agreed and handed some of his few remaining cigarettes to the young men. The one who had not yet spoken asked Gonzales if the question of expenses had been settled and whether an advance would be given.

"No," Gonzales said, "and you needn't bother about that; he's a pal of mine. He'll pay when he leaves."

Another meeting was arranged. Gonzales suggested their dining together on the next day but one, at the Spanish restaurant. It was at easy walking-distance from where the young men lived. "For the first night," he added, "I'll keep you company, old boy."

Next day on his way to his bedroom Rambert met Tarrou coming down the stairs at the hotel.

"Like to come with me?" he asked. "I'm just off to see Rieux."

Rambert hesitated.

"Well, I never feel sure I'm not disturbing him."

"I don't think you need worry about that; he's talked about you quite a lot."

The journalist pondered. Then, "Look here," he said. "If you've any time to spare after dinner, never mind how late, why not come to the hotel, both of you, and have a drink with me?"

"That will depend on Rieux." Tarrou sounded doubtful. "And on the plague," he added.

At eleven o'clock that night, however, Rieux and Tarrou entered the small, narrow bar of the hotel. Some thirty people were crowded into it, all talking at the top of their voices. Coming from the silence of the plague-bound town, the two newcomers were startled by the sudden burst of noise, and halted in the doorway. They understood the reason for it when they saw that liquor was still to be had here. Rambert, who was perched on a stool at a corner of the bar, beckoned to them. With complete coolness he elbowed away a noisy customer beside him to make room for his friends.

"You've no objection to a spot of something strong?"

"No," Tarrou replied. "Quite the contrary."

Rieux sniffed the pungency of bitter herbs in the drink that Rambert handed him. It was hard to make oneself heard in the din of voices, but Rambert seemed chiefly concerned with drinking. The doctor couldn't make up his mind whether he was drunk yet. At one of the two tables that occupied all the remaining space beyond the half-circle round the bar, a naval officer, with a girl on each side of him, was describing to a fat, red-faced man a typhus epidemic at Cairo. "They had camps, you know," he was saying, "for the natives, with tents for the sick ones and a ring of sentries all round. If a member of the family came along and tried to smuggle in one of those damn-fool native remedies, they fired at sight. A bit tough, I grant you, but it was the only thing to do." At the other table, round which sat a bevy of bright young people, the talk was incomprehensible, half drowned by the stridence of *St. James Infirmary* coming from a loud-speaker just above their heads.

"Any luck?" Rieux had to raise his voice.

"I'm getting on," Rambert replied. "In the course of the week, perhaps."

"A pity!" Tarrou shouted.

"Why?"

"Oh," Rieux put in, "Tarrou said that because he thinks you might be useful to us here. But, personally, I understand your wish to get away only too well."

Tarrou stood the next round of drinks. Rambert got off his stool and looked him in the eyes for the first time.

"How could I be useful?"

"Why, of course," Tarrou replied, slowly reaching toward his glass, "in one of our sanitary squads."

The look of brooding obstinacy that Rambert so often had came back to his face, and he climbed again on to his stool.

"Don't you think these squads of ours do any good?" asked Tarrou, who had just taken a sip of his glass and was gazing hard at Rambert.

"I'm sure they do," the journalist replied, and drank off his glass.

Rieux noticed that his hand was shaking, and he decided, definitely, that the man was far gone in drink.

Next day, when for the second time Rambert entered the Spanish restaurant, he had to make his way through a group of men who had taken chairs out on the sidewalk and were sitting in the green-gold evening light, enjoying the first breaths of cooler air. They were smoking an acrid-smelling tobacco. The restaurant itself was almost empty. Rambert went to the table at the back at which Gonzales had sat when they met for the first time. He told the waitress he would wait a bit. It was seven thirty.

In twos and threes the men from outside began to dribble in and seat themselves at the tables. The waitresses started serving them, and a tinkle of knives and forks, a hum of conversation, began to fill the cellarlike room. At eight Rambert was still waiting. The lights were turned on. A new set of people took the other chairs at his table. He ordered dinner. At half past eight he had finished without having seen either Gonzales or the two young men. He smoked several cigarettes. The restaurant was gradually emptying. Outside, night was falling rapidly. The curtains hung across the doorway were billowing in a warm breeze from the sea. At nine Rambert realized that the restaurant was quite empty and the waitress was eying him curiously. He paid, went out, and, noticing that a café across the street was open, settled down there at a place from which he could keep an eye on the entrance of the restaurant. At half past nine he walked slowly back to his hotel, racking his brains for some method of tracking down Gonzales, whose address he did not know, and bitterly discouraged by the not unlikely prospect of having to start the tiresome business all over again.

It was at this moment, as he walked in the dark streets along which ambulances were speeding, that it suddenly struck him—as he informed Dr. Rieux subsequently—that all this time he'd practically forgotten the woman he loved, so absorbed had he been in trying to find a rift in the walls that cut him off from her. But at this same moment, now that once more all ways of escape were sealed against him, he felt his longing for her blaze up again, with a violence so sudden, so intense, that he started running to his hotel, as if to escape the burning pain that none the less pervaded him, racing like wildfire in his blood.

Very early next day, however, he called on Rieux, to ask him where he could find Cottard.

"The only thing to do is to pick up the thread again where I dropped it."

"Come tomorrow night," Rieux said. "Tarrou asked me to invite Cottard here—I don't know why. He's due to come at ten. Come at half past ten."

When Cottard visited the doctor next day, Tarrou and Rieux were discussing the case of one of Rieux's patients who against all expectation had recovered.

"It was ten to one against," Tarrou commented. "He was in luck."

"Oh, come now," Cottard said. "It can't have been plague, that's all."

They assured him there was no doubt it was a case of plague.

"That's impossible, since he recovered. You know as well as I do, once you have plague your number's up."

"True enough, as a general rule," Rieux replied. "But if you refuse to be beaten, you have some pleasant surprises."

Cottard laughed.

"Precious few, anyhow. You saw the number of deaths this evening?"

Tarrou, who was gazing amiably at Cottard, said he knew the latest figures, and that the position was extremely serious. But what did that prove? Only that still more stringent measures should be applied.

"How? You can't make more stringent ones than those we have now."

"No. But every person in the town must apply them to himself."

Cottard stared at him in a puzzled manner, and Tarrou went on to say that there were far too many slackers, that this plague was everybody's business, and everyone should do his duty. For instance, any able-bodied man was welcome in the sanitary squads.

"That's an idea," said Cottard, "but it won't get you anywhere. The plague has the whip hand of you and there's nothing to be done about it."

"We shall know whether that is so"—Tarrou's voice was carefully controlled—"only when we've tried everything."

Meanwhile Rieux had been sitting at his desk, copying out reports. Tarrou was still gazing at the little business man, who was stirring uneasily in his chair.

"Look here, Monsieur Cottard, why don't you join us?"

Picking up his derby hat, Cottard rose from his chair with an offended expression.

"It's not my job," he said. Then, with an air of bravado, he added: "What's more, the plague suits me quite well and I see no reason why I should bother about trying to stop it."

As if a new idea had just waylaid him, Tarrou struck his forehead.

"Why, of course, I was forgetting. If it wasn't for that, you'd be arrested."

Cottard gave a start and gripped the back of the chair, as if he were about to

fall. Rieux had stopped writing and was observing him with grave interest.

"Who told you that?" Cottard almost screamed.

"Why, you yourself!" Tarrou looked surprised. "At least, that's what the doctor and I have gathered from the way you speak."

Losing all control of himself, Cottard let out a volley of oaths.

"Don't get excited," Tarrou said quietly. "Neither I nor the doctor would dream of reporting you to the police. What you may have done is no business of ours. And, anyway, we've never had much use for the police. Come, now! Sit down again."

Cottard looked at the chair, then hesitantly lowered himself into it. He heaved a deep sigh.

"It's something that happened ages ago," he began. "Somehow they've dug it up. I thought it had all been forgotten. But somebody started talking, damn him! They sent for me and told me not to budge till the inquiry was finished. And I felt pretty sure they'd end up by arresting me."

"Was it anything serious?" Tarrou asked.

"That depends on what you mean by 'serious.' It wasn't murder, anyhow."

"Prison or transportation with hard labor?"

Cottard was looking almost abject.

"Well, prison—if I'm lucky." But after a moment he grew excited again. "It was all a mistake. Everybody makes mistakes. And I can't bear the idea of being pulled in for that, of being torn from my home and habits and everyone I know."

"And is that the reason," Tarrou asked, "why you had the bright idea of hanging yourself?"

"Yes. It was a damn-fool thing to do, I admit."

For the first time Rieux spoke. He told

Cottard that he quite understood his anxiety, but perhaps everything would come right in the end.

"Oh, for the moment I've nothing to fear."

"I can see," Tarrou said, "that you're not going to join in our effort."

Twiddling his hat uneasily, Cottard gazed at Tarrou with shifty eyes.

"I hope you won't bear me a grudge."

"Certainly not. But"—Tarrou smiled—"do try at least not to propagate the microbe deliberately."

Cottard protested that he'd never wanted the plague, it was pure chance that it had broken out, and he wasn't to blame if it happened to make things easier for him just now. Then he seemed to pluck up courage again and when Rambert entered was shouting almost aggressively:

"What's more, I'm pretty sure you won't get anywhere."

Rambert learned to his chagrin that Cottard didn't know where Gonzales lived; he suggested that they'd better pay another visit to the small café. They made an appointment for the following day. When Rieux gave him to understand that he'd like to be kept posted, Rambert proposed that he and Tarrou should look him up one night at the end of the week. They could come as late as they liked and would be sure to find him in his room.

Next morning Cottard and Rambert went to the café and left a message for Garcia, asking him to come that evening, or if this could not be managed, next day. They waited for him in vain that evening. Next day Garcia turned up. He listened in silence to what Rambert had to say; then informed him he had no idea what had happened, but knew that several districts of the town had been isolated for twenty-four hours for a house-to-house inspection. Quite possibly Gonzales and the two youngsters hadn't been able to get through the cordon. All he could do was to put them in touch once more with Raoul. Naturally this couldn't be done before the next day but one.

"I see," Rambert said. "I'll have to start it all over again, from scratch."

On the next day but one, Raoul, whom Rambert met at a street corner, confirmed Garcia's surmise; the low-lying districts had, in fact, been isolated and a cordon put round them. The next thing was to get in contact with Gonzales. Two days later Rambert was lunching with the footballer.

"It's too damn silly," Gonzales said. "Of course you should have arranged some way of seeing each other."

Rambert heartily agreed.

"Tomorrow morning," Gonzales continued, "we'll look up the kids and try to get a real move on."

When they called next day, however, the youngsters were out. A note was left fixing a meeting for the following day at noon, outside the high school. When Rambert came back to his hotel, Tarrou was struck by the look on his face.

"Not feeling well?" he asked.

"It's having to start it all over again that's got me down." Then he added: "You'll come tonight, won't you?"

When the two friends entered Rambert's room that night, they found him lying on the bed. He got up at once and filled the glasses he had ready. Before lifting his to his lips, Rieux asked him if he was making progress. The journalist replied that he'd started the same round again and got to the same point as before; in a day or two he was to have his last appointment. Then he took a sip of his drink and added gloomily: "Needless to say, they won't turn up."

"Oh come! That doesn't follow because they let you down last time."

"So you haven't understood yet?" Rambert shrugged his shoulders almost scornfully.

"Understood what?"

"The plague."

"Ah!" Rieux exclaimed.

"No, you haven't understood that it means exactly that—the same thing over and over and over again."

He went to a corner of the room and started a small phonograph.

"What's that record?" Tarrou asked. "I've heard it before."

"It's *St. James Infirmary.*"

While the phonograph was playing, two shots rang out in the distance.

"A dog or a get-away," Tarrou remarked.

When, a moment later, the record ended, an ambulance bell could be heard clanging past under the window and receding into silence.

"Rather a boring record," Rambert remarked. "And this must be the tenth time I've put it on today."

"Are you really so fond of it?"

"No, but it's the only one I have." And after a moment he added: "That's what I said 'it' was—the same thing over and over again."

He asked Rieux how the sanitary groups were functioning. Five teams were now at work, and it was hoped to form others. Sitting on the bed, the journalist seemed to be studying his fingernails. Rieux was gazing at his squat, powerfully built form, hunched up on the edge of the bed. Suddenly he realized that Rambert was returning his gaze.

"You know, doctor, I've given a lot of thought to your campaign. And if I'm not with you, I have my reasons. No, I don't think it's that I'm afraid to risk my skin again. I took part in the Spanish Civil War."

"On which side?" Tarrou asked.

"The losing side. But since then I've done a bit of thinking."

"About what?"

"Courage. I know now that man is

capable of great deeds. But if he isn't capable of a great emotion, well, he leaves me cold."

"One has the idea that he is capable of everything," Tarrou remarked.

"I can't agree; he's incapable of suffering for a long time, or being happy for a long time. Which means that he's incapable of anything really worth while." He looked at the two men in turn, then asked: "Tell me, Tarrou, are you capable of dying for love?"

"I couldn't say, but I hardly think so—as I am now."

"You see. But you're capable of dying for an idea; one can see that right away. Well, personally, I've seen enough of people who die for an idea. I don't believe in heroism; I know it's easy and I've learned it can be murderous. What interests me is living and dying for what one loves."

Rieux had been watching the journalist attentively. With his eyes still on him he said quietly:

"Man isn't an idea, Rambert."

Rambert sprang off the bed, his face ablaze with passion.

"Man *is* an idea, and a precious small idea, once he turns his back on love. And that's my point; we—mankind—have lost the capacity for love. We must face that fact, doctor. Let's wait to acquire that capacity or, if really it's beyond us, wait for the deliverance that will come to each of us anyway, without his playing the hero. Personally, I look no farther."

Rieux rose. He suddenly appeared very tired.

"You're right, Rambert, quite right, and for nothing in the world would I try to dissuade you from what you're going to do; it seems to me absolutely right and proper. However, there's one thing I must tell you: there's no question of heroism in all this. It's a matter of common decency. That's an idea which may make some people smile, but the only means of fighting a plague is—common decency."

"What do you mean by 'common decency'?" Rambert's tone was grave.

"I don't know what it means for other people. But in my case I know that it consists in doing my job."

"Your job! I only wish I were sure what my job is!" There was a mordant edge to Rambert's voice. "Maybe I'm all wrong in putting love first."

Rieux looked him in the eyes.

"No," he said vehemently, "you are *not* wrong."

Rambert gazed thoughtfully at them.

"You two," he said, "I suppose you've nothing to lose in all this. It's easier, that way, to be on the side of the angels."

Rieux drained his glass.

"Come along," he said to Tarrou. "We've work to do."

He went out.

Tarrou followed, but seemed to change his mind when he reached the door. He stopped and looked at the journalist.

"I suppose you don't know that Rieux's wife is in a sanatorium, a hundred miles or so away."

Rambert showed surprise and began to say something; but Tarrou had already left the room.

At a very early hour next day Rambert rang up the doctor.

"Would you agree to my working with you until I find some way of getting out of the town?"

There was a moment's silence before the reply came.

"Certainly, Rambert. Thanks."

PART III

Thus week by week the prisoners of plague put up what fight they could. Some, like Rambert, even contrived to fancy they were still behaving as free men and had the power of choice. But actually it would have been truer to say that by this time, mid-August, the plague had swallowed up everything and everyone. No longer were there individual destinies; only a collective destiny, made of plague and the emotions shared by all. Strongest of these emotions was the sense of exile and of deprivation, with all the cross-currents of revolt and fear set up by these. That is why the narrator thinks this moment, registering the climax of the summer heat and the disease, the best for describing, on general lines and by way of illustration, the excesses of the living, burials of the dead, and the plight of parted lovers.

It was at this time that a high wind rose and blew for several days through the plague-stricken city. Wind is particularly dreaded by the inhabitants of Oran, since the plateau on which the town is built presents no natural obstacle, and it can sweep our streets with unimpeded violence. During the months when not a drop of rain had refreshed the town, a gray crust had formed on everything, and this flaked off under the wind, disintegrating into dust-clouds. What with the dust and scraps of paper whirled against peoples' legs, the streets grew emptier. Those few who went out could be seen hurrying along, bent forward, with handkerchiefs or their hands pressed to their mouths. At nightfall, instead of the usual throng of people, each trying to prolong a day that might well be his last, you met only small groups hastening home or to a favorite café. With the result that for several days when twilight came—it fell much quicker at this time of the year—the streets were almost empty, and silent but for the long-drawn stridence of the wind. A smell of brine and seaweed came from the unseen, storm-tossed sea. And in the growing darkness the almost empty town, palled in dust, swept by bitter sea-spray, and loud with the shrilling of the

wind, seemed a lost island of the damned.

Hitherto the plague had found far more victims in the more thickly populated and less well-appointed outer districts than in the heart of the town. Quite suddenly, however, it launched a new attack and established itself in the business center. Residents accused the wind of carrying infection, "broadcasting germs," as the hotel manager put it. Whatever the reason might be, people living in the central districts realized that their turn had come when each night they heard oftener and oftener the ambulances clanging past, sounding the plague's dismal, passionless tocsin under their windows.

The authorities had the idea of segregating certain particularly affected central areas and permitting only those whose services were indispensable to cross the cordon. Dwellers in these districts could not help regarding these regulations as a sort of taboo specially directed at themselves, and thus they came, by contrast, to envy residents in other areas their freedom. And the latter, to cheer themselves up in despondent moments, fell to picturing the lot of those others less free than themselves. "Anyhow, there are some worse off than I," was a remark that voiced the only solace to be had in those days.

About the same time we had a recrudescence of outbreaks of fire, especially in the residential area near the west gate. It was found, after inquiry, that people who had returned from quarantine were responsible for these fires. Thrown off their balance by bereavement and anxiety, they were burning their houses under the odd delusion that they were killing off the plague in the holocaust. Great difficulty was experienced in fighting these fires, whose numbers and frequency exposed whole districts to constant danger, owing to the high wind.

When the attempts made by the authorities to convince these well-meaning incendiaries that the official fumigation of their houses effectively removed any risk of infection had proved unavailing, it became necessary to decree very heavy penalties for this type of arson. And most likely it was not the prospect of mere imprisonment that deterred these unhappy people, but the common belief that a sentence of imprisonment was tantamount to a death sentence, owing to the very high mortality prevailing in the town jail. It must be admitted that there was some foundation for this belief. It seemed that, for obvious reasons, the plague launched its most virulent attacks on those who lived, by choice or by necessity, in groups: soldiers, prisoners, monks, and nuns. For though some prisoners are kept solitary, a prison forms a sort of community, as is proved by the fact that in our town jail the guards died of plague in the same proportion as the prisoners. The plague was no respecter of persons and under its despotic rule everyone, from the warden down to the humblest delinquent, was under sentence and, perhaps for the first time, impartial justice reigned in the prison.

Attempts made by the authorities to redress this leveling-out by some sort of hierarchy—the idea was to confer a decoration on guards who died in the exercise of their duties—came to nothing. Since martial law had been declared and the guards might, from a certain angle, be regarded as on active service, they were awarded posthumously the military medal. But though the prisoners raised no protest, strong exception was taken in military circles, and it was pointed out, logically enough, that a most regrettable confusion in the public mind would certainly ensue. The civil authority conceded the point and decided that the simplest solution was to bestow on guards who died at their post a "plague medal." Even so, since as regards the first recipients of the military medal the harm had been done and there was no question of withdrawing the decoration from them, the military were still dissatisfied. Moreover, the plague medal had the disadvantage of having far less moral effect than that attaching to a military award, since in time of pestilence a decoration of this sort is too easily acquired. Thus nobody was satisfied.

Another difficulty was that the jail administration could not follow the procedure adopted by the religious and, in a less degree, the military authorities. The monks in the two monasteries of the town had been evacuated and lodged for the time being with religious-minded families. In the same way, whenever possible, small bodies of men had been moved out of barracks and billeted in schools or public buildings. Thus the disease, which apparently had forced on us the solidarity of a beleaguered town, disrupted at the same time long-established communities and sent men out to live, as individuals, in relative isolation. This, too, added to the general feeling of unrest.

Indeed, it can easily be imagined that these changes, combined with the high wind, also had an incendiary effect on certain minds. There were frequent attacks on the gates of the town, and the men who made them now were armed. Shots were exchanged, there were casualties, and some few got away. Then the sentry posts were reinforced, and such attempts quickly ceased. None the less, they sufficed to start a wave of revolutionary violence, though only on a small scale. Houses that had been burnt or closed by the sanitary control were looted. However, it seemed unlikely that these excesses were premeditated. Usually it was some chance incentive that led normally well-behaved people to acts which promptly had their imitators.

Thus you sometimes saw a man, acting on some crazy impulse, dash into a blazing house under the eyes of its owner, who was standing by, dazed with grief, watching the flames. Seeing his indifference, many of the onlookers would follow the lead given by the first man, and presently the dark street was full of running men, changed to hunched, misshapen gnomes by the flickering glow from the dying flames and the ornaments or furniture they carried on their shoulders. It was incidents of this sort that compelled the authorities to declare martial law and enforce the regulations deriving from it. Two looters were shot, but we may doubt if this made much impression on the others; with so many deaths taking place every day, these two executions went unheeded—a mere drop in the ocean. Actually scenes of this kind continued to take place fairly often, without the authorities' making even a show of intervening. The only regulation that seemed to have some effect on the populace was the establishment of a curfew hour. From eleven onwards, plunged in complete darkness, Oran seemed a huge necropolis.

On moonlight nights the long, straight streets and dirty white walls, nowhere darkened by the shadow of a tree, their peace untroubled by footsteps or a dog's bark, glimmered in pale recession. The silent city was no more than an assemblage of huge, inert cubes, between which only the mute effigies of great men, carapaced in bronze, with their blank stone or metal faces, conjured up a sorry semblance of what the man had been. In lifeless squares and avenues these tawdry idols lorded it under the lowering sky; stolid monsters that might have personified the rule of immobility imposed on us, or, anyhow, its final aspect, that of a defunct city in which plague, stone, and darkness had effectively silenced every voice.

But there was darkness also in men's hearts, and the true facts were as little calculated to reassure our townsfolk as the wild stories going round about the burials. The narrator cannot help talking about these burials, and a word of excuse is here in place. For he is well aware of the reproach that might be made him in this respect; his justification is that funerals were taking place throughout this period and, in a way, he was compelled, as indeed everybody was compelled, to give heed to them. In any case it should not be assumed that he has a morbid taste for such ceremonies; quite the contrary, he much prefers the society of the living and—to give a concrete illustration—sea-bathing. But the bathing-beaches were out of bounds and the company of the living ran a risk, increasing as the days went by, of being perforce converted into the company of the dead. That was, indeed, self-evident. True, one could always refuse to face this disagreeable fact, shut one's eyes to it, or thrust it out of mind, but there is a terrible cogency in the self-evident; ultimately it breaks down all defenses. How, for instance, continue to ignore the funerals on the day when somebody you loved needed one?

Actually the most striking feature of our funerals was their speed. Formalities had been whittled down, and, generally speaking, all elaborate ceremonial suppressed. The plague victim died away from his family and the customary vigil beside the dead body was forbidden, with the result that a person dying in the evening spent the night alone, and those who died in the daytime were promptly buried. Needless to say, the family was notified, but in most cases, since the deceased had lived with them, its members were in quarantine and thus immobilized. When, however, the deceased had not lived with his family, they were asked to attend at a fixed time; after, that is to say, the body had been washed and put in the coffin and when the journey to the cemetery was about to begin.

Let us suppose that these formalities were taking place at the auxiliary hospital of which Dr. Rieux was in charge. This converted school had an exit at the back of the main building. A large storeroom giving on the corridor contained the coffins. On arrival, the family found a coffin already nailed up in the corridor. Then came the most important part of the business: the signing of official forms by the head of the family. Next the coffin was loaded on a motor-vehicle—a real hearse or a large converted ambulance. The mourners stepped into one of the few taxis still allowed to ply and the vehicles drove hell-for-leather to the cemetery by a route avoiding the center of the town. There was a halt at the gate, where police officers applied a rubber stamp to the official exit permit, without which it was impossible for our citizens to have what they called a last resting-place. The policeman stood back and the cars drew up near a plot of ground where a number of graves stood open, waiting for inmates. A priest came to meet the mourners, since church services at funerals were now prohibited. To an accompaniment of prayers the coffin was dragged from the hearse, roped up, and carried to the graveside; the ropes were slipped and it came heavily to rest at the bottom of the grave. No sooner had the priest begun to sprinkle holy water than the first sod rebounded from the lid. The ambulance had already left and was being sprayed with disinfectant, and while spadefuls of clay thudded more and more dully on the rising layer of earth, the family were bundling into the taxi. A quarter of an hour later they were back at home.

The whole process was put through with the maximum of speed and the minimum of risk. It cannot be denied that, anyhow in the early days, the natural feelings of the family were somewhat outraged by these lightning funerals. But obviously in time of plague such sentiments can't be taken into account, and all was sacrificed to efficiency. And though, to start with, the morale of the population was shaken by this summary procedure—for the desire to have a "proper funeral" is more widespread than is generally believed—as time went on, fortunately enough, the food problem became more urgent and the thoughts of our townsfolk were diverted to more instant needs. So much energy was expended on filling up forms, hunting round for supplies, and lining up that people had no time to think of the manner in which others were dying around them and they themselves would die one day. Thus the growing complications of our everyday life, which might have been an affliction, proved to be a blessing in disguise. Indeed, had not the epidemic, as already mentioned, spread its ravages, all would have been for the best.

For then coffins became scarcer; also there was a shortage of winding-sheets, and of space in the cemetery. Something had to be done about this, and one obvious step, justified by its practical convenience, was to combine funerals and, when necessary, multiply the trips between the hospital and the burial-place. At one moment the stock of coffins in Rieux's hospital was reduced to five. Once filled, all five were loaded together in the ambulance. At the cemetery they were emptied out and the iron-gray corpses put on stretchers and deposited in a shed reserved for that purpose, to wait their turn. Meanwhile the empty coffins, after being sprayed with antiseptic fluid, were rushed back to the hospital, and the process was repeated as often as necessary. This system worked excellently and won the approval of the Prefect. He even told Rieux that it was really a great improvement on the death-carts driven by Negroes of which one reads in accounts of former visitations of this sort.

"Yes," Rieux said, "And though the burials are much the same, we keep careful records of them. That, you will agree, is progress."

Successful, however, as the system proved itself in practice, there was something so distasteful in the last rites as now performed that the Prefect felt constrained to forbid relations of the deceased being present at the actual interment. They were allowed to come only as far as the cemetery gates, and even that was not authorized officially. For things had somewhat changed as regards the last stage of the ceremony. In a patch of open ground dotted with lentiscus trees at the far end of the cemetery, two big pits had been dug. One was reserved for the men, the other for the women. Thus, in this respect, the authorities still gave thought to propriety and it was only later that, by the force of things, this last remnant of decorum went by the board, and men and women were flung into the death-pits indiscriminately. Happily, this ultimate indignity synchronized with the plague's last ravages.

In the period we are now concerned with, the separation of the sexes was still in force and the authorities set great store by it. At the bottom of each pit a deep layer of quicklime steamed and seethed. On the lips of the pit a low ridge of quicklime threw up bubbles that burst in the air above it. When the ambulance had finished its trips, the stretchers were carried to the pits in Indian file. The naked, somewhat contorted bodies were slid off into the pit almost side by side, then covered with a layer of quicklime and another of earth, the latter only a few inches deep, so as to leave space for subsequent consignments. On the following day the next of kin were asked to sign the register of burials, which showed the distinction that can be made between men and, for example, dogs; men's deaths are checked and entered up.

Obviously all these activities called for a considerable staff, and Rieux was often on the brink of a shortage. Many of the gravediggers, stretcher-bearers, and the like, public servants to begin with, and later volunteers, died of plague. However stringent the precautions, sooner or later contagion did its work. Still, when all is said and done, the really amazing thing is that, so long as the epidemic lasted, there was never any lack of men for these duties. The critical moment came just before the outbreak touched high-water mark, and the doctor had good reason for feeling anxious. There was then a real shortage of man-power both for the higher posts and for the rough work, as Rieux called it. But, paradoxically enough, once the whole town was in the grip of the disease, its very prevalence tended to make things easier, since the disorganization of the town's economic life threw a great number of persons out of work. Few of the workers thus made available were qualified for administrative posts, but the recruiting of men for the "rough work" became much easier. From now on, indeed, poverty showed itself a stronger stimulus than fear, especially as, owing to its risks, such work was highly paid. The sanitary authorities always had a waiting-list of applicants for work; whenever there was a vacancy the men at the top of the list were notified, and unless they too had laid off work for good, they never failed to appear when summoned. Thus the Prefect, who had always been reluctant to employ the prisoners in the jail, whether short-term men or lifers, was able to avoid recourse to this distasteful measure. As long, he said, as there were unemployed, we could afford to wait.

Thus until the end of August our fellow citizens could be conveyed to their last resting-place, if not under very decorous conditions, at least in a manner orderly enough for the authorities to feel that they were doing their duty by the dead and the bereaved. However, we may here anticipate a little and describe the pass to which we came in the final phase. From August onwards the plague mortality was and continued such as far to exceed the capacity of our small cemetery. Such expedients as knocking down walls and letting the dead encroach on neighboring land proved inadequate; some new method had to be evolved without delay. The first step taken was to bury the dead by night, which obviously permitted a more summary procedure. The bodies were piled into ambulances in larger and larger numbers. And the few belated wayfarers who, in defiance of the regulations, were abroad in the outlying districts after curfew hour, or whose duties took them there, often saw the long white ambulances hurtling past, making the nightbound streets reverberate with the dull clangor of their bells. The corpses were tipped pell-mell into the pits and had hardly settled into place when spadefuls of quicklime began to sear their faces and the earth covered them indistinctively, in holes dug steadily deeper as time went on.

Shortly afterwards, however, it became necessary to find new space and to strike out in a new direction. By a special urgency measure the denizens of grants in perpetuity were evicted from their graves and the exhumed remains dispatched to the crematorium. And soon the plague victims likewise had to go to a fiery end. This meant that the old crematorium east of the town, outside the gates, had to be utilized. Accordingly the east-gate sentry post was moved farther out. Then a municipal employee had an idea that greatly helped the harassed authorities; he advised them to employ the streetcar line running along the coastal road, which was now unused. So the interiors of streetcars and trailers were adapted to this new purpose, and a branch line was laid down to the crematorium, which thus became a terminus.

During all the late summer and throughout the autumn there could daily be seen moving along the road skirting the cliffs above the sea a strange procession of passengerless streetcars swaying against the skyline. The residents in this area soon learned what was going on. And though the cliffs were patrolled day and night, little groups of people contrived to thread their way unseen between the rocks and would toss flowers into the open trailers as the cars went by. And in the warm darkness of the summer nights the cars could be heard clanking on their way, laden with flowers and corpses.

During the first few days an oily, foul-smelling cloud of smoke hung low upon the eastern districts of the town. These effluvia, all the doctors agreed, though unpleasant, were not in the least harmful. However, the residents of this part of the town threatened to migrate in a body, convinced that germs were raining down on them from the sky, with the result that an elaborate apparatus for diverting the smoke had to be installed to appease them. Thereafter only when a strong wind was blowing did a faint, sickly odor coming from the east remind them that they were living under a new order and that the plague fires were taking their nightly toll.

Such were the consequences of the epidemic at its culminating point. Happily it grew no worse, for otherwise, it may well be believed, the resourcefulness of our administration, the competence of our officials, not to mention the burning-capacity of our crematorium, would have proved unequal to their tasks. Rieux knew that desperate solutions had been mooted, such as throwing the corpses into the sea, and a picture had risen before him of hideous jetsam lolling in the shallows under the cliffs. He knew, too, that if there was another rise in the death-rate, no organization, however efficient, could stand up to it; that men would die in heaps, and corpses rot in the street, whatever the authorities might do, and the town would see in public squares the dying embrace the living in the frenzies of an all too comprehensible hatred or some crazy hope.

Such were the sights and apprehensions that kept alive in our townspeople their feeling of exile and separation. In this connection the narrator is well aware how regrettable is his inability to record at this point something of a really spectacular order—some heroic feat or memorable deed like those that thrill us in the chronicles of the past. The truth is that nothing is less sensational than pestilence, and by reason of their very duration great misfortunes are monotonous. In the memories of those who lived through them, the grim days of plague do not stand out like vivid flames, ravenous and inextinguishable, beaconing a troubled sky, but rather like the slow, deliberate progress of some monstrous thing crushing out all upon its path.

No, the real plague had nothing in common with the grandiose imaginings that had haunted Rieux's mind at its outbreak. It was, above all, a shrewd, unflagging adversary; a skilled organizer, doing his work thoroughly and well. That, it may be said in passing, is why, so as not to play false to the facts, and, still more, so as not to play false to himself, the narrator has aimed at objectivity. He has made hardly any changes for the sake of artistic effect, except those elementary adjustments needed to present his narrative in a more or less coherent form. And in deference to this scruple he is constrained to admit that, though the chief source of distress, the deepest as well as the most widespread, was separation—and it is his duty to say more about it as it existed in the later stages of the plague—it cannot be denied that even this distress was coming to lose something of its poignancy.

Was it that our fellow citizens, even those who had felt the parting from their loved ones most keenly, were getting used to doing without them? To assume this would fall somewhat short of the truth. It would be more correct to say that they were wasting away emotionally as well as physically. At the beginning of the plague they had a vivid recollection of the absent ones and bitterly felt their loss. But though they could clearly recall the face, the smile and voice of the beloved, and this or that occasion when (as they now saw in retrospect) they had been supremely happy, they had trouble in picturing what he or she might be doing at the moment when they conjured up these memories, in a setting so hopelessly remote. In short, at these moments memory played its part, but their imagination failed them. During the second phase of the plague their memory failed them, too. Not that they had forgotten the face itself, but—what came to the same thing—it had lost fleshly substance and they no longer saw it in memory's mirror.

Thus, while during the first weeks they were apt to complain that only shadows remained to them of what their love had been and meant, they now came to learn that even shadows can waste away, losing the faint hues of life that memory may give. And by the end of their long sundering they had also lost the power of imagining the intimacy that once was theirs or understanding what it can be to live with someone whose life is wrapped up in yours.

In this respect they had adapted themselves to the very condition of the plague, all the more potent for its mediocrity. None of us was capable any longer of an exalted emotion; all had trite, monotonous feelings. "It's high time it stopped," people would say, because in time of calamity the obvious thing is to desire its end, and in fact they wanted it to end. But when making such remarks, we felt none of the passionate yearning or fierce resentment of the early phase; we merely voiced one of the few clear ideas that lingered in the twilight of our minds. The furious revolt of the first weeks had given place to a vast despondency, not to be taken for resignation, though it was none the less a sort of passive and provisional acquiescence.

Our fellow citizens had fallen into line, adapted themselves, as people say, to the situation, because there was no way of doing otherwise. Naturally they retained the attitudes of sadness and suffering, but they had ceased to feel their sting. Indeed, to some, Dr. Rieux among them, this precisely was the most disheartening thing: that the habit of despair is worse than despair itself. Hitherto those who were parted had not been utterly unhappy; there was always a gleam of hope in the night of their distress; but that gleam had now died out. You could see them at street corners, in cafés or friends' houses, listless, indifferent, and looking so bored that, because of them, the whole town seemed like a railway waiting-room. Those who had jobs went about them at the exact tempo of the plague, with a dreary perseverance. Everyone was modest. For the first time exiles from those they loved had no reluctance to talk freely about them, using the same words as everybody else, and regarding their deprivation from the same angle as that from which they viewed the latest statistics of the epidemic. This change was striking since until now they had jealously withheld their personal grief from the common stock of suffering; now they accepted its inclusion. Without memories, without hope, they lived for the moment only. Indeed, the here and now had come to mean everything to them. For there is no denying that the plague had gradually killed off in all of us the faculty not of love only but even of friendship. Naturally enough, since love asks something of the future, and nothing was left us but a series of present moments.

However, this account of our predicament gives only the broad lines. Thus, while it is true that all who were parted came ultimately to this state, we must add that all did not attain it simultaneously; moreover, once this utter apathy had fallen on them, there were still flashes of lucidity, broken lights of memory that rekindled in the exiles a younger, keener sensibility. This happened when, for instance, they fell to making plans implying that the plague had ended. Or when, quite unexpectedly, by some kindly chance, they felt a twinge of jealousy, none the less acute for its objectlessness. Others, again, had sudden accesses of energy and shook off their languor on certain days of the week—for obvious reasons, on Sundays and Saturday afternoons, because these had been devoted to certain ritual pleasures in the days when the loved ones were still accessible. Sometimes the mood of melancholy that descended on them with the nightfall acted as a sort of warning, not always fulfilled, however, that old memories were floating up to the surface. That evening hour which for believers is the time to look into their consciences is hardest of all hours on the prisoner or exile who has nothing to look into but the void. For a moment it held them in suspense; then they sank back into their lethargy, the prison door had closed on them once again.

Obviously all this meant giving up what was most personal in their lives.

Whereas in the early days of the plague they had been struck by the host of small details that, while meaning absolutely nothing to others, meant so much to them personally, and thus had realized, perhaps for the first time, the uniqueness of each man's life; now, on the other hand, they took an interest only in what interested everyone else, they had only general ideas, and even their tenderest affections now seemed abstract, items of the common stock. So completely were they dominated by the plague that sometimes the one thing they aspired to was the long sleep it brought, and they caught themselves thinking: "A good thing if I get plague and have done with it!" But really they were asleep already; this whole period was for them no more than a long night's slumber. The town was peopled with sleepwalkers, whose trance was broken only on the rare occasions when at night their wounds, to all appearance closed, suddenly reopened. Then, waking with a start, they would run their fingers over the wounds with a sort of absentminded curiosity, twisting their lips, and in a flash their grief blazed up again, and abruptly there rose before them the mournful visage of their love. In the morning they harked back to normal conditions—in other words, the plague.

What impression, it may be asked, did these exiles of the plague make on the observer? The answer is simple; they made none. Or, to put it differently, they looked like everybody else, nondescript. They shared in the torpor of the town and in its puerile agitations. They lost every trace of a critical spirit, while gaining an air of *sang-froid*. You could see, for instance, even the most intelligent among them making a show like all the rest of studying the newspapers or listening to the radio, in the hope apparently of finding some reason to believe the plague would shortly end. They seemed to derive fantastic hopes or equally exaggerated fears from reading the lines that some journalist had scribbled at random, yawning with boredom at his desk. Meanwhile they drank their beer, nursed their sick, idled, or doped themselves with work, filed documents in offices, or played the phonograph at home, without betraying any difference from the rest of us. In other words, they had ceased to choose for themselves; plague had leveled out discrimination. This could be seen by the way nobody troubled about the quality of the clothes or food he bought. Everything was taken as it came.

And, finally, it is worth noting that those who were parted ceased to enjoy the curious privilege that had been theirs at the outset. They had lost love's egoism and the benefit they derived from it. Now, at least, the position was clear; this calamity was everybody's business. What with the gunshots echoing at the gates, the punctual thuds of rubber stamps marking the rhythm of lives and deaths, the files and fires, the panics and formalities, all alike were pledged to an ugly but recorded death, and, amidst noxious fumes and the muted clang of ambulances, all of us ate the same sour bread of exile, unconsciously waiting for the same reunion, the same miracle of peace regained. No doubt our love persisted, but in practice it served nothing; it was an inert mass within us, sterile as crime or a life sentence. It had declined on a patience that led nowhere, a dogged expectation. Viewed from this angle, the attitude of some of our fellow citizens resembled that of the long queues one saw outside the food-shops. There was the same resignation, the same long-sufferance, inexhaustible and without illusions. The only difference was that the mental state of the food-seekers would need to be raised to a vastly higher power to make it comparable with the gnawing pain of separation, since this latter came from a hunger fierce to the point of insatiability.

In any case, if the reader would have a correct idea of the mood of these exiles, we must conjure up once more those dreary evenings sifting down through a haze of dust and golden light upon the treeless streets filled with teeming crowds of men and women. For, characteristically, the sound that rose toward the terraces still bathed in the last glow of daylight, now that the noises of vehicles and motors—the sole voice of cities in ordinary times—had ceased, was but one vast rumor of low voices and incessant footfalls, the drumming of innumerable soles timed to the eerie whistling of the plague in the sultry air above, the sound of a huge concourse of people marking time, a never ending, stifling drone that, gradually swelling, filled the town from end to end, and evening after evening gave its truest, mournfulest expression to the blind endurance that had ousted love from all our hearts.

PART IV

Throughout September and October the town lay prostrate, at the mercy of the plague. There was nothing to do but to "mark time," and some hundreds of thousands of men and women went on doing this, through weeks that seemed interminable. Mist, heat, and rain rang their changes in our streets. From the south came silent coveys of starlings and thrushes, flying very high, but always giving the town a wide berth, as though the strange implement of the plague described by Paneloux, the giant flail whirling and shrilling over the housetops, warned them off us. At the beginning of October torrents of rain swept the streets clean. And all the time nothing more important befell us than that multitudinous marking time.

[99]

It was now that Rieux and his friends came to realize how exhausted they were. Indeed, the workers in the sanitary squads had given up trying to cope with their fatigue. Rieux noticed the change coming over his associates, and himself as well, and it took the form of a strange indifference to everything. Men, for instance, who hitherto had shown a keen interest in every scrap of news concerning the plague now displayed none at all. Rambert, who had been temporarily put in charge of a quarantine station—his hotel had been taken over for this purpose—could state at any moment the exact number of persons under his observation, and every detail of the procedure he had laid down for the prompt evacuation of those who suddenly developed symptoms of the disease was firmly fixed in his mind. The same was true of the statistics of the effects of anti-plague inoculations on the persons in his quarantine station. Nevertheless, he could not have told you the week's total of plague deaths, and he could not even have said if the figure was rising or falling. And meanwhile, in spite of everything, he had not lost hope of being able to "make his get-away" from one day to another.

As for the others, working themselves almost to a standstill throughout the day and far into the night, they never bothered to read a newspaper or listen to the radio. When told of some unlooked-for recovery, they made a show of interest, but actually received the news with the stolid indifference that we may imagine the fighting man in a great war to feel who, worn out by the incessant strain and mindful only of the duties daily assigned to him, has ceased even to hope for the decisive battle or the bugle-call of armistice.

Though he still worked out methodically the figures relating to the plague, Grand would certainly have been quite unable to say to what they pointed. Unlike Rieux, Rambert, and Tarrou, who obviously had great powers of endurance, he had never had good health. And now, in addition to his duties in the Municipal Office, he had his night work and his secretarial post under Rieux. One could see that the strain was telling on him, and if he managed to keep going, it was thanks to two or three fixed ideas, one of which was to take, the moment the plague ended, a complete vacation, of a week at least, which he would devote, "hats off," to his work in progress. He was also becoming subject to accesses of sentimentality and at such times would unburden himself to Rieux about Jeanne. Where was she now, he wondered; did her thoughts sometimes turn to him when she read the papers? It was Grand to whom one day Rieux caught himself talking—much to his own surprise—about his wife, and in the most common-place terms—something he had never done as yet to anyone.

Doubtful how far he could trust his wife's telegrams—their tone was always reassuring—he had decided to wire the house physician of the sanatorium. The reply informed him that her condition had worsened, but everything was being done to arrest further progress of the disease. He had kept the news to himself so far and could only put it down to his nervous exhaustion that he passed it on to Grand. After talking to the doctor about Jeanne, Grand had asked some questions about Mme Rieux and, on hearing Rieux's reply, said: "You know, it's wonderful, the cures they bring off nowadays." Rieux agreed, merely adding that the long separation was beginning to tell on him, and, what was more, he might have helped his wife to make a good recovery; whereas, as things were, she must be feeling terribly lonely. After which he fell silent and gave only evasive answers to Grand's further questions.

The others were in much the same state. Tarrou held his own better, but the entries in his diary show that while his curiosity had kept its depth, it had lost its diversity. Indeed, throughout this period the only person, apparently, who really interested him was Cottard. In the evening, at Rieux's apartment, where he had come to live now that the hotel was requisitioned as a quarantine center, he paid little or no attention to Grand and the doctor when they read over the day's statistics. At the earliest opportunity he switched the conversation over to his pet subject, small details of the daily life at Oran.

More perhaps than any of them, Dr. Castel showed signs of wear and tear. On the day when he came to tell Rieux that the anti-plague serum was ready, and they decided to try it for the first time on M. Othon's small son, whose case seemed all but hopeless, Rieux suddenly noticed, while he was announcing the latest statistics, that Castel was slumped in his chair, sound asleep. The difference in his old friend's face shocked him. The smile of benevolent irony that always played on it had seemed to endow it with perpetual youth; now, abruptly left out of control, with a trickle of saliva between the slightly parted lips, it betrayed its age and the wastage of the years. And, seeing this, Rieux felt a lump come to his throat.

It was by such lapses that Rieux could gauge his exhaustion. His sensibility was getting out of hand. Kept under all the time, it had grown hard and brittle and seemed to snap completely now and then, leaving him the prey of his emotions. No resource was left him but to tighten the stranglehold on his feelings and harden his heart protectively. For he knew this was the only way of carrying on. In any case, he had few illusions left, and fatigue was robbing him of even these remaining few. He knew that, over a period whose end he could not glimpse, his task was no longer to cure but to diagnose. To detect, to see, to describe, to register, and then condemn—that was his present function. Sometimes a woman would clutch his sleeve, crying shrilly: "Doctor, you'll save him, won't you?" But he wasn't there for saving life; he was there to order a sick man's evacuation. How futile was the hatred he saw on faces then! "You haven't a heart!" a woman told him on one occasion. She was wrong; he had one. It saw him through his twenty-hour day, when he hourly watched men dying who were meant to live. It enabled him to start anew each morning. He had just enough heart for that, as things were now. How could that heart have sufficed for saving life?

No, it wasn't medical aid that he dispensed in those crowded days—only information. Obviously that could hardly be reckoned a man's job. Yet, when all was said and done, who, in that terror-stricken, decimated populace, had scope for any activity worthy of his manhood? Indeed, for Rieux his exhaustion was a blessing in disguise. Had he been less tired, his senses more alert, that all-pervading odor of death might have made him sentimental. But when a man has had only four hours' sleep, he isn't sentimental. He sees things as they are; that is to say, he sees them in the garish light of justice—hideous, witless justice. And those others, the men and women under sentence to death, shared his bleak enlightenment. Before the plague he was welcomed as a savior. He was going to make them right with a couple of pills or an injection, and people took him by the arm on his way to the sickroom. Flattering, but dangerous. Now, on the contrary, he came accompanied by soldiers, and they had to hammer on the door with rifle-butts before the family would open it. They would have liked to drag him, drag the whole human race, with them to the grave. Yes, it was quite true that men can't do without their fellow men; that he was as helpless as these unhappy people and he, too, deserved the same faint thrill of pity that he allowed himself once he had left them.

Such, anyhow, were the thoughts that in those endless-seeming weeks ran in the doctor's mind, along with thoughts about his severance from his wife. And such, too, were his friends' thoughts, judging by the look he saw on their faces. But the most dangerous effect of the exhaustion steadily gaining on all engaged in the fight against the epidemic did not consist in their relative indifference to outside events and the feelings of others, but in the slackness and supineness that they allowed to invade their personal lives. They developed a tendency to shirk every movement that didn't seem absolutely necessary or called for efforts that seemed too great to be worth while. Thus these men were led to break, oftener and oftener, the rules of hygiene they themselves had instituted, to omit some of the numerous disinfections they should have practiced, and sometimes to visit the homes of people suffering from pneumonic plague without taking steps to safeguard themselves against infection, because they had been notified only at the last moment and could not be bothered with returning to a sanitary service station, sometimes a considerable distance away, to have the necessary instillations. There lay the real danger; for the energy they devoted to fighting the disease made them all the more liable to it. In short, they were gambling on their luck, and luck is not to be coerced.

There was, however, one man in the town who seemed neither exhausted nor discouraged; indeed, the living image of contentment. It was Cottard. Though maintaining contact with Rieux and Rambert, he still kept rather aloof,

whereas he deliberately cultivated Tarrou, seeing him as often as Tarrou's scanty leisure permitted. He had two reasons for this: one, that Tarrou knew all about his case, and the other, that he always gave him a cordial welcome and made him feel at ease. That was one of the remarkable things about Tarrou; no matter how much work he had put in, he was always a ready listener and an agreeable companion. Even when, some evenings, he seemed completely worn out, the next day brought him a new lease of energy. "Tarrou's a fellow one can talk to," Cottard once told Rambert, "because he's really human. He always understands."

This may explain why the entries in Tarrou's diary of this period tend to converge on Cottard's personality. It is obvious that Tarrou was attempting to give a full-length picture of the man and noted all his reactions and reflections, whether as conveyed to him by Cottard or interpreted by himself. Under the heading "Cottard and His Relations with the Plague," we find a series of notes covering several pages and, in the narrator's opinion, these are well worth summarizing here.

One of the entries gives Tarrou's general impression of Cottard at this time: "He is blossoming out. Expanding in geniality and good humor." For Cottard was anything but upset by the turn events were taking. Sometimes in Tarrou's company he voiced his true feelings in remarks of this order: "Getting worse every day, isn't it? Well, anyhow, everyone's in the same boat."

"Obviously," Tarrou comments, "he's in the same peril of death as everyone else, but that's just the point; he's in it *with the others.* And then I'm pretty sure he doesn't seriously think he runs much personal risk. He has got the idea into his head, apparently—and perhaps it's not so far-fetched as it seems—that a man suffering from a dangerous ailment or grave anxiety is immune to other ailments and anxieties. 'Have you noticed,' he asked me, 'that no one ever runs two diseases at once? Let's suppose you have an incurable disease like cancer or a galloping consumption—well, you'll never get plague or typhus; it's a physical impossibility. In fact, one might go farther; have you ever heard of a man with cancer being killed in an auto smash?' This theory, for what it's worth, keeps Cottard cheerful. The thing he'd most detest is being cut off from others; he'd rather be one of a beleaguered crowd than a prisoner alone. The plague has put an effective stop to police inquiries, sleuthings, warrants of arrest, and so forth. Come to that, we have no police nowadays; no crimes past or present, no more criminals—only condemned men hoping for the most capricious of pardons; and among these are the police themselves."

Thus Cottard (if we may trust Tarrou's diagnosis) had good grounds for viewing the symptoms of mental confusion and distress in those around him with an understanding and an indulgent satisfaction that might have found expression in the remark: "Prate away, my friends—but I had it first!"

"When I suggested to him," Tarrou continues, "that the surest way of not being cut off from others was having a clean conscience, he frowned. 'If that is so, everyone's always cut off from everyone else.' And a moment later he added: 'Say what you like, Tarrou, but let me tell you this. The one way of making people hang together is to give 'em a spell of plague. You've only got to look around you.' Of course I see his point, and I understand how congenial our present mode of life must be to him. How could he fail to recognize at every turn reactions that were his; the efforts everyone makes to keep on the right side of other people; the obligingness sometimes shown in helping someone who has lost his way, and the ill humor shown at other times; the way people flock to the luxury restaurants, their pleasure at being there and their reluctance to leave; the crowds lining up daily at the picture-houses, filling theaters and music halls and even dance halls, and flooding boisterously out into the squares and avenues; the shrinking from every contact and, notwithstanding, the craving for human warmth that urges people to one another, body to body, sex to sex? Cottard has been through all that obviously —with one exception; we may rule out women in his case. With that mug of his! And I should say that when tempted to visit a brothel he refrains; it might give him a bad name and be held up against him one day.

"In short, this epidemic has done him proud. Of a lonely man who hated loneliness it has made an accomplice. Yes, 'accomplice' is the word that fits, and doesn't he relish his complicity! He is happily at one with all around him, with their superstitions, their groundless panics, the susceptibilities of people whose nerves are always on the stretch; with their fixed idea of talking the least possible about plague and nevertheless talking of it all the time; with their abject terror at the slightest headache, now they know headache to be an early symptom of the disease; and, lastly, with their frayed, irritable sensibility that takes offense at trifling oversights and brings tears to their eyes over the loss of a trouser-button."

Tarrou often went out with Cottard in the evening, and he describes how they would plunge together into the dark crowds filling the streets at nightfall; how they mingled, shoulder to shoulder, in the black-and-white moving mass lit here and there by the fitful gleam of a street-lamp; and how they let themselves be swept along with the human herd toward resorts of pleasure whose companionable warmth seemed a safeguard from the plague's cold breath. What Cottard had some months previously been looking for in public places, luxury and the lavish life, the frenzied orgies he had dreamed of without being able to procure them— these were now the quest of a whole populace. Though prices soared inevitably, never had so much money been squandered, and while bare necessities were often lacking, never had so much been spent on superfluities. All the recreations of leisure, due though it now was to unemployment, multiplied a hundredfold. Sometimes Tarrou and Cottard would follow for some minutes one of those amorous couples who in the past would have tried to hide the passion drawing them to each other, but now, pressed closely to each other's side, paraded the streets among the crowd, with the trancelike self-absorption of great lovers, oblivious of the people around them. Cottard watched them gloatingly. "Good work, my dears!" he'd exclaim. "Go to it!" Even his voice had changed, grown louder; as Tarrou wrote, he was "blossoming out" in the congenial atmosphere of mass excitement, fantastically large tips clinking on café tables, love-affairs shaping under his eyes.

However, Tarrou seemed to detect little if any spitefulness in Cottard's attitude. His "I've been through the mill myself" had more pity than triumph in it. "I suspect," Tarrou wrote, "that he's getting quite fond of these people shut up under their little patch of sky within their city walls. For instance, he'd like to explain to them, if he had a chance, that it isn't so terrible as all that. 'You hear them saying,' he told me, ' "After the plague I'll do this or that." ' . . . They're eating their hearts out instead of staying put. And they don't even realize their privileges. Take my case: could I say

"After my arrest I'll do this or that"? Arrest's a beginning, not an end. Whereas plague. . . . Do you know what I think? They're fretting simply because they won't let themselves go. And I know what I'm talking about.' "

"Yes, he knows what he's talking about," Tarrou added. "He has an insight into the anomalies in the lives of the people here who, though they have an instinctive craving for human contacts, can't bring themselves to yield to it, because of the mistrust that keeps them apart. For it's common knowledge that you can't trust your neighbor; he may pass the disease to you without your knowing it, and take advantage of a moment of inadvertence on your part to infect you. When one has spent one's days, as Cottard has, seeing a possible police spy in everyone, even in persons he feels drawn to, it's easy to understand this reaction. One can have fellow-feelings toward people who are haunted by the idea that when they least expect it plague may lay its cold hand on their shoulders, and is, perhaps, about to do so at the very moment when one is congratulating oneself on being safe and sound. So far as this is possible, he is at ease under a reign of terror. But I suspect that, just because he has been through it before them, he can't wholly share with them the agony of this feeling of uncertainty that never leaves them. It comes to this: like all of us who have not yet died of plague he fully realizes that his freedom and his life may be snatched from him at any moment. But since he, personally, has learned what it is to live in a state of constant fear, he finds it normal that others should come to know this state. Or perhaps it should be put like this: fear seems to him more bearable under these conditions than it was when he had to bear its burden alone. In this respect he's wrong, and this makes him harder to understand than other people.

Still, after all, that's why he is worth a greater effort to understand."

Tarrou's notes end with a story illustrating the curious state of mind arrived at no less by Cottard than by other dwellers in the plague-stricken town. The story re-creates as nearly as may be the curiously feverish atmosphere of this period, and that is why the narrator attaches importance to it.

One evening Cottard and Tarrou went to the Municipal Opera House, where Gluck's *Orpheus* was being given. Cottard had invited Tarrou. A touring operatic company had come to Oran in the spring for a series of performances. Marooned there by the outbreak of plague and finding themselves in difficulties, the company and the management of the opera house had come to an agreement under which they were to give one performance a week until further notice. Thus for several months our theater had been resounding every Friday evening with the melodious laments of Orpheus and Eurydice's vain appeals. None the less, the opera continued in high favor and played regularly to full houses. From their seats, the most expensive, Cottard and Tarrou could look down at the orchestra seats filled to capacity with the cream of Oran society. It was interesting to see how careful they were, as they went to their places, to make an elegant entrance. While the musicians were discreetly tuning up, men in evening dress could be seen moving from one row to another, bowing gracefully to friends under the flood of light bathing the proscenium. In the soft hum of well-mannered conversation they regained the confidence denied them when they walked the dark streets of the town; evening dress was a sure charm against plague.

Throughout the first act Orpheus lamented suavely his lost Eurydice, with women in Grecian tunics singing melodious comments on his plight, and love was hymned in alternating strophes. The audience showed their appreciation in discreet applause. Only a few people noticed that in his song of the second act Orpheus introduced some tremolos not in the score and voiced an almost exaggerated emotion when begging the lord of the Underworld to be moved by his tears. Some rather jerky movements he indulged in gave our connoisseurs of stagecraft an impression of clever, if slightly overdone, effects, intended to bring out the emotion of the words he sang.

Not until the big duet between Orpheus and Eurydice in the third act—at the precise moment when Eurydice was slipping from her lover—did a flutter of surprise run through the house. And as though the singer had been waiting for this cue or, more likely, because the faint sounds that came to him from the orchestra seats confirmed what he was feeling, he chose this moment to stagger grotesquely to the footlights, his arms and legs splayed out under his antique robe, and fall down in the middle of the property sheepfold, always out of place, but now, in the eyes of the spectators, significantly, appallingly so. For at the same moment the orchestra stopped playing, the audience rose and began to leave the auditorium, slowly and silently at first, like worshippers leaving church when the service ends, or a death-chamber after a farewell visit to the dead, women lifting their skirts and moving with bowed heads, men steering the ladies by the elbow to prevent their brushing against the tip-up seats at the ends of the rows. But gradually their movements quickened, whispers rose to exclamations, and finally the crowd stampeded toward the exits, wedged together in the bottlenecks, and pouring out into the street in a confused mass, with shrill cries of dismay.

Cottard and Tarrou, who had merely

risen from their seats, gazed down at what was a dramatic picture of their life in those days: plague on the stage in the guise of a disarticulated mummer, and in the auditorium the toys of luxury, so futile now, forgotten fans and lace shawls derelict on the red plush seats.

During the first part of September Rambert had worked conscientiously at Rieux's side. He had merely asked for a few hours' leave on the day he was due to meet Gonzales and the two youngsters again outside the boys' school.

Gonzales kept the appointment, at noon, and while he and the journalist were talking, they saw the two boys coming toward them, laughing. They said they'd had no luck last time, but that was only to be expected. Anyhow, it wasn't their turn for guard duty this week. Rambert must have patience till next week; then they'd have another shot at it. Rambert observed that "patience" certainly was needed in this business. Gonzales suggested they should all meet again on the following Monday, and this time Rambert had better move in to stay with Marcel and Louis. "We'll make a date, you and I. If I don't turn up, go straight to their place. I'll give you the address." But Marcel, or Louis, told him that the safest thing was to take his pal there right away, then he'd be sure of finding it. If he wasn't too particular, there was enough grub for the four of them. That way he'd get the hang of things. Gonzales agreed it was a good idea, and the four of them set off toward the harbor.

Marcel and Louis lived on the outskirts of the dockyard, near the gate leading to the cliff road. It was a small Spanish house with gaily painted shutters and bare, dark rooms. The boys' mother, a wrinkled old Spanish woman with a smiling face, produced a dish of which the chief ingredient was rice. Gonzales showed surprise, as rice had been unprocurable for some time in the town. "We fix it up at the gate," Marcel explained. Rambert ate and drank heartily, and Gonzales informed him he was "a damned good sort." Actually the journalist was thinking solely of the coming week.

It turned out that he had a fortnight to wait, as the periods of guard duty were extended to two weeks, to reduce the number of shifts. During that fortnight Rambert worked indefatigably, giving every ounce of himself, with his eyes shut, as it were, from dawn till night. He went to bed very late and always slept like a log. This abrupt transition from a life of idleness to one of constant work had left him almost void of thoughts or energy. He talked little about his impending escape. Only one incident is worth noting: after a week he confessed to the doctor that for the first time he'd got really drunk. It was the evening before; on leaving the bar he had an impression that his groin was swollen and he had pains in his armpits when he moved his arms. "I'm in for it!" he thought. And his only reaction—an absurd one, as he frankly admitted to Rieux—had been to start running to the upper town and when he reached a small square, from which if not the sea, a fairly big patch of open sky could be seen, to call to his wife with a great cry, over the walls of the town. On returning home and failing to discover any symptoms of plague on his body, he had felt far from proud of having given way like that. Rieux, however, said he could well understand one's being moved to act thus. "Or, anyhow, one may easily feel inclined that way."

"Monsieur Othon was talking to me about you this morning," Rieux suddenly remarked, when Rambert was bidding him good night. "He asked me if I knew you, and I told him I did. Then he said: 'If he's a friend of yours advise him not to associate with smugglers. It's bound to attract attention.' "

"Meaning—what?"

"It means you'd better hurry up."

"Thanks." Rambert shook the doctor's hand.

In the doorway he suddenly swung round. Rieux noticed that, for the first time since the outbreak of plague, he was smiling.

"Then why don't you stop my going? You could easily manage it."

Rieux shook his head with his usual deliberateness. It was none of his business, he said. Rambert had elected for happiness, and he, Rieux, had no argument to put up against him. Personally he felt incapable of deciding which was the right course and which the wrong in such a case as Rambert's.

"If that's so, why tell me to hurry up?"

It was Rieux who now smiled.

"Perhaps because I, too, would like to do my bit for happiness."

Next day, though they were working together most of the time, neither referred to the subject. On the following Sunday Rambert moved into the little Spanish house. He was given a bed in the living-room. As the brothers did not come home for meals and he'd been told to go out as little as possible, he was always alone but for occasional meetings with the boys' mother. She was a dried-up little wisp of a woman, always dressed in black, busy as a bee, and she had a nut-brown, wrinkled face and immaculately white hair. No great talker, she merely smiled genially when her eyes fell on Rambert.

On one of the few occasions when she spoke, it was to ask him if he wasn't afraid of infecting his wife with plague. He replied that there might be some risk of that, but only a very slight one; while if he stayed in the town, there was a fair chance of their never seeing each other again.

The old woman smiled. "Is she nice?"

"Very nice."

"Pretty?"

"I think so."

"Ah," she nodded, "that explains it."

Rambert reflected. No doubt that explained it, but it was impossible that that alone explained it.

The old woman went to Mass every morning. "Don't you believe in God?" she asked him.

On Rambert's admitting he did not, she said again that "that explained it."

"Yes," she added, "you're right. You must go back to her. Or else—what would be left you?"

Rambert spent most of the day prowling round the room, gazing vaguely at the distempered walls, idly fingering the fans that were their only decoration, or counting the woolen balls on the table-cloth fringe. In the evening the youngsters came home; they hadn't much to say, except that the time hadn't come yet. After dinner Marcel played the guitar, and they drank an anise-flavored liqueur. Rambert seemed lost in thought.

On Wednesday Marcel announced: "It's for tomorrow night, at midnight. Be ready on time." Of the two men sharing the sentry post with them, he explained, one had got plague and the other, who had slept in the same room, was now under observation. Thus for two or three days Marcel and Louis would be alone at the post. They'd fix up the final details in the course of the night, and he could count on them to see it through. Rambert thanked them.

"Pleased?" the old woman asked.

He said yes, but his thoughts were elsewhere.

The next day was very hot and muggy and a heat-mist veiled the sun. The total of deaths had jumped up. But the old Spanish woman lost nothing of her serenity. "There's so much wickedness in the world," she said. "So what can you expect?"

Like Marcel and Louis, Rambert was stripped to the waist. But, even so, sweat was trickling down his chest and between his shoulder-blades. In the dim light of the shuttered room their torsos glowed like highly polished mahogany. Rambert kept prowling round like a caged animal, without speaking. Abruptly at four in the afternoon he announced that he was going out.

"Don't forget," Marcel said. "At midnight sharp. Everything's set."

Rambert went to the doctor's apartment. Rieux's mother told him he would find the doctor at the hospital in the upper town. As before, a crowd was circling in front of the entrance gates. "Move on, there!" a police sergeant with bulging eyes bawled every few minutes. And the crowd kept moving, but always in a circle. "No use hanging round here." The sergeant's coat was soaked in sweat. They knew it was "no use," but they stayed on, despite the devastating heat. Rambert showed his pass to the sergeant, who told him to go to Tarrou's office. Its door opened on the courtyard. He passed Father Paneloux, who was coming out of the office.

Tarrou was sitting at a black wood desk, with his sleeves rolled up, mopping up with his handkerchief a trickle of sweat in the bend of his arm. The office, a small, white-painted room, smelt of drugs and damp cloth.

"Still here?" asked Tarrou.

"Yes. I'd like to have a word with Rieux."

"He's in the ward. Look here! Don't you think you could fix up whatever you've come for without seeing him?"

"Why?"

"He's overdoing it. I spare him as much as I can."

Rambert gazed thoughtfully at Tarrou.

He'd grown thinner, his eyes and features were blurred with fatigue, his broad shoulders sagged. There was a knock at the door. A male attendant, wearing a white mask, entered. He laid a little sheaf of cards on Tarrou's desk and, his voice coming thickly through the cloth, said: "Six," then went out. Tarrou looked at the journalist and showed him the cards, spreading them fanwise.

"Neat little gadgets, aren't they? Well, they're deaths. Last night's deaths." Frowning, he slipped the cards together. "The only thing that's left us is accountancy!"

Taking his purchase on the table, Tarrou rose to his feet.

"You're off quite soon, I take it?"

"Tonight, at midnight."

Tarrou said he was glad to hear it, and Rambert had better look after himself for a bit.

"Did you say that—sincerely?"

Tarrou shrugged his shoulders.

"At my age one's got to be sincere. Lying's too much effort."

"Excuse me, Tarrou," the journalist said, "but I'd greatly like to see the doctor."

"I know. He's more human than I. All right, come along."

"It's not that." Rambert stumbled over his words and broke off.

Tarrou stared at him; then, unexpectedly, his face broke into a smile.

They walked down a narrow passage; the walls were painted pale green, and the light was glaucous, like that in an aquarium. Before they reached the glazed double door at the end of the passage, behind which shadowy forms could be seen moving, Tarrou took Rambert into a small room, all the wall space of which was occupied by cupboards. Opening one of these, he took from a sterilizer two masks of cotton-wool enclosed in muslin, handed one to Rambert, and told him to put it on.

The journalist asked if it was really any use. Tarrou said no, but it inspired confidence in others.

They opened the glazed door. It led into a very large room, all the windows of which were shut, in spite of the great heat. Electric fans buzzed near the ceiling, churning up the stagnant, overheated air above two long rows of gray beds. Groans shrill or stifled rose on all sides, blending in a monotonous dirgelike refrain. Men in white moved slowly from bed to bed under the garish light flooding in from high, barred windows. The appalling heat in the ward made Rambert ill at ease, and he had difficulty in recognizing Rieux, who was bending over a groaning form. The doctor was lancing the patient's groin, while two nurses, one on each side, held his legs apart. Presently Rieux straightened up, dropped his instruments into a tray that an attendant held out to him, and remained without moving for some moments, gazing down at the man, whose wound was now being dressed.

"Any news?" he asked Tarrou, who had come beside him.

"Paneloux is prepared to replace Rambert at the quarantine station. He has put in a lot of useful work already. All that remains is to reorganize group number three, now that Rambert's going."

Rieux nodded.

"Castel has his first lot of serum ready now," Tarrou continued. "He's in favor of its being tried at once."

"Good," Rieux said. "That's good news."

"And Rambert's come."

Rieux looked round. His eyes narrowed above the mask when he saw the journalist.

"Why have you come?" he asked. "Surely you should be elsewhere?"

Tarrou explained that it was fixed for midnight, to which Rambert added: "That's the idea, anyhow."

Whenever any of them spoke through the mask, the muslin bulged and grew moist over the lips. This gave a sort of unreality to the conversation; it was like a colloquy of statues.

"I'd like to have a word with you," Rambert said.

"Right. I'm just going. Wait for me in Tarrou's office."

A minute or so later Rambert and Rieux were sitting at the back of the doctor's car. Tarrou, who was at the wheel, looked round as he let in the gear.

"Gas is running out," he said. "We'll have to foot-slog it tomorrow."

"Doctor," Rambert said, "I'm not going. I want to stay with you."

Tarrou made no movement; he went on driving. Rieux seemed unable to shake off his fatigue.

"And what about *her?*" His voice was hardly audible.

Rambert said he'd thought it over very carefully, and his views hadn't changed, but if he went away, he would feel ashamed of himself, and that would embarrass his relations with the woman he loved.

Showing more animation, Rieux told him that was sheer nonsense; there was nothing shameful in preferring happiness.

"Certainly," Rambert replied. "But it may be shameful to be happy by oneself."

Tarrou, who had not spoken so far, now remarked, without turning his head, that if Rambert wished to take a share in other people's unhappiness, he'd have no time left for happiness. So the choice had to be made.

"That's not it," Rambert rejoined. "Until now I always felt a stranger in this town, and that I'd no concern with you people. But now that I've seen what I have seen, I know that I belong here whether I want it or not. This business is everybody's business." When there was no reply from either of the others, Rambert seemed to grow annoyed. "But you know that as well as I do, damn it! Or else what are you up to in that hospital of yours? Have *you* made a definite choice and turned down happiness?"

Rieux and Tarrou still said nothing, and the silence lasted until they were at the doctor's home. Then Rambert repeated his last question in a yet more emphatic tone.

Only then Rieux turned toward him, raising himself with an effort from the cushion.

"Forgive me, Rambert, only—well, I simply don't know. But stay with us if you want to." A swerve of the car made him break off. Then, looking straight in front of him, he said: "For nothing in the world is it worth turning one's back on what one loves. Yet that is what I'm doing, though why I do not know." He sank back on the cushion. "That's how it is," he added wearily, "and there's nothing to be done about it. So let's recognize the fact and draw the conclusions."

"What conclusions?"

"Ah," Rieux said, "a man can't cure and know at the same time. So let's cure as quickly as we can. That's the more urgent job."

At midnight Tarrou and Rieux were giving Rambert the map of the district he was to keep under surveillance. Tarrou glanced at his watch. Looking up, he met Rambert's gaze.

"Have you let them know?" he asked.

The journalist looked away.

"I'd sent them a note"—he spoke with an effort—"before coming to see you."

Toward the close of October Castel's antiplague serum was tried for the first time. Practically speaking, it was Rieux's last card. If it failed, the doctor was convinced the whole town would be at the mercy of the epidemic, which would either continue its ravages for an unpredictable period or perhaps die out abruptly of its own accord.

The day before Castel called on Rieux, M. Othon's son had fallen ill and all the family had to go into quarantine. Thus the mother, who had only recently come out of it, found herself isolated once again. In deference to the official regulations the magistrate had promptly sent for Dr. Rieux the moment he saw symptoms of the disease in his little boy. Mother and father were standing at the bedside when Rieux entered the room. The boy was in the phase of extreme prostration and submitted without a whimper to the doctor's examination. When Rieux raised his eyes he saw the magistrate's gaze intent on him, and, behind, the mother's pale face. She was holding a handkerchief to her mouth, and her big, dilated eyes followed each of the doctor's movements.

"He has it, I suppose?" the magistrate asked in a toneless voice.

"Yes." Rieux gazed down at the child again.

The mother's eyes widened yet more, but she still said nothing. M. Othon, too, kept silent for a while before saying in an even lower tone:

"Well, doctor, we must do as we are told to do."

Rieux avoided looking at Mme Othon, who was still holding her handkerchief to her mouth.

"It needn't take long," he said rather awkwardly, "if you'll let me use your phone."

The magistrate said he would take him to the telephone. But before going, the doctor turned toward Mme Othon.

"I regret very much indeed, but I'm afraid you'll have to get your things ready. You know how it is."

Mme Othon seemed disconcerted. She was staring at the floor.

Then, "I understand," she murmured,

slowly nodding her head. "I'll set about it at once."

Before leaving, Rieux on a sudden impulse asked the Othons if there wasn't anything they'd like him to do for them. The mother gazed at him in silence. And now the magistrate averted his eyes.

"No," he said, then swallowed hard. "But—save my son."

In the early days a mere formality, quarantine had now been reorganized by Rieux and Rambert on very strict lines. In particular they insisted on having members of the family of a patient kept apart. If, unawares, one of them had been infected, the risks of an extension of the infection must not be multiplied. Rieux explained this to the magistrate, who signified his approval of the procedure. Nevertheless, he and his wife exchanged a glance that made it clear to Rieux how keenly they both felt the separation thus imposed on them. Mme Othon and her little girl could be given rooms in the quarantine hospital under Rambert's charge. For the magistrate, however, no accommodation was available except in an isolation camp the authorities were now installing in the municipal stadium, using tents supplied by the highway department. When Rieux apologized for the poor accommodation, M. Othon replied that there was one rule for all alike, and it was only proper to abide by it.

The boy was taken to the auxiliary hospital and put in a ward of ten beds which had formerly been a classroom. After some twenty hours Rieux became convinced that the case was hopeless. The infection was steadily spreading, and the boy's body putting up no resistance. Tiny, half-formed, but acutely painful buboes were clogging the joints of the child's puny limbs. Obviously it was a losing fight.

Under the circumstances Rieux had no qualms about testing Castel's serum on the boy. That night, after dinner, they performed the inoculation, a lengthy process, without getting the slightest reaction. At daybreak on the following day they gathered round the bed to observe the effects of this test inoculation on which so much hung.

The child had come out of his extreme prostration and was tossing about convulsively on the bed. From four in the morning Dr. Castel and Tarrou had been keeping watch and noting, stage by stage, the progress and remissions of the malady. Tarrou's bulky form was slightly drooping at the head of the bed, while at its foot, with Rieux standing beside him, Castel was seated, reading, with every appearance of calm, an old leather-bound book. One by one, as the light increased in the former classroom, the others arrived. Paneloux, the first to come, leaned against the wall on the opposite side of the bed to Tarrou. His face was drawn with grief, and the accumulated weariness of many weeks, during which he had never spared himself, had deeply seamed his somewhat prominent forehead. Grand came next. It was seven o'clock, and he apologized for being out of breath; he could only stay a moment, but wanted to know if any definite results had been observed. Without speaking, Rieux pointed to the child. His eyes shut, his teeth clenched, his features frozen in an agonized grimace, he was rolling his head from side to side on the bolster. When there was just light enough to make out the half-obliterated figures of an equation chalked on a blackboard that still hung on the wall at the far end of the room, Rambert entered. Posting himself at the foot of the next bed, he took a package of cigarettes from his pocket. But after his first glance at the child's face he put it back.

From his chair Castel looked at Rieux over his spectacles.

"Any news of his father?"

"No," said Rieux. "He's in the isolation camp."

The doctor's hands were gripping the rail of the bed, his eyes fixed on the small tortured body. Suddenly it stiffened, and seemed to give a little at the waist, as slowly the arms and legs spread out X-wise. From the body, naked under an army blanket, rose a smell of damp wool and stale sweat. The boy had gritted his teeth again. Then very gradually he relaxed, bringing his arms and legs back toward the center of the bed, still without speaking or opening his eyes, and his breathing seemed to quicken. Rieux looked at Tarrou, who hastily lowered his eyes.

They had already seen children die—for many months now death had shown no favoritism—but they had never yet watched a child's agony minute by minute, as they had now been doing since daybreak. Needless to say, the pain inflicted on these innocent victims had always seemed to them to be what in fact it was: an abominable thing. But hitherto they had felt its abomination in, so to speak, an abstract way; they had never had to witness over so long a period the death-throes of an innocent child.

And just then the boy had a sudden spasm, as if something had bitten him in the stomach, and uttered a long, shrill wail. For moments that seemed endless he stayed in a queer, contorted position, his body racked by convulsive tremors; it was as if his frail frame were bending before the fierce breath of the plague, breaking under the reiterated gusts of fever. Then the storm-wind passed, there came a lull, and he relaxed a little; the fever seemed to recede, leaving him gasping for breath on a dank, pestilential shore, lost in a languor that already looked like death. When for the third time the fiery wave broke on him, lifting him a little, the child curled himself up and shrank away to the edge of the bed,

as if in terror of the flames advancing on him, licking his limbs. A moment later, after tossing his head wildly to and fro, he flung off the blanket. From between the inflamed eyelids big tears welled up and trickled down the sunken, leaden-hued cheeks. When the spasm had passed, utterly exhausted, tensing his thin legs and arms, on which, within forty-eight hours, the flesh had wasted to the bone, the child lay flat, racked on the tumbled bed, in a grotesque parody of crucifixion.

Bending, Tarrou gently stroked with his big paw the small face stained with tears and sweat. Castel had closed his book a few moments before, and his eyes were now fixed on the child. He began to speak, but had to give a cough before continuing, because his voice rang out so harshly.

"There wasn't any remission this morning, was there, Rieux?"

Rieux shook his head, adding, however, that the child was putting up more resistance than one would have expected. Paneloux, who was slumped against the wall, said in a low voice:

"So if he is to die, he will have suffered longer."

Light was increasing in the ward. The occupants of the other nine beds were tossing about and groaning, but in tones that seemed deliberately subdued. Only one, at the far end of the ward, was screaming, or rather uttering little exclamations at regular intervals, which seemed to convey surprise more than pain. Indeed, one had the impression that even for the sufferers the frantic terror of the early phase had passed, and there was a sort of mournful resignation in their present attitude toward the disease. Only the child went on fighting with all his little might. Now and then Rieux took his pulse—less because this served any purpose than as an escape from his utter helplessness—and when he closed his eyes, he seemed to feel its tumult mingling with the fever of his own blood. And then, at one with the tortured child, he struggled to sustain him with all the remaining strength of his own body. But, linked for a few moments, the rhythms of their heartbeats soon fell apart, the child escaped him, and again he knew his impotence. Then he released the small, thin wrist and moved back to his place.

The light on the whitewashed walls was changing from pink to yellow. The first waves of another day of heat were beating on the windows. They hardly heard Grand saying he would come back as he turned to go. All were waiting. The child, his eyes still closed, seemed to grow a little calmer. His clawlike fingers were feebly plucking at the sides of the bed. Then they rose, scratched at the blanket over his knees, and suddenly he doubled up his limbs, bringing his thighs above his stomach, and remained quite still. For the first time he opened his eyes and gazed at Rieux, who was standing immediately in front of him. In the small face, rigid as a mask of grayish clay, slowly the lips parted and from them rose a long, incessant scream, hardly varying with his respiration, and filling the ward with a fierce, indignant protest, so little childish that it seemed like a collective voice issuing from all the sufferers there. Rieux clenched his jaws, Tarrou looked away. Rambert went and stood beside Castel, who closed the book lying on his knees. Paneloux gazed down at the small mouth, fouled with the sordes of the plague and pouring out the angry death-cry that has sounded through the ages of mankind. He sank on his knees, and all present found it natural to hear him say in a voice hoarse but clearly audible across that nameless, never ending wail:

"My God, spare this child!"

But the wail continued without cease and the other sufferers began to grow restless. The patient at the far end of the ward, whose little broken cries had gone on without a break, now quickened their tempo so that they flowed together in one unbroken cry, while the others' groans grew louder. A gust of sobs swept through the room, drowning Paneloux's prayer, and Rieux, who was still tightly gripping the rail of the bed, shut his eyes, dazed with exhaustion and disgust.

When he opened them again, Tarrou was at his side.

"I must go," Rieux said. "I can't bear to hear them any longer."

But then, suddenly, the other sufferers fell silent. And now the doctor grew aware that the child's wail, after weakening more and more, had fluttered out into silence. Around him the groans began again, but more faintly, like a far echo of the fight that now was over. For it was over. Castel had moved round to the other side of the bed and said the end had come. His mouth still gaping, but silent now, the child was lying among the tumbled blankets, a small, shrunken form, with the tears still wet on his cheeks.

Paneloux went up to the bed and made the sign of benediction. Then gathering up his cassock, he walked out by the passage between the beds.

"Will you have to start it all over again?" Tarrou asked Castel.

The old doctor nodded slowly, with a twisted smile.

"Perhaps. After all, he put up a surprisingly long resistance."

Rieux was already on his way out, walking so quickly and with such a strange look on his face that Paneloux put out an arm to check him when he was about to pass him in the doorway.

"Come, doctor," he began.

Rieux swung round on him fiercely.

"Ah! That child, anyhow, was innocent, and you know it as well as I do!"

He strode on, brushing past Paneloux, and walked across the school playground. Sitting on a wooden bench under the dingy, stunted trees, he wiped off the sweat that was beginning to run into his eyes. He felt like shouting imprecations—anything to loosen the stranglehold that bound his heart with steel. Heat was flooding down between the branches of the fig trees. A white haze, spreading rapidly over the blue of the morning sky, made the air yet more stifling. Rieux lay back wearily on the bench. Gazing up at the ragged branches, the shimmering sky, he slowly got back his breath and fought down his fatigue.

He heard a voice behind him. "Why was there that anger in your voice just now? What we'd been seeing was as unbearable to me as it was to you."

Rieux turned toward Paneloux.

"I know. I'm sorry. But weariness is a kind of madness. And there are times when the only feeling I have is one of mad revolt."

"I understand," Paneloux said in a low voice. "That sort of thing is revolting because it passes our human understanding. But perhaps we should love what we cannot understand."

Rieux straightened up slowly. He gazed at Paneloux, summoning to his gaze all the strength and fervor he could muster against his weariness. Then he shook his head.

"No, Father. I've a very different idea of love. And until my dying day I shall refuse to love a scheme of things in which children are put to torture."

A shade of disquietude crossed the priest's face. "Ah, doctor," he said sadly, "I've just realized what is meant by 'grace.'"

Rieux had sunk back again on the bench. His lassitude had returned and from its depths he spoke, more gently:

"It's something I haven't got; that I know. But I'd rather not discuss that with you. We're working side by side for something that unites us—beyond blasphemy and prayers. And it's the only thing that matters."

Paneloux sat down beside Rieux. It was obvious that he was deeply moved.

"Yes, yes," he said, "you, too, are working for man's salvation."

Rieux tried to smile.

"Salvation's much too big a word for me. I don't aim so high. I'm concerned with man's health; and for me his health comes first."

Paneloux seemed to hesitate. "Doctor—" he began, then fell silent. Down his face, too, sweat was trickling. Murmuring: "Good-by for the present," he rose. His eyes were moist. When he turned to go, Rieux, who had seemed lost in thought, suddenly rose and took a step toward him.

"Again, please forgive me. I can promise there won't be another outburst of that kind."

Paneloux held out his hand, saying regretfully:

"And yet—I haven't convinced you!"

"What does it matter? What I hate is death and disease, as you well know. And whether you wish it or not, we're allies, facing them and fighting them together." Rieux was still holding Paneloux's hand. "So you see"—but he refrained from meeting the priest's eyes—"God Himself can't part us now."

Since joining Rieux's band of workers Paneloux had spent his entire time in hospitals and places where he came in contact with plague. He had elected for the place among his fellow workers that he judged incumbent on him—in the forefront of the fight. And constantly since then he had rubbed shoulders with death. Though theoretically immunized by periodical inoculations, he was well aware that at any moment death might claim him too, and he had given thought to this. Outwardly he had lost nothing of his serenity. But from the day on which he saw a child die, something seemed to change in him. And his face bore traces of the rising tension of his thoughts. When one day he told Rieux with a smile that he was working on a short essay entitled "Is a Priest Justified in Consulting a Doctor?" Rieux had gathered that something graver lay behind the question than the priest's tone seemed to imply. On the doctor's saying he would greatly like to have a look at the essay, Paneloux informed him that he would shortly be preaching at a Mass for men, and his sermon would convey some at least of his considered opinions on the question.

"I hope you'll come, doctor. The subject will interest you."

A high wind was blowing on the day Father Paneloux preached his second sermon. The congregation, it must be admitted, was sparser than on the first occasion, partly because this kind of performance had lost its novelty for our townsfolk. Indeed, considering the abnormal conditions they were up against, the very word "novelty" had lost all meaning. Moreover, most people, assuming they had not altogether abandoned religious observances, or did not combine them naïvely with a thoroughly immoral way of living, had replaced normal religious practice by more or less extravagant superstitions. Thus they were readier to wear prophylactic medals of St. Roch than to go to Mass.

An illustration may be found in the remarkable interest shown in prophecies of all descriptions. True, in the spring, when the epidemic was expected to end abruptly at any moment, no one troubled to take another's opinion as to its probable duration, since everyone had persuaded himself that it would have none. But as the days went by, a fear grew up that the calamity might last indefinitely, and then the ending of the plague became the target of all hopes. As a result copies of predictions attributed to soothsayers or saints of the Catholic Church circulated freely from hand to hand. The local printing firms were quick to realize the profit to be made by pandering to this new craze and printed large numbers of the prophecies that had been going round in manuscript. Finding that the public appetite for this type of literature was still unsated, they had researches made in the municipal libraries for all the mental pabulum of the kind available in old chronicles, memoirs, and the like. And when this source ran dry, they commissioned journalists to write up forecasts, and, in this respect at least, the journalists proved themselves equal to their prototypes of earlier ages.

Some of these prophetic writings were actually serialized in our newspapers and read with as much avidity as the love-stories that had occupied these columns in the piping times of health. Some predictions were based on far-fetched arithmetical calculations, involving the figures of the year, the total of deaths, and the number of months the plague had so far lasted. Others made comparisons with the great pestilences of former times, drew parallels (which the forecasters called "constants"), and claimed to deduce conclusions bearing on the present calamity. But our most popular prophets were undoubtedly those who in an apocalyptic jargon had announced sequences of events, any one of which might be construed as applicable to the present state of affairs and was abstruse enough to admit of almost any interpretation. Thus Nostradamus and St. Odilia were consulted daily, and always with happy results. Indeed, the one thing these prophecies had in common was that, ultimately, all were reassuring. Unfortunately, though, the plague was not.

Thus superstition had usurped the place of religion in the life of our town, and that is why the church in which Paneloux preached his sermon was only three-quarters full. That evening, when Rieux arrived, the wind was pouring in great gusts through the swing-doors and filling the aisles with sudden drafts. And it was in a cold, silent church, surrounded by a congregation of men exclusively, that Rieux watched the Father climb into the pulpit. He spoke in a gentler, more thoughtful tone than on the previous occasion, and several times was noticed to be stumbling over his words. A yet more noteworthy change was that instead of saying "you" he now said "we."

However, his voice grew gradually firmer as he proceeded. He started by recalling that for many a long month plague had been in our midst, and we now knew it better, after having seen it often seated at our tables or at the bedsides of those we loved. We had seen it walking at our side, or waiting for our coming at the places where we worked. Thus we were now, perhaps, better able to comprehend what it was telling us unceasingly; a message to which, in the first shock of the visitation, we might not have listened with due heed. What he, Father Paneloux, had said in his first sermon still held good—such, anyhow, was his belief. And yet, perhaps, as may befall any one of us (here he struck his breast), his words and thoughts had lacked in charity. However this might be, one thing was not to be gainsaid; a fact that always, under all circumstances, we should bear in mind. Appearances notwithstanding, all trials, however cruel, worked together for good to the Christian. And, indeed, what a Christian should always seek in his hour of trial was to discern that good, in what it consisted and how best he could turn it to account.

At this stage the people near Rieux seemed to settle in against the arm-rests of their pews and make themselves as comfortable as they could. One of the big padded entrance doors was softly thudding in the wind, and someone got up to secure it. As a result, Rieux's attention wandered and he did not follow well what Paneloux now went on to say. Apparently it came to this: we might try to explain the phenomenon of the plague, but, above all, should learn what it had to teach us. Rieux gathered that, to the Father's thinking, there was really nothing to explain.

His interest quickened when, in a more emphatic tone, the preacher said that there were some things we could grasp as touching God, and others we could not. There was no doubt as to the existence of good and evil and, as a rule, it was easy to see the difference between them. The difficulty began when we looked into the nature of evil, and among things evil he included human suffering. Thus we had apparently needful pain, and apparently needless pain; we had Don Juan cast into hell, and a child's death. For while it is right that a libertine should be struck down, we see no reason for a child's suffering. And, truth to tell, nothing was more important on earth than a child's suffering, the horror it inspires in us, and the reasons we must find to account for it. In other manifestations of life God made things easy for us and, thus far, our religion had no merit. But in this respect He put us, so to speak, with our backs to the wall. Indeed, we all were up against the wall that plague had built around us, and in its lethal shadow we must work out our salvation. He, Father Paneloux, refused to have recourse to simple devices enabling him to scale that wall. Thus he might easily have assured them that the child's sufferings would be compensated for by an eternity of bliss awaiting him. But how could he give that assurance when, to tell the truth, he knew nothing about it? For who would dare to assert that eternal happiness can compensate for a single moment's human suffering? He who asserted that would not be a true Christian, a follower of the Master who knew all the pangs of suffering in his body and his soul. No, he, Father Paneloux, would keep faith with that great symbol of all suffering, the tortured body on the Cross; he would stand fast, his back to the wall, and face honestly the terrible problem of a child's agony. And he would boldly say to those who listened to his words today: "My brothers, a time of testing has come for us all. We must believe everything or deny everything. And who among you, I ask, would dare to deny everything?"

It crossed Rieux's mind that Father Paneloux was dallying with heresy in speaking thus, but he had no time to follow up the thought. The preacher was declaring vehemently that this uncompromising duty laid on the Christian was at once his ruling virtue and his privilege. He was well aware that certain minds, schooled to a more indulgent and conventional morality, might well be dismayed, not to say outraged, by the seemingly excessive standard of Christian virtue about which he was going to speak. But religion in a time of plague could not be the religion of every day. While God might accept and even desire that the soul should take its ease and rejoice in happier times, in periods of extreme calamity He laid extreme demands on it. Thus today God had vouchsafed to His creatures an ordeal such that they must acquire and practice the greatest of all virtues: that of the All or Nothing.

Many centuries previously a profane writer had claimed to reveal a secret of the Church by declaring that purgatory did not exist. He wished to convey that there could be no half measures, there was only the alternative between heaven and hell; you were either saved or damned. That, according to Paneloux, was a heresy that could spring only from a blind, disordered soul. Nevertheless, there may well have been periods of history when purgatory could not be hoped for; periods when it was impossible to speak of venial sin. Every sin was deadly, and any indifference criminal. It was all or it was nothing.

The preacher paused, and Rieux heard more clearly the whistling of the wind outside; judging by the sounds that came in below the closed doors, it had risen to storm pitch. Then he heard Father Paneloux's voice again. He was saying that the total acceptance of which he had been speaking was not to be taken in the limited sense usually given to the words; he was not thinking of mere resignation or even of that harder virtue, humility. It involved humiliation, but a humiliation to which the person humiliated gave full assent. True, the agony of a child was humiliating to the heart and to the mind. But that was why we had to come to terms with it. And that, too, was why— and here Paneloux assured those present that it was not easy to say what he was about to say—since it was God's will, we, too, should will it. Thus and thus only the Christian could face the problem squarely and, scorning subterfuge, pierce to the heart of the supreme issue, the essential choice. And his choice would be to believe everything, so as not to be forced into denying everything. Like those worthy women who, after learning that buboes were the natural issues through which the body cast out infection, went to their church and prayed: "Please, God, give him buboes," thus the Christian should yield himself wholly to the divine will, even though it passed his understanding. It was wrong to say: *"This* I understand, but *that* I cannot accept"; we must go straight to the heart of that which is unacceptable, precisely because it is thus that we are constrained to make our choice. The sufferings of children were our bread of affliction, but without this bread our souls would die of spiritual hunger.

The shuffling sounds which usually followed the moment when the preacher paused were beginning to make themselves heard when, unexpectedly, he raised his voice, making as if to put himself in his hearers' place and ask what then was the proper course to follow. He made no doubt that the ugly word "fatalism" would be applied to what he said. Well, he would not boggle at the word, provided he were allowed to qualify it with the adjective "active." Needless to say, there was no question of imitating the Abyssinian Christians of whom he had spoken previously. Nor should one even think of acting like those Persians who in time of plague threw their infected garments on the Christian sanitary workers and loudly called on Heaven to give the plague to these infidels who were trying to avert a pestilence sent by God. But, on the other hand, it would be no less wrong to imitate the monks at Cairo who, when plague was raging in the town, distributed the Host with pincers at the Mass, so as to avoid contact with wet, warm mouths in which infection might be latent. The plague-stricken Persians and the monks were equally at fault. For the former a child's agony did not count; with the latter, on the contrary, the natural dread of suffering ranked highest in their conduct. In both cases the real problem had been shirked; they had closed their ears to God's voice.

But, Paneloux continued, there were other precedents of which he would now remind them. If the chronicles of the Black Death at Marseille were to be trusted, only four of the eighty-one monks in the Mercy Monastery survived the epidemic. And of these four three took to flight. Thus far the chronicler, and it was not his task to tell us more than the bare facts. But when he read that chronicle, Father Paneloux had found his thoughts fixed on that monk who stayed on by himself, despite the death of his seventy-seven companions, and, above all, despite the example of his three brothers who had fled. And, bringing down his fist on the edge of the pulpit, Father Paneloux cried in a ringing voice: "My brothers, each one of us must be the one who stays!"

There was no question of not taking precautions or failing to comply with the orders wisely promulgated for the public weal in the disorders of a pestilence. Nor should we listen to certain moralists who told us to sink on our knees and give up the struggle. No, we should go forward, groping our way through the darkness, stumbling perhaps at times, and try to do what good lay in our power. As for the rest, we must hold fast, trusting in the divine goodness, even as to the deaths of little children, and not seeking personal respite.

At this point Father Paneloux evoked the august figure of Bishop Belzunce during the Marseille plague. He reminded his hearers how, toward the close of the epidemic, the Bishop, having done all that it behooved him, shut himself up in his palace, behind high walls, after laying in a stock of food and drink. With a sudden revulsion of feeling, such as often comes in times of extreme tribulation, the inhabitants of Marseille, who had idolized him hitherto, now turned against him, piled up corpses round his house in order to infect it, and even flung bodies over the walls to make sure of his death. Thus in a moment of weakness the Bishop had proposed to isolate himself from the outside world—and, lo and behold, corpses rained down on his head! This had a lesson for us all; we must convince ourselves that there is no island of escape in time of plague. No, there was no middle course. We must accept the dilemma and choose either to hate God or to love God. And who would dare to choose to hate Him?

"My brothers"—the preacher's tone showed he was nearing the conclusion of his sermon—"the love of God is a hard love. It demands total self-surrender, disdain of our human personality. And yet it alone can reconcile us to suffering and the deaths of children, it alone can justify them, since we cannot understand them, and we can only make God's will ours. That is the hard lesson I would share with you today. That is the faith, cruel in men's eyes, and crucial in God's, which we must ever strive to compass. We must aspire beyond ourselves toward that high and fearful vision. And on that lofty plane all will fall into place, all discords be resolved, and truth flash forth from the dark cloud of seeming injustice. Thus in some churches of the south of France plague victims have lain sleeping many a century under the flagstones of the chancel, and priests now speak above their tombs, and the divine message they bring to men rises from that charnel, to which, nevertheless, children have contributed their share."

When Rieux was preparing to leave the church a violent gust swept up the nave through the half-open doors and buffeted the faces of the departing congregation. It brought with it a smell of rain, a tang of drenched sidewalks, warning them of the weather they would encounter outside. An old priest and a young deacon who were walking immediately in front of Rieux had much difficulty in keeping their headdress from blowing away. But this did not prevent the elder of the two from discussing the sermon they had heard. He paid tribute to the preacher's eloquence, but the boldness of thought Paneloux had shown gave him pause. In his opinion the sermon had displayed more uneasiness than real power, and at Paneloux's age a priest had no business to feel uneasy. The young deacon, his head bowed to protect his face from the wind, replied that he saw much of the Father, had followed the evolution of his views, and believed his forthcoming pamphlet would be bolder still; indeed it might well be refused the imprimatur.

"You don't mean to say so! What's the main idea?" asked the old priest.

They were now in the Cathedral square and for some moments the roar of the wind made it impossible for the younger man to speak. When there was a slight lull, he said briefly to his companion:

"That it's illogical for a priest to call in a doctor."

Tarrou, when told by Rieux what Paneloux had said, remarked that he'd known a priest who had lost his faith during the war, as the result of seeing a young man's face with both eyes destroyed.

"Paneloux is right," Tarrou continued. "When an innocent youth can have his eyes destroyed, a Christian should either lose his faith or consent to having his eyes destroyed. Paneloux declines to lose his faith, and he will go through with it to the end. That's what he meant to say."

It may be that this remark of Tarrou's throws some light on the regrettable events which followed, in the course of which the priest's conduct seemed inexplicable to his friends. The reader will judge for himself.

A few days after the sermon Paneloux had to move out of his rooms. It was a time when many people were obliged to change their residence owing to the new conditions created by the plague. Thus Tarrou, when his hotel was requisitioned, had gone to live with Rieux, and now the Father had to vacate the lodgings provided for him by his Order and stay in the house of a pious old lady who had so far escaped the epidemic. During the process of moving, Paneloux had been feeling more run down than ever, mentally as well as physically. And it was this that put him in the bad books of his hostess. One evening when she was enthusiastically vaunting the merits of St. Odilia's prophecies, the priest betrayed a slight impatience, due probably to fatigue. All his subsequent efforts to bring the good lady round to, anyhow, a state of benevolent neutrality came to nothing. He had made a bad impression and it went on rankling. So each night on his way to his bedroom, where almost all the furniture was dotted with crochet covers, he had to contemplate the back of his hostess seated in her drawing-room and carry away with him a memory of the sour "Good night, Father," she flung at him over her shoulder. It was on one such evening that he felt, like a flood bursting the dikes, the turbulent onrush in his wrists and temples of the fever latent in his blood for several days past.

The only available account of what followed comes from the lips of the old lady. Next morning she rose early, as was her wont. After an hour or so, puzzled at not seeing the Father leave his room, she brought herself, not without some hesitation, to knock at his door. She found him still in bed after a sleepless night. He had difficulty in breathing and looked more flushed than usual. She had suggested most politely (as she put it) that a doctor should be called in, but her suggestion had been brushed aside with a curtness that she described as "quite unmannerly." So she had no alternative but to leave the room. Later in the morning the Father rang and asked if he could see her. He apologized for his lack of courtesy and assured her that what he was suffering from could not be plague, as he

had none of the symptoms; it was no more than a passing indisposition. The lady replied with dignity that her suggestion had not been prompted by any apprehension of that sort—she took no thought for her personal security, which was in God's hands—but that she felt a certain measure of responsibility for the Father's welfare while he was under her roof. When he said nothing, his hostess, wishing (according to her account) to do her duty by him, offered to send for her doctor. Father Paneloux told her not to trouble, adding some explanations that seemed to the old lady incoherent, not to say nonsensical. The only thing she gathered, and it was precisely this that appeared to her so incomprehensible, was that the Father refused to hear of a doctor's visit because it was against his principles. Her impression was that her guest's mind had been unhinged by fever, and she confined herself to bringing him a cup of tea.

Resolutely mindful of the obligations imposed on her by the situation, she visited the invalid regularly every two hours. What struck her most about him was his restlessness, which continued throughout the day. He would throw off the blankets, then pull them back, and he kept running his hand over his forehead, which was glistening with sweat. Every now and then he sat up in bed and tried to clear his throat with a thick, grating cough, which sounded almost like retching. At these moments he seemed to be vainly struggling to force up from his lungs a clot of some semi-solid substance that was choking him. After each unavailing effort, he sank back, utterly exhausted, on the pillow. Then he would raise himself again a little and stare straight in front of him with a fixity even more dismaying than the paroxysms which had preceded it. Even now the old lady was reluctant to annoy her guest by calling in the doctor. After all, it might be no more than an attack of fever, spectacular as were its manifestations.

However, in the afternoon she made another attempt to talk to the priest, but she could get out of him no more than a few rambling phrases. She renewed her proposal to call in the doctor. Whereat Paneloux sat up and in a stifled voice emphatically declined to see a doctor. Under these circumstances it seemed best to the old lady to wait till the following morning; if the Father's condition showed no more improvement she would ring up the number announced ten times daily on the radio by the Ransdoc Information Bureau. Still conscious of her obligations, she resolved to visit the invalid from time to time in the course of the night and give him any attention he might need. But after bringing him a decoction of herbal tea she decided to lie down for a while. Only at daybreak did she wake up, and then she hurried to the priest's room.

Father Paneloux was lying quite still; his face had lost its deep flush of the previous day and had now a deathly pallor, all the more impressive because the cheeks had kept their fullness. He was gazing up at the bead fringe of a lamp hanging above the bed. When the old lady came in he turned his head to her. As she quaintly put it, he looked as if he'd been severely thrashed all the night long, and more dead than alive. She was greatly struck by the apathy of his voice when, on her asking how he was feeling, he replied that he was in a bad way, he did not need a doctor, and all he wished was to be taken to the hospital, so as to comply with the regulations. Panic-stricken, she hurried to the telephone.

Rieux came at noon. After hearing what the old lady had to say he replied briefly that Paneloux was right, but it was probably too late. The Father wel-comed him with the same air of complete indifference. Rieux examined him and was surprised to find none of the characteristic symptoms of bubonic or pneumonic plague, except congestion and obstruction of the lungs. But his pulse was so weak and his general state so alarming that there was little hope of saving him.

"You have none of the specific symptoms of the disease," Rieux told him. "But I admit one can't be sure, and I must isolate you."

The Father smiled queerly, as if for politeness' sake, but said nothing. Rieux left the room to telephone, then came back and looked at the priest.

"I'll stay with you," he said gently.

Paneloux showed a little more animation and a sort of warmth came back to his eyes when he looked up at the doctor. Then, speaking with such difficulty that it was impossible to tell if there was sadness in his voice, he said:

"Thanks. But priests can have no friends. They have given their all to God."

He asked for the crucifix that hung above the head of the bed; when given it, he turned away to gaze at it.

At the hospital Paneloux did not utter a word. He submitted passively to the treatment given him, but never let go of the crucifix. However, his case continued doubtful, and Rieux could not feel sure how to diagnose it. For several weeks, indeed, the disease had seemed to make a point of confounding diagnoses. In the case of Paneloux, what followed was to show that this uncertainty had no consequence.

His temperature rose. Throughout the day the cough grew louder, racking the enfeebled body. At last, at nightfall, Father Paneloux brought up the clot of matter that was choking him; it was red. Even at the height of his fever Paneloux's eyes kept their blank serenity, and when, next morning, he was found dead, his body drooping over the bedside, they betrayed nothing. Against his name the index card recorded: "Doubtful case."

All Souls' Day that year was very different from what it had been in former years. True, the weather was seasonable; there had been a sudden change, and the great heat had given place to mild autumnal air. As in other years a cool wind blew all day, and big clouds raced from one horizon to the other, trailing shadows over the houses upon which fell again, when they had passed, the pale gold light of a November sky.

The first waterproofs made their appearance. Indeed, one was struck by the number of glossy, rubberized garments to be seen. The reason was that our newspapers had informed us that two hundred years previously, during the great pestilences of southern Europe, the doctors wore oiled clothing as a safeguard against infection. The shops had seized this opportunity of unloading their stock of out-of-fashion waterproofs, which their purchasers fondly hoped would guarantee immunity from germs.

But these familiar aspects of All Souls' Day could not make us forget that the cemeteries were left unvisited. In previous years the rather sickly smell of chrysanthemums had filled the streetcars, while long lines of women could be seen making pilgrimage to the places where members of the family were buried, to lay flowers on the graves. This was the day when they made amends for the oblivion and dereliction in which their dead had slept for many a long month. But in the plague year people no longer wished to be reminded of their dead. Because, indeed, they were thinking all too much about them as it was. There

was no more question of revisiting them with a shade of regret and much melancholy. They were no longer the forsaken to whom, one day in the year, you came to justify yourself. They were intruders whom you would rather forget. This is why the Day of the Dead this year was tacitly but willfully ignored. As Cottard dryly remarked—Tarrou noted that the habit of irony was growing on him more and more—each day was for us a Day of the Dead.

And, in fact, the balefires of the pestilence were blazing ever more merrily in the crematorium. It is true that the actual number of deaths showed no increase. But it seemed that plague had settled in for good at its most virulent, and it took its daily toll of deaths with the punctual zeal of a good civil servant. Theoretically, and in the view of the authorities, this was a hopeful sign. The fact that the graph after its long rising curve had flattened out seemed to many, Dr. Richard for example, reassuring. "The graph's good today," he would remark, rubbing his hands. To his mind the disease had reached what he called high-water mark. Thereafter it could but ebb. He gave the credit of this to Dr. Castel's new serum, which, indeed, had brought off some quite unlooked-for recoveries. While not dissenting, the old doctor reminded him that the future remained uncertain; history proved that epidemics have a way of recrudescing when least expected. The authorities, who had long been desirous of giving a fillip to the morale of the populace, but had so far been prevented by the plague from doing so, now proposed to convene a meeting of the medical corps and ask for an announcement on the subject. Unfortunately, just before the meeting was due to take place, Dr. Richard, too, was carried off by the plague, then precisely at "high-water mark."

The effect of this regrettable event,

which, sensational as it was, actually proved nothing, was to make our authorities swing back to pessimism as inconsequently as they had previously indulged in optimism. As for Castel, he confined himself to preparing his serums with the maximum of care. By this time no public place or building had escaped conversion into a hospital or quarantine camp with the exception of the Prefect's offices, which were needed for administrative purposes and committee meetings. In a general way, however, owing to the relative stability of the epidemic at this time, Rieux's organizations were still able to cope with the situation. Though working constantly at high pressure, the doctors and their helpers were not forced to contemplate still greater efforts. All they had to do was to carry on automatically, so to speak, their all but superhuman task. The pneumonic type of infection, cases of which had already been detected, was now spreading all over the town; one could almost believe that the high winds were kindling and fanning its flames in people's chests. The victims of pneumonic plague succumbed much more quickly, after coughing up blood-stained sputum. This new form of the epidemic looked like being more contagious as well as even more fatal. However, the opinions of experts had always been divided on this matter. For greater safety all sanitary workers wore masks of sterilized muslin. On the face of it, the disease should have extended its ravages. But, the cases of bubonic plague showing a decrease, the death rate remained constant.

Meanwhile the authorities had another cause for anxiety in the difficulty of maintaining the food-supply. Profiteers were taking a hand and purveying at enormous prices essential foodstuffs not available in the shops. The result was that poor families were in great straits, while the rich went short of practically

nothing. Thus, whereas plague by its impartial ministrations should have promoted equality among our townsfolk, it now had the opposite effect and, thanks to the habitual conflict of cupidities, exacerbated the sense of injustice rankling in men's hearts. They were assured, of course, of the inerrable equality of death, but nobody wanted that kind of equality. Poor people who were feeling the pinch thought still more nostalgically of towns and villages in the near-by countryside, where bread was cheap and life without restrictions. Indeed, they had a natural if illogical feeling that they should have been permitted to move out to these happier places. The feeling was embodied in a slogan shouted in the streets and chalked up on walls: "Bread or fresh air!" This half-ironical battle-cry was the signal for some demonstrations that, though easily repressed, made everyone aware that an ugly mood was developing among us.

The newspapers, needless to say, complied with the instructions given them: optimism at all costs. If one was to believe what one read in them, our populace was giving "a fine example of courage and composure." But in a town thrown back upon itself, in which nothing could be kept secret, no one had illusions about the "example" given by the public. To form a correct idea about the courage and composure talked about by our journalists you had only to visit one of the quarantine depots or isolation camps established by our authorities. As it so happens, the narrator, being fully occupied elsewhere, had no occasion to visit any of them, and must fall back on Tarrou's diary for a description of the conditions in these places.

Tarrou gives an account of a visit he made, accompanied by Rambert, to the camp located in the municipal stadium. The stadium lies on the outskirts of the town, between a street along which runs a car line and a stretch of waste land extending to the extreme edge of the plateau on which Oran is built. It was already surrounded by high concrete walls and all that was needed to make escape practically impossible was to post sentries at the four entrance gates. The walls served another purpose: they screened the unfortunates in quarantine from the view of people on the road. Against this advantage may be set the fact that the inmates could hear all day, though they could not see them, the passing streetcars, and recognize by the increased volume of sound coming from the road the hours when people had knocked off work or were going to it. And this brought home to them that the life from which they were debarred was going on as before, within a few yards of them, and that those high walls parted two worlds as alien to each other as two different planets.

Tarrou and Rambert chose a Sunday afternoon for their visit to the stadium. They were accompanied by Gonzales, the football-player, with whom Rambert had kept in contact and who had let himself be persuaded into undertaking, in rotation with others, the surveillance of the camp. This visit was to enable Rambert to introduce Gonzales to the camp commandant. When they met that afternoon, Gonzales's first remark was that this was exactly the time when, before the plague, he used to start getting into his football togs. Now that the sports fields had been requisitioned, all that was of the past, and Gonzales was feeling— and showed it—at a loose end. This was one of the reasons why he had accepted the post proposed by Rambert, but he made it a condition that he was to be on duty during week-ends only.

The sky was overcast and, glancing up at it, Gonzales observed regretfully that a day like this, neither too hot nor rainy, would have been perfect for a game. And then he fell to conjuring up, as best he could, the once familiar smell of embrocation in the dressing-rooms, the stands crowded with people, the colored shirts of the players, showing up brightly against the tawny soil, the lemons at intermission or bottled lemonade that titillated parched throats with a thousand refreshing pin-pricks. Tarrou also records how on the way, as they walked the shabby outer streets, the footballer gave kicks to all the small loose stones. His object was to shoot them into the sewer-holes of the gutters, and whenever he did this, he would shout: "Goal!" When he had finished his cigarette he spat the stub in front of him and tried to catch it on his toe before it touched the ground. Some children were playing near the stadium, and when one of them sent a ball toward the three men, Gonzales went out of his way to return it neatly.

On entering the stadium they found the stands full of people. The field was dotted with several hundred red tents, inside which one had glimpses of bedding and bundles of clothes or rugs. The stands had been kept open for the use of the internees in hot or rainy weather. But it was a rule of the camp that everyone must be in his tent at sunset. Shower-baths had been installed under the stands, and what used to be the players' dressing-rooms converted into offices and infirmaries. The majority of the inmates of the camp were sitting about on the stands. Some, however, were strolling on the touchlines, and a few, squatting at the entrances of their tents, were listlessly contemplating the scene around them. In the stands many of those slumped on the wooden tiers had a look of vague expectancy.

"What do they do with themselves all day?" Tarrou asked Rambert.

"Nothing."

Almost all, indeed, had empty hands and idly dangling arms. Another curious thing about this multitude of derelicts was its silence.

"When they first came there was such a din you couldn't hear yourself speak," Rambert said. "But as the days went by they grew quieter and quieter."

In his notes Tarrou gives what to his mind would explain this change. He pictures them in the early days bundled together in the tents, listening to the buzz of flies, scratching themselves, and, whenever they found an obliging listener, shrilly voicing their fear or indignation. But when the camp grew overcrowded, fewer and fewer people were inclined to play the part of sympathetic listener. So they had no choice but to hold their peace and nurse their mistrust of everything and everyone. One had, indeed, a feeling that suspicion was falling, dewlike, from the grayly shining sky over the brick-red camp.

Yes, there was suspicion in the eyes of all. Obviously, they were thinking, there must be some good reason for the isolation inflicted on them, and they had the air of people who are puzzling over their problem and are afraid. Everyone Tarrou set eyes on had that vacant gaze and was visibly suffering from the complete break with all that life had meant to him. And since they could not be thinking of their death all the time, they thought of nothing. They were on vacation. "But worst of all," Tarrou writes, "is that they're forgotten, and they know it. Their friends have forgotten them because they have other things to think about, naturally enough. And those they love have forgotten them because all their energies are devoted to making schemes and taking steps to get them out of the camp. And by dint of always thinking about these schemes and steps they have ceased thinking about those whose release they're trying to secure. And that, too, is natural enough. In fact, it comes to this:

nobody is capable of really thinking about anyone, even in the worst calamity. For really to think about someone means thinking about that person every minute of the day, without letting one's thoughts be diverted by anything—by meals, by a fly that settles on one's cheek, by household duties, or by a sudden itch somewhere. But there are always flies and itches. That's why life is difficult to live. And these people know it only too well."

The camp manager came up; a gentleman named Othon, he said, would like to see them. Leaving Gonzales in the office, he led the others to a corner of the grandstand, where they saw M. Othon sitting by himself. He rose as they approached. The magistrate was dressed exactly as in the past and still wore a stiff collar. The only changes Tarrou noted were that the tufts of hair over his temples were not brushed back and that one of his shoelaces was undone. M. Othon appeared very tired and not once did he look his visitors in the face. He said he was glad to see them and requested them to thank Dr. Rieux for all he had done.

Some moments of silence ensued, then with an effort the magistrate spoke again:

"I hope Jacques did not suffer too much."

This was the first time Tarrou heard him utter his son's name, and he realized that something had changed. The sun was setting and, flooding through a rift in the clouds, the level rays raked the stands, tingeing their faces with a yellow glow.

"No," Tarrou said. "No, I couldn't really say he suffered."

When they took their leave, the magistrate was still gazing toward the light.

They called in at the office to say goodby to Gonzales, whom they found studying the duty roster. The footballer was laughing when he shook hands with them.

"Anyhow, I'm back in the good old dressing-room," he chuckled. "That's something to go on with."

Soon after, when the camp manager was seeing Tarrou and Rambert out, they heard a crackling noise coming from the stands. A moment later the loud-speakers, which in happier times served to announce the results of games or to introduce the teams, informed the in-mates of the camp that they were to go back to their tents for the evening meal. Slowly everyone filed off the stands and shuffled toward the tents. After all were under canvas two small electric trucks, of the kind used for transporting baggage on railroad platforms, began to wend their way between the tents. While the occupants held forth their arms, two ladles plunged into the two big caldrons on each truck and neatly tipped their contents into the waiting mess-kits. Then the truck moved on to the next tent.

"Very efficient," Tarrou remarked.

The camp manager beamed as he shook hands.

"Yes, isn't it? We're great believers in efficiency in this camp."

Dusk was falling. The sky had cleared and the camp was bathed in cool, soft light. Through the hush of evening came a faint tinkle of spoons and plates. Above the tents bats were circling, vanishing abruptly into the darkness. A streetcar squealed on a switch outside the walls.

"Poor Monsieur Othon!" Tarrou murmured as the gate closed behind them. "One would like to do something to help him. But how can you help a judge?"

There were other camps of much the same kind in the town, but the narrator, for lack of first-hand information and in deference to veracity, has nothing to add about them. This much, however, he can say; the mere existence of these camps, the smell of crowded humanity coming from them, the baying of their loud-speakers in the dusk, the air of mystery that clung about them, and the dread these forbidden places inspired told seriously on our fellow citizens' morale and added to the general nervousness and apprehension. Breaches of the peace and minor riots became more frequent.

As November drew to a close, the mornings turned much colder. Heavy downpours had scoured the streets and washed the sky clean of clouds. In the mornings a weak sunlight bathed the town in a cold, sparkling sheen. The air warmed up, however, as night approached. It was such a night that Tarrou chose for telling something of himself to Dr. Rieux.

After a particularly tiring day, about ten o'clock Tarrou proposed to the doctor that they should go together for the evening visit to Rieux's old asthma patient. There was a soft glow above the housetops in the Old Town and a light breeze fanned their faces at the street crossings. Coming from the silent streets, they found the old man's loquacity rather irksome at first. He launched into a long harangue to the effect that some folks were getting fed up, that it was always the same people had all the jam, and things couldn't go on like that indefinitely, one day there'd be—he rubbed his hands—"a fine old row." He continued expatiating on this theme all the time the doctor was attending to him.

They heard footsteps overhead. Noticing Tarrou's upward glance, the old woman explained that it was the girls from next door walking on the terrace. She added that one had a lovely view up there, and that as the terraces in this part of the town often joined up with the next one on one side, the women could visit their neighbors without having to go into the street.

"Why not go up and have a look?" the old man suggested. "You'll get a breath of nice fresh air."

They found nobody on the terrace—only three empty chairs. On one side, as far as eye could reach, was a row of terraces, the most remote of which abutted on a dark, rugged mass that they recognized as the hill nearest the town. On the other side, spanning some streets and the unseen harbor, their gaze came to rest on the horizon, where sea and sky merged in a dim, vibrant grayness. Beyond a black patch that they knew to be the cliffs a sudden glow, whose source they could not see, sprang up at regular intervals; the lighthouse at the entrance of the fairway was still functioning for the benefit of ships that, passing Oran's unused harbor, went on to other ports along the coast. In a sky swept crystal-clear by the night wind, the stars showed like silver flakes, tarnished now and then by the yellow gleam of the revolving light. Perfumes of spice and warm stone were wafted on the breeze. Everything was very still.

"A pleasant spot," said Rieux as he lowered himself into a chair. "You'd think that plague had never found its way up here."

Tarrou was gazing seawards, his back to the doctor.

"Yes," he replied after a moment's silence, "it's good to be here."

Then, settling into the chair beside Rieux, he fixed his eyes on his face. Three times the glow spread up the sky and died away. A faint clatter of crockery rose from a room opening on the street below. A door banged somewhere in the house.

"Rieux," Tarrou said in a quite ordinary tone, "do you realize that you've never tried to find out anything about

me—the man I am? Can I regard you as a friend?"

"Yes, of course, we're friends; only so far we haven't had much time to show it."

"Good. That gives me confidence. Suppose we now take an hour off—for friendship?"

Rieux smiled by way of answer.

"Well, here goes!"

There was a long faint hiss some streets off, the sound of a car speeding on the wet pavement. It died away; then some vague shouts a long way off broke the stillness again. Then, like a dense veil slowly falling from the starry sky on the two men, silence returned. Tarrou had moved and now was sitting on the parapet, facing Rieux, who was slumped back in his chair. All that could be seen of him was a dark, bulky form outlined against the glimmering sky. He had much to tell, what follows gives it more or less in his own words.

"To make things simpler, Rieux, let me begin by saying I had plague already, long before I came to this town and encountered it here. Which is tantamount to saying I'm like everybody else. Only there are some people who don't know it, or feel at ease in that condition; others know and want to get out of it. Personally, I've always wanted to get out of it.

"When I was young I lived with the idea of my innocence; that is to say, with no idea at all. I'm not the self-tormenting kind of person, and I made a suitable start in life. I brought off everything I set my hand to, I moved at ease in the field of the intellect, I got on excellently with women, and if I had occasional qualms, they passed as lightly as they came. Then one day I started thinking. And now—

"I should tell you I wasn't poor in my young days, as you were. My father had an important post—he was prosecuting attorney; but to look at him, you'd never have guessed it; he appeared, and was, a kindly, good-natured man. My mother was a simple, rather shy woman, and I've always loved her greatly; but I'd rather not talk about her. My father was always very kind to me, and I even think he tried to understand me. He wasn't a model husband. I know that now, but I can't say it shocks me particularly. Even in his infidelities he behaved as one could count on his behaving and never gave rise to scandal. In short, he wasn't at all original and, now he's dead, I realize that, while no plaster saint, he was a very decent man as men go. He kept the middle way, that's all; he was the type of man for whom one has an affection of the mild but steady order—which is the kind that wears best.

"My father had one peculiarity; the big railway directory was his bedside book. Not that he often took a train; almost his only journeys were to Brittany, where he had a small country house to which we went every summer. But he was a walking timetable; he could tell you the exact times of departure and arrival of the Paris-Berlin expresses; how to get from Lyon to Warsaw, which trains to take and at what hours; the precise distance between any two capital cities you might mention. Could you tell me offhand how to get from Briançon to Chamonix? Even a station-master would scratch his head, I should say. Well, my father had the answer pat. Almost every evening he enlarged his knowledge of the subject, and he prided himself on it. This hobby of his much amused me; I would put complicated travel problems to him and check his answers afterwards by the railway directory. They were invariably correct. My father and I got on together excellently, thanks largely to these railway games we played in the evenings; I was exactly the audience he needed, attentive and appreciative. Personally I regarded this accomplishment of his as quite as admirable in its way as most accomplishments.

"But I'm letting my tongue run away with me and attributing too much importance to that worthy man. Actually he played only an indirect role in the great change of heart about which I want to tell you. The most he did to me was to touch off a train of thoughts. When I was seventeen my father asked me to come to hear him speak in court. There was a big case on at the assizes, and probably he thought I'd see him to his best advantage. Also I suspect he hoped I'd be duly impressed by the pomp and ceremony of the law and encouraged to take up his profession. I could tell he was keen on my going, and the prospect of seeing a side of my father's character so different from that we saw at home appealed to me. Those were absolutely the only reasons I had for going to the trial. What happened in a court had always seemed to me as natural, as much in the order of things, as a military parade on the Fourteenth of July or a school speech day. My notions on the subject were purely abstract, and I'd never given it serious thought.

"The only picture I carried away with me of that day's proceedings was a picture of the criminal. I have little doubt he was guilty—of what crime is no great matter. That little man of about thirty, with sparse, sandy hair, seemed so eager to confess everything, so genuinely horrified at what he'd done and what was going to be done with him, that after a few minutes I had eyes for nothing and nobody else. He looked like a yellow owl scared blind by too much light. His tie was slightly awry, he kept biting his nails, those of one hand only, his right. . . . I needn't go on, need I? You've understood—he was a living human being.

"As for me, it came on me suddenly,

in a flash of understanding; until then I'd thought of him only under his commonplace official designation, as 'the defendant.' And though I can't say I quite forgot my father, something seemed to grip my vitals at that moment and riveted all my attention on the little man in the dock. I hardly heard what was being said; I only knew that they were set on killing that living man, and an uprush of some elemental instinct, like a wave, had swept me to his side. And I did not really wake up until my father rose to address the court.

"In his red gown he was another man, no longer genial or good-natured; his mouth spewed out long, turgid phrases like an endless stream of snakes. I realized he was clamoring for the prisoner's death, telling the jury that they owed it to society to find him guilty; he went so far as to demand that the man should have his head cut off. Not exactly in those words, I admit. 'He must pay the supreme penalty,' was the formula. But the difference, really, was slight, and the result the same. He had the head he asked for. Only of course it wasn't he who did the actual job. I, who saw the whole business through to its conclusion, felt a far closer, far more terrifying intimacy with that wretched man than my father can ever have felt. Nevertheless, it fell to him, in the course of his duties, to be present at what's politely termed the prisoner's last moments, but what would be better called murder in its most despicable form.

"From that day on I couldn't even see the railway directory without a shudder of disgust. I took a horrified interest in legal proceedings, death sentences, executions, and I realized with dismay that my father must have often witnessed those brutal murders—on the days when, as I'd noticed without guessing what it meant, he rose very early in the morning. I remembered he used to wind his alarm-clock on those occasions, to make sure. I didn't dare to broach the subject with my mother, but I watched her now more closely and saw that their life in common had ceased to mean anything, she had abandoned hope. That helped me to 'forgive her,' as I put it to myself at the time. Later on, I learned that there'd been nothing to forgive; she'd been quite poor until her marriage, and poverty had taught her resignation.

"Probably you're expecting me to tell you that I left home at once. No, I stayed on many months, nearly a year, in fact. Then one evening my father asked for the alarm-clock as he had to get up early. I couldn't sleep that night. Next day, when he came home, I'd gone.

"To cut a long story short, I had a letter from my father, who had set inquiries on foot to find me, I went to see him, and, without explaining my reasons, told him quite calmly that I'd kill myself if he forced me to return. He wound up by letting me have my way—he was, as I've said, a kindly man at bottom—gave me a lecture on the silliness of wanting to 'live my life' (that was how he accounted for my conduct and I didn't undeceive him), and plenty of good advice. I could see he really felt it deeply and it was an effort for him to keep back his tears. Subsequently—but quite a long time after that—I formed a habit of visiting my mother periodically, and I always saw him on these occasions. I imagine these infrequent meetings satisfied my father. Personally, I hadn't the least antipathy to him, only a little sadness of heart. When he died I had my mother come to live with me, and she'd still be with me if she were alive.

"I've had to dwell on my start in life, since for me it really was the start of everything. I'll get on more quickly now. I came to grips with poverty when I was eighteen, after an easy life till then. I tried all sorts of jobs, and I didn't do too badly. But my real interest in life was the death penalty; I wanted to square accounts with that poor blind owl in the dock. So I became an agitator, as they say. I didn't want to be pestiferous, that's all. To my mind the social order around me was based on the death sentence, and by fighting the established order I'd be fighting against murder. That was my view, others had told me so, and I still think that this belief of mine was substantially true. I joined forces with a group of people I then liked, and indeed have never ceased to like. I spent many years in close co-operation with them, and there's not a country in Europe in whose struggles I haven't played a part. But that's another story.

"Needless to say, I knew that we, too, on occasion, passed sentences of death. But I was told that these few deaths were inevitable for the building up of a new world in which murder would cease to be. That also was true up to a point—and maybe I'm not capable of standing fast where that order of truths is concerned. Whatever the explanation, I hesitated. But then I remembered that miserable owl in the dock and it enabled me to keep on. Until the day when I was present at an execution—it was in Hungary—and exactly the same dazed horror that I'd experienced as a youngster made everything reel before my eyes.

"Have you ever seen a man shot by a firing-squad? No, of course not; the spectators are hand-picked and it's like a private party, you need an invitation. The result is that you've gleaned your ideas about it from books and pictures. A post, a blindfolded man, some soldiers in the offing. But the real thing isn't a bit like that. Do you know that the firing-squad stands only a yard and a half from the condemned man? Do you know that if the victim took two steps forward his chest would touch the rifles? Do you know that, at this short range, the soldiers concentrate their fire on the region of the heart and their big bullets make a hole into which you could thrust your fist? No, you didn't know all that; those are things that are never spoken of. For the plague-stricken their peace of mind is more important than a human life. Decent folks must be allowed to sleep easy o' nights, mustn't they? Really it would be shockingly bad taste to linger on such details, that's common knowledge. But personally I've never been able to sleep well since then. The bad taste remained in my mouth and I've kept lingering on the details, brooding over them.

"And thus I came to understand that I, anyhow, had had plague through all those long years in which, paradoxically enough, I'd believed with all my soul that I was fighting it. I learned that I had had an indirect hand in the deaths of thousands of people; that I'd even brought about their deaths by approving of acts and principles which could only end that way. Others did not seem embarrassed by such thoughts, or anyhow never voiced them of their own accord. But I was different; what I'd come to know stuck in my gorge. I was with them and yet I was alone. When I spoke of these matters they told me not to be so squeamish; I should remember what great issues were at stake. And they advanced arguments, often quite impressive ones, to make me swallow what none the less I couldn't bring myself to stomach. I replied that the most eminent of the plague-stricken, the men who wear red robes, also have excellent arguments to justify what they do, and once I admitted the arguments of necessity and *force majeure* put forward by the less eminent, I couldn't reject those of the eminent. To which they retorted that the surest way of playing the game of the red robes was to leave to them the monopoly of the death penalty. My reply to this was that if you gave in once, there was no reason for not continuing to give in. It seems to me that history has borne me out; today there's a sort of competition who will kill the most. They're all mad over murder and they couldn't stop killing men even if they wanted to.

"In any case, my concern was not with arguments. It was with the poor owl; with that foul procedure whereby dirty mouths stinking of plague told a fettered man that he was going to die, and scientifically arranged things so that he should die, after nights and nights of mental torture while he waited to be murdered in cold blood. My concern was with that hole in a man's chest. And I told myself that meanwhile, so far anyhow as I was concerned, nothing in the world would induce me to accept any argument that justified such butcheries. Yes, I chose to be blindly obstinate, pending the day when I could see my way more clearly.

"I'm still of the same mind. For many years I've been ashamed, mortally ashamed, of having been, even with the best intentions, even at many removes, a murderer in my turn. As time went on I merely learned that even those who were better than the rest could not keep themselves nowadays from killing or letting others kill, because such is the logic by which they live; and that we can't stir a finger in this world without the risk of bringing death to somebody. Yes, I've been ashamed ever since; I have realized that we all have plague, and I have lost my peace. And today I am still trying to find it; still trying to understand all those others and not to be the mortal enemy of anyone. I only know that one must do what one can to cease being plague-stricken, and that's the only way in which we can hope for some peace or, failing that, a decent death. This, and only this, can bring relief to men and, if

not save them, at least do them the least harm possible and even, sometimes, a little good. So that is why I resolved to have no truck with anything which, directly or indirectly, for good reasons or for bad, brings death to anyone or justifies others' putting him to death.

"That, too, is why this epidemic has taught me nothing new, except that I must fight it at your side. I know positively—yes, Rieux, I can say I know the world inside out, as you may see—that each of us has the plague within him; no one, no one on earth is free from it. And I know, too, that we must keep endless watch on ourselves lest in a careless moment we breathe in somebody's face and fasten the infection on him. What's natural is the microbe. All the rest—health, integrity, purity (if you like)—is a product of the human will, of a vigilance that must never falter. The good man, the man who infects hardly anyone, is the man who has the fewest lapses of attention. And it needs tremendous willpower, a never ending tension of the mind, to avoid such lapses. Yes, Rieux, it's a wearying business, being plague-stricken. But it's still more wearying to refuse to be it. That's why everybody in the world today looks so tired; everyone is more or less sick of plague. But that is also why some of us, those who want to get the plague out of their systems, feel such desperate weariness, a weariness from which nothing remains to set us free except death.

"Pending that release, I know I have no place in the world of today; once I'd definitely refused to kill, I doomed myself to an exile that can never end. I leave it to others to make history. I know, too, that I'm not qualified to pass judgment on those others. There's something lacking in my mental make-up, and its lack prevents me from being a rational murderer. So it's a deficiency, not a superiority. But as things are, I'm willing to be as

I am; I've learned modesty. All I maintain is that on this earth there are pestilences and there are victims, and it's up to us, so far as possible, not to join forces with the pestilences. That may sound simple to the point of childishness; I can't judge if it's simple, but I know it's true. You see, I'd heard such quantities of arguments, which very nearly turned my head, and turned other people's heads enough to make them approve of murder; and I'd come to realize that all our troubles spring from our failure to use plain, clean-cut language. So I resolved always to speak—and to act—quite clearly, as this was the only way of setting myself on the right track. That's why I say there are pestilences and there are victims; no more than that. If, by making that statement, I, too, become a carrier of the plague-germ, at least I don't do it willfully. I try, in short, to be an innocent murderer. You see, I've no great ambitions.

"I grant we should add a third category: that of the true healers. But it's a fact one doesn't come across many of them, and anyhow it must be a hard vocation. That's why I decided to take, in every predicament, the victims' side, so as to reduce the damage done. Among them I can at least try to discover how one attains to the third category; in other words, to peace."

Tarrou was swinging his leg, tapping the terrace lightly with his heel, as he concluded. After a short silence the doctor raised himself a little in his chair and asked if Tarrou had an idea of the path to follow for attaining peace.

"Yes," he replied. "The path of sympathy."

Two ambulances were clanging in the distance. The dispersed shouts they had been hearing off and on drew together on the outskirts of the town, near the stony hill, and presently there was a sound like a gunshot. Then silence fell again. Rieux counted two flashes of the revolving light. The breeze freshened and a gust coming from the sea filled the air for a moment with the smell of brine. And at the same time they clearly heard the low sound of waves lapping the foot of the cliffs.

"It comes to this," Tarrou said almost casually; "what interests me is learning how to become a saint."

"But you don't believe in God."

"Exactly! Can one be a saint without God?—that's the problem, in fact the only problem, I'm up against today."

A sudden blaze sprang up above the place the shouts had come from and, stemming the wind-stream, a rumor of many voices came to their ears. The blaze died down almost at once, leaving behind it only a dull red glow. Then in a break of the wind they distinctly heard some strident yells and the discharge of a gun, followed by the roar of an angry crowd. Tarrou stood up and listened, but nothing more could be heard.

"Another skirmish at the gates, I suppose."

"Well, it's over now," Rieux said.

Tarrou said in a low voice that it was never over, and there would be more victims, because that was in the order of things.

"Perhaps," the doctor answered. "But, you know, I feel more fellowship with the defeated than with saints. Heroism and sanctity don't really appeal to me, I imagine. What interests me is being a man."

"Yes, we're both after the same thing, but I'm less ambitious."

Rieux supposed Tarrou was jesting and turned to him with a smile. But, faintly lit by the dim radiance falling from the sky, the face he saw was sad and earnest. There was another gust of wind and

Rieux felt it warm on his skin. Tarrou gave himself a little shake.

"Do you know," he said, "what we now should do for friendship's sake?"

"Anything you like, Tarrou."

"Go for a swim. It's one of these harmless pleasures that even a saint-to-be can indulge in, don't you agree?" Rieux smiled again, and Tarrou continued: "With our passes, we can get out on the pier. Really, it's too damn silly living only in and for the plague. Of course, a man should fight for the victims, but if he ceases caring for anything outside that, what's the use of his fighting?"

"Right," Rieux said. "Let's go."

Some minutes later the car drew up at the harbor gates. The moon had risen and a milk-white radiance, dappled with shadows, lay around them. Behind them rose the town, tier on tier, and from it came warm, fetid breaths of air that urged them toward the sea. After showing their passes to a guard, who inspected them minutely, they crossed some open ground littered with casks, and headed toward the pier. The air here reeked of stale wine and fish. Just before they reached the pier a smell of iodine and seaweed announced the nearness of the sea and they clearly heard the sound of waves breaking gently on the big stone blocks.

Once they were on the pier they saw the sea spread out before them, a gently heaving expanse of deep-piled velvet, supple and sleek as a creature of the wild. They sat down on a boulder facing the open. Slowly the waters rose and sank, and with their tranquil breathing sudden oily glints formed and flickered over the surface in a haze of broken lights. Before them the darkness stretched out into infinity. Rieux could feel under his hand the gnarled, weather-worn visage of the rocks, and a strange happiness possessed him. Turning to Tarrou, he caught a glimpse on his friend's face of the same happiness, a happiness that forgot nothing, not even murder.

They undressed, and Rieux dived in first. After the first shock of cold had passed and he came back to the surface the water seemed tepid. When he had taken a few strokes he found that the sea was warm that night with the warmth of autumn seas that borrow from the shore the accumulated heat of the long days of summer. The movement of his feet left a foaming wake as he swam steadily ahead, and the water slipped along his arms to close in tightly on his legs. A loud splash told him that Tarrou had dived. Rieux lay on his back and stayed motionless, gazing up at the dome of sky lit by the stars and moon. He drew a deep breath. Then he heard a sound of beaten water, louder and louder, amazingly clear in the hollow silence of the night. Tarrou was coming up with him, he now could hear his breathing.

Rieux turned and swam level with his friend, timing his stroke to Tarrou's. But Tarrou was the stronger swimmer and Rieux had to put on speed to keep up with him. For some minutes they swam side by side, with the same zest, in the same rhythm, isolated from the world, at last free of the town and of the plague. Rieux was the first to stop and they swam back slowly, except at one point, where unexpectedly they found themselves caught in an ice-cold current. Their energy whipped up by this trap the sea had sprung on them, both struck out more vigorously.

They dressed and started back. Neither had said a word, but they were conscious of being perfectly at one, and the memory of this night would be cherished by them both. When they caught sight of the plague watchman, Rieux guessed that Tarrou, like himself, was thinking that the disease had given them a respite, and this was good, but now they must set their shoulders to the wheel again.

Yes, the plague gave short shrift indeed, and they must set their shoulders to the wheel again. Throughout December it smoldered in the chests of our townsfolk, fed the fires in the crematorium, and peopled the camps with human jetsam. In short, it never ceased progressing with its characteristically jerky but unfaltering stride. The authorities had optimistically reckoned on the coming of winter to halt its progress, but it lasted through the first cold spells without the least remission. So the only thing for us to do was to go on waiting, and since after a too long waiting one gives up waiting, the whole town lived as if it had no future.

As for Dr. Rieux, that brief hour of peace and friendship which had been granted him was not, and could not be, repeated. Yet another hospital had been opened, and his only converse was with his patients. However, he noticed a change at this stage of the epidemic, now that the plague was assuming more and more the pneumonic form; the patients seemed, after their fashion, to be seconding the doctor. Instead of giving way to the prostration or the frenzies of the early period, they appeared to have a clearer idea of where their interests lay and on their own initiative asked for what might be most beneficial. Thus they were always clamoring for something to drink and insisted on being kept as warm as possible. And though the demands on him were as exhausting as before, Rieux no longer had the impression of putting up a solitary fight; the patients were co-operating.

Toward the end of December he received a letter from M. Othon, who was still in quarantine. The magistrate stated that his quarantine period was over; unfortunately the date of his admission to camp seemed to have been mislaid by the secretariat, and if he was still detained it was certainly due to a mistake. His wife, recently released from quarantine, had gone to the Prefect's office to protest and had been rudely treated; they had told her that the office never made mistakes. Rieux asked Rambert to look into the matter, and a few days later M. Othon called on him. There had, in fact, been a mistake, and Rieux showed some indignation. But M. Othon, who had grown thinner, raised a limp, deprecating hand; weighing his words, he said that everyone could make mistakes. And the doctor thought to himself that decidedly something had changed.

"What will you do now, Monsieur Othon?" Rieux asked. "I suppose you have a pile of work awaiting you."

"Well, as a matter of fact, I'm putting in for some leave."

"I quite understand. You need a rest."

"It's not that. I want to go back to the camp."

Rieux couldn't believe his ears. "But you've only just come out of it!"

"I'm afraid I did not make myself clear. I'm told there are some voluntary workers from government offices in that camp." The magistrate rolled his round eyes a little and tried to smooth down a tuft of hair. "It would keep me busy, you see. And also—I know it may sound absurd, but I'd feel less separated from my little boy."

Rieux stared at him. Could it be that a sudden gentleness showed in those hard, inexpressive eyes? Yes, they had grown misted, lost their steely glitter.

"Certainly," Rieux said. "Since that's your wish, I'll fix it up for you."

The doctor kept his word; and the life of the plague-ridden town resumed its course until Christmas. Tarrou continued to bring his quiet efficiency to bear on every problem. Rambert confided in the doctor that, with the connivance of the two young guards, he was sending letters to his wife and now and then receiving an answer. He suggested to Rieux that he should avail himself of this clandestine channel, and Rieux agreed to do so. For the first time for many months he sat down to write a letter. He found it a laborious business, as if he were manipulating a language that he had forgotten. The letter was dispatched. The reply was slow in coming. As for Cottard, he was prospering, making money hand over fist in small, somewhat shady transactions. With Grand, however, it was otherwise; the Christmas season did not seem to agree with him.

Indeed, Christmas that year had none of its old-time associations; it smacked of hell rather than of heaven. Empty, unlighted shops, dummy chocolates or empty boxes in the confectioners' windows, streetcars laden with listless, dispirited passengers—all was as unlike previous Christmastides as it well could be. In the past all the townspeople, rich and poor alike, indulged in seasonable festivity; now only a privileged few, those with money to burn, could do so, and they caroused in shamefast solitude in a dingy back shop or a private room. In the churches there were more supplications than carols. You saw a few children, too young to realize what threatened them, playing in the frosty, cheerless streets. But no one dared to bid them welcome-in the God of former days, bringer of gifts, and old as human sorrow, yet new as the hopes of youth. There was no room in any heart but for a very old, gray hope, that hope which keeps men from letting themselves drift into death and is nothing but a dogged will to live.

Grand had failed to show up as usual on the previous evening. Feeling somewhat anxious, Rieux called at his place early in the morning, but he wasn't at home. His friends were asked to keep a lookout for him. At about eleven Rambert came to the hospital with the news that he'd had a distant glimpse of Grand, who seemed to be wandering aimlessly, "looking very queer." Unfortunately he had lost sight of him almost at once. Tarrou and the doctor set out in the car to hunt for Grand.

At noon Rieux stepped out of his car into the frozen air; he had just caught sight of Grand some distance away, his face glued to a shop-window full of crudely carved wooden toys. Tears were steadily flowing down the old fellow's cheeks, and they wrung the doctor's heart, for he could understand them, and he felt his own tears welling up in sympathy. A picture rose before him of that scene of long ago—the youngster standing in front of another shop-window, like this one dressed for Christmas, and Jeanne turning toward him in a sudden access of emotion and saying how happy she was. He could guess that through the mists of the past years, from the depth of his fond despair, Jeanne's young voice was rising, echoing in Grand's ears. And he knew, also, what the old man was thinking as his tears flowed, and he, Rieux, thought it too: that a loveless world is a dead world, and always there comes an hour when one is weary of prisons, of one's work, and of devotion to duty, and all one craves for is a loved face, the warmth and wonder of a loving heart.

Grand saw the doctor's reflection in the window. Still weeping, he turned and, leaning against the shop-front, watched Rieux approach.

"Oh, doctor, doctor!" He could say no more.

Rieux, too, couldn't speak; he made a vague, understanding gesture. At this moment he suffered with Grand's sorrow, and what filled his breast was the passionate indignation we feel when confronted by the anguish all men share.

"Yes, Grand," he murmured.

"Oh, if only I could have time to write to her! To let her know . . . and to let her be happy without remorse!"

Almost roughly Rieux took Grand's arm and drew him forward. Grand did not resist and went on muttering broken phrases.

"Too long! It's lasted too long. All the time one's wanting to let oneself go, and then one day one has to. Oh, doctor, I know I look a quiet sort, just like anybody else. But it's always been a terrible effort only to be—just normal. And now—well, even that's too much for me."

He stopped dead. He was trembling violently, his eyes were fever-bright. Rieux took his hand; it was burning hot.

"You must go home."

But Grand wrenched himself free and started running. After a few steps he halted and stretched out his arms, swaying to and fro. Then he spun round on himself and fell flat on the pavement, his face stained with the tears that went on flowing. Some people who were approaching stopped abruptly and watched the scene from a little way off, not daring to come nearer. Rieux had to carry the old man to the car.

Grand lay in bed, gasping for breath; his lungs were congested. Rieux pondered. The old fellow hadn't any family. What would be the point of having him evacuated? He and Tarrou could look after him.

Grand's head was buried in the pillow, his cheeks were a greenish gray, his eyes had gone dull, opaque. He seemed to be gazing fixedly at the scanty fire Tarrou was kindling with the remains of an old packing-case. "I'm in a bad way," he muttered. A queer crackling sound came from his flame-seared lungs whenever he tried to speak. Rieux told him not to talk

and promised to come back. The sick man's lips parted in a curious smile, and a look of humorous complicity flickered across the haggard face. "If I pull through, doctor—hats off!" A moment later he sank into extreme prostration.

Visiting him again some hours later, they found him half sitting up in bed, and Rieux was horrified by the rapid change that had come over his face, ravaged by the fires of the disease consuming him. However, he seemed more lucid and almost immediately asked them to get his manuscript from the drawer where he always kept it. When Tarrou handed him the sheets, he pressed them to his chest without looking at them, then held them out to the doctor, indicating by a gesture that he was to read them. There were some fifty pages of manuscript. Glancing through them, Rieux saw that the bulk of the writing consisted of the same sentence written again and again with small variants, simplifications or elaborations. Persistently the month of May, the lady on horseback, the avenues of the Bois recurred, regrouped in different patterns. There were, besides, explanatory notes, some exceedingly long, and lists of alternatives. But at the foot of the last page was written in a studiously clear hand: *My dearest Jeanne, Today is Christmas Day and . . ."* Eight words only. Above it, in copperplate script, was the latest version of the famous phrase. "Read it," Grand whispered. And Rieux read:

"One fine morning in May, a slim young horsewoman might have been seen riding a glossy sorrel mare along the avenues of the Bois, among the flowers. . . ."

"Is that *it?"* There was a feverish quaver in the old voice. Rieux refrained from looking at him, and he began to toss about in the bed. "Yes, I know. I know what you're thinking. 'Fine' isn't the word. It's—"

Rieux clasped his hand under the coverlet.

"No, doctor. It's too late—no time . . ." His breast heaved painfully, then suddenly he said in a loud, shrill voice: "Burn it!"

The doctor hesitated, but Grand repeated his injunction in so violent a tone and with such agony in his voice that Rieux walked across to the fireplace and dropped the sheets on the dying fire. It blazed up, and there was a sudden flood of light, a fleeting warmth, in the room. When the doctor came back to the bed, Grand had his back turned, his face almost touching the wall. After injecting the serum Rieux whispered to his friend that Grand wouldn't last the night, and Tarrou volunteered to stay with him. The doctor approved.

All night Rieux was haunted by the idea of Grand's death. But next morning he found his patient sitting up in bed, talking to Tarrou. His temperature was down to normal and there were no symptoms other than a generalized prostration.

"Yes, doctor," Grand said. "I was overhasty. But I'll make another start. You'll see, I can remember every word."

Rieux looked at Tarrou dubiously. "We must wait," he said.

But at noon there was no change. By nightfall Grand could be considered out of danger. Rieux was completely baffled by this "resurrection."

Other surprises were in store for him. About the same time there was brought to the hospital a girl whose case Rieux diagnosed as hopeless, and he had her sent immediately to the isolation ward. She was delirious and had all the symptoms of pneumonic plague. Next morning, however, the temperature had fallen. As in Grand's case the doctor assumed this was the ordinary morning fall that his experience had taught him to regard as a bad sign. But at noon her temperature still showed no rise and at night it went up only a few points. Next morning it was down to normal. Though very exhausted, the girl was breathing freely. Rieux remarked to Tarrou that her recovery was "against all the rules!" But in the course of the next week four similar cases came to his notice.

The old asthma patient was bubbling over with excitement when Rieux and Tarrou visited him at the end of the week.

"Would you ever have believed it! They're coming out again," he said.

"Who?"

"Why, the rats!"

Not one dead or living rat had been seen in the town since April.

"Does that mean it's starting all over again?" Tarrou asked Rieux.

The old man was rubbing his hands.

"You should see 'em running, doctor! It's a treat, it is!"

He himself had seen two rats slipping into the house by the street door, and some neighbors, too, had told him they'd seen rats in their basements. In some houses people had heard those once familiar scratchings and rustlings behind the woodwork. Rieux awaited with much interest the mortality figures that were announced every Monday. They showed a decrease.

PART V

Though this sudden setback of the plague was as welcome as it was unlooked-for, our townsfolk were in no hurry to jubilate. While intensifying their desire to be set free, the terrible months they had lived through had taught them prudence, and they had come to count less and less on a speedy end of the epidemic. All the same, this new development was the talk of the town, and people began to nurse hopes none the less heartfelt for being unavowed. All else took a back place; that daily there were new victims counted for little beside that staggering fact: the weekly total showed a decrease. One of the signs that a return to the golden age of health was secretly awaited was that our fellow citizens, careful though they were not to voice their hope, now began to talk—in, it is true, a carefully detached tone—of the new order of life that would set in after the plague.

All agreed that the amenities of the past couldn't be restored at once; destruction is an easier, speedier process than reconstruction. However, it was thought that a slight improvement in the food-supply could safely be counted on, and this would relieve what was just now the acutest worry of every household. But in reality behind these mild aspirations lurked wild, extravagant hopes, and often one of us, becoming aware of this, would hastily add that, even on the rosiest view, you couldn't expect the plague to stop from one day to another.

Actually, while the epidemic did not stop "from one day to another," it declined more rapidly than we could reasonably have expected. With the first week of January an unusually persistent spell of very cold weather settled in and seemed to crystallize above the town. Yet never before had the sky been so blue; day after day its icy radiance flooded the town with brilliant light, and in the frost-cleansed air the epidemic seemed to lose its virulence, and in each of three consecutive weeks a big drop in the deathroll was announced. Thus over a relatively brief period the disease lost practically all the gains piled up over many months. Its setbacks with seemingly predestined victims, like Grand and Rieux's girl patient, its bursts of activity for two or three days in some districts synchronizing with its total disappearance from others, its new practice of multiplying its victims on, say, a Monday, and on Wednesday letting almost all escape—in short, its accesses of violence followed by spells of complete inactivity—all these gave an impression that its energy was flagging, out of exhaustion and exasperation, and it was losing, with its self-command, the ruthless, almost mathematical efficiency that had been its trump card hitherto. Of a sudden Castel's anti-plague injections scored frequent successes, denied it until now. Indeed, all the treatments the doctors had tentatively employed, without definite results, now seemed almost uniformly efficacious. It was as if the plague had been hounded down and cornered, and its sudden weakness lent new strength to the blunted weapons so far used against it. Only at rare moments did the disease brace itself and make as it were a blind and fatal leap at three or four patients whose recovery had been expected—a truly ill-starred few, killed off when hope ran highest. Such was the case of M. Othon, the magistrate, evacuated from the quarantine camp; Tarrou said of him that "he'd had no luck," but one couldn't tell if he had in mind the life or the death of M. Othon.

But, generally speaking, the epidemic was in retreat all along the line; the official communiqués, which had at first encouraged no more than shadowy, half-hearted hopes, now confirmed the popular belief that the victory was won and the enemy abandoning his positions. Really, however, it is doubtful if this could be called a victory. All that could be said was that the disease seemed to be leaving as unaccountably as it had come. Our strategy had not changed, but whereas yesterday it had obviously failed, today it seemed triumphant. Indeed, one's chief impression was that the epidemic had called a retreat after reaching all its objectives; it had, so to speak, achieved its purpose.

Nevertheless, it seemed as if nothing

had changed in the town. Silent as ever by day, the streets filled up at nightfall with the usual crowds of people, now wearing overcoats and scarves. Cafés and picture-houses did as much business as before. But on a closer view you might notice that people looked less strained, and they occasionally smiled. And this brought home the fact that since the outbreak of plague no one had hitherto been seen to smile in public. The truth was that for many months the town had been stifling under an airless shroud, in which a rent had now been made, and every Monday when he turned on the radio, each of us learned that the rift was widening; soon he would be able to breathe freely. It was at best a negative solace, with no immediate impact on men's lives. Still, had anyone been told a month earlier that a train had just left or a boat put in, or that cars were to be allowed on the streets again, the news would have been received with looks of incredulity; whereas in mid-January an announcement of this kind would have caused no surprise. The change, no doubt, was slight. Yet, however slight, it proved what a vast forward stride our townsfolk had made in the way of hope. And indeed it could be said that once the faintest stirring of hope became possible, the dominion of the plague was ended.

It must, however, be admitted that our fellow citizens' reactions during that month were diverse to the point of incoherence. More precisely, they fluctuated between high optimism and extreme depression. Hence the odd circumstance that several more attempts to escape took place at the very moment when the statistics were most encouraging. This took the authorities by surprise, and, apparently, the sentries too—since most of the "escapists" brought it off. But, looking into it, one saw that people who tried to escape at this time were prompted by quite understandable motives. Some of them plague had imbued with a skepticism so thorough that it was now a second nature; they had become allergic to hope in any form. Thus even when the plague had run its course, they went on living by its standards. They were, in short, behind the times. In the case of others—chiefly those who had been living until now in forced separation from those they loved—the rising wind of hope, after all these months of durance and depression, had fanned impatience to a blaze and swept away their self-control. They were seized with a sort of panic at the thought that they might die so near the goal and never see again the ones they loved, and their long privation have no recompense. Thus, though for weary months and months they had endured their long ordeal with dogged perseverance, the first thrill of hope had been enough to shatter what fear and hopelessness had failed to impair. And in the frenzy of their haste they tried to outstrip the plague, incapable of keeping pace with it up to the end.

Meanwhile, there were various symptoms of the growing optimism. Prices, for instance, fell sharply. This fall was unaccountable from the purely economic viewpoint. Our difficulties were as great as ever, the gates were kept rigorously closed, and the food situation was far from showing any improvement. Thus it was a purely psychological reaction—as if the dwindling of the plague must have repercussions in all fields. Others to profit by the spread of optimism were those who used to live in groups and had been forced to live apart. The two convents reopened and their communal life was resumed. The troops, too, were regrouped in such barracks as had not been requisitioned, and settled down to the garrison life of the past. Minor details, but significant.

This state of subdued yet active ferment prevailed until January 25, when the weekly total showed so striking a decline that, after consulting the medical board, the authorities announced that the epidemic could be regarded as definitely stemmed. True, the communiqué went on to say that, acting with a prudence of which the population would certainly approve, the Prefect had decided that the gates of the town were to remain closed for two weeks more, and the prophylactic measures to remain in force for another month. During this period, at the least sign of danger "the standing orders would be strictly enforced and, if necessary, prolonged thereafter for such a period as might be deemed desirable." All, however, concurred in regarding these phrases as mere official verbiage, and the night of January 25 was the occasion of much festivity. To associate himself with the popular rejoicings, the Prefect gave orders for the street lighting to be resumed as in the past. And the townspeople paraded the brilliantly lighted streets in boisterous groups, laughing and singing.

True, in some houses the shutters remained closed, and those within listened in silence to the joyful shouts outside. Yet even in these houses of mourning a feeling of deep relief prevailed; whether because at last the fear of seeing other members of the household taken from them was calmed or because the shadow of personal anxiety was lifted from their hearts. The families that perforce withdrew themselves the most from the general jubilation were those who at this hour had one of their members down with plague in hospital and, whether in a quarantine camp or at home, waited in enforced seclusion for the epidemic to have done with them as it had done with the others. No doubt these families had hopes, but they hoarded them and forbade themselves to draw on them before feeling quite sure they were justified. And this time of waiting in silence and exile, in a limbo between joy and grief, seemed still crueler for the gladness all around them.

But these exceptions did not diminish the satisfaction of the great majority. No doubt the plague was not yet ended—a fact of which they were to be reminded; still, in imagination they could already hear, weeks in advance, trains whistling on their way to an outside world that had no limit, and steamers hooting as they put out from the harbor across shining seas. Next day these fancies would have passed and qualms of doubt returned. But for the moment the whole town was on the move, quitting the dark, lugubrious confines where it had struck its roots of stone, and setting forth at last, like a shipload of survivors, toward a land of promise.

That night Tarrou, Rieux, Rambert, and their colleagues joined for a while the marching crowds and they, too, felt as if they trod on air. Long after they had turned off the main streets, even when in empty byways they walked past shuttered houses, the joyful clamor followed them up, and because of their fatigue somehow they could not disassociate the sorrow behind those closed shutters from the joy filling the central streets. Thus the coming liberation had a twofold aspect, of happiness and tears.

At one moment, when the cries of exultation in the distance were swelling to a roar, Tarrou stopped abruptly. A small, sleek form was scampering along the roadway: a cat, the first cat any of them had seen since the spring. It stopped in the middle of the road, hesitated, licked a paw and quickly passed it behind its right ear; then it started forward again and vanished into the darkness. Tarrou smiled to himself; the little old man on the balcony, too, would be pleased.

But in those days when the plague seemed to be retreating, slinking back to the obscure lair from which it had stealthily emerged, at least one person in the town viewed this retreat with consternation, if Tarrou's notes are to be trusted; and that man was Cottard.

To tell the truth, these diary notes take a rather curious turn from the date on which the death returns began to drop. The handwriting becomes much harder to read—this may have been due to fatigue—and the diarist jumps from one topic to another without transition. What is more, these later notes lack the objectivity of the earlier ones; personal considerations creep in. Thus, sandwiched between long passages dealing with the case of Cottard, we find a brief account of the old man and the cats. Tarrou conveys to us that the plague had in no wise lessened his appreciation of the old fellow, who continued equally to interest him after the epidemic had run its course; unfortunately, he could not go on interesting him, and this through no lack of good intentions on Tarrou's part. He had done his best to see him again. Some days after that memorable 25th of January he stationed himself at the corner of the little street. The cats were back at their usual places, basking in the patches of sunlight. But at the ritual hour the shutters stayed closed. And never once did Tarrou see them open on the following days. He drew the rather odd conclusion that the old fellow was either dead or vexed—if vexed, the reason being that he had thought that he was right and the plague had put him in the wrong; if dead, the question was (as in the case of the old asthmatic) had he been a saint? Tarrou hardly thought so, but he found in the old man's case "a pointer." "Perhaps," he wrote, "we can only reach approximations of sainthood. In which case we must make shift with a mild, benevolent diabolism."

Interspersed with observations relating to Cottard are remarks, scattered here and there, about Grand—he was now convalescent and had gone back to work as if nothing had happened—and about Rieux's mother. The occasional conversations he had with her, when living under the same roof, the old lady's attitudes, her opinions on the plague, are all recorded in detail in the diary. Tarrou lays stress above all on Mme Rieux's self-effacement, her way of explaining things in the simplest possible words, her predilection for a special window at which she always sat in the early evening, holding herself rather straight, her hands at rest, her eyes fixed on the quiet street below, until twilight filled the room and she showed among the gathering shadows as a motionless black form which gradually merged into the invading darkness. He remarks on the "lightness" with which she moved from one room to the other; on her kindness—though no precise instances had come to his notice he discerned its gentle glow in all she said and did; on the gift she had of knowing everything without (apparently) taking thought; and lastly that, dim and silent though she was, she quailed before no light, even the garish light of the plague. At this point Tarrou's handwriting began to fall off oddly; indeed, the following lines were almost illegible. And, as if in confirmation of this loss of grip upon himself, the last lines of the entry deal—for the first time in the diary—with his personal life. "She reminds me of my mother; what I loved most in Mother was her self-effacement, her 'dimness,' as they say, and it's she I've always wanted to get back to. It happened eight years ago; but I can't say she died. She only effaced herself a trifle more than usual, and when I looked round she was no longer there."

But to return to Cottard. When the weekly totals began to show a decline, he visited Rieux several times on various pretexts. But obviously what he really wanted was to get from Rieux his opinion on the probable course of the epidemic. "Do you really think it can stop like that, all of a sudden?" He was skeptical about this, or anyhow professed to be. But the fact that he kept on asking the question seemed to imply he was less sure than he professed to be. From the middle of January Rieux gave him fairly optimistic answers. But these were not to Cottard's liking, and his reactions varied on each occasion, from mere petulance to great despondency. One day the doctor was moved to tell him that, though the statistics were highly promising, it was too soon to say definitely that we were out of the wood.

"In other words," Cottard said promptly, "there's no knowing. It may start again at any moment."

"Quite so. Just as it's equally possible the improvement may speed up."

Distressing to everyone else, this state of uncertainty seemed to agree with Cottard. Tarrou observed that he would enter into conversations with shopkeepers in his part of the town, with the obvious desire of propagating the opinion expressed by Rieux. Indeed, he had no trouble in doing this. After the first exhilaration following the announcement of the plague's decline had worn off, doubts had returned to many minds. And the sight of their anxiety reassured Cottard. Just as at other times he yielded to discouragement. "Yes," he said gloomily to Tarrou, "one of these days the gates will be opened. And then, you'll see, they'll drop me like a live coal!"

Everyone was struck by his abrupt changes of mood during the first three weeks of January. Though normally he spared no pains to make himself liked by neighbors and acquaintances, now, for whole days, he deliberately cold-shouldered them. On these occasions, so Tarrou gathered, he abruptly cut off outside contacts and retired morosely into his shell. He was no more to be seen in restaurants or at the theater or in his favorite cafés. However, he seemed unable to resume the obscure, humdrum life he had led before the epidemic. He stayed in his room and had his meals sent up from a near-by restaurant. Only at nightfall did he venture forth to make some small purchases, and on leaving the shop he would furtively roam the darker, less-frequented streets. Once or twice Tarrou ran into him on these occasions, but failed to elicit more than a few gruff monosyllables. Then, from one day to another, he became sociable again, talked volubly about the plague, asking everyone for his views on it, and mingled in the crowd with evident pleasure.

On January 25, the day of the official announcement, Cottard went to cover again. Two days later Tarrou came across him loitering in a side-street. When Cottard suggested he should accompany him home, Tarrou demurred; he'd had a particularly tiring day. But Cottard wouldn't hear of a refusal. He seemed much agitated, gesticulated freely, spoke very rapidly and in a very loud tone. He began by asking Tarrou if he really thought the official communiqué meant an end of the plague. Tarrou replied that obviously a mere official announcement couldn't stop an epidemic, but it certainly looked as if, barring accidents, it would shortly cease.

"Yes," Cottard said. "Barring accidents. And accidents *will* happen, won't they?"

Tarrou pointed out that the authorities had allowed for the possibility by refusing to open the gates for another fortnight.

"And very wise they were!" Cottard exclaimed in the same excited tone. "By the way things are going, I should say they'll have to eat their words."

Tarrou agreed this might be so; still,

he thought it wiser to count on the opening of the gates and a return to normal life in the near future.

"Granted!" Cottard rejoined. "But what do you mean by 'a return to normal life'?"

Tarrou smiled. "New films at the picture-houses."

But Cottard didn't smile. Was it supposed, he asked, that the plague wouldn't have changed anything and the life of the town would go on as before, exactly as if nothing had happened? Tarrou thought that the plague would have changed things and not changed them; naturally our fellow citizens' strongest desire was, and would be, to behave as if nothing had changed and for that reason nothing would be changed, in a sense. But—to look at it from another angle—one can't forget everything, however great one's wish to do so; the plague was bound to leave traces, anyhow, in people's hearts.

To this Cottard rejoined curtly that he wasn't interested in hearts; indeed, they were the last thing he bothered about. What interested him was knowing whether the whole administration wouldn't be changed, lock, stock, and barrel; whether, for instance, the public services would function as before. Tarrou had to admit he had no inside knowledge on the matter; his personal theory was that after the upheaval caused by the epidemic, there would be some delay in getting these services under way again. Also, it seemed likely that all sorts of new problems would arise and necessitate at least some reorganization of the administrative system.

Cottard nodded. "Yes, that's quite on the cards; in fact everyone will have to make a fresh start."

They were nearing Cottard's house. He now seemed more cheerful, determined to take a rosier view of the future. Obviously he was picturing the town entering on a new lease of life, blotting out its past and starting again with a clean sheet.

"So that's that," Tarrou smiled. "Quite likely things will pan out all right for you, too—who can say? It'll be a new life for all of us, in a manner of speaking."

They were shaking hands at the door of the apartment house where Cottard lived.

"Quite right!" Cottard was growing more and more excited. "That would be a great idea, starting again with a clean sheet."

Suddenly from the lightless hall two men emerged. Tarrou had hardly time to hear his companion mutter: "Now, what do those birds want?" when the men in question, who looked like subordinate government employees in their best clothes, cut in with an inquiry if his name was Cottard. With a stifled exclamation Cottard swung round and dashed off into the darkness. Taken by surprise, Tarrou and the two men gazed blankly at each other for some moments. Then Tarrou asked them what they wanted. In noncommittal tones they informed him that they wanted "some information," and walked away, unhurrying, in the direction Cottard had taken.

On his return home Tarrou wrote out an account of this peculiar incident, following it up with a "Feeling very tired tonight"—which is confirmed by his handwriting in this entry. He added that he had still much to do, but that was no reason for not "holding himself in readiness," and he questioned if he were ready. As a sort of postscript—and, in fact, it is here that Tarrou's diary ends—he noted that there is always a certain hour of the day and of the night when a man's courage is at its lowest ebb, and it was that hour only that he feared.

When next day, a few days before the date fixed for the opening of the gates, Dr. Rieux came home at noon, he was wondering if the telegram he was expecting had arrived. Though his days were no less strenuous than at the height of the epidemic, the prospect of imminent release had obliterated his fatigue. Hope had returned and with it a new zest for life. No man can live on the stretch all the time, with his energy and will-power strained to the breaking-point, and it is a joy to be able to relax at last and loosen nerves and muscles that were braced for the struggle. If the telegram, too, that he awaited brought good news, Rieux would be able to make a fresh start. Indeed, he had a feeling that everyone in those days was making a fresh start.

He walked past the concierge's room in the hall. The new man, old Michel's successor, his face pressed to the window looking on the hall, gave him a smile. As he went up the stairs, the man's face, pale with exhaustion and privation, but smiling, hovered before his eyes.

Yes, he'd make a fresh start, once the period of "abstractions" was over, and with any luck—He was opening the door with these thoughts in his mind when he saw his mother coming down the hall to meet him. M. Tarrou, she told him, wasn't well. He had risen at the usual time, but did not feel up to going out and had returned to bed. Mme Rieux felt worried about him.

"Quite likely it's nothing serious," her son said.

Tarrou was lying on his back, his heavy head deeply indenting the pillow, the coverlet bulging above his massive chest. His head was aching and his temperature up. The symptoms weren't very definite, he told Rieux, but they might well be those of plague.

After examining him Rieux said: "No, there's nothing definite as yet."

But Tarrou also suffered from a raging thirst, and in the hallway the doctor told his mother that it might be plague.

"Oh!" she exclaimed. "Surely that's not possible, not now!" And after a moment added: "Let's keep him here, Bernard."

Rieux pondered. "Strictly speaking, I've no right to do that," he said doubtfully. "Still, the gates will be opened quite soon. If you weren't here, I think I'd take it on myself."

"Bernard, let him stay, and let me stay too. You know, I've just had another inoculation."

The doctor pointed out that Tarrou, too, had had inoculations, though it was possible, tired as he was, he'd overlooked the last one or omitted to take the necessary precautions.

Rieux was going to the surgery as he spoke, and when he returned to the bedroom Tarrou noticed that he had a box of the big ampoules containing the serum.

"Ah, so it *is* that," he said.

"Not necessarily; but we mustn't run any risks."

Without replying Tarrou extended his arm and submitted to the prolonged injections he himself had so often administered to others.

"We'll judge better this evening." Rieux looked Tarrou in the eyes.

"But what about isolating me, Rieux?"

"It's by no means certain that you have plague."

Tarrou smiled with an effort.

"Well, it's the first time I've known you do the injection without ordering the patient off to the isolation ward."

Rieux looked away.

"You'll be better here. My mother and I will look after you."

Tarrou said nothing and the doctor, who was putting away the ampoules in the box, waited for him to speak before looking round. But still Tarrou said nothing, and finally Rieux went up to the bed.

The sick man was gazing at him steadily, and though his face was drawn, the gray eyes were calm. Rieux smiled down on him.

"Now try to sleep. I'll be back soon."

As he was going out he heard Tarrou calling, and turned back. Tarrou's manner had an odd effect, as though he were at once trying to keep back what he had to say and forcing himself to say it.

"Rieux," he said at last, "you must tell me the whole truth. I count on that."

"I promise it."

Tarrou's heavy face relaxed in a brief smile.

"Thanks. I don't want to die, and I shall put up a fight. But if I lose the match, I want to make a good end of it."

Bending forward, Rieux pressed his shoulder.

"No. To become a saint, you need to live. So fight away!"

In the course of that day the weather, which after being very cold had grown slightly milder, broke in a series of violent hailstorms followed by rain. At sunset the sky cleared a little, and it was bitterly cold again. Rieux came home in the evening. His overcoat still on, he entered his friend's bedroom. Tarrou did not seem to have moved, but his set lips, drained white by fever, told of the effort he was keeping up.

"Well?" Rieux asked.

Tarrou raised his broad shoulders a little out of the bedclothes.

"Well," he said, "I'm losing the match."

The doctor bent over him. Ganglia had knotted under the burning skin and there was a rumbling in his chest, like the sound of a hidden forge. The strange thing was that Tarrou showed symptoms of both varieties of plague at once.

Rieux straightened up and said the serum hadn't yet had time to take effect. An uprush of fever in his throat drowned the few words that Tarrou tried to utter.

After dinner Rieux and his mother took up their posts at the sick man's bedside. The night began with a struggle, and Rieux knew that this grim wrestling with the angel of plague was to last until dawn. In this struggle Tarrou's robust shoulders and chest were not his greatest assets; rather, the blood that had spurted under Rieux's needle and, in this blood, that something more vital than the soul, which no science could bring to light. The doctor's task could be only to watch his friend's struggle. As to what he was about to do, the stimulants to inject, the abscesses to deal with—many months' repeated failures had taught him to appreciate such expedients at their true value. Indeed, the only way in which he might help was to provide opportunities for the beneficence of chance, which too often stays dormant unless roused to action. Luck was an ally he could not dispense with. For Rieux was confronted by an aspect of the plague that baffled him. Yet again it was doing all it could to confound the tactics used against it; it launched attacks in unexpected places and retreated from those where it seemed definitely lodged. Once more it was out to darken counsel.

Tarrou struggled without moving. Not once in the course of the night did he counter the enemy's attacks by restless agitation; only with all his stolid bulk, with silence, did he carry on the fight. Nor did he even try to speak, thus intimating, after his fashion, that he could no longer let his attention stray. Rieux could follow the vicissitudes of the struggle only in his friend's eyes, now open and now shut; in the eyelids, now more closely welded to the eyeball, now distended; and in his gaze fixed on some object in the room or brought back to the doctor and his mother. And each time it met the doctor's gaze, with a great effort Tarrou smiled.

At one moment there came a sound of hurrying footsteps in the street. They were in flight before a distant throbbing which gradually approached until the street was loud with the clamor of the downpour; another rain-squall was sweeping the town, mingled presently with hailstones that clattered on the sidewalk. Window awnings were flapping wildly. Rieux, whose attention had been diverted momentarily by the noises of the squall, looked again across the shadows at Tarrou's face, on which fell the light of a small bedside lamp. His mother was knitting, raising her eyes now and then from her work to gaze at the sick man. The doctor had done everything that could be done. When the squall had passed, the silence in the room grew denser, filled only by the silent turmoil of the unseen battle. His nerves overwrought by sleeplessness, the doctor fancied he could hear, on the edge of the silence, that faint eerie sibilance which had haunted his ears ever since the beginning of the epidemic. He made a sign to his mother, indicating she should go to bed. She shook her head, and her eyes grew brighter; then she examined carefully, at her needle-tips, a stitch of which she was unsure. Rieux got up, gave the sick man a drink, and sat down again.

Footsteps rang on the pavement, nearing, then receding; people were taking advantage of the lull to hurry home. For the first time the doctor realized that this night, without the clang of ambulances and full of belated wayfarers, was just like a night of the past—a plague-free night. It was as if the pestilence, hounded away by cold, the street-lamps, and the crowd, had fled from the depths of the town and taken shelter in this warm room and was launching its last offensive at Tarrou's inert body. No longer did it thresh the air above the houses with its flail. But it was whistling softly in the stagnant air of the sickroom, and this it was that Rieux had been hearing since the long vigil began. And now it was for him to wait and watch until that strange sound ceased here too, and here as well the plague confessed defeat.

A little before dawn Rieux leaned toward his mother and whispered:

"You'd better have some rest now, as you'll have to relieve me at eight. Mind you take your drops before going to bed."

Mme Rieux rose, folded her knitting, and went to the bedside. Tarrou had had his eyes shut for some time. Sweat had plastered his hair on his stubborn forehead. Mme Rieux sighed, and he opened his eyes. He saw the gentle face bent over him and, athwart the surge of fever, that steadfast smile took form again. But at once the eyes closed. Left to himself, Rieux moved into the chair his mother had just left. The street was silent and no sound came from the sleeping town. The chill of daybreak was beginning to make itself felt.

The doctor dozed off, but very soon an early cart rattling down the street awakened him. Shivering a little, he looked at Tarrou and saw that a lull had come; he, too, was sleeping. The iron-shod wheels rumbled away into the distance. Darkness still was pressing on the windowpanes. When the doctor came beside the bed, Tarrou gazed at him with expressionless eyes, like a man still on the frontier of sleep.

"You slept, didn't you?" Rieux asked.

"Yes."

"Breathing better?"

"A bit. Does that mean anything?"

Rieux kept silent for some moments; then he said

"No, Tarrou, it doesn't mean anything. You know as well as I that there's often a remission in the morning."

"Thanks." Tarrou nodded his approval. "Always tell me the exact truth."

Rieux was sitting on the side of the bed. Beside him he could feel the sick man's legs, stiff and hard as the limbs of an effigy on a tomb. Tarrou was breathing with more difficulty.

"The fever'll come back, won't it, Rieux?" he gasped.

"Yes. But at noon we shall know where we stand."

Tarrou shut his eyes; he seemed to be mustering up his strength. There was a look of utter weariness on his face. He was waiting for the fever to rise and already it was stirring somewhat in the depths of his being. When he opened his eyes, his gaze was misted. It brightened only when he saw Rieux bending over him, a tumbler in his hand.

"Drink."

Tarrou drank, then slowly lowered his head on to the pillow.

"It's a long business," he murmured.

Rieux clasped his arm, but Tarrou, whose head was averted, showed no reaction. Then suddenly, as if some inner dike had given way without warning, the fever surged back, dyeing his cheeks and forehead. Tarrou's eyes came back to the doctor, who, bending again, gave him a look of affectionate encouragement. Tarrou tried to shape a smile, but it could not force its way through the set jaws and lips welded by dry saliva. In the rigid face only the eyes lived still, glowing with courage.

At seven Mme Rieux returned to the bedroom. The doctor went to the surgery to ring up the hospital and arrange for a substitute. He also decided to postpone his consultations; then lay down for some moments on the surgery couch. Five minutes later he went back to the bedroom. Tarrou's face was turned toward Mme Rieux, who was sitting close beside the bed, her hands folded on her lap; in the dim light of the room she seemed no more than a darker patch of shadow. Tarrou was gazing at her so intently that, putting a finger to her lips, Mme Rieux rose and switched off the bedside lamp. Behind the curtains the light was growing, and presently, when the sick man's face grew visible, Mme Rieux could see his eyes still intent on her. Bending above the bed, she smoothed out the bolster and, as she straightened up, laid her hand for a moment on his moist, tangled hair. Then she heard a muffled voice, which seemed to come from very far away, murmur: "Thank you," and that all was well now. By the time she was back in her chair Tarrou had shut his eyes, and, despite the sealed mouth, a faint smile seemed to hover on the wasted face.

At noon the fever reached its climax. A visceral cough racked the sick man's body and he now was spitting blood. The ganglia had ceased swelling, but they were still there, like lumps of iron embedded in the joints. Rieux decided that lancing them was impracticable. Now and then, in the intervals between bouts of fever and coughing fits, Tarrou still gazed at his friends. But soon his eyes opened less and less often and the glow that shone out from the ravaged face in the brief moments of recognition grew steadily fainter. The storm, lashing his body into convulsive movement, lit it up with ever rarer flashes, and in the heart of the tempest he was slowly drifting, derelict. And now Rieux had before him only a masklike face, inert, from which the smile had gone forever. This human form, his friend's, lacerated by the spear-thrusts of the plague, consumed by searing, superhuman fires, buffeted by all the raging winds of heaven, was foundering under his eyes in the dark flood of the pestilence, and he could do nothing to avert the wreck. He could only stand, unavailing, on the shore, empty-handed and sick at heart, unarmed and helpless yet again under the onset of calamity. And thus, when the end came, the tears that blinded Rieux's eyes were tears of impotence; and he did not see Tarrou roll over, face to the wall, and die with a short, hollow groan as if somewhere within him an essential cord had snapped.

The next night was not one of struggle but of silence. In the tranquil death-chamber, beside the dead body now in everyday clothing—here, too, Rieux felt it brooding, that elemental peace which, when he was sitting many nights before on the terrace high above the plague, had followed the brief foray at the gates. Then, already, it had brought to his mind the silence brooding over the beds in which he had let men die. There as here it was the same solemn pause, the lull that follows battle; it was the silence of defeat. But the silence now enveloping his dead friend, so dense, so much akin to the nocturnal silence of the streets and of the town set free at last, made Rieux cruelly aware that this defeat was final, the last disastrous battle that ends a war and makes peace itself an ill beyond all remedy. The doctor could not tell if Tarrou had found peace, now that all was over, but for himself he had a feeling that no peace was possible to him hence-forth, any more than there can be an armistice for a mother bereaved of her son or for a man who buries his friend.

The night was cold again, with frosty stars sparkling in a clear, wintry sky. And in the dimly lit room they felt the cold pressing itself to the windowpanes and heard the long, silvery suspiration of a polar night. Mme Rieux sat near the bed in her usual attitude, her right side lit up by the bedside lamp. In the center of the room, outside the little zone of light, Rieux sat, waiting. Now and then thoughts of his wife waylaid him, but he brushed them aside each time.

When the night began, the heels of passers-by had rung briskly in the frozen air.

"Have you attended to everything?" Mme Rieux had asked.

"Yes, I've telephoned."

Then they had resumed their silent vigil. From time to time Mme Rieux stole a glance at her son, and whenever he caught her doing this, he smiled. Out in the street the usual night-time sounds bridged the long silences. A good many cars were on the road again, though officially this was not yet permitted; they sped past with a long hiss of tires on the pavement, receded, and returned. Voices, distant calls, silence again, a clatter of horse hoofs, the squeal of streetcars rounding a curve, vague murmurs—then once more the quiet breathing of the night.

"Bernard?"

"Yes?"

"Not too tired?"

"No."

At that moment he knew what his mother was thinking, and that she loved him. But he knew, too, that to love someone means relatively little; or, rather, that love is never strong enough to find the words befitting it. Thus he and his mother would always love each other silently. And one day she—or he—would die, without ever, all their lives long, hav-ing gone farther than this by way of making their affection known. Thus, too, he had lived at Tarrou's side, and Tarrou had died this evening without their friendship's having had time to enter fully into the life of either. Tarrou had "lost the match," as he put it. But what had he, Rieux, won? No more than the experience of having known plague and remembering it, of having known friend-ship and remembering it, of knowing affection and being destined one day to remember it. So all a man could win in the conflict between plague and life was

[148]

knowledge and memories. But Tarrou, perhaps, would have called that winning the match.

Another car passed, and Mme Rieux stirred slightly. Rieux smiled toward her. She assured him she wasn't tired and immediately added:

"You must go and have a good long rest in the mountains, over there."

"Yes, Mother."

Certainly he'd take a rest "over there." It, too, would be a pretext for memory. But if that was what it meant, winning the match—how hard it must be to live only with what one knows and what one remembers, cut off from what one hopes for! It was thus, most probably, that Tarrou had lived, and he realized the bleak sterility of a life without illusions. There can be no peace without hope, and Tarrou, denying as he did the right to condemn anyone whomsoever—though he knew well that no one can help condemning and it befalls even the victim sometimes to turn executioner—Tarrou had lived a life riddled with contradictions and had never known hope's solace. Did that explain his aspiration toward saintliness, his quest of peace by service in the cause of others? Actually Rieux had no idea of the answer to that question, and it mattered little. The only picture of Tarrou he would always have would be the picture of a man who firmly gripped the steering-wheel of his car when driving, or else the picture of that stalwart body, now lying motionless. Knowing meant that: a living warmth, and a picture of death.

That, no doubt, explains Dr. Rieux's composure on receiving next morning the news of his wife's death. He was in the surgery. His mother came in, almost running, and handed him a telegram; then went back to the hall to give the telegraph-boy a tip. When she returned, her son was holding the telegram open in his hand. She looked at him, but his eyes were resolutely fixed on the window; it was flooded with the effulgence of the morning sun rising above the harbor.

"Bernard," she said gently.

The doctor turned and looked at her almost as if she were a stranger.

"The telegram?"

"Yes," he said, "that's it. A week ago."

Mme Rieux turned her face toward the window. Rieux kept silent for a while. Then he told his mother not to cry, he'd been expecting it, but it was hard all the same. And he knew, in saying this, that this suffering was nothing new. For many months, and for the last two days, it was the selfsame suffering going on and on.

At last, at daybreak on a fine February morning, the ceremonial opening of the gates took place, acclaimed by the populace, the newspapers, the radio, and official communiqués. It only remains for the narrator to give what account he can of the rejoicings that followed, though he himself was one of those debarred from sharing in them wholeheartedly.

Elaborate day and night fêtes were organized, and at the same time smoke began to rise from locomotives in the station, and ships were already heading for our harbor—reminders in their divers ways that this was the long-awaited day of reuniting, and the end of tears for all who had been parted.

We can easily picture, at this stage, the consequences of that feeling of separation which had so long rankled in the hearts of so many of our townsfolk. Trains coming in were as crowded as those that left the town in the course of the day. Every passenger had reserved his seat long in advance and had been on tenterhooks during the past fortnight lest at the last moment the authorities should go back on their decision. Some of these incoming travelers were still somewhat nervous; though as a rule they knew the lot of those nearest and dearest to them, they were still in the dark about others and the town itself, of which their imagination painted a grim and terrifying picture. But this applies only to people who had not been eating their hearts out during the long months of exile, and not to parted lovers.

The lovers, indeed, were wholly wrapped up in their fixed idea, and for them one thing only had changed. Whereas during those months of separation time had never gone quickly enough for their liking and they were always wanting to speed its flight, now that they were in sight of the town they would have liked to slow it down and hold each moment in suspense, once the brakes went on and the train was entering the station. For the sensation, confused perhaps, but none the less poignant for that, of all those days and weeks and months of life lost to their love made them vaguely feel they were entitled to some compensation; this present hour of joy should run at half the speed of those long hours of waiting. And the people who awaited them at home or on the platform—among the latter Rambert, whose wife, warned in good time, had got busy at once and was coming by the first train—were likewise fretting with impatience and quivering with anxiety. For even Rambert felt a nervous tremor at the thought that soon he would have to confront a love and a devotion that the plague months had slowly refined to a pale abstraction, with the flesh-and-blood woman who had given rise to them.

If only he could put the clock back and be once more the man who, at the outbreak of the epidemic, had had only one thought and one desire: to escape and return to the woman he loved! But that, he knew, was out of the question now; he had changed too greatly. The plague had forced on him a detachment which, try as he might, he couldn't think away, and which like a formless fear haunted his mind. Almost he thought the plague had ended too abruptly, he hadn't had time to pull himself together. Happiness was bearing down on him full speed, the event outrunning expectation. Rambert understood that all would be restored to him in a flash, and joy break on him like a flame with which there is no dallying.

Everyone indeed, more or less consciously, felt as he did, and it is of all those people on the platform that we wish to speak. Each was returning to his personal life, yet the sense of comradeship persisted and they were exchanging smiles and cheerful glances among themselves. But the moment they saw the smoke of the approaching engine, the feeling of exile vanished before an uprush of overpowering, bewildering joy. And when the train stopped, all those interminable-seeming separations which often had begun on this same platform came to an end in one ecstatic moment, when arms closed with hungry possessiveness on bodies whose living shape they had forgotten. As for Rambert, hadn't time to see that form running toward him; already she had flung herself upon his breast. And with his arms locked around her, pressing to his shoulder the head of which he saw only the familiar hair, he let his tears flow freely, unknowing if they rose from present joy or from sorrow too long repressed; aware only that they would prevent his making sure if the face buried in the hollow of his shoulder were the face of which he had dreamed so often or, instead, a stranger's face. For the moment he wished to behave like all those others around him who believed, or made believe, that plague can come and go without changing anything in men's hearts.

Nestling to one another, they went to their homes, blind to the outside world and seemingly triumphant over the plague, forgetting every sadness and the plight of those who had come by the same train and found no one awaiting them, and were bracing themselves to hear in their homes a confirmation of the fear that the long silence had already implanted in their hearts. For these last, who had now for company only their new-born grief, for those who at this moment were dedicating themselves to a lifelong memory of bereavement—for these unhappy people matters were very different, the pangs of separation had touched their climax. For the mothers, husbands, wives, and lovers who had lost all joy, now that the loved one lay under a layer of quicklime in a death-pit or was a mere handful of indistinctive ashes in a gray mound, the plague had not yet ended.

But who gave a thought to these lonely mourners? Routing the cold flaws that had been threshing the air since early morning, the sun was pouring on the town a steady flood of tranquil light. In the forts on the hills, under the sky of pure, unwavering blue, guns were thundering without a break. And everyone was out and about to celebrate those crowded moments when the time of ordeal ended and the time of forgetting had not yet begun.

In streets and squares people were dancing. Within twenty-four hours the motor traffic had doubled and the ever more numerous cars were held up at every turn by merry-making crowds. Every church bell was in full peal throughout the afternoon, and the bells filled the blue and gold sky with their reverberations. Indeed, in all the churches thanksgiving services were being held. But at the same time the places of entertainment were packed, and the cafés, caring nothing for the morrow, were producing their last bottles of liquor. A noisy concourse surged round every bar, including loving couples who fondled each other without a thought for appearances. All were laughing or shouting. The reserves of emotion pent up during those many months when for everybody the flame of life burned low were being recklessly squandered to celebrate this, the red-letter day of their survival. Tomorrow real life would begin again, with its restrictions. But for the moment people in very different walks of life were rubbing shoulders, fraternizing. The leveling-out that death's imminence had failed in practice to accomplish was realized at last, for a few gay hours, in the rapture of escape.

But this rather tawdry exuberance was only one aspect of the town that day; not a few of those filling the streets at sundown, among them Rambert and his wife, hid under an air of calm satisfaction subtler forms of happiness. Many couples, indeed, and many families, looked like people out for a casual stroll, no more than that; in reality most of them were making sentimental pilgrimages to places where they had gone to school with suffering. The newcomers were being shown the striking or obscurer tokens of the plague, relics of its passage. In some cases the survivor merely played the part of guide, the eyewitness who has "been through it," and talked freely of the danger without mentioning his fear. These were the milder forms of pleasure, little more than recreation. In other cases, however, there was more emotion to these walks about the town, as when a man, pointing to some place charged for him with sad yet tender associations, would say to the girl or woman beside him: "This is where, one evening just like this, I longed for you so desperately—and you weren't there!" These passionate pilgrims could readily be distinguished; they formed oases of whispers, aloof, self-centered, in the turbulence of the crowd. Far more effectively than the bands playing in the squares they vouched for the vast joy of liberation. These ecstatic couples, locked together, hardly speaking, proclaimed in the midst of the tumult of rejoicing, with the proud egoism and injustice of happy people, that the plague was over, the reign of terror ended. Calmly they denied, in the teeth of the evidence, that we had ever known a crazy world in which men were killed off like flies, or that precise savagery, that calculated frenzy of the plague, which instilled an odious freedom as to all that was not the here and now; or those charnel-house stenches which stupefied whom they did not kill. In short, they denied that we had ever been the hag-ridden populace a part of which was daily fed into a furnace and went up in oily fumes, while the rest, in shackled impotence, waited their turn.

That, anyhow, was what seemed evident to Rieux when towards the close of the afternoon, on his way to the outskirts of the town, he walked alone in an uproar of bells, guns, bands, and deafening shouts. There was no question of his taking a day off; sick men have no holidays. Through the cool, clear light bathing the town rose the familiar smells of roasting meat and anise-flavored liquor. All around him happy faces were turned toward the shining sky, men and women with flushed cheeks embraced one another with low, tense cries of desire. Yes, the plague had ended with the terror, and those passionately straining arms told what it had meant: exile and deprivation in the profoundest meaning of the words.

For the first time Rieux found that he could give a name to the family likeness that for several months he had detected in the faces in the streets. He had only to look around him now. At the end of the plague, with its misery and privations, these men and women had come to wear the aspect of the part they had been playing for so long, the part of emigrants whose faces first, and now their clothes, told of long banishment from a distant homeland. Once plague had shut the gates of the town, they had settled down to a life of separation, debarred from the living warmth that gives forgetfulness of all. In different degrees, in every part of the town, men and women had been yearning for a reunion, not of the same kind for all, but for all alike ruled out. Most of them had longed intensely for an absent one, for the warmth of a body, for love, or merely for a life that habit had endeared. Some, often without knowing it, suffered from being deprived of the company of friends and from their inability to get in touch with them through the usual channels of friendship—letters, trains, and boats. Others, fewer these— Tarrou may have been one of them—had desired reunion with something they couldn't have defined, but which seemed to them the only desirable thing on earth. For want of a better name, they sometimes called it peace.

Rieux walked on. As he progressed, the crowds grew thicker, the din multiplied, and he had a feeling that his destination was receding as he advanced. Gradually he found himself drawn into the seething, clamorous mass and understanding more and more the cry that went up from it, a cry that, for some part at least, was his. Yes, they had suffered together, in body no less than in soul, from a cruel leisure, exile without redress, thirst that was never slaked. Among the heaps of corpses, the clanging bells of ambulances, the warnings of what goes by the name of fate, among unremitting waves of fear and agonized revolt, the horror that such things could be, always a great voice had been ringing in the ears of these forlorn, panicked people, a voice calling them back to the land of their desire, a homeland. It lay outside the walls of the stifled, strangled town, in the fragrant brushwood of the hills, in the waves of the sea, under free skies, and in the custody of love. And it was to this, their lost home, toward happiness, they longed to return, turning their backs disgustedly on all else.

As to what that exile and that longing for reunion meant, Rieux had no idea. But as he walked ahead, jostled on all sides, accosted now and then, and gradually made his way into less crowded streets, he was thinking it has no importance whether such things have or have not a meaning; all we need consider is the answer given to men's hope.

Henceforth he knew the answer, and he perceived it better now he was in the outskirts of the town, in almost empty streets. Those who, clinging to their little own, had set their hearts solely on returning to the home of their love had sometimes their reward—though some of them were still walking the streets alone, without the one they had awaited. Then, again, those were happy who had not suffered a twofold separation, like some of us who, in the days before the epidemic, had failed to build their love on a solid basis at the outset, and had spent years blindly groping for the pact, so slow and hard to come by, that in the long run binds together ill-assorted lovers. Such people had had, like Rieux himself, the rashness of counting overmuch on time; and now they were parted forever. But others—like Rambert, to whom the doctor had said early that morning: "Courage! It's up to you *now* to prove you're right"—had, without faltering, welcomed back the loved one who they thought was lost to them. And for some time, anyhow, they would be happy. They knew now that if there is one thing one can always yearn for and sometimes attain, it is human love.

But for those others who aspired beyond and above the human individual toward something they could not even imagine, there had been no answer. Tarrou might seem to have won through to that hardly-come-by peace of which he used to speak; but he had found it only in death, too late to turn it to account. If others, however—Rieux could see them in the doorways of houses, passionately embracing and gazing hungrily at one another in the failing sunset glow—had got what they wanted, this was because they had asked for the one thing that depended on them solely. And as he turned the corner of the street where Grand and Cottard lived, Rieux was thinking it was only right that those whose desires are limited to man and his humble yet formidable love should enter, if only now and then, into their reward.

This chronicle is drawing to an end, and this seems to be the moment for Dr. Bernard Rieux to confess that he is the narrator. But before describing the closing scenes, he would wish anyhow to justify his undertaking and to set it down that he expressly made a point of adopting the tone of an impartial observer. His profession put him in touch with a great many of our townspeople while plague was raging, and he had opportunities of hearing their various opinions. Thus he was well placed for giving a true account of all he saw and heard. But in so doing he has tried to keep within the limits that seemed desirable. For instance, in a general way he has confined himself to describing only such things as he was enabled to see for himself, and has refrained from attributing to his fellow sufferers thoughts that, when all is said and done, they were not bound to have. And as for documents, he has used only such as chance, or mischance, put in his way.

Summoned to give evidence regarding what was a sort of crime, he has exercised the restraint that behooves a conscientious witness. All the same, following the dictates of his heart, he has deliberately taken the victims' side and tried to share with his fellow citizens the only certitudes they had in common—love, exile, and suffering. Thus he can truly say there was not one of their anxieties in which he did not share, no predicament of theirs that was not his.

To be an honest witness, it was for him to confine himself mainly to what people did or said and what could be gleaned from documents. Regarding his personal troubles and his long suspense, his duty was to hold his peace. When now and then he refers to such matters, it is only for the light they may throw on his fellow citizens and in order to give a picture, as well defined as possible, of what most of the time they felt confusedly. Actually, this self-imposed reticence cost him little effort. Whenever tempted to add his personal note to the myriad voices of the plague-stricken, he was deterred by the thought that not one of his sufferings but was common to all the others and that in a world where sorrow is so often lonely, this was an advantage. Thus, decidedly, it was up to him to speak for all.

But there was at least one of our townsfolk for whom Dr. Rieux could not speak, the man of whom Tarrou said one day to Rieux: "His only real crime is that of having in his heart approved of something that killed off men, women, and children. I can understand the rest, but for *that* I am obliged to pardon him." It is fitting that this chronicle should end with some reference to that man, who had an ignorant, that is to say lonely, heart.

On turning out of the main thoroughfares where the rejoicings were in full swing, and entering the street where Grand and Cottard lived, Dr. Rieux was held up by a police cordon. Nothing could have surprised him more. This quiet part of the town seemed all the quieter for the sounds of festivity in the distance, and the doctor pictured it as deserted as it was tranquil.

"Sorry, doctor," a policeman said, "but I can't let you through. There's a crazy fellow with a gun, shooting at everybody. But you'd better stay; we may need you."

Just then Rieux saw Grand coming toward him. Grand, too, had no idea what was happening and the police had stopped him, too. He had been told that the shots came from the house where he lived. They could see, some way down the street, the front of the house, bathed in cool evening light. Farther down the street was another line of policemen like the one that had prevented Rieux and Grand from advancing, and behind the line some of the local residents could be seen crossing and recrossing the street hastily. The street immediately in front of the house was quite empty and in the middle of the hollow square lay a hat and a piece of dirty cloth. Looking more carefully, they saw more policemen, revolver in hand, sheltering in doorways facing the house. All the shutters in Grand's house were closed, except one on the third floor that seemed to be hanging loose on one hinge only. Not a sound could be heard in the street but for occasional snatches of music coming from the center of the town.

Suddenly two revolver-shots rang out; they came from one of the buildings opposite and some splinters flew off the dismantled shutter. Then silence came again. Seen from a distance, after the tumult of the day, the whole business seemed to Rieux fantastically unreal, like something in a dream.

"That's Cottard's window," Grand suddenly exclaimed. "I can't make it out. I thought he'd disappeared."

"Why are they shooting?" Rieux asked the policeman.

"Oh, just to keep him busy. We're waiting for a car to come with the stuff that's needed. He fires at anyone who tries to get in by the front door. He got one of our men just now."

"But why did he fire?"

"Ask me another! Some folks were having fun in the street, and he let off at them. They couldn't make it out at first. When he fired again, they started yelling, one man was wounded, and the rest took to their heels. Some fellow out of his head, I should say."

The minutes seemed interminable in the silence that had returned. Then they noticed a dog, the first dog Rieux had seen for many months, emerging on the other side of the street, a draggled-looking spaniel that its owners had, presumably, kept in hiding. It ambled along the wall, stopped in the doorway, sat down, and began to dig at its fleas. Some of the policemen whistled for it to come away. It raised its head, then walked out into the road and was sniffing at the hat when a revolver barked from the third-floor window. The dog did a somersault like a tossed pancake, lashed the air with its legs, and floundered on to its side, its body writhing in long convulsions. As if by way of reprisal five or six shots from the opposite house knocked more splinters off the shutter. Then silence fell again. The sun had moved a little and the shadow-line was nearing Cottard's window.

There was a low squeal of brakes in the street, behind the doctor.

"Here they are," the policeman said.

A number of police officers jumped out of the car and unloaded coils of rope, a ladder, and two big oblong packages wrapped in oilcloth. Then they turned into a street behind the row of houses facing Grand's. A minute or so later there were signs of movement, though little could be seen, in the doorways of the houses. Then came a short spell of waiting. The dog had ceased moving; it now was lying in a small, dark, glistening pool.

Suddenly from the window of one of the houses that the police officers had entered from behind there came a burst of machine-gun fire. They were still aiming at the shutter, which literally shredded itself away, disclosing a dark gap into which neither Grand nor Rieux could see from where they stood. When the first machine-gun stopped firing, another opened up from a different angle, in a house a little farther up the street. The shots were evidently directed into the window space, and a fragment of the brickwork clattered down upon the pavement. At the same moment three police officers charged across the road and disappeared into the doorway. The machine-gun ceased fire. Then came another wait. Two muffled detonations sounded inside the house, followed by a confused hubbub growing steadily louder until they saw a small man in his shirt-sleeves, screaming at the top of his voice, being carried more than dragged out by the doorway.

As if at an expected signal all the shutters in the street flew open and excited faces lined the windows, while people streamed out of the houses and jostled the lines of police. Rieux had a brief glimpse of the small man, on his feet now, in the middle of the road, his arms pinioned behind him by two police officers. He was still screaming. A policeman went up and dealt him two hard blows with his fists, quite calmly, with a sort of conscientious thoroughness.

"It's Cottard!" Grand's voice was shrill with excitement. "He's gone mad!"

Cottard had fallen backwards, and the policeman launched a vigorous kick into the crumpled mass sprawling on the ground. Then a small, surging group began to move toward the doctor and his old friend.

"Stand clear!" the policeman bawled.

Rieux looked away when the group, Cottard and his captors, passed him.

The dusk was thickening into night when Grand and the doctor made a move at last. The Cottard incident seemed to have shaken the neighborhood out of its normal lethargy and even these remote streets were becoming crowded with noisy merry-makers. On his doorstep Grand bade the doctor good night; he was going to put in an evening's work, he said. Just as he was starting up the stairs he added that he'd written to Jeanne and was feeling much happier. Also he'd made a fresh start with his phrase. "I've cut out all the adjectives."

And, with a twinkle in his eye, he took his hat off, bringing it low in a courtly sweep. But Rieux was thinking of Cottard, and the dull thud of fists belaboring the wretched man's face haunted him as he went to visit his old asthma patient. Perhaps it was more painful to think of a guilty man than of a dead man.

It was quite dark by the time he reached his patient's house. In the bedroom the distant clamor of a populace rejoicing in its new-won freedom could be faintly heard, and the old fellow was as usual transposing peas from one pan to another.

"They're quite right to amuse themselves," he said. "It takes all sorts to make a world, as they say. And your colleague, doctor, how's he getting on?"

"He's dead." Rieux was listening to his patient's rumbling chest.

"Ah, really?" The old fellow sounded embarrassed.

"Of plague," Rieux added.

"Yes," the old man said after a moment's silence, "it's always the best who go. That's how life is. But he was a man who knew what he wanted."

"Why do you say that?" The doctor was putting back his stethoscope.

"Oh, for no particular reason. Only— well, he never talked just for talking's sake. I'd rather cottoned to him. But there you are! All those folks are saying: 'It was plague. We've had the plague here.' You'd almost think they expected to be given medals for it. But what does that mean—'plague'? Just life, no more than that."

"Do your inhalations regularly."

"Don't worry about me, doctor! There's lots of life in me yet, and I'll see 'em all into their graves. *I* know how to live."

A burst of joyful shouts in the distance seemed an echo of his boast. Halfway across the room the doctor halted.

"Would you mind if I go up on the terrace?"

"Of course not. You'd like to have a look at 'em—that it? But they're just the same as ever, really." When Rieux was leaving the room, a new thought crossed his mind. "I say, doctor. Is it a fact they're going to put up a memorial to the people who died of plague?"

"So the papers say. A monument, or just a tablet."

"I could have sworn it! And there'll be speeches." He chuckled throatily. "I can almost hear them saying: 'Our dear departed . . .' And then they'll go off and have a good snack."

Rieux was already halfway up the stairs. Cold, fathomless depths of sky glimmered overhead, and near the hilltops stars shone hard as flint. It was much like the night when he and Tarrou had come to the terrace to forget the plague. Only, tonight the sea was breaking on the cliffs more loudly and the air was calm and limpid, free of the tang of brine the autumn wind had brought. The noises of the town were still beating like waves at the foot of the long line of terraces, but tonight they told not of revolt, but of deliverance. In the distance a reddish glow hung above the big central streets and squares. In this night of new-born freedom desires knew no limits, and it was their clamor that reached Rieux's ears.

From the dark harbor soared the first rocket of the firework display organized by the municipality, and the town acclaimed it with a long-drawn sigh of delight. Cottard, Tarrou, the men and the women Rieux had loved and lost—all alike, dead or guilty, were forgotten. Yes, the old fellow had been right; these people were "just the same as ever." But this was at once their strength and their innocence, and it was on this level, beyond all grief, that Rieux could feel himself at one with them. And it was in the midst of shouts rolling against the terrace wall in massive waves that waxed in volume and duration, while cataracts of colored fire fell thicker through the darkness, that Dr. Rieux resolved to compile this chronicle, so that he should not be one of those who hold their peace but should bear witness in favor of those plague-stricken people; so that some memorial of the injustice and outrage done them might endure; and to state quite simply what we learn in a time of pestilence: that there are more things to admire in men than to despise.

None the less, he knew that the tale he had to tell could not be one of a final victory. It could be only the record of what had had to be done, and what assuredly would have to be done again in the never ending fight against terror and its relentless onslaughts, despite their personal afflictions, by all who, while unable to be saints but refusing to bow down to pestilences, strive their utmost to be healers.

And, indeed, as he listened to the cries of joy rising from the town, Rieux remembered that such joy is always imperiled. He knew what those jubilant crowds did not know but could have learned from books: that the plague bacillus never dies or disappears for good; that it can lie dormant for years and years in furniture and linen-chests; that it bides its time in bedrooms, cellars, trunks, and bookshelves; and that perhaps the day would come when, for the bane and the enlightening of men, it would rouse up its rats again and send them forth to die in a happy city.

THE LIFE AND WORKS OF
ALBERT CAMUS

By PIERRE DE BOISDEFERRE

SINCE JANUARY 4, 1960, we have had to speak of Albert Camus in the past tense, as a man whose existence is circumscribed by history, and one whose work is no longer simply signed, but dated. Camus, so full of life and fun (despite the myth of his unsmiling formality), so fond of football and dancing, is now one with the red soil of Lourmarin beneath the Mediterranean sky he loved so much. He streaked across the half-century like a meteor, trailing the hopes and dreams of the generation he extolled "to serve man's dignity by means that remain worthy in the midst of an unworthy history."

"Man is not entirely to blame, it was not he who started history; nor is he entirely innocent since he continues it." Camus brooded over this dilemma all his life. He began by affirming the innocence of man, a stranger in a society that denies him, an outsider in a world that condemns him to death, overshadowed by the outrageous and inhuman fact of death: "No morality, no effort is a priori justifiable in face of the implacable mathematics that determine our lot." The source of Camus' metaphysical anguish is probably to be found in the contrasts presented by his native Algeria. He was born in Mondovi, Algeria, on November 7, 1913. Less than a year later, his father, a French farm laborer, was killed in the Battle of the Marne. He was brought up by his Spanish peasant mother and his grandmother, a woman of implacable severity, in a small apartment in Belcourt, the Montmartre or Belleville of Algiers. Thanks to his schoolmasters—Louis Germain and the philosopher Jean Grenier—he was able to continue his education and obtain a scholarship to the Algiers lycée instead of being condemned to some humdrum job. When tuberculosis cut short his studies for a degree in philosophy, he was already conditioned to the harsh realities of poverty. But he found solace in Algeria, its blue sky, its curving beaches, luxuriant orchards, and beautiful girls, and while his experience made it impossible for him to believe that "all is well under the sun and in history," the sun itself taught him that "history isn't everything."

Unlike so many intellectuals, Albert Camus knew what he was talking about when he spoke of hard times. When he was twenty, he refused to escape from his poverty into the colorless existence of a civil servant: "The finality of it frightened me." He was already eager to prove himself, to justify his existence creatively, even if he could do nothing to alter the fundamental problem of "destiny."

The Algiers Camus knew was still wholly European in spirit, way of life, and appearance. It had not yet developed into the boom town—complete with skyscrapers and huge outlying apartment blocks such as the Climat de France and Diar El Maçoul—it was to become in the space of a few years as a result of the war. The Algiers of Albert Camus was still that of the interwar period: a large and handsome town, busy and densely populated, it is true, but not so much a metropolis as an overseas prefecture with a colonial flavor, lulled to torpor by the summer heat.

Like so many of his compatriots, Camus spent his Sundays on the beaches between Madrague and Cherchell bathing and lounging in the shade of the pines. He enjoyed swimming and football, and he spoke of the University of Algiers with love, saying it "stands out from its French counterparts in that its natural setting and way of life make it much closer to the Stoa of antiquity than the prison-houses of the mother country. Sport was our main interest and continued to be mine for a long time afterward. It gave me my only real lessons in morality."

Two places in particular seem to have shaped his sensibilities, though in very different ways: Oran and Tipasa. Oran—now a town without a soul—was the Marseilles of French North Africa: Camus wrote of it in *La Peste* (*The Plague*, 1947), "its ordinariness is what strikes one first about the town of Oran, which is merely a large French port on the Algerian coast, headquarters of the Prefect of a French 'Department.' The town itself, let us admit, is ugly . . . a town without pigeons, without any trees or gardens, where you never hear the beat of wings or the rustle of leaves." This could not be bettered as an objective description of Oran, a sprawling, haphazard town with a business district de-

pressingly like those of Marseilles or Toulouse. But Camus loved it for its vitality. Its people were less settled than those of Algiers, more varied and boisterous, the product of a melting pot into which just as many Spaniards and Maltese as *Francouais* had been thrown. From this hodgepodge had emerged a generation of tall, dark, well-built young men and women justly celebrated for their glowing health and golden ripeness.

Camus spent a year and a half in Oran, from 1941 to 1942, and it now seems inevitable that he should have chosen its crowded, carefree streets and boulevards as the compelling background for the most significant of his novels, *The Plague,* a novel that has become as prophetic as Kafka's *The Trial* for the same reasons.

The opposite pole of Camus's Algerian experience is represented by Tipasa, which he rescued from two millennia of obscurity and which will always be associated with his name. He described it unforgettably not only in *Noces* (*Nuptials,* 1938) but in *L'Été* (*Summer,* 1954), which sings the praises of its sky, "fresh as an eye, washed and rewashed by the waters," of its "vibrant" light and the "pristine wonder" the light evokes not only from the sea but from every tree and house it touches: "It was in such a light that the earth must have emerged at the dawn of creation."

For Camus, every one of the thirty-five miles between Algiers and Tipasa was crammed with memories and sensations. "The violence of childhood, adolescent daydreams to the purring of the bus, the mornings, the shining girls, the beaches, the taut young muscles, the melancholy in the heart of a sixteen-year-old at nightfall, the lust for life, the glory, and always the same sky, year after year, inexhaustible in its power and brilliance, insatiably devouring one by one, over the months, its victims spreadeagled on the

[160]

beach at the deadly hour of noon." All this he felt when the road, leaving the Sahel and "its hills with their bronze-colored vines," began to plunge down to the coast. In the worst moments of the occupation during World War II, Camus took refuge in his memory of the sky at Tipasa: "In the end, it saved me from despair. I had always known that the ruins of Tipasa were younger than our own scaffolding or rubble."

For Tipasa, an unpretentious resort on the Algerian coast, has outlived the glories of its past, and its ruins are far more eloquent than its modern villas nestling in their bougainvillea. Every stone bears witness to the frailty of civilization, the barbarians at the temple gates, their tragic irruption into the jaded pleasures of a civilization in its decline. If you are lucky enough to be there in springtime, the opening words of *Nuptials* must surely ring like a "Hallelujah" in your ears: "Tipasa is the abode of the gods, and their voices can be heard in the sun and the scent of wormwood, the silver glitter on the sea, the raw blue sky, the flower-covered ruins, and the light dappling the piled-up stones. At certain times of day, the countryside is black with sun. The eye tries in vain to recapture something other than the beads of light and color trembling at the edge of the lashes."

Tipasa's very soil relates the history, alternately happy and tragic, of what was once a city rivaling Iconium and Caesarea. It has yielded traces of many bygone societies: chipped flint tools from the later Paleolithic period, the remains of Punic vaults bearing the sign of Tanit, of Carthaginian houses and Roman villas, of Christian and Byzantine basilicas. The cathedral of Tipasa was the largest in Africa (its monumental apse, flanked by pre-Romanesque buttresses, towered over the old episcopal district) until it was rebuilt on a smaller scale by the Byzantines. I can still visualize the theater, which was supported by arcades and not—as might be expected—anchored to the hillside; the magnificent *nymphaeum* where the water splashed down between statues and pillars of red, yellow, and green marble; the Caesarea gate, not unlike a medieval postern; the monumental basilica and the impressive forum with its perfect vaulting.

One evening at Tipasa, when we were having an aperitif on the terrace of a friend's home—a comfortable, old-fashioned house, spacious and civilized, full of fine furniture and books, pottery and Roman statues—shooting started up in the mountains, reminding us of the precariousness of our situation. Camus himself felt it even more acutely when he returned to rain-drenched Tipasa and found the little square hedged in by barbed wire, soldiers in battledress stationed around the old ruins, and the people of the town robbed by the curfew of their stroll in the cool of the evening.

Two thousand years ago Tipasa had already much to teach: the right to "love without measure," to spend time "crushing wormwood between one's fingers, trying to synchronize one's breathing with the turbulent sighs of the world," to understand the patiently acquired "science of living that is worth all worldly wisdom." And it could also have taught the inexorable end that shapes the destiny of every man on earth and turns our existence, which could be such a beautiful thing, into "a horrible, dirty adventure." What point is there in celebrating the earth and its beauty when they will inevitably end in a meaningless void? "Accomplish what? O bitter bed, royal couch, the crown is at the bottom of the waters."

Midway between happiness and tragedy comes everyday life and the small pleasures that make it bearable, its moments of unconscious comedy which

Camus could appreciate. He spoke of Algiers and Oran with tender irony, and congratulated the people of Oran for raising an altar to themselves—La Maison du Colon (Colonial House)—on which certain virtues of colonialism are symbolized. "To judge from the building, these virtues were three in number: outrageous taste, love of violence, and a leaning toward historical synthesis. Egypt, Byzantium, and Munich all had a hand in the construction of this delicate confection in the form of an enormous upturned goblet . . . on which a condescending colonist wearing a bow tie and a pith helmet accepts the homage of a procession of slaves in classical robes." As for the majestic, if somewhat squat, lions of the Place d'Armes, Camus liked to imagine that they came down from their pedestals at night and silently prowled round the dark square "to urinate against the great, dusty fig trees." Few people had a keener ear for the *pataouète,* the vernacular speech of Algiers, and Camus noted down the more colorful expressions in his *Carnets (Notebooks),* and used them frequently in *L'Étranger (The Stranger).*

Camus was not, however, destined to languish in Algiers. He had become a journalist in Algeria, working for the *Alger Républicain,* in which he vigorously pleaded the cause of the Arabs, uprooted and deprived of their homeland, advocating twenty years ahead of his time the integration that was granted only when it was too late. He soon took advantage of his career to discover Europe for himself, working for *Paris-Soir* as well as his Algerian paper.

His European travels, carried out on a shoestring, confirmed his unshakable attachment to the beauty of the world. In the baroque Prague of the Hrad and in the Italy of the Renaissance, the youthful Camus experienced that almost physical sense of identity with the universe that

gives his best passages their special quality. Writing of the gilded rooftops of Prague, the lilacs of Seville, the Bobboli Gardens, and the little Monastery of San Francisco in Palma, the author of *Nuptials* recaptured a note that had been lost since Barrès and Gide. In art, he discovered a school of life, a pledge of liberty that made the creator the equal of God. He saw the beauty of the world continued through the intermediary of the artist, who works "in that trivial and magnificent material known as the present."

Paris and France itself constituted the last lap of his travels and Camus was to discover them at the worst moments of their history, in the somber atmosphere of the war. At the age of twenty-six, he was "advised" to leave Algiers: the journalist who had dared to say that at Titi-Ouzo he had seen "children in rags fighting with dogs for the contents of a dustbin" had no place in colonial-minded Algeria, and when the armistice was signed, he was working as a sub-editor on *Paris-Soir.* He found a refuge in Lyons, but he also experienced the unfathomable sadness of those all-devouring cities that even the sun cannot brighten. When he returned to Paris, Malraux introduced him to Gallimard's, the firm that eventually published *The Stranger* and *Le Mythe de Sisyphe (The Myth of Sisyphus)* (both 1942). He soon joined the Resistance (with René Leynaud, who was executed in the summer of 1944), and the liberation of Paris found him on the staff of *Combat* with a group of friends that included Pascal Pia, Roger Grenier, Albert Olivier, and Jacques Lemarchand. It was now that his rapid climb to fame began: in the autumn of 1944, Gérard Philippe performed his play *Caligula,* three years later came the triumph of *The Plague,* and ten years later, the Nobel Prize.

At the age of thirty, as Sartre pointed

out, Camus was a key figure for his generation, both as writer and as man of action. Racing ahead in his career, Camus had soon assumed the place held thirty years earlier by André Gide, that of a goader of consciences. His work at first trailed after Sartre's, like some tiny boat in the wake of an ocean liner. But, despite superficial resemblances, the truths developed by Sartre and Camus could in the long run only defeat or cancel one another. An argument between Mersault and Mathieu, or between Rieux and Brunet, could only have ended in a slanging match. What Camus called "the absurd"—the discrepancy between man's impulse toward immortality and the finite nature of his existence—"the most shattering passion of all," was quite alien to Sartre, whose morality was one of "doing" and whose logic was of a strictly rational kind. Sartre's experience of nature—the "nausea" that has inspired his few poetic passages—was poles apart from Camus's impassioned sense of communion with the Algerian summer, the wind at Djemila, the warmth of the sea.

"We think only in images. To be a philosopher, you must write novels," Camus wrote in his *Notebooks*. A student of philosophy, the author of a dissertation on Plotinus and St. Augustine, he did not consider the real philosophers —Descartes, Kant, Spinoza—to be the creators of systems, but they were "witnesses to the truth" in the Kierkegaardian sense. Hence his affinity with Pascal and his admiration for Nietzsche, a number of whose themes he developed, starting with that of "conscious death," which he dealt with in his own fashion in *The Myth of Sisyphus*.

Camus's ideas thus stem from sensations and images intimately bound up with his own experience. *L'Envers et l'Endroit* (The Bad Side and the Good, 1937) and *Nuptials,* both of which appeared on the eve of the war, were the works of a poet with a seasoning of Pascal and Nietzsche and with a lyricism reminiscent of the youthful rapture of Gide's *Fruits of Earth:* "I wish to proclaim that I love life to distraction; it makes me proud to be a man. And yet I have often been told that there is nothing to be proud of. Yes, there is: the sun, the sea, my heart brimming with youth, the salt tang of my body, and that vast backcloth of yellow and blue where tenderness and genius meet. I must devote all my energy and resources to capturing this."

At the dawn of his career, then, as in the heart of his work, there is "an invincible sun." But this sun has its dark side: the "truth to which the sun bears witness is also that of my death." The world is beautiful, but man is not its master; he cannot fathom its depth or its duration. "The impenetrability and strangeness of the world constitute the absurd," he wrote, and he was to experience this sense of the absurd with a passionate intensity. Yet, in opposition to the excesses of human history crammed with violence and death he would always set the sovereign measure of art, seeking always to overcome the basic contradiction that separates man from his experience. Transposed into the realm of art, this separation becomes bearable, and in his work Camus tried to find the means of remolding "this sorry scheme of things . . . nearer to the heart's desire."

After being awarded the Nobel Prize in 1957, which brought him at last financial independence, Camus settled in Provence, far from Algeria then plunged into "excess," a prey to the very "plague" he had described in his writings. He was justly enchanted by Provence; by the impressive range of the Luberon, the old sun-warmed stones, the Romanesque castles and churches, and the graveyards clinging to the hillside. From among twenty equally delightful villages he chose Lourmarin. For the past thirty years, the castle there had been a sort of Villa Medici reserved for the use of painters and writers and particularly appreciated by those born beside the Mediterranean. Camus could often be seen crossing its narrow, French-style garden with friends such as Emmanuel Roblès and Jean Amrouche, Gabriel Audisio and Henri Bosco. A house nearby—vast but sparsely furnished, served him as a retreat; it was there he did his writing, standing at a walnut desk. He often went for walks in the mountains, taking one of those overgrown, herb-scented paths that tourists avoid because vipers and scorpions lurk there in the summer. In the evenings he would sometimes consult one of the forty thousand books in the castle library, which had been assembled by Laurent-Vibert. He felt at home at Lourmarin and it was there, in the half-light of a Provençal winter morning, that his publisher Michel Gallimard stopped by and offered him a lift to Paris in his powerful, low-built Facel Vega. Camus accepted, though he had originally intended to go by train. It was January 4, 1960. At 1:55 P.M. the car skidded off the road at Villeblevin, not far from Sens, and crashed into a tree. Camus was killed instantly.

The Myth of Sisyphus and *The Stranger,* both of which appeared in 1942, in the middle of a war whose outcome was still doubtful, attracted attention by their combination of youthful lyricism and maturity. Starting from the "only truly serious philosophical problem," that of suicide, Camus reexamines our accepted ideas in the harsh light of death. He begs each one of us to face the divorce between man's striving for the eternal and the finite nature of his life, to experience the absurdity of this world like "a passion": "From the moment it is recognized, absurdity becomes a passion,

the most shattering passion of all." Once a man has become aware of it, he must continue his desperate quest to the very end. Camus demonstrates this in the triumphant cry of Sisyphus, who, with no future, freed from the bondage of the eternal, affirms that he can stake his life on the moment, risk all on a fleeting venture, break every record, live at the very highest pitch.

Camus pictures Sisyphus as being happy and shows how his long punishment enabled him to become master of his fate again. He has lost the illusion of another world and rediscovered "the face, gestures, and drama of this world, compounded of a hard-earned wisdom and a passion that knows no aftermath," for "the struggle toward the peaks is enough to fill a man's heart." Yet Camus still felt something missing in man's life: What would remain of him on earth if he were deprived of his creations? Camus liked to imagine heroes of the absurd: Don Juan without love, for "if to love were enough, things would be too simple"; the actor without conviction; the illusionless conqueror who knows that "action is useless in itself." With such heroes he filled his works, from the victim of *The Stranger*—by way of Caligula, that prototype of the absurd superman—to humanity itself in *The Plague.*

Unjustifiable in itself, the creative process nevertheless comes to man's aid by giving him an extra dimension. Art would thus appear to be the only possible revenge we can take on nature and its indifference, for "everything that constitutes the dignity of art is opposed to such a world and rejects it." For Camus, the "perpetual dialogue of resurrections and metamorphoses" that—according to Malraux—the artist, knowing he must die, wrings from the implacable nebulae, is the "shattering witness of man's sole dignity: unrelenting rebellion against his fate." Better still, it is a "moral discipline." And, like Proust plunging into time lost and then regained, Camus immersed himself in creative work. Starting from the "sense of the absurd that may seem rare in this century" and that determines his view of the world, Camus takes us on a journey of spiritual liberation, from crime to heroism and from solitude to communion.

In *The Myth of Sisyphus,* Camus drew a portrait of the hero of the absurd. "His contempt for the gods, his hatred of death, and his passion for life incurred a punishment that consisted of applying his whole being to the accomplishment of precisely nothing. Such is the price we have to pay for the passions of this world . . . The myth is tragic because of its hero's awareness . . . Sisyphus, a proletarian among the gods, powerless and rebellious, understands the full extent of his wretched predicament."

But Camus gave us his real "hero of the absurd" in a short book that was to be his masterpiece, *The Stranger.* Sartre refused to call it a novel, defining it instead to be "one of those short moralist's novels like *Zadig* or *Candide* . . . at the heart it remains very close to a *conte* by Voltaire." In his analysis of the book, Sartre also observed that "with time, good novels become exactly like natural phenomena; we forget that they have authors, and they are accepted like stones or trees because they are there, because they exist." This aptly describes the quality of *The Stranger.* With each rereading of this story one feels again that obsessive sense of anguish that found no outlet in action, as in most novels, but settled back on the reader, and clung to his awareness, shadowing his life with its inexorable presence.

The art of *The Stranger* resides in its very unpretentiousness. Its construction is so perfect and unobtrusive that it creates an illusion of utter simplicity; it is not a story but something that exists as naturally as air or light. The sentences are short and impersonal, and there are no long speeches. The details of the action are slight and simple, and this makes them all the more disquieting. There is no emotion whatsoever, and yet the tears come to our eyes.

"Mother died today. Or, maybe, yesterday; I can't be sure. The telegram from the Home says: Your mother passed away . . ." This is how the hero, Mersault, lives: in the present, a present over which he has no control. There is a sardonic, rather touching humor in these dry laconic statements, so effective in their restraint. Who is this man with such elementary reactions, so manifestly a stranger in the world and yet so close to us? Who is this spiritual proletarian, who obviously has no control over what happens to him and yet endures it, submits to it, and makes us experience it with painful intensity?

Camus has already given us the answer in *The Myth of Sisyphus:* Mersault is each one of us, the human animal of our time par excellence. He is man the absurd, man born into a totalitarian universe, man the robot, man without hope, without love, without God. He could well have been Don Juan, a rebel, a hero, or merely a victim—and in fact he is all these things since he is the epitome of man, the incarnation of human misery in the guise of a humble Algerian employee. He has that meager share of love that even the least favored among us still manage to glean from life—in short, he is happy, but happy at the lowest level. But even this scrap of happiness, which he has neither sought nor earned, will be snatched away from him by the absurdity of life.

With superb artistry, Camus describes Mersault's day-to-day existence and the way in which he is gradually and unwittingly brought to the threshold of death. After each warning signal, there is a breathing space in which he has the impression—as in Kafka's *Trial*—that nothing has really happened. "As I was coming back after shutting the window, I glanced at the mirror and saw reflected in it a corner of the table with my spirit lamp and some bits of bread beside it. It occurred to me that somehow I'd got through another Sunday, that Mother now was buried, and tomorrow I'd be going back to work as usual. Really, nothing in my life had changed."

And, in fact, life resumes its course. Mersault's boss offers him a job in Paris, his mistress asks him to marry her, but it is all the same to him. Paris or Algiers, marriage or an affair—what difference can it make? Then one Sunday, as he is taking a walk in the suburbs of Algiers, something happens and it is as if we were watching a film in slow motion. A fight breaks out between some friends of Mersault's and two Arabs who have followed them to pick a quarrel. At first, everything seems to dissolve in the glare of the sun: a revolver is thrust into Mersault's hands, but he does not use it; the episode is finished and he will take his siesta and forget it. Then he sees one of the Arabs lying on the ground and steps forward to avoid the sun. The Arab draws a knife, and Mersault loses his head: "Then everything began to reel before my eyes . . . Every nerve in my body was a steel spring, and my grip closed on the revolver . . . with that crisp, whipcrack sound, it all began . . . I knew I'd shattered the balance of the day, the supreme calm of the beach on which I had been happy. But I fired four shots more . . . and each successive shot was another loud, fateful rap on the door of my undoing."

Legally, Mersault's guilt is never in doubt: he has killed a man. For nothing. It is an utterly gratuitous, motiveless crime. Mersault finds himself in prison. His past will be brought to bear on his future, and the most trivial details of his life will be seized on by the prosecution. Mersault is innocent as a man, but in the eyes of the law his act has revealed him as he really is: a *born* criminal. In Kafka's book, there are no judges or prosecutors, only an absurd trial held by night. Here, everything is strictly motivated, but the sense of the absurd is produced by the contrast between the subjective and the objective, between Mersault's experience of his own life and the way in which society sees it. Mersault is present at his trial without really being involved in it; he cannot identify himself with the person described by his accusers. He learns that he never loved his mother: the concierge "said I'd declined to see Mother's body, I'd smoked cigarettes and slept, and drunk coffee. It was then I felt a sort of wave of indignation spreading through the courtroom, and for the first time I understood that I was guilty."

Here we come to the very heart of the absurd: a series of trivial acts are given a significance Mersault neither foresaw nor intended. A particularly unfavorable impression is produced on the public and the jury when they learn that Mersault went to a Fernandel film the day after his mother's death. From that moment, all evidence in favor of the accused is of little avail since his behavior when his mother died proves that "he was already a criminal at heart." After that, it all goes very quickly, and for a moment Mersault hears again all the familiar sounds of the town he loved: "The shouts of newspaperboys in the already languid air, the last calls of birds in the public gardens . . . the screech of trams at the steep corners of hills," and he is astonished to see that "familiar paths may lead as well to prison as to innocent, carefree sleep."

There is one incident when the chaplain visits Mersault in his cell. Mersault had raised no protest when the death sentence was pronounced, but now something snaps inside him: "He [the chaplain] seemed so cocksure, you see. And yet none of his certainties was worth one strand of a woman's hair. What difference could they make to me, the death of others, or a mother's love, or his God, the fate one thinks one chooses, since one and the same fate was bound to 'choose' me? His turn too would come like the others. And what difference could it make if, after being charged with murder, he were executed because he didn't weep at his mother's funeral?"

Now we suddenly understand: and this is the only artistic flaw in the novel, the only moment when we are aware that a thesis is being presented to us in the guise of life, that the whole book has been built up toward the point at which the "stranger" reveals himself in this ultimate negation.

After that, it matters little that he regains peace of mind, sleeps quietly, rediscovers the sounds of the countryside, can savor the fragrance of the night and the earth, the salt tang of the air, the drowsy calm of summer, and that, apparently purged of evil by his angry outburst, he can accept the "benign indifference" of the world. He now hopes that the crowd will revile him on the day of his execution. He has renounced human friendship, refusing to look beyond his death. He has stopped being a victim, and may even believe himself a hero. When he was unhappy, he won our affection, but this intellectual happiness leaves us cold. We thought we loved a man, but it was only a philosophy.

Camus's subsequent work displays, on one hand, a sense of human misery and, on the other, an affirmation, a demand for a world commensurate with man; on one hand, the death cell and, on the other, an apotheosis of human dignity, an obstinate celebration of the act of living.

His stories are almost always the same, and his characters are practically interchangeable. The basic theme is that of unsuspecting humanity struck down by unpredictable misfortune. Take, for example, the plot of *Le Malentendu* (*Cross Purpose*, 1944): "One of the villagers had left his home [in Czechoslovakia] to try his luck abroad. After twenty-five years, having made a fortune, he returned to his country with his wife and child. Meanwhile his mother and sister had been running a small hotel in the village where he was born. He decided to give them a surprise and . . . went to stay at his mother's place under an assumed name. His mother and his sister completely failed to recognize him . . . he showed them a large amount of money he had on him, and in the course of the night they slaughtered him with a hammer."

The plot of *Cross Purpose* offers the key to Camus's work: the irreparable misunderstanding between man and his world. In the play, staged by Marcel Herrand in 1944 at the Théâtre des Mathurins with a cast that included Hélène Vercors and Maria Casarès, Camus shows this misunderstanding in its starkest form, without a ray of hope. As a result, the play lacks credibility and also humanity, the characters being mere abstractions, and it was a failure on the stage. But its philosophical conclusion is of some interest. It expresses the earlier Camus, the Camus of absurd revolt, frozen hopes, and life without a future: "One can hardly call it a home, that place of clotted darkness underground, to which we go from here, to feed blind animals . . . What do they serve, those blind impulses that surge up in us, the yearnings that rack our souls? Why cry out for the sea, or for love? What futility. Your husband knows now what the answer is: that charnel house where in the end we shall lie huddled together . . . Try to realize that no grief of yours can ever equal the injustice done to man . . . Pray your God to harden you to stone. It's . . . the one true happiness."

The difference between *Cross Purpose* and *Caligula* (1944) is that between the absurd and the baroque, between a "black" play and one with colorful overtones. The story centers around a hero of the absurd, intoxicated by unbridled freedom. In history, Nero was such a hero, but Camus chose instead to deal with Caligula, the mad emperor who had his horse created consul.

In this play, Camus is not greatly concerned about historical accuracy (Caligula's madness is supposed to be due to an attack of meningitis); the important thing was that in the character of Caligula (in turn a capricious, sulky child, an oriental potentate, and a sadistic tyrant), he could portray an obsession with freedom carried to the point of absurdity: "This world of ours, this scheme of things, as they call it, is quite intolerable. That's why I want the moon, or happiness, or eternal life—something, in fact, that may sound crazy, but which isn't of this world."

In the course of his career, Caligula has encountered "a very simple truth that is hard to bear": men die and they are not happy. This truth, and no other, is what he wishes to teach his fellowmen so that they may learn to die, despairing but aware. He expects his people to be grateful, but he only succeeds in inspiring hatred and revolt; he is accompanied everywhere by "the same weight of the future and the past"; his solitude is poisoned by his victims. He thought he was wresting them from their detestable security by violence, when all that was needed was a little love. Finally, confronted by an empire littered with corpses, he learns that "killing is no solu-

tion" and cannot even find a judge "in this world where no one is innocent." The logical crime is no solution. In this sense, *Caligula* marks the end of one phase of Camus's work. What he had sought in death and torture, he would now seek in sanctity.

The immediate impact of *The Plague* is well known—in six months it achieved a degree of success for which Malraux's *La Condition Humaine* (*Man's Fate*) had to wait fifteen years. It was at once recognized as a profound commentary on the modern world, and quickly found an international audience.

When we read *The Plague* we are at once struck by its urgency but also by a certain weakness in the handling. Admittedly it is more difficult to compose a fully orchestrated novel than a novella, like *The Stranger,* on a single theme whose tone sustains itself. But *The Plague* shows that Camus had few of the gifts of the imaginative novelist. In his books, cold, hunger, poverty, love, sickness, death, and joy cease to be natural human conditions and take on an abstract quality. Though he was often classified as an existentialist, Camus was actually an even more essentialist novelist than Balzac. The characters of *The Plague,* like those of *The Stranger,* are stereotyped: Father Paneloux is simply a Jesuit, that is, the defender of an absurd belief that refuses to reveal itself in its true colors. The judge and the prefect are similarly treated.

Another striking feature is Camus's difficulty in encompassing reality: he must have a bare stage, characters without costumes. The physical seems to embarrass him, and he wants us to be interested only in ideas. *The Plague* contains that kind of basic inhumanity that was Mersault's real crime. And yet Camus makes every effort in the way of documentation. He speaks of "Athens, a charnel-house reeking to heaven and deserted even by the birds; Chinese towns cluttered up with victims silent in their agony; the convicts of Marseille piling rotting corpses into pits." Most of his characters are faceless ghosts (Judge Othon is just a little bit of a caricature), all condemned to the same fate by an anonymous, implacable, and absurd misfortune. But their life is portrayed for us with an art that is all the more effective for its poverty of resources. The trappings of realism are replaced by a broader outline, a starker truth; we are free to fill in the details, to hang the bedclothes from the windows to air, pack the trams with people, stick colorful posters on the walls. If we do not have the setting, at least we have its framework—a framework terrifying in its implications.

The Plague may be simply an allegory, but it is an allegory for the times, and was immediately recognized as such on its appearance. Here we have the German occupation, the concentration camps, and the prospect of a third world war—the age of inhumanity, the all-powerful state, the tyranny of the machine, and the irresponsibility of our rulers. Seen in this light, the anonymity of *The Plague* takes on its full significance: its characters are those of our own everyday life, their faces are our own, and, like us, they are condemned to death.

The book is in the form of a diary kept by an eyewitness, Dr. Rieux. It is a physician's account of events, precise, dry, lyrical only in its moments of protest. Like *The Stranger,* the book starts out with a series of warning signals: Rieux's wife, who is suffering from tuberculosis, leaves the town, rats are found dead, people come down with suspicious fevers. We also find those breathing spaces in which we can imagine that the disaster is abating and we almost come to terms with an epidemic that is carrying off a mere fifteen hundred people a week.

The town undergoes no basic changes during the plague: as soon as the danger has passed, it immediately returns to its absurd daily round of work and pleasure. But the best of its inhabitants have learned the real nature of the evil that was eating them away and know they must fight it. Tarrou, one of the victims, remarks to his friend Rieux:

I had the plague already, long before I came to this town and encountered it here . . . Only there are people who don't know it or who feel at ease in that condition. Personally, I've always wanted to get out of it. Others did not seem embarrassed by such thoughts . . . they advanced arguments, often quite impressive ones . . .

In any case, my concern was not with arguments. It was with . . . that foul procedure whereby . . . a fettered man was going to die . . . after nights and nights of mental torture while he waited to be murdered in cold blood . . . And I told myself that meanwhile, so far anyhow as I was concerned, nothing in the world would induce me to accept any argument that justified such butcheries. Yes, I chose to be blindly obstinate, pending the day when I could see my way more clearly . . . That, too, is why this epidemic has taught me nothing new, except that I must fight at your side. I know positively . . . that each of us has the plague within him . . . What's natural is the microbe . . . The good man, the man who infects hardly anyone, is the man who has the fewest lapses of attention . . . once I'd definitely refused to kill, I doomed myself to an exile that can never end. I leave it to others to "make history" . . . on this earth there are pestilences and there are victims, and it's up to us, so far as possible, not to join forces with the pestilences.

And Tarrou concludes his long monologue with these words: "I grant we should add a third category: that of the true healers. But it's a fact one doesn't come across many of them, and anyhow it must be a hard vocation. That's why I decided to take, in every predicament, the victim's side—so as to reduce the damage done."

And Tarrou goes even further in baring his soul to his new friend as they walk together a few days before his death. "It comes to this"—he says almost casually—"what interests me is learning how to become a saint." And, in reply to Rieux, who exclaims "But you don't believe in God," he says: "Exactly. Can one be a saint without God?—that's the problem, in fact the only problem I'm up against today."

It is true that in a world of absurdity saintliness may be the only solution. Dostoevsky was the first to understand this, then Bernanos, whose priests, ranged against the evil of the world, are unforgettable figures. The experience of the concentration camps showed what the quiet heroism of the defeated, their solidarity in face of the hell created by the S.S., could accomplish. Communists and Christians were in the forefront of the struggle, which was as much a fight for life as an affirmation of human dignity, of the nobility of man at the moment of his most abject humiliation.

But the author of *The Plague* refuses his characters any form of justification—nothing can justify Tarrou's death. We have no assurance that he does not die in utter despair. He chose sainthood as a form of escape, but he might just as well have chosen suicide or the tortures Caligula inflicted on his courtiers, for it is clear that in Camus's eyes everything is

on the same level. The absurdity of the universe makes no allowance for sainthood, which is its own justification or else does not exist. In the absence of any explicit reference to the divinity of Christ, all sainthood implies is that perfection is possible. Sainthood is not a privilege; it is not even a form of heroism. It is not the prerogative of a single man, or even an end in itself, but it is total man placed at the service of total humanity.

In other words, sainthood presupposes the existence of a specifically human *nature;* the saint takes upon himself the whole essence of man, embodies an experience that is universal. In the purely existentialist view—man is what he *does* and nothing else—sainthood makes no sense. A man can be a hero but he cannot be a saint without accepting his fate completely, without acquiescing in his own death in order that the world may be saved. Gandhi came close to this kind of sainthood; for him, nonviolence was only the means to an end that was greater than himself. But what if there were a Gandhi for whom nonviolence was only an absurd gesture, a purposeless moral discipline?

L'État de siège (State of Siege), produced at the Théâtre Marigny on October 27, 1948, by Jean-Louis Barrault, is an essay in dramatic counterpoint, containing obvious allusions to Franco's Spain and the German occupation and it tended to emphasize the weakness in Camus's outlook. The same, however, cannot be said of *Les Justes* (The Just), first produced on December 15, 1949, at the Théâtre Hébertot, in which Camus returns to the give-and-take of ideas he had abandoned in *State of Siege* in favor of the lyrical monologue. The characters who have something to tell us are Stepan Federov and Yanek Kaliayev, nineteenth-century Russian terrorists. In Stepan's opinion "only the bomb is revolutionary" and revolution within the framework of legitimacy is criminal. He has learned in prison that, if tyranny is to be overthrown, discipline is essential. He would not hesitate to kill a child, if ordered to do so by the Organization. He "does not love life, but justice, which is above life."

Yanek, on the contrary, seeks a more human kind of justification. He is a poet who loves "beauty and happiness" and who agrees to become a criminal only "that the earth may at last be filled with the innocent." Thus he hesitates to throw a bomb at the Grand Duke's carriage when he sees there are children in it. In the end, Yanek keeps his appointment with his brothers-in-arms and is able to die reconciled with them and with himself—to die the death of a "just" man.

In his last phase, Camus moved toward the definition of a practical morality with service to mankind taking the place of the Christian notion of salvation. "Man's salvation is too grand a concept for me. What I am really interested in is his health." The morality of revolt (carried to its utmost limit by the mad Caligula) is succeeded by one based rather on human brotherhood, although metaphysically it is no less pessimistic: "Since the world is ordered by death, it might be better for God if we refused to believe in Him and fought death with all our strength, without raising our eyes to the silent heavens."

Condemned to a "definitive exile" on earth, determined to leave it to others to "make history," Camus moved quietly from revolt to testimony in L'Homme révolté (The Rebel, 1951). Because he had pleaded guilty before history and imposed moral limits on revolt, Camus fell into disfavor with the intellectuals of the left—mostly as the result of an attack on his views in the magazine Temps modernes—and became a somewhat isolated figure. Admittedly, he himself had not been sparing in his judgments: "In

the purely historical universe that they have chosen," he writes, at the end of a long analysis of revolutions in Europe, "rebellion and revolution end in the same dilemma: either police rule or insanity." In opposition to those overambitious thinkers and statesmen who try to assimilate the absolute into history and religion into politics, the author of The Rebel sets the apparent detachment of "thought at the meridian," the timeless wisdom of the Mediterranean peoples. Above all, Camus sets his own limit on revolution: respect for man, for man's dignity and his personality. Camus formulates this rule as follows: "Instead of killing and dying in order to produce the being that we are not, we have to live and let live in order to create what we are." By comparison with his trenchant criticism of the deification of revolution, the positive answer of the book is inadequate, but at least it shows a praiseworthy modesty. In fighting what is evil, Camus refuses to follow the totalitarian ideologies in imposing a fabricated idea of what is good.

The three volumes of Actuelles (1950, 1953, and 1958), the essays collected in Summer (1954), the short stories of L'Exil et le Royaume (Exile and the Kingdom, 1957), and the touching posthumous Carnets (Notebooks, 1962 and 1964) do not show any appreciable change in Camus's outlook after The Rebel. "We cannot always live by struggle or hatred. We cannot always die with weapons in our hands. There is history and there is something else—simple happiness . . . beauty." To the modern world, Camus holds up the example of Greece "which never pushed anything to extremes in the realm of the sacred or the reasonable," and which "took everything into consideration, balancing darkness with light. By contrast, our own Europe, dedicated to the conquest of the absolute, is the daughter of excess."

It was not that suffering and injustice

could be considered as any less outrageous than they were at the time of *The Stranger*. But the Camusian hero no longer sought to do more than to diminish suffering quantitatively, after mastering in himself everything that should be mastered and rectifying in creation everything that should be rectified: "Every undertaking which is more ambitious than this proves to be contradictory. The absolute is not attained, nor, above all, created, through history. Politics is not religion, or, if it is, then it is nothing but the Inquisition." And Camus goes on to quote René Char: "Obsession with the harvest and indifference to history are the two extremities of my bow."

What will survive of Camus, who died at the height of his fame soon after the crowning recognition of the Nobel Prize, but before the contradictions that troubled him had been resolved in his work? Not his plays—even though his most instinctive vocation was for the theater—since they too often substitute philosophic dialogue for action. As for his fiction, it draws its symbolic power and depth from actual events. Thus, *The Stranger* expresses the "absurd" atmosphere of the German occupation, and *The Plague* gives the power of myth to the discovery, dating from 1940, that every society carries its own hell within it, that a happy city can perish from the plague. This power is lacking in *La Chute* (*The Fall*, 1956)—an ambiguous, pitiless indictment of modern man, that cold-hearted monster who judges himself only that he may better accuse his fellows—and also in the despairing stories collected in *Exile and the Kingdom*,

though two or three of them are admirable. On the other hand, his descriptions of the sun-drenched Mediterranean landscape will long be quoted, and certain poignant passages in his essays, from *The Myth of Sisyphus* to *Summer*, will become standard texts in the schools. For the rest, it is enough to know that Albert Camus shared our history, our misfortunes, and our hopes, sustained by an obscure feeling that writing was an *honor*. Few writers nowadays could claim as much.

Camus—who, by some curious misapprehension, was long considered an existentialist—is still regarded by the general public, if not as a revolutionary, at least as an innovator. Yet the most striking thing about his style and thought is his classicism. I was not surprised, when I once asked him about the writers who had influenced him, to hear him mention not only Malraux and the Gide of *Fruits of the Earth* but also Montherlant and even Barrès. One could also include Vigny, Vauvernargues, and of course the Pascal of the *Pensées*. As a moralist, Camus takes his rightful place in a group that includes Montaigne and Saint-Evremond on one hand and Corneille and Pascal on the other. His period— that of the German occupation, the concentration camps, the atom bomb, and the all-powerful state—inspired most of his subjects and shaped his sensibility. But it did not supply him with his style or with the obsession underlying his work: the horror of death, hidden at the heart of the world like a worm in a fruit, "that physical fear of the animal that loves the sun" faced with a destiny that nothing can justify.

Translated by Helga Harrison.
Pierre de Boisdeffre, diplomat, literary critic, and historian, was the winner of the French Grand Prix du Critique in 1950.

THE 1957 PRIZE

By KJELL STRÖMBERG

IN THE competition for the Nobel Prize for Literature for 1957, France was represented by nine candidates; and for the ninth time a French writer was to win the award, although he was an outsider whom few expected to win so early in his career. The name of André Malraux, proposed by various literary associations in both France and Sweden, was on everyone's lips, especially since he had just been received by the King and widely fêted when he came to Stockholm to deliver a brilliant lecture on Rembrandt. The perennial candidacy of Jean-Paul Sartre also had ardent defenders in the Swedish press, but finally, it was Albert Camus, disciple of the one and emulator of the other, who was proclaimed winner of the award on October 17, 1957, chiefly for "his important literary production, which with clearsighted earnestness illuminates the problems of the human conscience of our times."

The Nobel Committee's choice caused some astonishment, as it also had in the case of Roger Martin du Gard, twenty years before, when he was chosen over his elder and master, André Gide, who had to wait another ten years before being selected by the Academy on the eve of his death. The first gesture made by the new laureate, Camus, was to praise Malraux as precursor and master of an entire literary generation. Moreover, like Sartre, Malraux had temporarily abandoned literature in the strict sense to take an active part in politics, at a time when Camus's creative genius was at its peak, as shown most convincingly by his admirable story *The Fall*, published in 1956.

There is no need to name all the other candidates, some fifty all told, but we must mention four who were later to win the Prize. Boris Pasternak and Saint-John Perse had both been proposed by influential members of the Swedish Academy. Also for the first time appeared the names of two candidates who were to become perennials and the subject of vigorous discussion—Samuel Beckett, the Irish chief of the French "absurdist" school, who won the Prize in 1969, and Vainno Linna, the author of a vast epic on the great deeds of the Finns during their most recent struggle with their powerful Russian neighbor.

Camus had first been proposed for the Prize in 1947 by the Academy itself after the publication of *The Plague*, an unquestionable masterpiece in which Camus treated the essential problem of the human condition, the problem of evil, with an artistic power and a sense of the present day which brought him the attention and the admiration of everyone in the civilized world. One after another various members of the Swedish Academy took up his candidacy again—in 1949, in 1954, in the following years, without waiting for his name to be proposed from abroad. Few proposals for Camus arrived from abroad, obviously because everyone had gradually and with good reason become convinced that the Nobel Prize could crown only the finished work of an entire career, not the work, no matter how great, of a young author who had not yet said his final word. When he received the award, Albert Camus was only forty-four years old, the youngest laureate after Rudyard Kipling, who was forty-three when he won the Prize in 1907. With the exception of Sinclair Lewis, who won his award at forty-five, no writer had reached this summit of glory before the age of fifty, and most had to wait until they were much older.

The first report on Camus, prepared at the request of the Nobel Prize Committee of the Swedish Academy for the consideration of its members, was written in 1949 by Holger Ahlenius, the same expert who had been consulted on André Gide. Ahlenius also wrote two other reports on Camus, as conscientious and as extensive as the first. Also submitted was a kind of confirmation by Anders Österling, permanent secretary of the Academy.

Following a tradition initiated during World War II, the Swedish ambassador to France, Ragnar Kumlin, was the first to break the news to the writer. Smiling but visibly moved, the young laureate received the grave diplomat in his little office at his publisher's, Gallimard, where he was soon joined by the directors and a crowd of journalists who had got wind of the event.

In France, the fact that a young writer with few books to his credit could be so honored created no little surprise. In some cases this surprise took the form of anger, especially in certain extremist circles on both the left and the right, because in the moribund Fourth Republic politics took precedence over everything else. But most of the leading newspapers and weeklies devoted full-page articles to the event which reminded the world that France, in spite of the political vexations of the moment, was still a great cultural power.

Similar expressions of satisfaction came from the leading newspapers of England and America, but the *Manchester Guardian* noted that the choice of Camus might meet with strong opposition from certain influential critics in Sweden—and indeed the literary editor of the liberal *Dagens Nyheter,* a newspaper with a large circulation, wrote that he found the choice of Camus inexplicable, arguing that not only Malraux but also Sartre were "immensely superior" to the new laureate.

Even so, a laureate has rarely been awaited in Stockholm with such curiosity and affection. Anders Österling delivered the speech in his honor at the awards ceremony in the Concert Palace. At the banquet which followed the ceremony, Albert Camus escorted the wife of the great Marshal of the Kingdom, S. E. M. Birger Ekberg, president of the Nobel Foundation, who as a member of the Swedish Academy had been one of Camus's most faithful supporters; while his wife, Mme Francine Camus, whose delicate beauty impressed everyone, was seated between the King, Gustav VI, and his brother, Prince William.

The high point of the banquet was Camus's speech, one of the best ever given in the luxurious Gilded Room of the Stockholm Town Hall. The speech got a tremendous response in both the Swedish and French press.

During his stay in Sweden, Camus discussed the thorniest questions of the day as the guest of honor of various student groups.

Two years later, Albert Camus was dead.

Translated by Dale McAdoo.

Winston Churchill

1953

"For his mastery of historical and biographical description as well as for brilliant oratory in defending exalted human values"

Maps by *RAFAEL D. PALACIOS*

PRESENTATION ADDRESS

By S. SIWERTZ

MEMBER OF THE SWEDISH ACADEMY

VERY SELDOM have great statesmen and warriors also been great writers. One thinks of Julius Caesar, Marcus Aurelius, and even Napoleon, whose letters to Josephine during the first Italian campaign certainly have passion and splendor. But the man who can most readily be compared with Sir Winston Churchill is Disraeli, who also was a versatile author. It can be said of Disraeli as Churchill says of Rosebery, that "he flourished in an age of great men and small events." He was never subjected to any really dreadful ordeals. His writing was partly a political springboard, partly an emotional safety valve. Through a series of romantic and self-revealing novels, at times rather difficult to read, he avenged himself for the humiliation and setbacks that he, the Jewish stranger in an England ruled by aristocrats, suffered despite his fantastic career. He was not a great writer but a great actor, who played his leading part dazzlingly. He could very well repeat Augustus' words of farewell: "Applaud, my friends, the comedy is over!"

Churchill's John Bull profile stands out effectively against the elder statesman's chalk-white, exotic mask with the black lock of hair on the forehead. The conservative Disraeli revered the English way of life and tradition which Churchill, radical in many respects, has in his blood, including steadfastness in the midst of the storm and the resolute impetus which marks both word and deed. He wears no mask, shows no sign of cleavage, has no complex, enigmatic nature. The analytical *morbidezza,* without which the modern generation finds it hard to imagine an author, is foreign to him. He is a man for whom reality's block has not fallen apart. There, simply, lies the world with its roads and goals under the sun, the stars, and the banners. His prose is just as conscious of the goal and the glory as a runner in the stadium. His every word is half a deed. He is heart and soul a late Victorian who has been buffeted by the gale, or rather one who chose of his own accord to breast the storm.

Churchill's political and literary achievements are of such magnitude that one is tempted to resort to portray him as a Caesar who also has the gift of Cicero's pen. Never before has one of history's leading figures been so close to us by virtue of such an outstanding combination. In his great work about his ancestor, Marlborough, Churchill writes, "Words are easy and many, while great deeds are difficult and rare." Yes, but great, living, and persuasive words are also difficult and rare. And Churchill has shown that they too can take on the character of great deeds.

It is the exciting and colorful side of Churchill's writing which perhaps first strikes the reader. Besides much else, *My Early Life* (1930) is also one of the world's most entertaining adventure stories. Even a very youthful mind can follow with the keenest pleasure the hero's spirited start in life as a problem child in school, as a polo-playing lieutenant in the cavalry (he was considered too dense for the infantry), and as a war correspondent in Cuba, in the Indian border districts, in the Sudan, and in South Africa during the Boer War. Rapid movement, undaunted judgments, and a lively perception distinguish him even here. As a word-painter the young Churchill has not only verve but visual acuteness. Later he took up painting as a hobby, and in *Thoughts and Adventures* (1932) discourses charmingly on the joy it has given him. He loves brilliant colors and feels sorry for the poor brown ones. Nevertheless, Churchill paints better with words. His battle scenes have a matchless coloring. Danger is man's oldest mistress and in the heat of action the young officer was fired to an almost visionary clear-sightedness. On a visit to Omdurman many years ago I discovered how the final struggle in the crushing of the Mahdi's rebellion, as it is depicted in *The River War* (1899), was branded on my memory. I could see in front of me the dervish hordes brandishing their spears and guns, the ochre-yellow sand ramparts shot to pieces, the Anglo-Egyptian troops' methodical advance, and the cavalry charge which nearly cost Churchill his life.

Even old battles which must be dug out of dusty archives are described by Churchill with awesome clarity. Trevelyan masterfully depicts Marlborough's campaigns, but in illusory power it is doubtful that

Churchill's historic battle scenes can be surpassed. Take, for instance, the Battle of Blenheim. One follows in fascination the moves of the bloody chess game, one sees the cannon balls plow their furrows through the compact squares, one is carried away by the thundering charge and fierce hand-to-hand fighting of the cavalry; and after putting the book down one can waken in the night in a cold sweat, imagining he is right in the front rank of English redcoats who, without wavering, stand among the piles of dead and wounded loading their rifles and firing their flashing salvoes.

But Churchill became far more than a soldier and a delineator of war. Even in the strict but brilliant school of the parliamentary gamble for power he was, perhaps from the outset, something of a problem child. The young Hotspur learned, however, to bridle his impetuosity, and he quickly developed into an eminent political orator with the same gift of repartee as Lloyd George. His sallies, often severe, excluded neither warmth nor chivalry. In his alternation between Toryism and Liberalism, he followed in the footsteps of his father, Lord Randolph Churchill. He has also portrayed the latter's short, uneasy, tragically interrupted political and personal life in a work which has an undisputed place of honor in England's profuse biographical literature.

Even World War I, despite all setbacks, meant a vast expansion for Churchill as both politician and writer. In his historical works the personal and the factual elements have been intimately blended. He knows what he is talking about. In gauging the dynamics of events, his profound experience is unmistakable. He is the man who has himself been through the fire, taken risks, and withstood extreme pressure. This gives his words a vibrating power. Occasionally, perhaps, the personal side gets the upper hand. Balfour called *The World Crisis* (1923–1929) "Winston's brilliant autobiography, disguised as world history." With all due respect to archives and documents, there is something special about history written by a man who has himself helped to make it.

In his great book on the Duke of Marlborough (1933–1938), whose life's work is so similar to Churchill's own, he makes an intrepid attack on his ancestor's detractors. I do not know what professional historians say of his polemic against Macaulay, but these diatribes against the great general's persistent haters and revilers are certainly diverting and temperamental.

The Marlborough book is not only a series of vivid battle scenes and a skillful defense of the statesman and warrior. It is also a penetrating study of an enigmatic and unique personality; it shows that Churchill, in addition to all else, is capable of real character-drawing. He returns again and again to the confusing mixture in Marlborough of methodical niggardliness and dazzling virtuosity: "His private fortune was amassed," he says, "upon the same principles as marked the staff-work of his campaigns, and was a part of the same design. It was only in love or on the battlefield that he took all risks. In these supreme exaltations he was swept from his system and rule of living, and blazed resplendent with the heroic virtues. In his marriage and in his victories the worldly prudence, the calculation, the reinsurance, which regulated his ordinary life and sustained his strategy, fell from him like a too heavily embroidered cloak, and the genius within sprang forth in sure and triumphant commands." In his military enthusiasm Churchill forgets for a moment that Marlborough's famous and dearly loved Sarah was by no means one to let herself be ordered about. But it is a wonderful passage.

Churchill regretted that he had never been able to study at Oxford. He had to devote his leisure hours to educating himself. But there are certainly no educational gaps noticeable in his mature prose. Take, for example, *Great Contemporaries* (1937), one of his most charming books. He is said to have molded his style on Gibbon, Burke, and Macaulay, but here he is supremely himself. What a deft touch and at the same time what a fund of human knowledge, generosity, and gay malice are in this portrait gallery!

Churchill's reaction to Bernard Shaw is very amusing, a piquant meeting between two of England's greatest literary personalities. Churchill cannot resist poking fun at Shaw's blithely irresponsible talk and flippancy, which contrasted with the latter's fundamental gravity. Half amused, half appalled, he winces at the way in which the incorrigibly clowning genius was forever tripping himself up and turning somersaults between the most extreme antitheses. It is contrast between the writer, who must at all costs create surprises, and the stateman, whose task it is to meet and master them.

It is not easy to sum up briefly the greatness of Churchill's style. He says of his old friend, the Liberal statesman, John Morley, "Though in conversation he paraded and manœuvred nimbly and elegantly around his own convictions, offering his salutations and the gay compliments of old-time war to the other side, [he] always returned to his fortified camp to sleep." As a stylist Churchill himself, despite his mettlesome chivalry, is not prone to such amiable arabesques. He does not beat about the bush, but is a man of plain speaking. His fervor is realistic, his striking power is tempered only by broad-mindedness and humor. He knows that a good story tells itself. He scorns unnecessary frills and his metaphors are rare but expressive.

Behind Churchill the writer is Churchill the orator—hence the resilience and pungency of his phrases. We often characterize ourselves unconsciously through the praise we give others. Churchill, for instance, says of another of his friends, Lord Birkenhead, "As he warmed to his subject, there grew that glow of conviction and appeal, instinctive and priceless, which constitutes true eloquence." The words might with greater justification have been said of Churchill himself.

The famous desert warrior, Lawrence of Arabia, the author of *The Seven Pillars of Wisdom,* is another who has both made and written history. Of him Churchill says, "Just as an aeroplane only flies by its speed and pressure against the air, so he flew best and easiest in the hurricane." It is again striking how Churchill here too speaks of the same genius that carried his own words through the storm of events.

Churchill's mature oratory is swift, unerring in its aim, and moving in its grandeur. There is the power which forges the links of history. Napoleon's proclamations were often effective in their lapidary style. But Churchill's eloquence in the fateful hours of freedom and human dignity was heart-stirring in quite another way. With his great speeches he has, perhaps, himself erected his most enduring monument.

Lady Churchill—The Swedish Academy expresses its joy at your presence and asks you to convey to Sir Winston a greeting of deep respect. A literary prize is intended to cast luster over the author, but here it is the author who gives luster to the prize. I ask you now to accept, on behalf of your husband, the 1953 Nobel Prize for Literature from the hands of His Majesty the King.

ACCEPTANCE SPEECH

By WINSTON CHURCHILL

THE NOBEL PRIZE FOR LITERATURE is an honor for me alike unique and unexpected and I grieve that my duties have not allowed me to receive it myself here in Stockholm from the hands of His Majesty your beloved and justly respected Sovereign. I am grateful that I am allowed to confide this task to my wife.

The roll on which my name has been inscribed represents much that is outstanding in the world's literature of the twentieth century. The judgment of the Swedish Academy is accepted as impartial, authoritative, and sincere throughout the civilized world. I am proud but also, I must admit, awestruck at your decision to include me. I do hope you are right. I feel we are both running a considerable risk and that I do not deserve it. But I shall have no misgivings if you have none.

Since Alfred Nobel died in 1896 we have entered an age of storm and tragedy. The power of man has grown in every sphere except over himself. Never in the field of action have events seemed so harshly to dwarf personalities. Rarely in history have brutal facts so dominated thought or has such a widespread, individual virtue found so dim a collective focus. The fearful question confronts us; have our problems got beyond our control? Undoubtedly we are passing through a phase where this may be so. Well may we humble ourselves, and seek for guidance and mercy.

We in Europe and the Western world, who have planned for health and social security, who have marveled at the triumphs of medicine and science, and who have aimed at justice and freedom for all, have nevertheless been witnesses of famine, misery, cruelty, and destruction before which pale the deeds of Attila and Genghis Khan. And we who, first in the League of Nations, and now in the United Nations, have attempted to give an abiding foundation to the peace of which men have dreamed so long, have lived to see a world marred by cleavages and threatened by discords even graver and more violent than those which convulsed Europe after the fall of the Roman Empire.

It is upon this dark background that we can appreciate the majesty and hope which inspired the conception of Alfred Nobel. He has left behind him a bright and enduring beam of culture, of purpose, and of inspiration to a generation which stands in sore need. This world-famous institution points a true path for us to follow. Let us therefore confront the clatter and rigidity we see around us with tolerance, variety, and calm.

The world looks with admiration and indeed with comfort to Scandinavia, where three countries, without sacrificing their sovereignty, live united in their thought, in their economic practice, and in their healthy way of life. From such fountains new and brighter opportunities may come to all mankind. These are, I believe, the sentiments which may animate those whom the Nobel Foundation elects to honor, in the sure knowledge that they will thus be respecting the ideals and wishes of its illustrious founder.

MY EARLY LIFE

By WINSTON CHURCHILL

[Excerpt]

CHAPTER XXI

I Escape from the Boers—I

During the first three weeks of my captivity, although I was a party to all plans of revolt or escape, I was engaged in arguing with the Boer Authorities that they should release me as a Press Correspondent. They replied that I had forfeited my non-combatant status by the part I had taken in the armored train fight. I contended that I had not fired a shot and had been taken unarmed. This was strictly true. But the Natal newspapers had been captured by the Boers. These contained glowing accounts of my activities, and attributed the escape of the engine and the wounded entirely to me. General Joubert therefore intimated that even if I had not fired a shot myself, I had injured the Boer operations by freeing the engine, and that I must therefore be treated as a prisoner-of-war. As soon as I learned of this decision, in the first week of December, I resolved to escape.

I shall transcribe what I wrote at the time where I cannot improve upon it.

"The State Model Schools stood in the midst of a quadrangle, and were surrounded on two sides by an iron grille and on two by a corrugated-iron fence about ten feet high. These boundaries offered little obstacle to anyone who possessed the activity of youth, but the fact that they were guarded on the inside by sentries, fifty yards apart, armed with rifle and revolver, made them a well-nigh insuperable barrier. No walls are so hard to pierce as living walls.

"After anxious reflection and continual watching, it was discovered by several of the prisoners that when the sentries along the eastern side walked about on their beats they were at certain moments unable to see the top of a few yards of the wall near the small circular lavatory office which can be seen on the plan. The electric lights in the middle of the quadrangle brilliantly lighted the whole place, but the eastern wall was in shadow. The first thing was therefore to pass the two sentries near the office. It was necessary to hit off the exact moment when both their backs should be turned together. After the wall was scaled we should be in the garden of the villa next door. There the plan came to an end. Everything after this was vague and uncertain. How to get out of the garden, how to pass unnoticed through the streets, how to evade the patrols that surrounded the town, and above all how to cover the two hundred and eighty miles to the Portuguese frontier, were questions which would arise at a later stage."

"Together with Captain Haldane and Lieutenant Brockie I made an abortive attempt, not pushed with any decision, on December 11. There was no difficulty in getting into the circular office. But to climb out of it over the wall was a hazard of the sharpest character. Anyone doing so must at the moment he was on the top of the wall be plainly visible to the sentries fifteen yards away, if they were in the right place and happened to look! Whether the sentries would challenge or fire depended entirely upon their individual dispositions, and no one could tell what they would do. Nevertheless I was determined that nothing should stop my taking the plunge the next day. As the 12th wore away my fears crystallized more and more into desperation. In the evening, after my two friends had made an attempt, but had not found the moment propitious, I strolled across the quadrangle and secreted myself in the circular office. Through an aperture in the metal casing of which it was built I watched the sentries. For some time they remained stolid and obstructive. Then all of a sudden one turned and walked up to his comrade, and they began to talk. Their backs were turned.

"Now or never! I stood on a ledge, seized the top of the wall with my hands, and drew myself up. Twice I let myself down again in sickly hesitation, and then with a third resolve scrambled up and over. My waistcoat got entangled with the ornamental metal-work on the top. I had to pause for an appreciable moment to extricate myself. In this posture I had one parting glimpse of the sentries still talking with their backs turned fifteen yards away. One of them was lighting his cigarette, and I remember the glow on the inside of his hands as a distinct impression which my mind recorded. Then I lowered myself lightly down into the adjoining garden and crouched among the shrubs. I was free! The first step had been taken, and it was irrevocable. It now remained to await the arrival of my comrades. The bushes in the garden gave a good deal of cover, and in the moonlight their shadows fell dark on the ground. I lay here for an hour in great impatience and anxiety. People were continually moving about in the garden, and once a man came and apparently looked straight at me only a few yards away. Where were the others? Why did they not make the attempt?"

"Suddenly I heard a voice from within the quadrangle say, quite loud, 'All up.' I crawled back to the wall. Two officers were walking up and down inside, jabbering Latin words, laughing and talking all manner of nonsense—amid which I caught my name. I risked a cough. One of the officers immediately began to chatter alone. The other said, slowly and clearly, 'They cannot get out. The sentry suspects. It's all up. Can you get back again?' But now all my fears fell from me at once. To go back was impossible. I could not hope to climb the wall unnoticed. There was no helpful ledge on the outside. Fate pointed onwards. Besides, I said to myself, 'Of course, I shall be recaptured, but I will at least have a run for my money.' I said to the officers, 'I shall go on alone.'

"Now I was in the right mood for these undertakings—failure being almost certain, no odds against success affected me. All risks were less than the certainty. A glance at the plan will show that the gate which led into the road was only a few yards from another sentry. I said to myself, '*Toujours de l'audace,*' put my hat on my head, strode into the middle of the garden, walked past the windows of the house without any attempt at concealment, and so went through the gate and turned to the left. I passed the sentry at less than five yards. Most of them knew me by sight. Whether he looked at me or not I do not know, for I never turned my head. I restrained with the utmost difficulty an impulse to run. But after walking a hundred yards and hearing no challenge, I knew that the second obstacle had been surmounted. I was at large in Pretoria.

"I walked on leisurely through the night, humming a tune and choosing the middle of the road. The streets were full of burghers, but they paid no attention to me. Gradually I reached the suburbs, and on a little bridge I sat down to reflect and consider. I was in the heart of the enemy's country. I knew no one to whom I could apply for succor. Nearly three hundred miles stretched between me and Delagoa Bay. My escape must be known at dawn. Pursuit would be immediate. Yet all exits were barred. The town was picketed, the country was patrolled, the trains were searched, the line was guarded. I wore a civilian brown flannel suit. I had seventy-five pounds in my pocket and four slabs of chocolate, but the compass and the map which might have guided me, the opium tablets and meat lozenges which should have sustained me, were in my friends' pockets in the State Model Schools. Worst of all, I could not speak a word of Dutch or Kaffir, and how was I to get food or direction?

"But when hope had departed, fear had gone as well. I formed a plan. I would find the Delagoa Bay Railway. Without map or compass, I must follow that in spite of the pickets. I looked at the stars. Orion shone brightly. Scarcely a year before he had guided me when lost in the desert to the banks of the Nile. He had given me water. Now he should lead to freedom. I could not endure the want of either.

"After walking south for half a mile I struck the railroad. Was it the line to Delagoa Bay or the Pietersburg branch? If it were the former, it should run east. But, so far as I could see, this line ran northwards. Still, it might be only wind-ing its way out among the hills. I resolved to follow it. The night was delicious. A cool breeze fanned my face, and a wild feeling of exhilaration took hold of me. At any rate, I was free, if only for an hour. That was something. The fascination of the adventure grew. Unless the stars in their courses fought for me, I could not escape. Where, then, was the need of caution? I marched briskly along the line. Here and there the lights of a picket fire gleamed. Every bridge had its watchers. But I passed them all, making very short *détours* at the dangerous places, and really taking scarcely any precautions. Perhaps that was the reason I succeeded.

"As I walked I extended my plan. I could not march three hundred miles to the frontier. I would board a train in motion and hide under the seats, on the roof, on the couplings—anywhere. I thought of Paul Bultitude's escape from school in *Vice Versa*. I saw myself emerging from under the seat, and bribing or persuading some fat first-class passenger to help me. What train should I take? The first, of course. After walking for two hours I perceived the signal lights of a station. I left the line, and circling round it, hid in the ditch by the track about two hundred yards beyond the platform. I argued that the train would stop at the station and that it would not have got up too much speed by the time it reached me. An hour passed. I began to grow impatient. Suddenly I heard the whistle and the approaching rattle. Then the great yellow headlights of the engine flashed into view. The train waited five minutes at the station, and started again with much noise and steaming. I crouched by the track. I rehearsed the act in my mind. I must wait until the engine had passed, otherwise I should be seen. Then I must make a dash for the carriages.

"The train started slowly, but gathered

speed sooner than I had expected. The flaring lights drew swiftly near. The rattle became a roar. The dark mass hung for a second above me. The engine-driver silhouetted against his furnace glow, the black profile of the engine, the clouds of steam rushed past. Then I hurled myself on the trucks, clutched at something, missed, clutched again, missed again, grasped some sort of hand-hold, was swung off my feet—my toes bumping on the line, and with a struggle seated myself on the couplings of the fifth truck from the front of the train. It was a goods train, and the trucks were full of sacks, soft sacks covered with coal-dust. They were in fact bags filled with empty coal bags going back to their colliery. I crawled on top and burrowed in among them. In five minutes I was completely buried. The sacks were warm and comfortable. Perhaps the engine-driver had seen me rush up to the train and would give the alarm at the next station; on the other hand, perhaps not. Where was the train going to? Where would it be unloaded? Would it be searched? Was it on the Delagoa Bay line? What should I do in the morning? Ah, never mind that. Sufficient for the night was the luck thereof. Fresh plans for fresh contingencies. I resolved to sleep, nor can I imagine a more pleasing lullaby than the clatter of the train that carries an escaping prisoner at twenty miles an hour away from the enemy's capital.

"How long I slept I do not know, but I woke up suddenly with all feelings of exhilaration gone, and only the consciousness of oppressive difficulties heavy on me. I must leave the train before daybreak, so that I could drink at a pool and find some hiding-place while it was still dark. I would not run the risk of being unloaded with the coal bags. Another night I would board another train. I crawled from my cosy hiding-place among the sacks and sat again on the

couplings. The train was running at a fair speed, but I felt it was time to leave it. I took hold of the iron handle at the back of the truck, pulled strongly with my left hand, and sprang. My feet struck the ground in two gigantic strides, and the next instant I was sprawling in the ditch considerably shaken but unhurt. The train, my faithful ally of the night, hurried on its journey.

"It was still dark. I was in the middle of a wide valley, surrounded by low hills, and carpeted with high grass drenched in dew. I searched for water in the nearest gully, and soon found a clear pool. I was very thirsty, but long after I had quenched my thirst I continued to drink, that I might have sufficient for the whole day.

"Presently the dawn began to break, and the sky to the east grew yellow and red, slashed across with heavy black clouds. I saw with relief that the railway ran steadily towards the sunrise. I had taken the right line, after all.

"Having drunk my fill, I set out for the hills, among which I hoped to find some hiding-place, and as it became broad daylight I entered a small grove of trees which grew on the side of a deep ravine. Here I resolved to wait till dusk. I had one consolation: no one in the world knew where I was—I did not know myself. It was now four o'clock. Fourteen hours lay between me and the night. My impatience to proceed while I was still strong doubled their length. At first it was terribly cold, but by degrees the sun gained power, and by ten o'clock the heat was oppressive. My sole companion was a gigantic vulture, who manifested an extravagant interest in my condition, and made hideous and ominous gurglings from time to time. From my lofty position I commanded a view of the whole valley. A little tin-roofed town lay three miles to the westward. Scattered farmsteads, each with a clump of trees, relieved the monotony of the undulating ground. At the foot of the hill stood a Kaffir kraal, and the figures of its inhabitants dotted the patches of cultivation or surrounded the droves of goats and cows which fed on the pasture. . . . During the day I ate one slab of chocolate, which, with the heat, produced a violent thirst. The pool was hardly half a mile away, but I dared not leave the shelter of the little wood, for I could see the figures of white men riding or walking occasionally across the valley, and once a Boer came and fired two shots at birds close to my hiding-place. But no one discovered me.

"The elation and the excitement of the previous night had burnt away, and a chilling reaction followed. I was very hungry, for I had had no dinner before starting, and chocolate, though it sustains, does not satisfy. I had scarcely slept, but yet my heart beat so fiercely and I was so nervous and perplexed about the future that I could not rest. I thought of all the chances that lay against me; I dreaded and detested more than words can express the prospect of being caught and dragged back to Pretoria. I found no comfort in any of the philosophical ideas which some men parade in their hours of ease and strength and safety. They seemed only fairweather friends. I realized with awful force that no exercise of my own feeble wit and strength could save me from my enemies, and that without the assistance of that High Power which interferes in the eternal sequence of causes and effects more often than we are always prone to admit, I could never succeed. I prayed long and earnestly for help and guidance. My prayer, as it seems to me, was swiftly and wonderfully answered."

I wrote these lines many years ago while the impression of the adventure was strong upon me. Then I could tell no more. To have done so would have compromised the liberty and perhaps the lives of those who had helped me. For many years these reasons have disappeared. The time has come when I can relate the events which followed, and which changed my nearly hopeless position into one of superior advantage.

During the day I had watched the railway with attention. I saw two or three trains pass along it each way. I argued that the same number would pass at night. I resolved to board one of these. I thought I could improve on my procedure of the previous evening. I had observed how slowly the trains, particularly long goods-trains, climbed some of the steep gradients. Sometimes they were hardly going at a foot's pace. It would probably be easy to choose a point where the line was not only on an up grade but also on a curve. Thus I could board some truck on the convex side of the train when both the engine and the guard's van were bent away, and when consequently neither the engine-driver nor the guard would see me. This plan seemed to me in every respect sound. I saw myself leaving the train again before dawn, having been carried forward another sixty or seventy miles during the night. That would be scarcely one hundred and fifty miles from the frontier. And why should not the process be repeated? Where was the flaw? I could not see it. With three long bounds on three successive nights I could be in Portuguese territory. Meanwhile I still had two or three slabs of chocolate and a pocketful of crumbled biscuit— enough, that is to say, to keep body and soul together at a pinch without running the awful risk of recapture entailed by accosting a single human being. In this mood I watched with increasing impatience the arrival of darkness.

The long day reached its close at last. The western clouds flushed into fire; the shadows of the hills stretched out across the valley; a ponderous Boer wagon with its long team crawled slowly along the track towards the township; the Kaffirs collected their herds and drew them round their kraal; the daylight died, and soon it was quite dark. Then, and not until then, I set forth. I hurried to the railway line, scrambling along through the boulders and high grass and pausing on my way to drink at a stream of sweet cold water. I made my way to the place where I had seen the trains crawling so slowly up the slope, and soon found a point where the curve of the track fulfilled all the conditions of my plan. Here, behind a little bush, I sat down and waited hopefully. An hour passed; two hours passed; three hours—and yet no train. Six hours had now elapsed since the last, whose time I had carefully noted, had gone by. Surely one was due. Another hour slipped away. Still no train! My plan began to crumble and my hopes to ooze out of me. After all, was it not quite possible that no trains ran on this part of the line during the dark hours? This was in fact the case, and I might well have continued to wait in vain till daylight. However, between twelve and one in the morning I lost patience and started along the track, resolved to cover at any rate ten or fifteen miles of my journey. I did not make much progress. Every bridge was guarded by armed men; every few miles were huts. At intervals there were stations with tin-roofed villages clustering around them. All the veldt was bathed in the bright rays of the full moon, and to avoid these dangerous places I had to make wide circuits and even to creep along the ground. Leaving the railroad I fell into bogs and swamps, brushed through high grass dripping with dew, and waded across the streams over which the bridges carried the railway. I was soon drenched to the waist. I had been able to take very little exercise during my month's imprison-

ment, and I was quickly tired with walking and with want of food and sleep. Presently I approached a station. It was a mere platform in the veldt, with two or three buildings and huts around it. But laid up on the sidings, obviously for the night, were three long goods-trains. Evidently the flow of traffic over the railway was uneven. These three trains, motionless in the moonlight, confirmed my fears that traffic was not maintained by night on this part of the line. Where, then, was my plan which in the afternoon had looked so fine and sure?

It now occurred to me that I might board one of these stationary trains immediately, and hiding amid its freight be carried forward during the next day—and night too if all were well. On the other hand, where were they going to? Where would they stop? Where would they be unloaded? Once I entered a wagon my lot would be cast. I might find myself ignominiously unloaded and recaptured at Witbank or Middleburg, or at any station in the long two hundred miles which separated me from the frontier. It was necessary at all costs before taking such a step to find out where these trains were going. To do this I must penetrate the station, examine the labels on the trucks or on the merchandise, and see if I could extract any certain guidance from them. I crept up to the platform and got between two of the long trains on the siding. I was proceeding to examine the markings on the trucks when loud voices rapidly approaching on the outside of the trains filled me with fear. Several Kaffirs were laughing and shouting in their unmodulated tones, and I heard, as I thought, a European voice arguing or ordering. At any rate, it was enough for me. I retreated between the two trains to the extreme end of the siding, and slipped stealthily but rapidly into the grass of the illimitable plain.

There was nothing for it but to plod

on—but in an increasingly purposeless and hopeless manner. I felt very miserable when I looked around and saw here and there the lights of houses and thought of the warmth and comfort within them, but knew that they meant only danger to me. Far off on the moonlit horizon there presently began to shine the row of six or eight big lights which marked either Witbank or Middleburg station. Out in the darkness to my left gleamed two or three fires. I was sure they were not the lights of houses, but how far off they were or what they were I could not be certain. The idea formed in my mind that they were the fires of a Kaffir kraal. Then I began to think that the best use I could make of my remaining strength would be to go to these Kaffirs. I had heard that they hated the Boers and were friendly to the British. At any rate, they would probably not arrest me. They might give me food and a dry corner to sleep in. Although I could not speak a word of their language, yet I thought perhaps they might understand the value of a British bank-note. They might even be induced to help me. A guide, a pony—but, above all, rest, warmth, and food—such were the promptings which dominated my mind. So I set out towards the fires.

I must have walked a mile or so in this resolve before a realization of its weakness and imprudence took possession of me. Then I turned back again to the railway line and retraced my steps perhaps half the distance. Then I stopped and sat down, completely baffled, destitute of any idea what to do or where to turn. Suddenly without the slightest reason all my doubts disappeared. It was certainly by no process of logic that they were dispelled. I just felt quite clear that I would go to the Kaffir kraal. I had sometimes in former years held a "Planchette" pencil and written while others had touched my wrist or hand. I acted in exactly the same unconscious or subconscious manner now.

I walked on rapidly towards the fires, which I had in the first instance thought were not more than a couple of miles from the railway line. I soon found they were much farther away than that. After about an hour or an hour and a half they still seemed almost as far off as ever. But I persevered, and presently between two and three o'clock in the morning I perceived that they were not the fires of a Kaffir kraal. The angular outline of buildings began to draw out against them, and soon I saw that I was approaching a group of houses around the mouth of a coal-mine. The wheel which worked the winding gear was plainly visible, and I could see that the fires which had led me so far were from the furnaces of the engines. Hard by, surrounded by one or two slighter structures, stood a small but substantial stone house two stories high.

I halted in the wilderness to survey this scene and to resolve my action. It was still possible to turn back. But in that direction I saw nothing but the prospect of further futile wanderings terminated by hunger, fever, discovery, or surrender. On the other hand, here in front was a chance. I had heard it said before I escaped that in the mining district of Witbank and Middleburg there were a certain number of English residents who had been suffered to remain in the country in order to keep the mines working. Had I been led to one of these? What did this house which frowned dark and inscrutable upon me contain? A Briton or a Boer; a friend or a foe? Nor did this exhaust the possibilities. I had my seventy-five pounds in English notes in my pocket. If I revealed my identity, I thought that I could give reasonable assurance of a thousand. I might find some indifferent neutral-minded person who out of good nature or for a large sum of money would aid me in my bitter and desperate need. Certainly I would try to make what bargain I could now—now while I still had the strength to plead my cause and perhaps to extricate myself if the results were adverse. Still the odds were heavy against me, and it was with faltering and reluctant steps that I walked out of the shimmering gloom of the veldt into the light of the furnace fires, advanced towards the silent house, and struck with my fist upon the door.

There was a pause. Then I knocked again. And almost immediately a light sprang up above and an upper window opened.

"Wer ist da?" cried a man's voice.

I felt the shock of disappointment and consternation to my fingers.

"I want help; I have had an accident," I replied.

Some muttering followed. Then I heard steps descending the stairs, the bolt of the door was drawn, the lock was turned. It was opened abruptly, and in the darkness of the passage a tall man hastily attired, with a pale face and dark moustache, stood before me.

"What do you want?" he said, this time in English.

I had now to think of something to say. I wanted above all to get into parley with this man, to get matters in such a state that instead of raising an alarm and summoning others he would discuss things quietly.

"I am a burgher," I began. "I have had an accident. I was going to join my commando at Komati Poort. I have fallen off the train. We were skylarking. I have been unconscious for hours. I think I have dislocated my shoulder."

It is astonishing how one thinks of these things. This story leaped out as if I had learned it by heart. Yet I had not the slightest idea what I was going to say or what the next sentence would be.

The stranger regarded me intently, and after some hesitation said at length, "Well, come in." He retreated a little into the darkness of the passage, threw open a door on one side of it, and pointed with his left hand into a dark room. I walked past him and entered, wondering if it was to be my prison. He followed, struck a light, lit a lamp, and set it on the table at the far side of which I stood. I was in a small room, evidently a dining-room and office in one. I noticed besides the large table, a roll desk, two or three chairs, and one of those machines for making soda-water, consisting of two glass globes set one above the other and encased in thin wire-netting. On his end of the table my host had laid a revolver, which he had hitherto presumably been holding in his right hand.

"I think I'd like to know a little more about this railway accident of yours," he said, after a considerable pause.

"I think," I replied, "I had better tell you the truth."

"I think you had," he said, slowly.

So I took the plunge and threw all I had upon the board.

"I am Winston Churchill, War Correspondent of the *Morning Post*. I escaped last night from Pretoria. I am making my way to the frontier." (Making my way!) "I have plenty of money. Will you help me?"

There was another long pause. My companion rose from the table slowly and locked the door. After this act, which struck me as unpromising, and was certainly ambiguous, he advanced upon me and suddenly held out his hand.

"Thank God you have come here! It is the only house for twenty miles where you would not have been handed over. But we are all British here, and we will see you through."

It is easier to recall across the gulf of years the spasm of relief which swept over me, than it is to describe it. A moment before I had thought myself trapped; and now friends, food, resources, aid were all at my disposal. I felt like a drowning man pulled out of the water and informed he has won the Derby!

My host now introduced himself as Mr. John Howard, manager of the Transvaal Collieries. He had become a naturalized burgher of the Transvaal some years before the war. But out of consideration for his British race and some inducements which he had offered to the local Field Cornet, he had not been called up to fight against the British. Instead he had been allowed to remain with one or two others on the mine, keeping it pumped out and in good order until coal-cutting could be resumed. He had with him at the mine-head, besides his secretary, who was British, an engineman from Lancashire and two Scottish miners. All these four were British subjects and had been allowed to remain only upon giving their parole to observe strict neutrality. He himself as burgher of the Transvaal Republic would be guilty of treason in harboring me, and liable to be shot if caught at the time or found out later on.

"Never mind," he said, "we will fix it up somehow." And added, "The Field Cornet was round here this afternoon asking about you. They have got the hue and cry out all along the line and all over the district."

I said that I did not wish to compromise him.

Let him give me food, a pistol, a guide, and if possible a pony, and I would make my own way to the sea, marching by night across country far away from the railway line or any habitation.

He would not hear of it. He would fix up something. But he enjoined the utmost caution. Spies were everywhere. He had two Dutch servant-maids actually sleeping in the house. There were many Kaffirs employed about the mine premises and on the pumping-machinery of the mine. Surveying these dangers he became very thoughtful.

Then: "But you are famishing."

I did not contradict him. In a moment he had bustled off into the kitchen, telling me meanwhile to help myself from a whisky bottle and the soda-water machine which I have already mentioned. He returned after an interval with the best part of a cold leg of mutton and various other delectable commodities, and, leaving me to do full justice to these, quitted the room and let himself out of the house by a back door.

Nearly an hour passed before Mr. Howard returned. In this period my physical well-being had been brought into harmony with the improvement in my prospects. I felt confident of success and equal to anything.

"It's all right," said Mr. Howard. "I have seen the men, and they are all for it. We must put you down the pit tonight, and there you will have to stay till we can see how to get you out of the country. One difficulty," he said, "will be the *skoff* (food). The Dutch girl sees every mouthful I eat. The cook will want to know what has happened to her leg of mutton. I shall have to think it all out during the night. You must get down the pit at once. We'll make you comfortable enough."

Accordingly, just as the dawn was breaking, I followed my host across a little yard into the enclosure in which stood the winding-wheel of the mine. Here a stout man, introduced as Mr. Dewsnap, of Oldham, locked my hand in a grip of crushing vigor.

"They'll all vote for you next time," he whispered.

A door was opened and I entered the cage. Down we shot into the bowels of the earth. At the bottom of the mine were the two Scottish miners with lanterns and a big bundle which afterwards proved to be a mattress and blankets. We walked for some time through the pitchy labyrinth, with frequent turns, twists, and alterations of level, and finally stopped in a sort of chamber where the air was cool and fresh. Here my guide set down his bundle, and Mr. Howard handed me a couple of candles, a bottle of whisky, and a box of cigars.

"There's no difficulty about these," he said. "I keep them under lock and key. Now we must plan how to feed you tomorrow."

"Don't you move from here, whatever happens," was the parting injunction. "There will be Kaffirs about the mine after daylight, but we shall be on the look-out that none of them wanders this way. None of them has seen anything so far."

My four friends trooped off with their lanterns, and I was left alone. Viewed from the velvety darkness of the pit, life seemed bathed in rosy light. After the perplexity and even despair through which I had passed I counted upon freedom as certain. Instead of a humiliating recapture and long months of monotonous imprisonment, probably in the common jail, I saw myself once more rejoining the Army with a real exploit to my credit, and in that full enjoyment of freedom and keen pursuit of adventure dear to the heart of youth. In this comfortable mood, and speeded by intense fatigue, I soon slept the sleep of the weary—but of the triumphant.

CHAPTER XXII

I Escape from the Boers—II

I do not know how many hours I slept, but the following afternoon must have been far advanced when I found myself thoroughly awake. I put out my hand for the candle, but could feel it nowhere. I did not know what pitfalls these mining-galleries might contain, so I thought it better to lie quiet on my mattress and await developments. Several hours passed before the faint gleam of a lantern showed that someone was coming. It proved to be Mr. Howard himself, armed with a chicken and other good things. He also brought several books. He asked me why I had not lighted my candle. I said I couldn't find it.

"Didn't you put it under the mattress?" he asked.

"No."

"Then the rats must have got it."

He told me there were swarms of rats in the mine, that some years ago he had introduced a particular kind of white rat, which was an excellent scavenger, and that these had multiplied and thriven exceedingly. He told me he had been to the house of an English doctor twenty miles away to get the chicken. He was worried at the attitude of the two Dutch servants, who were very inquisitive about the depredations upon the leg of mutton for which I had been responsible. If he could not get another chicken cooked for the next day, he would have to take double helpings on his own plate and slip the surplus into a parcel for me while the servant was out of the room. He said that inquiries were being made for me all over the district by the Boers, and that the Pretoria Government was making a tremendous fuss about my escape. The fact that there were a number of English remaining in the Middleburg mining region indicated it as a likely place for me to have turned to, and all persons of English origin were more or less suspect.

I again expressed my willingness to go on alone with a Kaffir guide and a pony, but this he utterly refused to entertain. It would take a lot of planning, he said, to get me out of the country, and I might have to stay in the mine for quite a long time.

"Here," he said, "you are absolutely safe. Mac" (by which he meant one of the Scottish miners) "knows all the disused workings and places that no one else would dream of. There is one place here where the water actually touches the roof for a foot or two. If they searched the mine, Mac would dive under that with you into the workings cut off beyond the water. No one would ever think of looking there. We have frightened the Kaffirs with tales of ghosts, and anyhow, we are watching their movements continually."

He stayed with me while I dined, and then departed, leaving me, among other things, half-a-dozen candles which, duly warned, I tucked under my pillow and mattress.

I slept again for a long time, and woke suddenly with a feeling of movement about me. Something seemed to be pulling at my pillow. I put out my hand quickly. There was a perfect scurry. The rats were at the candles. I rescued the candles in time, and lighted one. Luckily for me, I have no horror of rats as such, and being reassured by their evident timidity, I was not particularly uneasy. All the same, the three days I passed in the mine were not among the most pleasant which my memory re-illumines. The patter of little feet and a perceptible sense of stir and scurry were continuous. Once I was waked up from a doze by one actually galloping across me. On the candle being lighted these beings became invisible.

The next day—if you can call it day—arrived in due course. This was December 14, and the third day since I had escaped from the State Model Schools. It was relieved by a visit from the two Scottish miners, with whom I had a long confabulation. I then learned, to my surprise, that the mine was only about two hundred feet deep.

There were parts of it, said Mac, where one could see the daylight up a disused shaft. Would I like to take a turn around the old workings and have a glimmer? We passed an hour or two wandering round and up and down these subterranean galleries, and spent a quarter of an hour near the bottom of the shaft, where, grey and faint, the light of the sun and of the upper world was discerned. On this promenade I saw numbers of rats. They seemed rather nice little beasts, quite white, with dark eyes which I was assured in the daylight were a bright pink. Three years afterwards a British officer on duty in the district wrote to me that he had heard my statement at a lecture about the white rats and their pink eyes, and thought it was the limit of mendacity. He had taken the trouble to visit the mine and see for himself, and he proceeded to apologize for having doubted my truthfulness.

On the 15th Mr. Howard announced that the hue and cry seemed to be dying away. No trace of the fugitive had been discovered throughout the mining district. The talk among the Boer officials was now that I must be hiding at the house of some British sympathizer in Pretoria. They did not believe that it was possible I could have got out of the town. In these circumstances he thought that I might come up and have a walk on the veldt that night, and that if all was quiet the next morning I might shift my quarters to the back room of the office. On the one hand he seemed reassured, and on the other increasingly excited by the adventure. Accordingly, I had a fine stroll in the glorious fresh air and moonlight, and thereafter, anticipating slightly our program, I took up my quarters behind packing-cases in the inner room of the office. Here I remained for three more days, walking each night on the endless plain with Mr. Howard or his assistant.

On the 16th, the fifth day of escape,

Mr. Howard informed me he had made a plan to get me out of the country. The mine was connected with the railway by a branch line. In the neighborhood of the mine there lived a Dutchman, Burgener by name, who was sending a consignment of wool to Delagoa Bay on the 19th. This gentleman was well disposed to the British. He had been approached by Mr. Howard, had been made a party to our secret, and was willing to assist. Mr. Burgener's wool was packed in great bales and would fill two or three large trucks. These trucks were to be loaded at the mine's siding. The bales could be so packed as to leave a small place in the center of the truck in which I could be concealed. A tarpaulin would be fastened over each truck after it had been loaded, and it was very unlikely indeed that, if the fastenings were found intact, it would be removed at the frontier. Did I agree to take this chance?

I was more worried about this than almost anything that had happened to me so far in my adventure. When by extraordinary chance one has gained some great advantage or prize and actually had it in one's possession and been enjoying it for several days, the idea of losing it becomes almost insupportable. I had really come to count upon freedom as a certainty, and the idea of having to put myself in a position in which I should be perfectly helpless, without a move of any kind, absolutely at the caprice of a searching party at the frontier, was profoundly harassing. Rather than face this ordeal I would much have preferred to start off on the veldt with a pony and a guide, and far from the haunts of man to make my way march by march beyond the wide territories of the Boer Republic. However, in the end I accepted the proposal of my generous rescuer, and arrangements were made accordingly.

I should have been still more anxious if I could have read some of the telegrams which were reaching English newspapers. For instance:

Pretoria, December 13.—Though Mr. Churchill's escape was cleverly executed there is little chance of his being able to cross the border.

Pretoria, December 14.—It is reported that Mr. Winston Churchill has been captured at the border railway station of Komati Poort.

Lourenço Marques, December 16.—It is reported that Mr. Churchill has been captured at Waterval Boven.

London, December 16.—With reference to the escape from Pretoria of Mr. Winston Churchill, fears are expressed that he may be captured again before long and if so may probably be shot;

or if I had read the description of myself and the reward for my recapture which were now widely distributed or posted along the railway line. I am glad I knew nothing of all this.

The afternoon of the 18th dragged slowly away. I remember that I spent the greater part of it reading Stevenson's *Kidnapped*. Those thrilling pages which describe the escape of David Balfour and Alan Breck in the glens awakened sensations with which I was only too familiar. To be a fugitive, to be a hunted man, to be "wanted," is a mental experience by itself. The risks of the battlefield, the hazards of the bullet or the shell are one thing. Having the police after you is another. The need for concealment and deception breeds an actual sense of guilt very undermining to morale. Feeling that at any moment the officers of the law may present themselves or any stranger may ask the questions, "Who are you?" "Where do you come from?" "Where are you going?"—to which questions no satisfactory answer could be given—gnawed the structure of self-confidence. I dreaded in every fiber the ordeal which awaited me at Komati Poort and which I must impotently and passively endure if I was to make good my escape from the enemy.

In this mood I was startled by the sound of rifle-shots close at hand, one after another at irregular intervals. A sinister explanation flashed through my mind. The Boers had come! Howard and his handful of Englishmen were in open rebellion in the heart of the enemy's country! I had been strictly enjoined upon no account to leave my hiding-place behind the packing-cases in any circumstances whatever, and I accordingly remained there in great anxiety. Presently it became clear that the worst had not happened. The sounds of voices and presently of laughter came from the office. Evidently a conversation amicable, sociable in its character was in progress. I resumed my companionship with Alan Breck. At last the voices died away, and then after an interval my door was opened and Mr. Howard's pale, sombre face appeared, suffused by a broad grin. He relocked the door behind him and walked delicately towards me, evidently in high glee.

"The Field Cornet has been here," he said. "No, he was not looking for you. He says they caught you at Waterval Boven yesterday. But I didn't want him messing about, so I challenged him to a rifle match at bottles. He won two pounds off me and has gone away delighted.

"It is all fixed up for to-night," he added.

"What do I do?" I asked.

"Nothing. You simply follow me when I come for you."

At two o'clock on the morning of the 19th I awaited, fully dressed, the signal. The door opened. My host appeared. He beckoned. Not a word was spoken on either side. He led the way through the front office to the siding where three large bogie trucks stood. Three figures, evidently Dewsnap and the miners, were strolling about in different directions in the moonlight. A gang of Kaffirs were busy lifting an enormous bale into the rearmost truck. Howard strolled along to the first truck and walked across the line past the end of it. As he did so he pointed with his left hand. I nipped on to the buffers and saw before me a hole between the wool bales and the end of the truck, just wide enough to squeeze into. From this there led a narrow tunnel formed of wool bales into the center of the truck. Here was a space wide enough to lie in, high enough to sit up in. In this I took up my abode.

Three or four hours later, when gleams of daylight had reached me through the interstices of my shelter and through chinks in the boards of the floorings of the truck, the noise of an approaching engine was heard. Then came the bumping and banging of coupling up. And again, after a further pause, we started rumbling off on our journey into the unknown.

I now took stock of my new abode and of the resources in munitions and supplies with which it was furnished. First there was a revolver. This was a moral support, though it was not easy to see in what way it could helpfully be applied to any problem I was likely to have to solve. Secondly, there were two roast chickens, some slices of meat, a loaf of bread, a melon, and three bottles of cold tea. The journey to the sea was not expected to take more than sixteen hours, but no one could tell what delay might occur to ordinary commercial traffic in time of war.

There was plenty of light now in the recess in which I was confined. There were many crevices in the boards composing the sides and floor of the truck, and through these the light found its way between the wool bales. Working along the tunnel to the end of the truck, I found a chink which must have been nearly an eighth of an inch in width, and through which it was possible to gain a partial view of the outer world. To check the progress of the journey I had learned by heart beforehand the names of all the stations on the route. I can remember many of them today: Witbank, Middleburg, Bergendal, Belfast, Dalmanutha, Machadodorp, Waterval Boven, Waterval Onder, Elands, Nooidgedacht, and so on to Komati Poort. We had by now reached the first of these. At this point the branch line from the mine joined the railway. Here, after two or three hours' delay and shunting, we were evidently coupled up to a regular train, and soon started off at a superior and very satisfactory pace.

All day long we traveled eastward through the Transvaal, and when darkness fell we were laid up for the night at a station which, according to my reckoning, was Waterval Boven. We had accomplished nearly half of our journey. But how long should we wait on this siding? It might be for days; it would certainly be until the next morning. During all the dragging hours of the day I had lain on the floor of the truck occupying my mind as best I could, painting bright pictures of the pleasures of freedom, of the excitement of rejoining the army, of the triumph of a successful escape—but haunted also perpetually by anxieties about the search at the frontier, an ordeal inevitable and constantly approaching. Now another apprehension laid hold upon me. I wanted to go to sleep. Indeed, I did not think I could possibly keep awake. But if I slept I might snore! And if I snored while the train was at rest in the silent siding, I might be heard. And if I were heard! I decided in principle that it was only prudent to abstain from sleep, and

shortly afterwards fell into a blissful slumber from which I was awakened the next morning by the banging and jerking of the train as the engine was again coupled to it.

Between Waterval Boven and Waterval Onder there is a very steep descent which the locomotive accomplishes by means of a rack and pinion. We ground our way down this at three or four miles an hour, and this feature made my reckoning certain that the next station was, in fact, Waterval Onder. All this day, too, we rattled through the enemy's country, and late in the afternoon we reached the dreaded Komati Poort. Peeping through my chink, I could see this was a considerable place, with numerous tracks of rails and several trains standing on them. Numbers of people were moving about. There were many voices and much shouting and whistling. After a preliminary inspection of the scene I retreated, as the train pulled up, into the very center of my fastness, and covering myself up with a piece of sacking lay flat on the floor of the truck and awaited developments with a beating heart.

Three or four hours passed, and I did not know whether we had been searched or not. Several times people had passed up and down the train talking in Dutch. But the tarpaulins had not been removed, and no special examination seemed to have been made of the truck. Meanwhile darkness had come on, and I had to resign myself to an indefinite continuance of my uncertainties. It was tantalizing to be held so long in jeopardy after all these hundreds of miles had been accomplished, and I was now within a few hundred yards of the frontier. Again I wondered about the dangers of snoring. But in the end I slept without mishap.

We were still stationary when I awoke. Perhaps they were searching the train so thoroughly that there was consequently a great delay! Alternatively, perhaps we were forgotton on the siding and would be left there for days or weeks. I was greatly tempted to peer out, but I resisted. At last, at eleven o'clock, we were coupled up, and almost immediately started. If I had been right in thinking that the station in which we had passed the night was Komati Poort, I was already in Portuguese territory. But perhaps I had made a mistake. Perhaps I had miscounted. Perhaps there was still another station before the frontier. Perhaps the search still impended. But all these doubts were dispelled when the train arrived at the next station. I peered through my chink and saw the uniform caps of the Portuguese officials on the platform and the name Resana Garcia painted on a board. I restrained all expression of my joy until we moved on again. Then, as we rumbled and banged along, I pushed my head out of the tarpaulin and sang and shouted and crowed at the top of my voice. Indeed, I was so carried away by thankfulness and delight that I fired my revolver two or three times in the air as a *feu de joie*. None of these follies led to any evil results.

It was late in the afternoon when we reached Lourenço Marques. My train ran into a goods yard, and a crowd of Kaffirs advanced to unload it. I thought the moment had now come for me to quit my hiding-place, in which I had passed nearly three anxious and uncomfortable days. I had already thrown out every vestige of food and had removed all traces of my occupation. I now slipped out at the end of the truck between the couplings, and mingling unnoticed with the Kaffirs and loafers in the yard— which my slovenly and unkempt appearance well fitted me to do—I strolled my way towards the gates and found myself in the streets of Lourenço Marques.

Burgener was waiting outside the gates. We exchanged glances. He turned and walked off into the town, and I followed twenty yards behind. We walked through several streets and turned a number of corners. Presently he stopped and stood for a moment gazing up at the roof of the opposite house. I looked in the same direction, and there—blest vision!—I saw floating the gay colors of the Union Jack. It was the British Consulate.

The secretary of the British Consul evidently did not expect my arrival.

"Be off," he said. "The Consul cannot see you to-day. Come to his office at nine to-morrow, if you want anything."

At this I became so angry, and repeated so loudly that I insisted on seeing the Consul personally at once, that that gentleman himself looked out of the window and finally came down to the door and asked me my name. From that moment every resource of hospitality and welcome was at my disposal. A hot bath, clean clothing, an excellent dinner, means of telegraphing—all I could want.

I devoured the file of newspapers which was placed before me. Great events had taken place since I had climbed the wall of the States Model Schools. The Black Week of the Boer War had descended on the British Army. General Gatacre at Stormberg, Lord Methuen at Magersfontein, and Sir Redvers Buller at Colenso, had all suffered staggering defeats, and casualties on a scale unknown to England since the Crimean War. All this made me eager to rejoin the army, and the Consul himself was no less anxious to get me out of Lourenço Marques, which was full of Boers and Boer sympathizers. Happily the weekly steamer was leaving for Durban that very evening; in fact, it might almost be said it ran in connection with my train. On this steamer I decided to embark.

The news of my arrival had spread like wildfire through the town, and while we were at dinner the Consul was at first disturbed to see a group of strange figures in the garden. These, however, turned out to be Englishmen fully armed who had hurried up to the Consulate determined to resist any attempt at my recapture. Under the escort of these patriotic gentlemen I marched safely through the streets to the quay, and at about ten o'clock was on salt water in the steamship *Induna*.

I reached Durban to find myself a popular hero. I was received as if I had won a great victory. The harbor was decorated with flags. Bands and crowds thronged the quays. The Admiral, the General, the Mayor pressed on board to grasp my hand. I was nearly torn to pieces by enthusiastic kindness. Whirled along on the shoulders of the crowd, I was carried to the steps of the town hall, where nothing would content them but a speech, which after a becoming reluctance I was induced to deliver. Sheaves of telegrams from all parts of the world poured in upon me, and I started that night for the Army in a blaze of triumph.

Here, too, I was received with the greatest goodwill. I took up my quarters in the very plate-layer's hut within one hundred yards of which I had a little more than a month before been taken prisoner, and there with the rude plenty of the Natal campaign celebrated by a dinner to many friends my good fortune and Christmas Eve.

THE ISLAND RACE
By WINSTON CHURCHILL

CONTENTS

THE ISLAND RACE

By WINSTON CHURCHILL

Our story centers in an island, not widely sundered from the Continent, and so titled that its mountains lie all to the west and north, while south and east is a gently undulating landscape of wooded valleys, open downs, and slow rivers. It is very accessible to the invader, whether he comes in peace or war, as pirate or merchant, conqueror or missionary. Those who dwell there are not insensitive to any shift of power, any change of faith, or even fashion, on the mainland, but they give to every practice, every doctrine that comes to it from abroad, its peculiar turn and imprint. . . .

CHAPTER ONE

The Island Race

In the summer of the Roman year 699, now described as the year 55 before the birth of Christ, the Proconsul of Gaul, Gaius Julius Cæsar, turned his gaze upon Britain. He knew that it was inhabited by the same type of tribesmen who confronted the Roman arms in Germany, Gaul, and Spain. To Cæsar the Island presented itself as an integral part of his task of subjugating the Northern barbarians to the rule and system of Rome. All that mattered was to choose a good day in the fine August weather, throw a few legions on to the nearest shore, and see what there was in this strange Island. Cæsar's vision pierced the centuries, and where he conquered civilization dwelt.

What was, in fact, this Island which now for the first time in coherent history was to be linked with the great world? We have dug up in the present age from the gravel of Swanscombe a human skull which is certainly a quarter of a million years old. It is said that the whole of Southern Britain could in this period support upon its game no more than seven hundred families. Already man had

found out that a flint was better than a fist. His descendants would burrow deep in the chalk and gravel for battle-axe flints of the best size and quality, and gain survival thereby. But so far he had only learned to chip his flints into rough tools.

At the close of the Ice Age changes in climate brought about the collapse of the hunting civilizations of Old Stone Age Man, and after a very long period of time the tides of invasion brought Neolithic culture into the Western forests. The newcomers had a primitive agriculture. Presently they constructed earthwork enclosures on the hilltops, into which they drove their cattle at night-time. Moreover, Neolithic man had developed a means of polishing his flints into perfect shape for killing. This betokened a great advance; but others were in prospect.

In early days Britain was part of the Continent. A wide plain joined England and Holland, in which the Thames and the Rhine met together and poured their waters northward. In some slight movement of the earth's surface this plain sank a few hundred feet, and admitted the ocean to the North Sea and the

Baltic. Another tremor, important for our story, sundered the cliffs of Dover from those of Cape Gris Nez, and the scour of the ocean and its tides made the Straits of Dover and the English Channel. Britain was still little more than a promontory of Europe, or divided from it by a narrow tide race which has gradually enlarged into the Straits of Dover, when the Pyramids were a-building, and when learned Egyptians were laboriously exploring the ancient ruins of Sakkara.

While what is now our Island was still joined to the Continent another great improvement was made in human methods of destruction. Copper and tin were discovered and worried out of the earth; the one too soft and the other too brittle for the main purpose, but, blended by human genius, they opened the Age of Bronze. Other things being equal, the men with bronze could beat the men with flints. The discovery was hailed, and the Bronze Age began. The Late Bronze Age in the southern parts of Britain, according to most authorities, began about 1000 B.C. and lasted until about 400 B.C.

At this point the march of invention brought a new factor upon the scene. Iron was dug and forged. Men armed with iron entered Britain from the Continent and killed the men of bronze. The Iron Age immigrations brought with them a revival of the hill-top camps, which had ceased to be constructed since the Neolithic Age.

The last of the successive waves of Celtic inroad and supersession which marked the Iron Age came in the early part of the first century B.C. There is no doubt that the Belgæ were by far the most enlightened invaders who had hitherto penetrated the recesses of the Island. This active, alert, conquering, and ruling race established themselves wherever they went with ease and celerity, and might have looked forward to a long dominion. But the tramp of the legions

had followed hard behind them, and they must soon defend the prize they had won against still better men and higher systems of government and war.

Meanwhile, in Rome, at the center and summit, only vague ideas prevailed about the Western islands. These were the ultimate fringes of the world. Still, there was the tin trade, in which important interests were concerned, and Polybius, writing about 140 B.C., shows that this aspect at least had been fully discussed by commercial writers.

Late in August 55 B.C. Cæsar sailed with eighty transports and two legions at midnight, and descended upon Albion on the low, shelving beach between Deal and Walmer. There was a short, ferocious fight amid the waves, but the Romans reached the shore, and, once arrayed, forced the Britons to flight. Cæsar's landing, however, was only the first of his troubles. His cavalry, in eighteen transports, caught by a sudden gale, drifted far down the Channel, and were thankful to regain the Continent. The high tide of the full moon wrought grievous damage to his fleet at anchor. The Britons had sued for peace after the battle on the beach, but now in great numbers they attacked the Roman foragers. Discipline and armor once again told their tale. The British submitted. Their conqueror imposed only nominal terms. He never even pretended that his expedition had been a success.

To supersede the record of it he came again the next year, this time with five legions and some cavalry conveyed in eight hundred ships. The landing was unimpeded, but again the sea assailed him. He was forced to spend ten days in hauling all his ships on to the shore, and in fortifying the camp of which they then formed part. This done he renewed his invasion and crossed the Thames near Brentford. But the British had found a leader in the chief Cassivellaunus, who was a master of war under the prevailing conditions. Dismissing to their homes the mass of untrained foot-soldiers and peasantry, he kept pace with the invaders march by march with his chariots and horsemen. None the less Cæsar captured his first stronghold; the tribes began to make terms for themselves; a well-conceived plan for destroying Cæsar's base on the Kentish shore was defeated. Cassivellaunus negotiated a further surrender of hostages and a promise of tribute and submission, in return for which Cæsar was again content to quit the Island. Cæsar had his triumph, and British captives trod their dreary path at his tail through the streets of Rome; but for nearly a hundred years no invading army landed upon the Island coasts.

In the year A.D. 41 the murder of the Emperor Caligula, and a chapter of accidents, brought his uncle, the clownish scholar Claudius, to the throne of the world. He was attracted by the idea of gaining a military reputation. In the year 43, almost one hundred years after Julius Cæsar's evacuation, a powerful, well-organized Roman army of some twenty thousand men was prepared for the subjugation of Britain.

The internal situation favored the invaders. Cunobelinus (Shakespeare's Cymbeline) had established an overlordship over the South-East of the Island, with his capital at Colchester. But in his old age dissensions had begun to impair his authority, and on his death the kingdom was ruled jointly by his sons Caractacus and Togodumnus. They were not everywhere recognized, and they had no time to form a union of the tribal kingdom before the Roman commander, Plautius, and his legions arrived. The people of Kent fell back on the tactics of Cassivellaunus, and Plautius had much trouble in searching them out; but when he did find them he first defeated Carac-

tacus, and then his brother somewhere in East Kent. Then, advancing along Cæsar's old line of march, he came on a river he had not heard of, the Medway. "The barbarians thought that the Romans would not be able to cross without a bridge, and consequently bivouacked in rather careless fashion on the opposite bank";[1] nevertheless, the Britons faced them on the second day, and were only broken by a flank attack, Vespasian —some day to be Emperor himself— having discovered a ford higher up. This victory marred the stage-management of the campaign. Plautius won his battle too soon, and in the wrong place. Something had to be done to show that the Emperor's presence was necessary to victory. So Claudius, who had been waiting on events in France, crossed the seas, bringing substantial reinforcements, including a number of elephants. A battle was procured, and the Romans won. Claudius returned to Rome to receive from the Senate the title of "Britannicus" and permission to celebrate a triumph. But the British war continued. Caractacus escaped to the Welsh border, and, rousing its tribes, maintained an indomitable resistance for more than six years.

"In this year A.D. 61," according to Tacitus,[2] "a severe disaster was sustained in Britain." Suetonius, the new Governor, had engaged himself deeply in the West. The King of the East Anglican Iceni had died. "His kingdom was plundered by centurions, and his private property by slaves, as if they had been captured in war; his widow Boadicea [relished by the learned as Boudicca] was flogged, and his daughters outraged; the chiefs of the Iceni were robbed of

[1] Dio Cassius, Book LX.
[2] Extracts from Tacitus' *Annals* are from G. G. Ramsay's translation; passages from the *Agricola* come from the translation of Church and Brodribb.

their ancestral properties as if the Romans had received the whole country as a gift, and the king's own relatives were reduced to slavery."

In all Britain there were only four legions, at most twenty thousand men. The Fourteenth and Twentieth were with Suetonius on his Welsh campaign. The Ninth was at Lincoln, and the Second at Gloucester. The first target of the revolt was Camulodunum (Colchester), the center of Roman authority and Roman religion. The town was burned to ashes. Everyone, Roman or Romanized, was massacred and everything destroyed. Meanwhile, the Ninth Legion was marching to the rescue. The victorious Britons advanced from the sack of Colchester to meet it. By sheer force of numbers they overcame the Roman infantry and slaughtered them to a man, and the commander, Petilius Cerialis, was content to escape with his cavalry. Such were the tidings which reached Suetonius in Anglesey. He, "undaunted, made his way through a hostile country to Londinium, a town which, though not dignified by the title of colony, was a busy emporium for traders." This is the first mention of London in literature. The citizens implored Suetonius to protect them, but when he heard that Boadicea, having chased Cerialis towards Lincoln, had turned and was marching south he took the hard but right decision to leave them to their fate. The slaughter which fell upon London was universal. Boadicea then turned upon Verulamium (St. Albans). A like total slaughter and obliteration was inflicted. "No less," according to Tacitus, "than seventy thousand citizens and allies were slain" in these three cities. This is probably the most horrible episode which our Island has known.

"And now Suetonius, having with him the Fourteenth Legion, with the veterans of the Twentieth, and the auxiliaries nearest at hand, making up a force of about ten thousand fully armed men, resolved . . . for battle." At heavy adverse odds Roman discipline and tactical skill triumphed. Boadicea poisoned herself.

Suetonius now thought only of vengeance, and the extermination of the entire ancient British race might have followed but for the remonstrances of a new Procurator, supported by his Treasury seniors at Rome, who saw themselves about to be possessed of a desert instead of a province. In the end it was resolved to make the best of the Britons. The Emperor Nero sent a new Governor, who made a peace with the desperate tribesmen which enabled their blood to be perpetuated in the Island race.

In A.D. 78 Agricola, a Governor of talent and energy, was sent to Britannia. With military ability Agricola united a statesmanlike humanity and showed "such a preference for the natural powers of the Britons over the more labored style of the Gauls" that the well-to-do classes were conciliated and became willing to adopt the toga and other Roman fashions. Although in the Senate and governing circles in Rome it was constantly explained that the Imperial policy adhered to the principle of the great Augustus, that the frontiers should be maintained but not extended, Agricola was permitted to conduct six campaigns of expansion in Britannia. But there was no safety or permanent peace for the British province unless he could subdue the powerful tribes and large bands of desperate warriors who had been driven northwards by his advance. The decisive battle was fought in A.D. 83 at Mons Graupius, a place unidentified, though some suggest the Pass of Killiecrankie. Here, according to the Roman account, "ten thousand of the enemy were slain, and on our side there were about three hundred and sixty men." The way to the entire subjugation of the Island was now open, and had Agricola been encouraged or at least supported by the Imperial Government the course of history might have been altered. But Caledonia was to Rome only a sensation: the real strain was between the Rhine and the Danube. Counsels of prudence prevailed, and the remnants of the British fighting men were left to molder in the Northern mists. In the wild North and West freedom found refuge among the mountains, but elsewhere the conquest and pacification were at length complete and Britannia became one of the forty-five provinces of the Roman Empire.

For nearly three hundred years Britain, reconciled to the Roman system, enjoyed in many respects the happiest, most comfortable, and most enlightened times its inhabitants have had. In all, the army of occupation numbered less than forty thousand men, and after a few generations was locally recruited and almost of purely British birth. In this period, almost equal to that which separates us from the reign of Queen Elizabeth I, well-to-do persons in Britain lived better than they ever did until Late Victorian times. In culture and learning Britain was a pale reflection of the Roman scene, not so lively as the Gallic. But there was law; there was order; there was peace; there was warmth; there was food, and a long-established custom of life. The population was free from barbarism without being sunk in sloth or luxury. Indeed, it may be said that of all the provinces few assimilated the Roman system with more aptitude than the Islanders. A poll in the fourth century would have declared for an indefinite continuance of the Roman régime.

Towns were planned in chessboard squares for communities dwelling under orderly government. During the first century the builders evidently took a san-

guine view of the resources and future of Britannia, and all their towns were projected to meet an increasing population. We may assume a population of at least a million in the Romanized area. But there are no signs that any large increase of population accompanied the Roman system. The conquerors who so easily subdued and rallied the Britons to their method of social life brought with them no means, apart from stopping tribal war, of increasing the annual income derived from the productivity of the soil. The cultivated ground was still for the most part confined to the lighter and more easily cultivated upland soils, which had for thousands of years been worked in a primitive fashion. Such mining of lead and tin, such smelting, as had existed from time immemorial may have gained something from orderly administration; but there was no new science, no new thrust of power and knowledge in the material sphere. These conditions soon cast their shadows upon the boldly planned towns. The surrounding agricultural prosperity was not sufficient to support the hopes of their designers. Nevertheless, men dwelt safely, and what property they had was secured by iron laws. Urban life in Britannia was a failure, not of existence, but of expansion.

We owe London to Rome. An extensive and well-planned city with mighty walls took the place of the wooden trading settlement of A.D. 61, and soon achieved a leading place in the life of the Roman province of Britain, superseding the old Belgic capital, Colchester, as the commercial center. The comparative unsuccess of urban life led the better-class Roman Britons to establish themselves in the country, and thus the villa system was the dominant feature of Roman Britain in its heyday. A very large number of comfortable dwellings, each with its lands around it, rose and thrived. At least five hundred have been explored in the

Southern counties. None is found farther north than Yorkshire or farther west than the Glamorgan sea-plain. The towns were shrunken after the third century. The villas still flourished in the fourth, and in some cases lingered on into the darkening days of the fifth.

The work of Agricola in Northern Britain had been left unfinished and the position which he had won in Scotland had to be gradually abandoned. The accession of Hadrian was marked by a serious disaster. Hadrian came himself to Britain in 122, and the reorganization of the frontier began. During the next five years a military barrier was built between the Tyne and the Solway seventy-three miles long. It consisted of a stone rampart eight to ten feet thick, sustained by seventeen forts, each garrisoned by an auxiliary cohort, about eighty castles, and double that number of signal towers. In front of the wall was a thirty-foot ditch, and behind it another ditch which seems to have been designed as a customs frontier and was probably controlled and staffed by the financial administration. Twenty years later, in the reign of the Emperor Antoninus Pius, the Roman troops pushed northwards again over the ground of Agricola's conquests, and a new wall was built across the Forth–Clyde isthmus thirty-seven miles in length. Somewhere about the year 186 the Antonine Wall was abandoned and the troops were concentrated on the original line of defense.

The first half-century after the Claudian invasion was very active in road-building. In the second century we find most of the work concentrated upon the frontiers of the military districts. By the third century the road system was complete and needed only to be kept in repair. These pedestrian facts are one measure of the rise and decline of the Roman power.

By the end of the third century Rome seemed as powerful and stable as ever. But below the surface the foundations were cracking, and through the fissures new ideas and new institutions were thrusting themselves. The essence of the Roman peace was toleration of all religions and the acceptance of a universal system of government. Every generation after the middle of the second century saw an increasing weakening of the system and a gathering movement towards a uniform religion. The institution of slavery, by which a third of Roman society was bound, could not withstand indefinitely the new dynamic thoughts which Christianity brought with it.

From outside the uncouth barbarians smote upon the barriers. We see these forces swelling like a flood against all the threatened dykes of the Roman world, not only brimming at the lip of the dam, but percolating insidiously, now by a breach, now in a mere ooze, while all the time men become conscious of the frailty of the structure itself.

From the end of the third century, when Roman civilization in Britain and the challenge to the supreme structure were equally at their height, inroads of barbarian peoples began, both from Europe and from the forlorn Island to the westward. The Scots, whom nowadays we should call the Irish, and the Picts from Scotland began to press on Hadrian's Wall, to turn both flanks of it by sea raids on a growing scale. At the same time the Saxons rowed in longboats across the North Sea and lay heavy all along the East coast from Newcastle to Dover. But although the process of wearing down was spread over many years, and misery deepened by inches, we must recognize in the year 367 circumstances of supreme and murderous horror. In that fatal year the Picts, the Scots, and the Saxons seemed to work in combination. A wide-open breach was made in the defenses, and murderous hordes poured in upon the fine world of country houses and homesteads. The villa life of Britain only feebly recovered from the disaster. The towns were already declining. Now people took refuge in them. At least they had walls.

The pages of history reveal the repeated efforts made by the Imperial Government to protect Britannia. Again and again, in spite of revolts and ingratitude, officers and troops were sent to restore order or drive back the barbarians. By the beginning of the fifth century all the legions had gone on one errand or another, and to frantic appeals for aid the helpless Emperor Honorius could only send his valedictory message in 410, that "the cantons should take steps to defend themselves."

The first glimpse we have of the British after the Roman Government had withdrawn its protection is afforded by the visit of St. Germanus in 429. He speaks of a land of wealth. There is treasure; there are flocks and herds; food is abundant; institutions, civil and religious, function; the country is prosperous, but at war. Another twelve years passed, and a Gaulish chronicler records this somber note in A.D. 441 or 442: "The Britons in these days by all kinds of calamities and disasters are falling into the power of the Saxons." What had happened? Something more than the forays of the fourth century: the mass migration from North Germany had begun. Thereafter the darkness closes in.

Imitating a common Roman practice, the dominant British chief about A.D. 450 sought to strengthen himself by bringing in a band of mercenaries from over the seas. They proved a trap. Hengist, a name frequently mentioned in Northern story, like a medieval mercenary was ready to sell his sword and his ships to anyone who would give him land on which to support his men; and what he took was the future kingdom of Kent. But the British resistance stiffened as the invaders got away from the coast, and their advance was brought to a standstill for nearly fifty years by a great battle won at Mount Badon.

Nennius tells us the name of the British soldier who won the crowning mercy of Mount Badon, and that name takes us out of the mist of dimly remembered history into the daylight of romance. There looms, large, uncertain, dim but glittering, the legend of King Arthur and the Knights of the Round Table. Somewhere in the Island a great captain gathered the forces of Roman Britain and fought the barbarian invaders to the death. Around him, around his name and his deeds, shine all that romance and poetry can bestow. True or false, they have gained an immortal hold upon the thoughts of men. If we could see exactly what happened we should find ourselves in the presence of a theme as well founded, as inspired, and as inalienable from the inheritance of mankind as the *Odyssey* or the Old Testament. It is all true, or it ought to be; and more and better besides. And wherever men are fighting against barbarism, tyranny, and massacre, for freedom, law, and honor, let them remember that the fame of their deeds, even though they themselves be exterminated, may perhaps be celebrated as long as the world rolls round. Let us then declare that King Arthur and his noble knights, guarding the Sacred Flame of Christianity and the theme of a world order, sustained by valor, physical strength, and good horses and armor, slaughtered innumerable hosts of foul barbarians and set decent folk an example for all time.

Did the invaders exterminate the native population, or did they superimpose themselves upon them and become to some extent blended with them? The invaders themselves were not without their yearnings for settled security. Their hard laws, the rigors they endured, were but the results of the immense pressures behind them as the hordes of avid humanity spread westward from Central Asia. To these savage swords Britain seemed a refuge. In the wake of the raiders there grew steadily the plan and system of settlement.

Serious writers contend that the Anglo-Saxon conquest was for the bulk of the British community mainly a change of masters. The rich were slaughtered; the brave and proud fell back in large numbers upon the Western mountains. The Saxon was moreover a valley-settler. But in many places a long time must have passed before these lower grounds could be cleared and drained, and while this work was in progress what did he live on but the produce of the upland British farms? It is more natural to suppose that he would keep his natives working as serfs on the land with which they were familiar until the valley was ready for sowing. Then the old British farms would go down to grass, and the whole population would cluster in the village by the stream or the spring. But the language of the valley-settlers, living in compact groups, would be dominant over that of the hill-cultivators, scattered in small and isolated holdings. The study of modern English place-names has shown that hill, wood, and stream names are often Celtic in origin, even in regions where the village names are Anglo-Saxon. In this way, without assuming any wholesale extermination, the disappearance of the British language can be explained even in areas where we know a British population to have survived. No uniformity of practice prevailed in the Island. There was no color bar. In physical type the two races resembled each other; and the probabilities are that in many districts a substantial British element was incorporated in the Saxon stock.

Of all the tribes of the Germanic race none was more cruel than the Saxons. Although tradition and the Venerable Bede assign the conquest of Britain to the Angles, Jutes, and Saxons together, and although the various settlements have tribal peculiarities, it is probable that before their general exodus from Schleswig-Holstein the Saxons had virtually incorporated the other two strains.

In the tribal conceptions of the Germanic nation lie, no doubt, many of those principles which are now admired, and which have formed a recognizable part of the message which the English-speaking peoples have given to the world. But the conquerors of Roman Britain, far from practicing these ideals, introduced a whole scheme of society which was fundamentally sordid and vicious. The invaders brought into Britain a principle common to all Germanic tribes, namely, the use of the money power to regulate all the legal relations of men. An elaborate tariff prescribed in shillings the "wergild" or exact value or worth of every man. The life of a slaughtered man could be compounded for cash. With money all was possible; without it only retribution or loss of liberty.

The great transition which we witness among the emigrants is the abandonment of blood and kin as the theme of their society and its replacement by local societies and lordship based on the ownership of land. The armed farmer-colonists found themselves forced to accept a stronger State authority owing to the stresses of continued military action. In Germany they had no kings. They developed them in Britain from leaders who claimed descent from the ancient gods. The position of the king continually increased in importance, and his supporters or companions gradually formed a new class in society, which carried with it the germ of feudalism, and was in the end to dominate all other conventions. The spoils of war were soon consumed, but the land remained for ever. Insensibly, at first, but with growing speed from the seventh century onwards, a landed aristocracy was created owing all it had to the king.

But with this movement towards a more coherent policy or structure of society there came also a welter of conflicting minor powers. For a long time the Island presented only the spectacle of a chaos arising from the strife of small fiercely organized entities. Although from the time of the immigration the people south of the Humber were generally subject to a common overlord, they were never able to carry the evolution of kingship forward to a national throne.

Christianity had not been established as the religion of the Empire during the first two centuries of the Roman occupation of Britain. There arose, however, a British Christian Church which sent its bishops to the early councils, and fell back with other survivors upon the Western parts of the Island. Such was the gulf between the warring races that no attempt was made at any time by the British bishops to Christianize the invaders.

After an interval one of their leading luminaries, afterwards known as St. David, accomplished the general conversion of what is now Wales. St. Patrick sailed back in 432 to the wild regions which he had quitted, converted kingdoms which were still pagan, and brought Ireland into touch with the Church of Western Europe. Columba, born half a century after St. Patrick's death, but an offspring of his Church, and imbued with his grace and fire, proved a new champion of the faith. From the monastery which he established in the island of Iona his disciples went forth to the British kingdom of Strathclyde, to the Pictish tribes of the North, and to the Anglian kingdom of North-umbria. He is the founder of the Scottish Christian Church. There was, however, a distinction in the form of Christianity which reached England through the mission of St. Columba and that which was more generally accepted throughout the Christianized countries of Europe. It was monastic in its form, and it traveled from the East through Northern Ireland to its new home without touching at any moment the Roman center.

These were the days when it was the first care of the Bishop of Rome that all Christ's sheep should be gathered into one fold. It was decided in the closing decade of the sixth century that a guide and teacher should be sent to England to diffuse and stimulate the faith, to convert the heathen, and also to bring about an effective working union between British Christians and the main body of the Church. The King of Kent had married Bertha, a daughter of the Frankish King, the descendant of Clovis, now enthroned in Paris. St. Augustine, as he is known to history, began his mission in 596 under hopeful auspices. With the aid of the Frankish Princess he converted King Ethelbert, who had for reasons of policy long meditated this step. Ethelbert, as overlord of England, exercised an effective authority over the kingdoms of the South and West. He was himself, as the only English Christian ruler, in a position where he might hold out the hand to the British princes, and, by using the Christian faith as a bond of union, establish his supremacy over the whole country. This, no doubt, was also in accordance with the ideas which Augustine had carried from Rome. Thus, at the opening of the seventh century, Ethelbert and Augustine summoned a conference of the British Christian bishops. It failed for two separate reasons: first, the sullen and jealous temper of the British bishops, and, secondly, the tactless arrogance of St. Augustine. All further efforts by Rome through Ethelbert and the Kentish kingdom to establish even the slightest contact with Christian Britain were inexorably repulsed. Augustine's mission therefore drew to a dignified but curtailed end.

Almost a generation passed before envoys from Rome began to penetrate into Northern England and rally its peoples to Christianity, and then it came about in the wake of political and dynastic developments. The Crown of Northumbria was gained by an exiled prince, Edwin, who by his abilities won his way, step by step, to the foremost position in England. Edwin married a Christian princess of Kent, whose religion he had promised to respect. Consequently, in her train from Canterbury to Edwin's capital at York there rode in 625 the first Roman missionary to Northern England, Paulinus, an envoy who had first come to Britain in the days of St. Augustine, twenty-four years before. Paulinus converted Edwin, and the ample kingdom of Northumbria, shaped like England itself in miniature, became Christian. But this blessed event brought with it swift and dire consequences. The overlordship of Northumbria was fiercely resented by King Penda of Mercia, or, as we should now say, of the Midlands. In 633 Penda, the heathen, made an unnatural alliance with Cadwallon, the Christian British King of North Wales, with the object of overthrowing the suzerainty of Edwin and breaking the Northumbrian power. Here for the first time noticed in history British and English fought side by side. In a savage battle near Doncaster Edwin was defeated and slain, and his head— not the last—was exhibited on the ramparts of captured York. But the inherent power of Northumbria was great. The destruction of Cadwallon and the clearance from Northumbria of the wild Western Britons, whose atrocities had united all the Saxon forces in the North,

was the prelude to the struggle with King Penda. Much of Mercia and East Anglia, as well as Northumbria, was recovered to Christianity by the Celtic missionaries. With the defeat and death of Penda, and upon the surge of all the passions which had been loosed, Anglo-Saxon England was definitely rallied to the Christian faith.

Henceforward the issue is no longer whether the Island shall be Christian or pagan, but whether the Roman or the Celtic view of Christianity shall prevail. These differences persisted across the centuries, much debated by all the parties concerned. The celebrated and largely successful attempt to solve them took place at the Synod of Whitby in 663. The issues hung in the balance, but in the end after much pious dissertation the decision was taken that the Church of Northumbria should be a definite part of the Church of Rome and of the Catholic system. Mercia soon afterwards conformed. These events brought Northumbria to her zenith. In Britain for the first time there was achieved a unity of faith, morals, and Church government covering five-sixths of the Island.

The Papacy realized that its efforts to guide and govern British Christianity through the kingdom of Kent had been misplaced. Two fresh emissaries were chosen in 668 to carry the light into the Northern mists, the first a native of Asia Minor, Theodore of Tarsus, the second an African named Hadrian from Carthage. When their work was finished the Anglican Church raised its mitred front in a majesty which has not yet been dimmed. Before he died in 690 Theodore had increased the number of bishoprics from seven to fourteen, and by his administrative skill he gave the Church a new cohesion. This remarkable Asiatic was the earliest of the statesmen of England, and guided her steps with fruitful wisdom.

There followed a long and intricate rivalry for leadership between the various Anglo-Saxon kings which occupied the seventh and eighth centuries. Bede, a monk of high ability, alone attempts to paint for us, and, so far as he can, explain the spectacle of Anglo-Saxon England in its first phase: seven kingdoms of varying strength, all professing the Gospel of Christ, and striving over each other for mastery by force and fraud.

The leadership of Saxon England passed to Mercia. For nearly eighty years two Mercian kings asserted or maintained their ascendancy over all England south of the Humber. Ethelbald took to styling himself "King of the Southern English" and "King of Britain." Little is known of Offa, who reigned for the second forty years, but the imprint of his power is visible not only throughout England but upon the Continent; he was reputed to be the first "King of all the English," and he had the first quarrel since Roman times with the mainland. Charlemagne wished one of his sons to marry one of Offa's daughters. Here we have an important proof of the esteem in which the Englishman was held. Offa stipulated that his son must simultaneously marry a daughter of Charlemagne. The founder of the Holy Roman Empire appeared at first incensed at this assumption of equality, but after a while he found it expedient to renew his friendship with Offa. It seems that "the King of the English" had placed an embargo upon Continental merchandise, and the inconvenience of this retaliation speedily overcame all points of pride and sentiment. Here was an English king who ruled over the greatest part of the Island, whose trade was important, and whose daughters were fit consorts for the sons of Charles the Great. We have a tangible monument of Offa in the immense dyke which he caused to be built between con-verted Saxon England and the still unconquered British. It conveys to us an idea of the magnitude and force of Offa's kingdom.

Art and culture grew in the track of order. The English had brought with them from their Continental home a vigorous barbaric art and a primitive poetry. Once established in the Island, this art was profoundly affected by the Celtic genius for curve and color, a genius suppressed by Roman provincialism, but breaking out again as soon as the Roman hand was removed. Christianity gave them a new range of subjects to adorn. The results are seen in such masterpieces as the Lindisfarne Gospels and the sculptured crosses of Northern England. A whole world of refinement and civilization of which the monasteries were the home, and of which only fragments have come down to us, had come into being. Bede was universally honored as the greatest scholar of his day. In the eighth century indeed England had claims to stand in the van of Western culture. England, with an independent character and personality, might scarcely yet be a part of a world civilization as in Roman times, but there was a new England, closer than ever before to national unity, and with a native genius of her own.

Measure for measure, what the Saxon pirates had given to the Britons was meted out to the English after the lapse of four hundred years. In the eighth century a vehement manifestation of conquering energy appeared in Scandinavia. Norway, Sweden, and Denmark threw up bands of formidable fighting men, who, in addition to all their other martial qualities, were the hardy rovers of the sea. The relations between the Danes and the Norwegians were tangled and varying. Sometimes they raided in collusion; sometimes they fought each other in desperate battles; but to Saxon England they presented themselves in the common guise of a merciless scourge.

In 793, on a January morning, the wealthy monastic settlement of Lindisfarne (or Holy Island), off the Northumbrian coast, was suddenly attacked by a powerful fleet from Denmark. The news of the atrocity traveled far and wide, not only in England but throughout Europe, and the loud cry of the Church sounded a general alarm. The Vikings, having a large choice of action, allowed an interval of recovery before paying another visit. It was not till 835 that the storm broke in fury, and fleets, sometimes of three or four hundred vessels, rowed up the rivers of England, France, and Russia in predatory enterprises on the greatest scale. For thirty years Southern England was constantly attacked. Paris was more than once besieged. Constantinople was assaulted. The harbor towns in Ireland were captured and held. The Swedish element penetrated into the heart of Russia, ruling the river towns and holding the trade to ransom. The Norwegian Vikings, coming from a still more severe climate, found the Scottish islands good for settlement. They reached Greenland and Stoneland (Labrador). They sailed up the St. Lawrence. They discovered America; but they set little store by the achievement.

For a long time no permanent foothold was gained in Britain or France. It was not until 865, when resistance on the Continent had temporarily stiffened, that the great Danish invasion of Northumbria and Eastern England began. Saxon England was at this time ripe for the sickle. On all sides were abbeys and monasteries, churches, and even cathedrals, possessed in that starveling age of treasures of gold and silver, of jewels, and also large stores of food, wine, and such luxuries as were known. To an undue subservience to the Church the English at this time added military mismanagement. The local noble, upon the summons of his chief or king, could call upon the able-bodied cultivators of the soil to serve in their own district for about forty days. This service, in the "fyrd," was grudgingly given, and when it was over the army dispersed without paying regard to the enemies who might be afoot for the purposes for which the campaign had been undertaken. The Danes and Norsemen had not only the advantages of surprise which sea-power so long imparted, but they showed both mobility and skill on land. Their stratagems have been highly praised. Among these "feigned flight" was foremost. They were in fact, the most audacious and treacherous type of pirate and shark that had ever yet appeared, and, owing to the very defective organization of the Saxons and the conditions of the period, they achieved a fuller realization of their desires than any of those who have emulated their proficiency—and there have been many.

Ivar "the Boneless" was a warrior of command and guile. He was the mastermind behind the Scandinavian invasion of England in the last quarter of the ninth century. In the spring of 866 his powerful army, organized on the basis of ships' companies, but now all mounted not for fighting but for locomotion, rode north along the old Roman road and was ferried across the Humber. He laid siege to York. And now—too late—the Northumbrians, who had been divided in their loyalties between two rival kings, forgot their feuds and united in one final effort. They attacked the Danish army before York. The defenders sallied out, and in the confusion the Vikings defeated them all with grievous slaughter, killing both their kings and destroying completely their power of resistance. This was the end of Northumbria.

But Ivar's object was nothing less than

the conquest of Mercia, which, as all men knew, had for nearly a hundred years represented the strength of England. The King of Mercia called for help from Wessex. The old King of Wessex was dead, but his two sons, Ethelred and Alfred, answered the appeal. They marched to his aid, but the Mercians flinched and preferred a parley. Ivar warred with policy as well as arms. While the Danes in their formidable attempt at conquest spread out from East Anglia, subdued Mercia, and ravaged Northumbria, the King of Wessex and his brother Alfred quietly built up their strength.

The Danish raiders now stayed longer every year. Thus again behind piracy and rapine there grew the process of settlement. But these settlements of the Danes differed from those of the Saxons; they were the encampment of armies, and their boundaries were the fighting fronts sustained by a series of fortified towns. Stamford, Nottingham, Lincoln, Derby, Leicester were the bases of the new invading force. The Saxons, now for four centuries entitled to be deemed the owners of the soil, very nearly succumbed completely to the Danish inroads. That they did not was due—as almost every critical turn of historic fortune has been due—to the sudden apparition in an era of confusion and decay of one of the great figures of history.

When the dynasties of Kent, Northumbria, and Mercia had disappeared all eyes turned to Wessex, where there was a royal House going back without a break to the first years of the Saxon settlement. The Danes had occupied London, not then the English capital, but a town in the kingdom of Mercia, and their army had fortified itself at Reading. Moving forward, they met the forces of the West Saxons on the Berkshire Downs, and here, in January 871, was fought the Battle of Ashdown. The fight was long

and hard. At last the Danes gave way, and, hotly pursued, fled back to Reading. This was the first time the invaders had been beaten in the field. The last of the Saxon kingdoms had withstood the assault upon it.

All through the year 871 the two armies waged deadly war. At twenty-four Alfred became King, and entered upon a desperate inheritance. Seven or eight battles were fought, and we are told the Danes usually held the field. At Wilton, in the summer, about a month after Alfred had assumed the Crown, he sustained a definite defeat in the heart of his own country. On the morrow of this misfortune Alfred thought it best to come to terms while he still had an army. We do not know the conditions, but there is no doubt that a heavy payment was among them. By this inglorious treaty and stubborn campaign Alfred secured five years in which to consolidate his power. Still maintaining their grip on London, the Danes moved back to the Midlands, which were now in complete submission.

Alfred and the men of Wessex had proved too stubborn a foe for easy subjugation. Some of the Danes wished to settle on the lands they already held. Henceforward they began to till the ground for a livelihood. From Yorkshire to Norfolk this sturdy, upstanding stock took root. As time passed they forgot the sea; they forgot the army; they thought only of the land—their own land. Although they were sufficiently skillful agriculturists, there was nothing they could teach the older inhabitants; they brought no new implements or methods, but they were resolved to learn. Thus the Danish differs in many ways from the Saxon settlement four hundred years earlier. There was no idea of exterminating the older population. The two languages were not very different; the way of life, the methods of cultivation, very much the same. The blood-stream of these vigorous individualists, proud and successful men of the sword, mingled henceforward in the Island race. They had a different view of social justice from that entertained by the manorialized Saxons. Their customary laws as they gradually took shape were an undoubted improvement upon the Saxon theme. Scandinavian England reared a free peasant population which the burdens of taxation and defense had made difficult in Wessex and English Mercia. It remained only for conversion to Christianity to mingle these races inextricably in the soul and body of a nation.

Alfred's dear-bought truce was over, and in January 878 occurred the most surprising reversal of his fortunes. His headquarters and Court lay at Chippenham, in Wiltshire. It was Twelfth Night, and the Saxons, who in these days of torment refreshed and fortified themselves by celebrating the feasts of the Church, were off their guard, engaged in pious exercises, or perhaps even drunk. Down swept the ravaging foe. The whole army of Wessex, sole guarantee of England south of the Thames, was dashed into confusion. A handful of officers and personal attendants hid themselves with Alfred in the marshes and forests of Somerset and the Isle of Athelney which rose from the quags. We see the warrior-king disguised as a minstrel harping in the Danish camps. We see him acting as kitchen-boy to a Saxon housewife in the celebrated story of Alfred and the cakes. Low were the fortunes of the once ruthless English.

The leaders of the Danish army felt sure at this time that mastery was in their hands. To the people of Wessex it seemed that all was over. Their forces were dispersed, the country overrun; their King, if alive, was a fugitive in hiding. It is the supreme proof of Alfred's quality that he was able in such a plight to exercise his full authority and keep contact with his subjects.

Towards the end of Lent the Danes suffered an unexpected misfortune in an attack on one of Alfred's strongholds on Exmoor.

> The Christians . . . judged it to be better either to suffer death or to gain the victory. Accordingly at daybreak they suddenly rushed forth against the heathen, and at the first attack they laid low most of the enemy, including their king. A few only by flight escaped to their ships.[1]

Eight hundred Danes were killed. Alfred, cheered by this news and striving to take the field again, continued a brigand warfare against the enemy while sending his messengers to summon the "fyrd," or local militia, for the end of May. All the fighting men came back. Battle must be sought before they lost interest. Alfred advanced to Ethandun—now Edington— and on the bare downs was fought the largest and culminating battle of Alfred's wars. All was staked. But the heathen had lost the favor of God through their violated oath, and eventually from this or other causes they fled from the cruel and clanging field. This time Alfred's pursuit was fruitful. Guthrum, King of the Viking army, so lately master of the one unconquered English kingdom, found himself penned in his camp. Bishop Asser says, "the heathen, terrified by hunger, cold, and fear, and at the last full of despair, begged for peace." They offered to give without return as many hostages as Alfred should care to pick and to depart forthwith. But Alfred had had longer ends in view. He could have starved them into surrender and slaughtered them to a man. He wished instead

---

[1] Quoted in Hodgkin, vol. ii, pp. 565–6.

to divide the land with them, and that the two races, in spite of fearful injuries given and received, should dwell together in amity. He received Guthrum with thirty prominent buccaneers in his camp. He stood godfather to Guthrum; he raised him from the font; he entertained him for twelve days; he presented him and his warriors with costly gifts; he called him his son. This sublime power to rise above the whole force of circumstances, to remain unbiased by the extremes of victory or defeat, to persevere in the teeth of disaster, to greet returning fortune with a cool eye, to have faith in men after repeated betrayals, raises Alfred far above the turmoil of barbaric wars to his pinnacle of deathless glory.

Fourteen years intervened between the victory of Ethandun and any serious Danish attack. Alfred worked ceaselessly to strengthen his realm. He reorganized the "fyrd," dividing it into two classes which practiced a rotation of service. He saw too the vision of English sea-power. He made great departures in ship design, and hoped to beat the Viking numbers by fewer ships of much larger size. These conclusions have only recently become antiquated. In spite of the disorders a definite treaty was achieved after the reconquest of London in 886. The treaty defined a political boundary running up the Thames, up the Lea, along the Lea to its source, then straight to Bedford, and after by the Ouse to Watling Street, beyond which no agreement was made. This line followed no natural frontiers. It recognized a war front.

King Alfred's Book of Laws, or Dooms, as set out in the existing laws of Kent, Wessex, and Mercia, attempted to blend the Mosaic code with Christian principles and old Germanic customs. The Laws of Alfred, continually amplified by his successors, grew into that body of customary law administered by the shire and hundred courts which, under the name of the Laws of St. Edward (the Confessor), the Norman kings undertook to respect, and out of which, with much manipulation by feudal lawyers, the Common Law was founded. He sought to reform the monastic life, which in the general confusion had grossly degenerated. He it was who set on foot the compiling of the *Saxon Chronicle*. The Christian culture of his Court sharply contrasted with the feckless barbarism of Viking life. The older race was to tame the warriors and teach them the arts of peace, and show them the value of a settled common existence. We are watching the birth of a nation. The result of Alfred's work was the future mingling of Saxon and Dane in a common Christian England.

One final war awaited Alfred. It was a crisis in the Viking story. Guthrum died in 891, and the pact which he had sworn with Alfred, and loosely kept, ended. Suddenly in the autumn of 892 a hostile armada of two hundred and fifty ships appeared off Lympne, carrying to the invasion of England "the Great Heathen Army" that had ravaged France. Unlike Charlemagne, Alfred had a valiant son. The King, in ill-health, is not often seen in this phase at the head of armies; we have glimpses of him, but the great episodes of the war were centered, as they should be, upon the young leaders. The English beat the Vikings. In 896 this third war petered out, and the Vikings, whose strength seemed at this time to be in decline, dispersed, some settling in the Danelaw, some going back to France.

Alfred died in 899, but the struggle with the Vikings had yet to pass through strangely contrasted phases. In his son Edward, who was immediately acclaimed King, the armies had already found a redoubtable leader. Edward the Elder, as he was afterwards called, and his sister

Ethelfleda, "the Lady of the Mercians," conducted the national war in common, and carried its success to heights which Alfred never knew. In 917 the whole resistance of East Anglia collapsed, and all the Danish leaders submitted to Edward as their protector and lord. In this hour of success Ethelfleda died, and Edward, hastening to Tamworth, was invited by the nobles of Mercia to occupy the vacant throne. Alfred's son was now undisputed King of all England south of the Humber, and the British princes of North and South Wales hastened to offer their perpetual allegiance. Edward the Elder reigned five years more in triumphant peace, and when he died in 924 his authority and his gifts passed to a third remarkable sovereign.

Athelstan, the third of the great West Saxon kings, sought at first, in accordance with the traditions of his House, peaceful relations with the unconquered parts of the Danelaw; but upon disputes arising he marched into Yorkshire in 926, and there established himself. Northumbria submitted; the Kings of the Scots and of Strathclyde acknowledged him as their "father and lord," and the Welsh princes agreed to pay tribute. There was an uneasy interlude; then in 933 came a campaign against the Scots, and in 937 a general rebellion and renewed war, organized by all the hitherto defeated characters in the drama. The victory of the English was overwhelming. Thus did King Alfred's grandson, the valiant Athelstan, become one of the first sovereigns of Western Europe. He styled himself on coin and charter *Rex totius Britanniæ*.

For eighty years five warrior-kings— Alfred, Edward, Athelstan, Edmund, and Edred—defeated the invaders. The English rule was now restored, though in a form changed by the passage of time, over the whole country. Yet underneath it there had grown up, deeply rooted in the soil, a Danish settlement covering the great Eastern plain, in which Danish blood and Danish customs survived under the authority of the English king. Finally, with this military and political revival marched a great rebirth of monastic life and learning and the beginning of our native English literature. From whatever point of view we regard it, the tenth century is a decisive step forward in the destinies of England. In the brilliant and peaceful reign of Edgar all this long building had reached its culmination. It must have seemed to contemporaries that with the magnificent Coronation at Bath in 973 the seal was set on the unity of the realm. Everywhere the courts are sitting regularly, in shire and borough and hundred; there is one coinage, and one system of weights and measures. The arts of building and decoration are reviving; learning begins to flourish again in the Church; there is a literary language, a King's English, which all educated men write. Civilization had been restored to the Island.

But now the political fabric which nurtured it was about to be overthrown. Now a child, a weakling, a vacillator, a faithless, feckless creature, succeeded to the warrior throne. We have reached the days of Ethelred the Unready. In 980 serious raids began again. We have an epic poem upon "The Battle of Maldon," fought in 991. No sooner had it begun than the English were worsted. Then followed the most shameful period of Danegeld. We have seen that Alfred in his day had never hesitated to use money as well as arms. Ethelred used money instead of arms. Panic-stricken, he planned the slaughter of all Danes in the South of England, whether in his pay or living peaceably on the land. This atrocious design was executed in 1002 on St. Brice's Day. Among the victims was Gunnhild, the wife of one of the principal Vikings, and sister of Sweyn, King of

Denmark. Sweyn swore implacable revenge, and for two years executed it upon the wretched Islanders. The fury of the avenger was not slaked by blood. A desperate effort was now made to build a fleet. Its leaders quarreled. Some ships were sunk in the fighting; others were lost in a storm, and the rest were shamefully abandoned by the naval commanders. It is vain to recount further the catalogue of miseries. It suffices to note that in 1013 Sweyn, accompanied by his younger son, Canute, though repulsed from London, was proclaimed King of England, while Ethelred fled for refuge to the Duke of Normandy, whose sister he had married. On these triumphs Sweyn died at the beginning of 1014. But soon the young Danish prince, Canute, set forth to claim the English Crown.

At this moment the flame of Alfred's line rose again in Ethelred's son, Edmund—Edmund Ironside, as he soon was called. He gained battles, he relieved London, he contended with every form of treachery; the hearts of all men went out to him. Ethelred died, and Edmund, last hope of the English, was acclaimed King. In spite of all odds and a heavy defeat he was strong enough to make a partition of the realm, and then set himself to rally his forces for the renewal of the struggle; but in 1016, at twenty-two years of age, Edmund Ironside died, and the whole realm abandoned itself to despair. All resistance, moral and military, collapsed before the Dane.

Canute became the ruling sovereign of the North, and was reckoned as having five or six kingdoms under him. But of all his realms Canute chose England for his home and capital. He married Emma of Normandy, the widow of Ethelred, and so forestalled any action by the Duke of Normandy on behalf of her descendants by Ethelred. He ruled according to the laws, and he made it known that these were to be administered in austere detachment from his executive authority. He built churches, he professed high devotion to the Christian faith and to the Papal diadem. His daughter was married to the Emperor Conrad's eldest son, who ultimately carried his empire across Schleswig to the banks of the Eider. Here again we see the power of a great man to bring order out of ceaseless broils and command harmony and unity to be his servants, and how the lack of such men has to be paid for by the inestimable suffering of the many.

Meanwhile, across the waters of the English Channel, a new military power was growing up. The Viking settlement founded in Normandy in the early years of the tenth century had become the most vigorous military State in France. In Normandy a class of knights and nobles arose who held their lands in return for military service, and sublet to inferior tenants upon the same basis. The Normans, with their craving for legality and logic, framed a general scheme of society, from which there soon emerged an excellent army. The dukes of Normandy created relations with the Church which became a model for medieval Europe. It was from this virile and well-organized land that the future rulers of England were to come.

In 1035 Canute died, and his empire with him. He left three sons, two by a former wife and one, Hardicanute, by Emma. Sweyn reigned in Norway for a spell, but his two brothers who ruled England were short-lived, and within seven years the throne of England was again vacant. There was still living in exile in Normandy Edward, the remaining son of Ethelred and Emma. The West Saxon line was the oldest in Europe. A Wessex earl, Godwin, was the leader of the Danish party in England. Godwin saw that he could consolidate his power

ATLANTIC
OCEAN

INVASIONS OF ENGLAND
8th – 11th Centuries

NORTH SEA

SCOTLAND

Scone

ANTONINE WALL

STRATHCLYDE

LINDISFARNE

Bamborough

NORTHUMBRIA

HADRIAN'S WALL

Durham

Armagh

IRISH SEA

York

HUMBER R.

DANELAW

Lincoln

Dublin

IRELAND

Nottingham

Derby

Tamworth

Leicester

Stamford

EAST
ANGLIA

WALES

M E R C I A

N

Gloucester

Maldon

Caerwent

Ashdown

Reading

London

Canterbury

Chippenham

Ethandum

WESSEX

Lympne

Glastonbury

Wilton

Winchester

Wareham

Hastings

Exeter

0   Miles   100

ENGLISH CHANNEL

FRANCE

and combine both English and Danish support by making Edward King.

Edward was a quiet, pious person, without liking for war or much aptitude for administration. His Norman upbringing made him the willing though gentle agent of Norman influence, so far as Earl Godwin would allow. For some years a bitter intrigue was carried on between Norman and Anglo-Danish influences at the English Court. A crisis came in the year 1051, when the Norman party at Court succeeded in driving Godwin into exile. But in the following year Godwin returned, backed by a force raised in Flanders, and with the active help of his son Harold. Many of the principal Norman agents in the country were expelled, and the authority of the Godwin family was felt again throughout the land.

The political condition of England at the close of the reign of Edward the Confessor was one of widespread weakness. Illuminated manuscripts, sculpture, metalwork, and architecture of much artistic merit were still produced, religious life flourished, and a basis of sound law and administration remained, but the virtues and vigor of Alfred's posterity were exhausted and the Saxon monarchy itself was in decline. The Island had come to count for little on the Continent, and had lost the thread of its own progress. The defenses, both of the coast and of the towns, were neglected. To the coming conquerors the whole system, social, moral, political, and military, seemed effete.

The figure of Edward the Confessor comes down to us faint, misty, frail. The medieval legend, carefully fostered by the Church, whose devoted servant he was, surpassed the man. Canonized in 1161, he lived for centuries in the memories of the Saxon folk. The Normans also had an interest in his fame. For them he was the King by whose wisdom the Crown had been left, or so they claimed, to their

Duke. Hence both sides blessed his memory, and until England appropriated St. George during the Hundred Years War St. Edward the Confessor was the kingdom's patron saint. St. George proved undoubtedly more suitable to the Islanders' needs, moods, and character.

CHAPTER TWO

The Making of the Nation

William of Normandy had a virile origin and a hard career. The Normans claimed that their Duke held his cousin Edward's promise of the throne. He and his knights looked out upon the world with fearless and adventurous eyes. William was in close touch with the Saxon Court, and had watched every move on the part of the supporters of the Anglo-Danish party, headed by Godwin and his son Harold.

Fate played startlingly into the hands of the Norman Duke. On some visit of inspection, probably in 1064, Harold was driven by the winds on to the French coast. The Count of Ponthieu reluctantly relinquished his windfall and conducted Harold to the Norman Court. All this story is told with irresistible charm in the tapestry chronicle of the reign commonly attributed to William's wife, Queen Matilda, but actually designed by English artists under the guidance of his half-brother, Odo, Bishop of Bayeux. It is probable that Harold swore a solemn oath to William to renounce all rights or designs upon the English Crown, and it is likely that if he had not done so he might never have seen either crown or England again.

At length, in January 1066, Edward the Confessor died, absolved, we trust, from such worldly sins as he had been tempted to commit. With his dying breath, in spite of his alleged promise to William, he is supposed to have commended Harold, his young, valiant counselor and guide, as the best choice for the Crown which the Witan, or Council, could make. At any rate, Harold, at the beginning of the fateful year 1066, was blithely accepted by London, the Midlands, and the South, and crowned King with all solemnity in Westminster Abbey. This event opened again the gates of war. Every aspiring thane who heard the news of Harold's elevation was conscious of an affront, and also of the wide ranges open to ability and the sword. Moreover, the entire structure of the feudal world rested upon the sanctity of oaths. Against the breakers of oaths the censures both of chivalry and the Church were combined with blasting force. Two rival projects of invasion were speedily prepared. The successors of Canute in Norway determined to revive their traditions of English sovereignty. An expedition was already being organized when Tostig, Harold's exiled and revengeful half-brother, ousted from his Earldom of Northumbria, arrived with full accounts of the crisis in the Island and of the weak state of its defenses. King Harold Hardrada set forth to conquer the English Crown.

Harold of England was thus faced with a double invasion from the North-East and from the South. In September 1066 he heard that a Norwegian fleet, with Hardrada and Tostig on board, had sailed up the Humber, beaten the local levies under Earls Edwin and Morcar, and encamped near York at Stamford Bridge. He now showed the fighting qualities he possessed. Within five days of the defeat of Edwin and Morcar Harold reached York, and the same day marched to confront the Norwegian army ten miles from the city. Hardrada was hit by an arrow in the throat, and Tostig, assuming the command, paid for his restless malice with his life. Though the Battle of Stamford Bridge has been over-shadowed by Hastings it has a claim to be regarded as one of the decisive contests of English history. Never again was a Scandinavian army able seriously to threaten the power of an English king or the unity of the realm.

William the Conqueror's invasion of England was planned like a business enterprise. The resources of Normandy were obviously unequal to the task; but the Duke's name was famous throughout the feudal world, and the idea of seizing and dividing England commended itself to the martial nobility of many lands. During the summer of 1066 this great gathering of audacious buccaneers, land-hungry, war-hungry, assembled in a merry company around St. Valery, at the mouth of the Somme. But the winds were contrary. For six whole weeks there was no day when the south wind blew. The bones of St. Edmund were brought from the Church of St. Valery and carried with military and religious pomp along the sea-shore. This proved effective, for the very next day the wind changed, not indeed to the south, but to the south-west. William thought this sufficient, and gave the signal. On September 28 the fleet hove in sight, and all came safely to anchor in Pevensey Bay.

Meanwhile, Harold and his house-carls, sadly depleted by the slaughter of Stamford Bridge, jingled down Ermine Street on their ponies. Remaining only five days in London, Harold marched out towards Pevensey, and in the evening of October 13 took up his position upon the slope of a hill which barred the direct march upon the capital. The military opinion of those as of these days has criticized his staking all upon an immediate battle. Some have suggested that he should have used the tactics which eleven hundred years before Cassivellaunus had employed against Cæsar. But these critics overlook the fact that whereas the Roman army consisted only of infantry, and the British only of charioteers and horsemen, Duke William's was essentially a cavalry force assisted by archers, while Harold had nothing but foot-soldiers who used horses only as transport. King Harold had great confidence in his redoubtable axe-men, and it was in good heart that he formed his shield-wall on the morning of October 14. There is a great dispute about the numbers engaged. Some modern authorities suppose the battle was fought by five or six thousand Norman knights and men-at-arms, with a few thousand archers, against eight to ten thousand axe- and spear-men, and the numbers on both sides may have been fewer. However it may be, at the first streak of dawn William set out from his camp at Pevensey, resolved to put all to the test; and Harold, eight miles away, awaited him in resolute array.

The cavalry charges of William's mail-clad knights, cumbersome in maneuver, beat in vain upon the dense, ordered masses of the English. Neither the arrow hail nor the assaults of the horsemen could prevail against them. Never, it was said, had the Norman knights met foot-soldiers of this stubbornness. The autumn afternoon was far spent before any result had been achieved, and it was then that William adopted the time-honored ruse of a feigned retreat. The house-carls around Harold preserved their discipline and kept their ranks, but the sense of relief to the less trained forces after these hours of combat was such that seeing their enemy in flight proved irresistible. They surged forward on the impulse of victory, and when half-way down the hill were savagely slaughtered by William's horsemen. There remained, as the dusk grew, only the valiant bodyguard who fought round the King and his standard. His brothers, Gyrth and Leofwine, had already been killed. William now directed his archers to shoot high into the air, so that the

arrows would fall behind the shield-wall, and one of these pierced Harold in the right eye, inflicting a mortal wound. He fell at the foot of the royal standard, unconquerable except by death, which does not count in honor. The hard-fought battle was now decided.

Duke William knew that his work was but begun. He was a prime exponent of the doctrine, so well known in this civilized age as "frightfulness"[1]—of mass terrorism through the spectacle of bloody and merciless examples. When William arrived near London he marched round the city by a circuitous route, isolating it by a belt of cruel desolation. On Christmas Day Aldred, Archbishop of York, crowned him King of England at Westminster. He rapidly established his power over all England south of the Humber.

The North still remained under its Saxon lords, Edwin and Morcar, unsubdued and defiant. From coast to coast the whole region was laid desolate, and hunted men took refuge in the wooded valleys of Yorkshire, to die of famine and exposure, or to sell themselves into slavery for food. The Saxon resistance died hard. Legends and chroniclers have painted for us the last stand of Hereward the Wake in the broad wastes of the fens round Ely. Not until five years after Hastings, in 1071, was Hereward put down. For at least twenty years after the invasion the Normans were an army camped in a hostile country, holding the population down by the castles at key points.

Here were the Normans entrenched on English soil, masters of the land and the fullness thereof. An armed warrior from Anjou or Maine or Brittany, or even from beyond the Alps and the Pyrenees, took possession of manor and county, according to his rank and prowess, and

---

[1] Written early in 1939.

set to work to make himself secure. Everywhere castles arose. These were not at first the massive stone structures of a later century; they were simply fortified military posts consisting of an earthen rampart and a stockade, and a central keep made of logs. In their early days the Normans borrowed no manners and few customs from the Islanders. The only culture was French. Surviving Saxon notables sent their sons to the monasteries of France for education. The English repeated the experience of the ancient Britons; all who could learned French, as formerly the contemporaries of Boadicea had learned Latin. At first the conquerors, who despised the uncouth English as louts and boors, ruled by the force of sharpened steel. But very soon in true Norman fashion they intermarried with the free population and identified themselves with their English past.

William's work in England is the more remarkable from the fact that all the time as Duke of Normandy he was involved in endless intrigues and conflicts with the King of France. Queen Matilda was a capable regent at Rouen, but plagued by the turbulence of her sons. Matilda died, and with increasing years William became fiercer in mood. When death drew near, his sons William and Henry came to him. William, whose one virtue had been filial fidelity, was named to succeed the Conqueror in England. The graceless Robert would rule in Normandy at last. For the youngest, Henry, there was nothing but five thousand pounds of silver, and the prophecy that he would one day reign over a united Anglo-Norman nation. On Thursday, September 9, 1087, as the early bells of Rouen Cathedral echoed over the hills, William and his authority died.

The Normans introduced into England their system of land tenure based upon military service. A military caste was imposed from above. The essence of Norman feudalism was that the land remained under the lord, whatever the man might do. Thus the landed pyramid rose up tier by tier to the King, until every acre in the country could be registered as held of somebody by some form of service. But the mass of the inhabitants were only indirectly affected by the change, and the feudal superstructure was for many years as unsure as it was impressive. The history of many an English village begins with an entry in Domesday Book. The result of this famous survey showed that the underlying structure of England and its peasant life were little changed by the shock of the invasion.

The Normans were administrators and lawyers rather than legislators. Their center of government was the royal Curia, the final court of appeal and the instrument of supervision; here were preserved and developed the financial and secretarial methods of the Anglo-Saxon kingdom. Not only the courts, but also the dues and taxes such as Danegeld, were preserved for the sake of the Norman revenues. Thus in the future government of England both Norman and Saxon institutions were unconsciously but profoundly blended. This survival of the hundred, the county court, and the sheriff makes the great difference between English and Continental feudalism.

In the Norman settlement lay the germ of a constitutional Opposition, with the effect if not the design of controlling the Government, not breaking it up. The seat of this potential Opposition was found in the counties, among the smaller nobility and their untitled descendants, Justices of the Peace and knights of the shire. This is the class—people of some consideration in the neighborhood, with leisure to go to the sheriff's court and thereafter to Westminster. Out of this process in time the Pyms and Hampdens arose.

The Conquest was the supreme achievement of the Norman race. It linked the history of England anew to Europe, and prevented for ever a drift into the narrower orbit of a Scandinavian empire. Henceforward English history marched with that of races and lands south of the Channel.

Once the secular conquest had been made secure William turned to the religious sphere. The key appointment was the Archbishopric of Canterbury. In 1070 the Saxon Stigand was deposed and succeeded by Lanfranc. In a series of councils such as had not been held in England since the days of Theodore organization and discipline were reformed. Older sees were transplanted from villages to towns—Crediton to Exeter, and Selsey to Chichester. New episcopal seats were established, and by 1087 the masons were at work on seven new cathedrals. At the same time the monastic movement, which had sprung from the Abbey of Cluny, began to spread in England. The English Church was rescued by the Conquest from the backwater in which it had languished. Under Lanfranc and his successor, Anselm, it came once again into contact with the wider European life of the Christian Church and its heritage of learning.

During the thirteen years of the reign of William Rufus the Anglo-Norman realms were vexed by fratricidal strife and successive baronial revolts. The Saxon inhabitants of England, fearful of a relapse into the chaos of pre-Conquest days, stood by the King against all rebels. In August 1100 he was mysteriously shot through the head by an arrow while hunting in the New Forest, leaving a memory of shameless exactions and infamous morals, but also a submissive realm to his successor.

Prince Henry, the youngest of the royal brothers, made straight for the royal Treasury at Winchester, and gained possession of it after sharp argument with its custodians. He set the precedent, which his successor followed, of proclaiming a charter upon his accession. Henry's desire to base himself in part at least upon the Saxon population of England led him, much to the suspicion of the Norman barons, to make a marriage with Matilda, niece of the last surviving Saxon claimant to the English throne and descendant of the old English line of kings. He knew that the friction caused by the separation of Normandy from England was by no means soothed. In September 1106 the most important battle since Hastings was fought at Tinchebrai. King Henry's victory was complete. Duke Robert was carried to his perpetual prison in England. There was now no challenged succession. The King of England's authority was established on both sides of the Channel.

There survived in medieval Europe a tradition of kingship more exalted than that of feudal overlord. The king was not merely the apex of the feudal pyramid, but the anointed Viceregent of God upon earth. The collapse of the Roman Empire had not entirely destroyed this Roman conception of sovereignty, and Henry now set himself to inject this idea of kingship into the Anglo-Norman State. The chroniclers spoke well of Henry I. We must regard his reign as a period when the central Government, by adroit and sharp accountancy and clerking, established in a more precise form the structure and resources of the State. In the process the feudatory chiefs upon whom the local government of the land depended were angered. We see therefore the beginning of an attachment to the King or central Government on the part of the people, which invested the Crown with a new source of strength, sometimes forthcoming and sometimes estranged, but always to be gathered, especially after periods of weakness and disorder, by a strong and righteous ruler.

The King had a son, his heir apparent, successor indisputable. In the winter of 1120 he was coming back from a visit to France in the royal yacht called the *White Ship*. Off the coast of Normandy the vessel struck a rock and all but one were drowned. The King had a daughter, Matilda, or Maud as the English called her, but although there was no Salic Law in the Norman code this clanking, jangling aristocracy, mailed and spurred, did not take kindly to the idea of a woman's rule. Against her stood the claim of Stephen, son of the Conqueror's daughter Adela. At the age of thirteen Maud had been married to the Holy Roman Emperor. In 1125, five years after the *White Ship* sank, he died, and at twenty-two she was a widow and an Empress. Fierce, proud, hard, cynical, living for politics above all other passions, however turbulent, she was fitted to bear her part in any war and be the mother of one of the greatest English kings. Upon this daughter, after mature consideration, Henry founded all his hopes. In order to enhance her unifying authority, and to protect Normandy from the claims of Anjou after his death, he married her to the Count of Anjou, thus linking the interests of the most powerful State in Northern France with the family and natural succession in England.

After giving the Island thirty years of peace and order and largely reconciling the Saxon population to Norman rule, Henry I expired on December 1, 1135, in the confident hope that his daughter Maud would carry on his work. But she was with her husband in Anjou and Stephen was the first on the spot. Swiftly returning from Blois, he made his way to London and claimed the Crown. A succession established on such disputable grounds could only be maintained unchallenged by skilful sovereignty. There

were grievous discontents among the high, the middle, and the low. In 1139 Maud, freed from entanglements that had kept her in France, entered the kingdom to claim her rights. The civil war developed into the first successful baronial reaction against the centralizing policy of the kings. Over large parts of England fighting was sporadic and local in character. It was the Central Southern counties that bore the brunt of civil war. But these commotions bit deep into the consciousness of the people. It was realized how vital an institution a strong monarchy was for the security of life and property. No better reasons for monarchy could have been found than were forced upon all minds by the events of Stephen's reign.

In 1147 Robert of Gloucester died and the leadership of Maud's party devolved upon her son. To contemporaries he was best known as Henry Fitz-Empress; but he carried into English history the emblem of his House, the broom, the *Planta Genesta,* which later generations were to make the name of this great dynasty, the Plantagenets. In his high feudal capacity Henry repaired to Paris to render homage to his lord the King of France, of which country he already possessed, by the accepted law of the age, a large part. Louis VII was a French Edward the Confessor; he practiced with faithful simplicity the law of Christ. These pious and exemplary habits did not endear him to his Queen. Eleanor of Aquitaine was in her own right a reigning princess, with the warmth of the South in her veins. The Papacy bowed to strong will in the high feudal chiefs, and Eleanor obtained a divorce from Louis VII in 1152 on the nominal grounds of consanguinity. But what staggered the French Court and opened the eyes of its prayerful King was the sudden marriage of Eleanor to Henry two months later. Thus half of France passed out of royal control into the hands of Henry. From all sides the potentates confronted the upstart. A month after the marriage these foes converged upon Normandy. But the youthful Duke Henry beat them back, ruptured and broken. He turned forthwith to England.

It was a valiant figure that landed in January 1153, and from all over England, distracted by civil war, hearts and eyes turned towards him. Merlin had prophesied a deliverer; had he not in his veins blood that ran back to William the Conqueror, and beyond him, through his grandmother Matilda, wife of Henry I, to Cerdic and the long-vanished Anglo-Saxon line? Glamour, terror, success, attended this youthful, puissant warrior, who had not only his sword, but his title-deeds. A treaty was concluded at Winchester in 1153 whereby Stephen made Henry his adopted son and his appointed heir. On this Henry did homage and made all the formal submissions, and when a year later Stephen died he was acclaimed and crowned King of England with more general hope and rejoicing than had ever uplifted any monarch in England since the days of Alfred the Great.

The accession of Henry II began one of the most pregnant and decisive reigns in English history. The new sovereign ruled an empire, and, as his subjects boasted, his warrant ran "from the Arctic Ocean to the Pyrenees." A vivid picture is painted of this gifted and, for a while, enviable man: square, thick-set, bull-necked, with powerful arms and coarse, rough hands; his legs bandy from endless riding; a large, round head and closely cropped red hair; a freckled face; a voice harsh and cracked. Intense love of the chase; other loves, which the Church deplored and Queen Eleanor resented; frugality in food and dress; days entirely concerned with public business; travel unceasing; moods various. Everything was stirred and molded by him in England, as also in his other much greater estates, which he patrolled with tireless attention.

England has had greater soldier-kings and subtler diplomatists than Henry II, but no man has left a deeper mark upon our laws and institutions. Fastening upon the elastic Saxon concept of the King's Peace, Henry used it to draw all criminal cases into his courts. Civil cases he attracted by straining a different principle, the old right of the King's court to hear appeals in cases where justice had been refused and to protect men in possession of their lands.

A bait was needed with which to draw litigants to the royal courts; the King must offer them better justice than they could have at the hands of their lords. Henry accordingly threw open to litigants in the royal courts a new procedure for them—trial by jury. Henry did not invent the jury; he put it to a new purpose. The idea of the jury is the one great contribution of the Franks to the English legal system, for, unknown in this country before the Conquest, the germ of it lies far back in the practice of the Carolingian kings. It was through this early form of jury that William the Conqueror had determined the Crown rights in the great Domesday survey. The genius of Henry II, perceiving new possibilities in such a procedure, turned to regular use in the courts an instrument which so far had only been used for administrative purposes. It was an astute move. Until this time both civil and criminal cases had been decided through the oath, the ordeal, or the duel. The jury of Henry II was not the jury that we know. Good men and true were picked, not yet for their impartiality, but because they were the men most likely to know the truth. In time the jurors with local knowledge would cease to be jurors at all and become witnesses, giving their evidence in open court to a jury entirely composed of bystanders. Very gradually, as the laws of evidence developed, the change came.

These methods gave good justice. Trial by jury became popular. Professional judges, removed from local prejudice, secured swifter decisions, and a strong authority to enforce them. Henry accordingly had to build up almost from nothing a complete system of royal courts, capable of absorbing a great rush of new work. The instrument to which he turned was the royal Council, the organ through which all manner of governmental business was already regularly carried out. It was to be the common parent of Chancery and Exchequer, of Parliament, of the Common Law courts, and those Courts of Prerogative on which the Tudors and Stuarts relied.

Henry also had to provide means whereby the litigant, eager for royal justice, could remove his case out of the court of his lord into the King's court. The device which Henry used was the royal writ. It was not until de Montfort's revolt against the third Henry in the thirteenth century that the multiplication of writs was checked and the number fixed at something under two hundred. This system then endured for six hundred years.

It was in these fateful and formative years that the English-speaking peoples began to devise methods of determining legal disputes which survive in substance to this day. A man can only be accused of a civil or criminal offense which is clearly defined and known to the law. The judge is an umpire. Witnesses must testify in public and on oath. The truth of their testimony is weighed not by the judge but by twelve "good men and true." Under Roman law, and systems derived from it, a trial in those turbulent

centuries, and in some countries even today, is often an inquisition. The judge makes his own investigation into the civil wrong or the public crime, and such investigation is largely uncontrolled. The suspect can be interrogated in private. And only when these processes have been accomplished is the accusation or charge against him formulated and published. Thus often arise secret intimidation, enforced confessions, torture, and blackmailed pleas of guilty. These sinister dangers were extinguished from the Common Law of England more than six centuries ago. By the time Henry II's great-grandson, Edward I, had died English criminal and civil procedure had settled into a mold and a tradition which in the mass govern the English-speaking peoples today. In all claims and disputes, whether they concerned the grazing lands of the Middle West, the oilfields of California, the sheep-runs and gold-mines of Australia, or the territorial rights of the Maoris, these rules have obtained, at any rate in theory, according to the procedure and mode of trial evolved by the English Common Law.

The military State in feudal Christendom bowed to the Church in things spiritual; it never accepted the idea of the transference of secular power to priestly authority. But the Church, enriched continually by the bequests of hardy barons, anxious in the death agony about their life beyond the grave, became the greatest landlord and capitalist in the community. The power of the State was held in constant challenge by this potent interest.

The Church in England, like the baronage, had gained greatly in power since the days of William the Conqueror and his faithful Archbishop Lanfranc. Stephen in his straits had made sweeping concessions to the Church, whose political influence then reached its zenith. These concessions, Henry felt, compromised his royal rights. He schemed to regain what had been lost, and as the first step in 1162 appointed his trusted servant Becket to be Archbishop of Canterbury, believing he would thus secure the acquiescence of the Episcopacy. In fact he provided the Church with a leader of unequaled vigor and obstinacy. He ignored or missed the ominous signs of the change in Becket's attitude, and proceeded to his second step, the publication in 1164 of the Constitutions of Clarendon. But Becket resisted. He regarded Stephen's yieldings as irrevocable gains by the Church. Stiff in defiance, Becket took refuge on the Continent, where the same conflict was already distracting both Germany and Italy. Only in 1170 was an apparent reconciliation brought about between him and the King at Fréteval, in Touraine. After the Fréteval agreement Henry supposed that bygones were to be bygones. But Becket had other views. His welcome home after the years of exile was astonishing. Henry Plantagenet was transported with passion. "What a pack of fools and cowards," he cried, "I have nourished in my house, that not one of them will avenge me of this turbulent priest!" Another version says "of this upstart clerk." A council was immediately summoned to devise measures for reasserting the royal authority. But meanwhile another train of action was in process. Four knights had heard the King's bitter words spoken in the full circle. They crossed the Channel. They called for horses and rode to Canterbury. There on December 29, 1170, they found the Archbishop in the cathedral. The scene and the tragedy are famous. After haggard parleys they fell upon him, cut him down with their swords, and left him bleeding like Julius Cæsar, with a score of wounds to cry for vengeance.

This tragedy was fatal to the King. The immediately following years were spent in trying to recover what he had lost by a great parade of atonement for his guilt. By the Compromise of Avranches in 1172 he made his peace with the Papacy on comparatively easy terms. But Becket's somber sacrifice had not been in vain. Until the Reformation the Church retained the system of ecclesiastical courts independent of the royal authority, and the right of appeal to Rome, two of the major points upon which Becket had defied the King.

All Europe marveled at the extent of Henry's domains, to which in 1171 he had added the lordship of Ireland. Yet Henry knew well that his splendor was personal in origin, tenuous and transient in quality; and he had also deep-clouding family sorrows. During these years he was confronted with no fewer than four rebellions by his sons. On each occasion they could count on the active support of the watchful King of France. These boys were typical sprigs of the Angevin stock. They wanted power as well as titles, and they bore their father no respect. In 1188 Richard, his eldest surviving son, after the death of young Henry, was making war upon him in conjunction with King Philip of France. Already desperately ill, Henry was defeated at Le Mans and recoiled into Touraine. When he saw in the list of conspirators against him the name of his son John, upon whom his affection had strangely rested, he abandoned the struggle with life. "Let things go as they will," he gasped. "Shame, shame on a conquered King." So saying, this hard, violent, brilliant, and lonely man expired at Chinon on July 6, 1189.

The new King affected little grief at the death of a father against whom he was in arms. Richard, with all his characteristic virtues and faults cast in a heroic mold, is one of the most fascinating medieval figures. When Richard's contemporaries called him "Cœur de Lion" they paid a lasting compliment to the king of beasts. Little did the English people owe him for his services, and heavily did they pay for his adventures. He was in England only twice for a few short months in his ten years' reign; yet his memory has always stirred English hearts, and seems to present throughout the centuries the pattern of the fighting man. Although a man of blood and violence, Richard was too impetuous to be either treacherous or habitually cruel. He was as ready to forgive as he was hasty to offend; he was open-handed and munificent to profusion; in war circumspect in design and skilful in execution; in politics a child, lacking in subtlety and experience. His political alliances were formed upon his likes and dislikes; his political schemes had neither unity nor clearness of purpose. The advantages gained for him by military genius were flung away through diplomatic ineptitude. His life was one magnificent parade, which, when ended, left only an empty plain.

The King's heart was set upon the new Crusade. Richard was crowned with peculiar state, by a ceremonial which, elaborating the most ancient forms and traditions of the Island monarchy, is still in all essentials observed today. Thereafter the King, for the sake of Christ's Sepulchre, virtually put the realm up for sale. Confiding the government to two Justiciars, William Longchamp, Bishop of Ely, and Hugh de Puiset, Bishop of Durham, under the supervision of the one trustworthy member of his family, his mother, the old Queen, Eleanor of Aquitaine, he started for the wars in the winter of 1189. The glamours of chivalry illumine the tale of the Third Crusade. King Richard dominated the scene. By the time Acre fell King Richard's glory as a warrior and also his skill as a general were the talk of all nations. But the quarrels of the allies paralyzed the campaign. The Crusading army, ably led by

Richard, in spite of the victory at Arsuf, where many thousand infidels were slain, could do no more than reach an eminence which commanded a distant view of the Holy City. In the next year, 1192, he captured Jaffa. Once again the distant prospect of Jerusalem alone rewarded the achievements of the Crusaders. By now the news from England was so alarming that the King felt it imperative to return home. A peace or truce for three years was at length effected, by which the coastal towns were divided and the Holy Sepulchre opened as a place of pilgrimage to small parties of Crusaders. Late in 1192 the King set out for home. Wrecked in the Adriatic, he sought to make his way through Germany in disguise, but his enemy the Duke of Austria was soon upon his track. He was arrested, and held prisoner in a castle. So valuable a prize was not suffered to remain in the Duke's hands. The Emperor himself demanded the famous captive. For many months his prison was a secret, but, as a pretty legend tells us, Blondel, Richard's faithful minstrel, went from castle to castle striking the chords which the King loved best, and at last was rewarded by an answer from Richard's own harp.

William Longchamp, Bishop of Ely, and, with magnificent pluralism, Papal Legate, Chancellor, and Justiciar, had addressed himself with fidelity and zeal to the task of governing England, entrusted to him by Richard in 1189. As the King's faithful servant he saw that the chief danger lay in the over-mighty position of Prince John. In the summer of 1191 there was open conflict between the two parties, and Longchamp marched against a revolt of John's adherents in the North Midlands. The French King saw in Richard's absence the chance of breaking up the Angevin power and driving the English out of France. In John he found a willing partner. Early in 1193, at a moment already full of peril, the grave news reached England that the King was prisoner "somewhere in Germany." John declared that Richard was dead, appeared in arms, and claimed the Crown. That England was held for Richard in his long absence against all these powerful and subtle forces is a proof of the loyalties of the Feudal Age. John's forces melted. The Holy Roman Emperor demanded the prodigious ransom of a hundred and fifty thousand marks, twice the annual revenue of the English Crown. At the end of 1193 the stipulated first instalment was paid, and at the beginning of February 1194 Richard Cœur de Lion was released from bondage. The King was re-crowned in London with even more elaborate ceremony than before. These processes well started, he crossed the Channel to defend his French possessions. He never set foot in England again.

The five remaining years of Richard's reign were spent in defending his French domains and raising money for that purpose from England. Once again the country was ruled by a deputy, this time Hubert Walter, a man bred in the traditions of Henry II's official Household, Archbishop of Canterbury, and Richard's Justiciar. With determination, knowledge, and deft touch he developed the system of strong centralized government devised by Henry II. Hubert Walter stands out as one of the great medieval administrators.

In France the war with Philip proceeded in a curious fashion. The negotiations were unceasing. Every year there was a truce, which every year was broken as the weather and general convenience permitted. In 1199, when the difficulties of raising revenue for the endless war were at their height, good news was brought to King Richard. It was said there had been dug up near the Castle of Chaluz, on the lands of one of his vassals, a treasure of wonderful quality. The King claimed this treasure as lord paramount. The lord of Chaluz resisted the demand, and the King laid siege to his small, weak castle. On the third day, as he rode daringly near the wall, confident in his hard-tried luck, a bolt from a crossbow struck him in the left shoulder by the neck. For seven years he had not confessed for fear of being compelled to be reconciled to Philip, but now he received the offices of the Church with sincere and exemplary piety, and died in the forty-second year of his age on April 6, 1199, worthy, by the consent of all men, to sit with King Arthur and Roland and other heroes of martial romance at some Eternal Round Table.

There is no animal in nature that combines the contradictory qualities of John. He united the ruthlessness of a hardened warrior with the craft and subtlety of a Machiavellian. Although from time to time he gave way to furious rages, in which "his eyes darted fire and his countenance became livid," his cruelties were conceived and executed with a cold, inhuman intelligence. Monkish chroniclers have emphasized his violence, greed, malice, treachery, and lust. But other records show that he was often judicious, always extremely capable, and on occasions even generous. He possessed an original and inquiring mind, and to the end of his life treasured his library of books. In him the restless energy of the Plantagenet race was raised to a furious pitch of instability. Although Richard had declared John to be King there were two views upon the succession. Geoffrey, his elder brother, had left behind him a son, Arthur, Prince of Brittany. It was already possible to hold that this grandson of Henry II of an elder branch had a prior right against John, and that is now the law of primogeniture. John was accepted without demur in

England. In the French provinces however the opposite view prevailed. Brittany in particular adopted Arthur. The King of France and all French interests thought themselves well served by a disputed succession and the espousal of a minor's cause. John felt that he would never be safe so long as Arthur lived. The havoc of disunity that was being wrought throughout the French provinces by the French King using Arthur as a pawn might well have weighed with a better man than John. Arthur, caught in open fight besieging his own grandmother, was a prisoner of war. No one knows what happened to Arthur. Hubert de Burgh, of whom more and better hereafter, gave out that upon the King's order he had delivered his prisoner at Easter 1203 to the hands of agents sent by John to castrate him, and that Arthur had died of the shock. That he was murdered by John's orders was not disputed at the time nor afterwards, though the question whether or not he was mutilated or blinded beforehand remains unanswered.

With the accession of John there emerges plainly in the Northern French provinces a sense of unity with one another and with the kingdom of France; at the same time on this side of the Channel the English baronage became ever more inclined to insular and even nationalistic ideas. Ties with the Continent were weakening through the gradual division of honors and appanages in England and Normandy between different branches of Anglo-Norman families. Moreover, the growing brilliance of the French Court and royal power in the late twelfth century was a powerful magnet which drew Continental loyalties to Paris. King John found himself compelled to fight at greater odds than his predecessors for his possessions on the Continent. He was also opposed by an increasing resistance to taxation for that purpose in England.

Arthur had been removed, but John failed to profit by his crime. Brittany and the central provinces of the Angevin Empire revolted. Having encircled Normandy, Philip prepared to strike at the stronghold of the Angevin power. In March 1204 King Richard's "fair child," the frowning Château Gaillard, fell, and the road to Rouen lay open. Three months later the capital itself was taken, and Normandy finally became French. No English tears need have been shed over this loss. The Angevin Empire at its peak had no real unity. Time and geography lay on the side of the French. The separation proved as much in the interest of England as of France. It rid the Island of a dangerous, costly distraction and entanglement, turned its thought and energies to its own affairs, and above all left a ruling class of alien origin with no interest henceforth that was not English or at least insular.

John, like William Rufus, pressed to logical limits the tendencies of his father's system. By systematic abuse of his feudal prerogatives John drove the baronage to violent resistance. The year 1205 brought a crisis. It also reopened the thorny question of who should elect the Primate of England. The Papal throne at this time was occupied by Innocent III; setting aside the candidates both of the Crown and of the Canterbury clergy, he caused Stephen Langton to be selected with great pomp and solemnity at Rome in December 1206. In his wrath, and without measuring the strength of his opponents, the King proceeded to levy a bloodless war upon the Church. When John began to persecute the clergy and seize Church lands the Pope retaliated by laying all England under an interdict. When John hardened his heart to the interdict and redoubled the attacks upon Church property, the Pope, in 1209, took the supreme step of excommunication. But John was stubborn and unabashed. The royal administration, never more efficient, found little difficulty in coping with the fiscal and legal problems presented to it or in maintaining order. But for the combination of the Church quarrel with stresses of mundane politics, the Crown might have established a position not reached till the days of Henry VIII.

After the loss of Normandy John had embarked upon a series of grandiose schemes for a Continental alliance against Philip Augustus; but his breach with the Church hastened a far more formidable league between the King of France and the Papacy, and in 1213 he had to choose between submission and a French invasion, backed by all the military and spiritual resources which Innocent III could set in motion. John, however, was not at the end of his devices, and by a stroke of cunning choice enough to be called political genius he turned defeat into something very like triumph. He offered to make England a fief of the Papacy, and to do homage to the Pope as his feudal lord. Innocent leapt at this addition to his worldly dignities. He accepted the sovereignty of England from the hands of John, and returned it to him as his vassal with his blessing.

This turned the tables upon John's secular enemies. Stephen Langton himself, the Pope's elect, was as good an Englishman as he was a Churchman. He foresaw the unbridled exploitation by Rome of the patronage of the English Church and the wholesale engrossment of its benefices by Italian nominees. Both John and Innocent persevered in their new partnership, and the disaffected barons drew together under the leadership of Stephen Langton. In 1214 an English expedition which John had led to Poitou failed. In Northern France the army commanded by his nephew, Otto of Saxony, and by the Earl of Salisbury, was defeated by King Philip at Bouvines. Here again was the opportunity of the King's domestic enemies. But John had still one final resource. Encouraged by the Pope, he took the vows of a Crusader and invoked sentence of excommunication upon his opponents. This was not denied him. But this agile use of the Papal thunders had robbed them of some of their virtues as a deterrent. The barons, encouraged by the King's defeat abroad, persisted in their demands in spite of the Papal Bull. Armed revolt seemed the only solution.

Although in the final scene of the struggle the Archbishop showed himself unwilling to go to the extreme of civil war, it was he who persuaded the barons to base their demands upon respect for ancient custom and law, and who gave them some principle to fight for besides their own class interests. The leaders of the barons in 1215 groped in the dim light toward a fundamental principle. Government must henceforward mean something more than the arbitrary rule of any man, and custom and the law must stand even above the King. It was this idea, perhaps only half understood, that gave unity and force to the barons' opposition and made the Charter which they now demanded imperishable. On a Monday morning in June, between Staines and Windsor, the barons and Churchmen began to collect on the great meadow at Runnymede. An uneasy hush fell on them from time to time. Many had failed to keep their tryst; and the bold few who had come knew that the King would never forgive this humiliation. He would hunt them down when he could, and the laymen at least were staking their lives in the cause they served.

They had arranged a little throne for the King and a tent. The handful of resolute men had drawn up, it seems, a short document on parchment. Their retainers and the groups and squadrons of horsemen in sullen steel kept at some distance and well in the background. For was not armed rebellion against the Crown the supreme feudal crime? Then events followed rapidly. A small cavalcade appeared from the direction of Windsor. Gradually men made out the faces of the King, the Papal Legate, the Archbishop of Canterbury, and several bishops. They dismounted without ceremony. Someone, probably the Archbishop, stated briefly the terms that were suggested. The King declared at once that he agreed. He said the details should be arranged immediately in his Chancery. The original "Articles of the Barons" on which Magna Carta is based exist today in the British Museum. They were sealed in a quiet, short scene, which has become one of the most famous in our history, on June 15, 1215.

If we set aside the rhetorical praise which has been so freely lavished upon the Charter and study the document itself we may find it rather surprising reading. It is entirely lacking in any spacious statement of the principles of democratic government or the rights of man. It is not a declaration of constitutional doctrine, but a practical document to remedy current abuses in the feudal system. Magna Carta must not, however, be dismissed lightly, in the words of a modern writer, as "a monument of class selfishness." In securing themselves the barons of Runnymede were in fact establishing the rights of the whole landed class, great and small—the simple knight with two hundred acres, the farmer or small yeoman with sixty. And there is evidence that their action was so understood throughout the country. If the thirteenth-century magnates understood little and

cared less for popular liberties or Parliamentary democracy, they had all the same laid hold of a principle which was to be of prime importance for the future development of English society and English institutions. Throughout the document it is implied that here is a law which is above the King and which even he must not break. This reaffirmation of a supreme law and its expression in a general charter is the great work of Magna Carta; and this alone justifies the respect in which men have held it. The underlying idea of the sovereignty of law, long existent in feudal custom, was raised by it into a doctrine for the national State. And when in subsequent ages the State, swollen with its own authority, has attempted to ride roughshod over the rights or liberties of the subject it is to this doctrine that appeal has again and again been made, and never, as yet, without success.

King John died in the toils; but he died at bay. He was at war with the English barons who had forced him to grant the Charter. They had invited Louis, son of the implacable Philip, King of France, into the country to be their liege lord, and with him came foreign troops and hardy adventurers. Everything threatened a long, stubborn civil war and a return to the anarchy of Stephen and Maud. Shakespeare has limned John's final agony:

> And none of you will bid the winter come
> To thrust his icy fingers in my maw. . . .
> I beg cold comfort, and you are so strait
> And so ungrateful, you deny me that.

Yet the sole reason and justification for revolt died with John.

Henry, a child of nine, was the undoubted heir to all the rights and loyalties of his grandfather's wide empire. The boy-King was crowned at Gloucester, and began his reign of fifty-six years on October 28, 1216. William the Marshal, aged seventy, reluctantly undertook what we should now call the Regency. He joined to himself the Earl of Chester, who might well have been his rival but did not press his claims, and Hubert de Burgh, John's faithful servant. The rebellion of the barons was quelled by fights on land and sea. After a year of fighting Louis of France was compelled to leave the country in 1217, his hopes utterly dashed. In 1219 the old victorious Marshal died, and Hubert ruled the land for twelve years. In 1225, as a sign of pacification, the Great Charter was again reissued in what was substantially its final form. Thus it became an unchallenged part of English law and tradition. But for the turbulent years of Henry III's minority, it might have moldered in the archives of history as a merely partisan document.

No long administration is immune from mistakes, and every statesman must from time to time make concessions to wrong-headed superior powers. But Hubert throughout his tenure stood for the policy of doing the least possible to recover the King's French domains. He resisted the Papacy in its efforts to draw money at all costs out of England for its large European schemes. He maintained order, and as the King grew up he restrained the Court party which was forming about him from making inroads upon the Charter. His was entirely the English point of view. In 1232 he was driven from power by a small palace clique. The leader of this intrigue was his former rival Peter des Roches, the Bishop of Winchester. De Burgh was the last of the great Justiciars who had wielded plenary and at times almost sovereign power. Henceforward the Household offices like the Wardrobe, largely dependent upon the royal will and favor, began to overshadow the great "national" offices, like the Justiciarship, filled by the baronial magnates. Des Roches himself kept in the background, but at the Christmas Council of 1232 nearly every post of consequence in the administration was conferred upon his friends, most of them, like him, men of Poitou. Under the leadership of Richard the Marshal, a second son of the faithful William, the barons began to growl against the foreigners. In alliance with Prince Llewellyn the young Marshal drove the King among the Welsh Marches, sacked Shrewsbury, and harried des Roches's lands. In the spring of 1234 Henry was forced to accept terms.

The Poitevins were the first of the long succession of foreign favorites whom Henry III gathered round him in the middle years of his reign. In 1236 he married Eleanor, the daughter of Raymond of Provence. A new wave of foreigners descended upon the profitable wardships, marriages, escheats, and benefices, which the disgusted baronage regarded as their own. An even more copious source of discontent in England was the influence of the Papacy over the grateful and pious King. Robert Grosseteste, scholar, scientist, and saint, a former Master of the Oxford Schools and since 1235 Bishop of Lincoln, led the English clergy in evasion or refusal of Papal demands. The Church, writhing under Papal exactions, and the baronage, offended by Court encroachments, were united in hatred of foreigners. The final stroke was the King's complete failure to check the successes of Llewellyn, who in 1256 had swept the English out of Wales and intrigued to overthrow the English faction in Scotland. Despised, discredited, and frightened, without money or men, the King faced an angered and powerful opposition. A letter of a Court official, written in July 1258, has been preserved. The King, so it says, had yielded to what he felt was overwhelming pressure. A commission for reform of government was set up.

The later years of Henry III's troubled reign were momentous in their consequences for the growth of English institutions. The commission for reform set about its work seriously, and in 1258 its proposals were embodied in the Provisions of Oxford, supplemented and extended in 1259 by the Provisions of Westminster. The staple of the barons' demand was that the King in future should govern by a Council of Fifteen, to be elected by four persons, two from the baronial and two from the royal party. It is significant that the King's proclamation accepting the arrangement in English as well as French is the first public document to be issued in both languages since the time of William the Conqueror. For a spell this Council, animated and controlled by Simon de Montfort, governed the land.

It is about this time that the word "Parlement"—Parliament—began to be current. In 1086 William the Conqueror had "deep speech" with his wise men before launching the Domesday inquiry. In Latin this would have appeared as *colloquium;* and "colloquy" is the common name in the twelfth century for the consultations between the King and his magnates. The occasional colloquy "on great affairs of the Kingdom" can at this point be called a Parliament. But more often the word means the permanent Council of officials and judges which sat at Westminster to receive petitions, redress grievances, and generally regulate the course of the law. By the thirteenth century Parliament establishes itself as the name of two quite different, though united, institutions. If we translate their functions into modern terms we may say that the first of these assemblies deals with policy, the second with legislation and administration. In the reign of Henry III, and even of Edward I, it was by no means a foregone conclusion that the two assemblies would be amalgamated. Rather did it look as if the English Constitution would develop as did the French Constitution, with a King in Council as the real Government, with the magnates reduced to a mere nobility, and "Parlement" only a clearing-house for legal business. Our history did not take this course. In the first place the magnates during the century that followed succeeded in mastering the Council and identifying their interests with it. Secondly, the English counties had a life of their own, and their representatives at Westminster were to exercise increasing influence. But without the powerful impulse of Simon de Montfort these forces might not have combined to shape a durable legislative assembly.

The King, the Court party, and the immense foreign interests associated therewith had no intention of submitting indefinitely to the thralldom of the Provisions. His son Edward was already the rising star of all who wished to see a strong monarchy. Supporters of this cause appeared among the poor and turbulent elements in London and the towns. It is the merit of Simon de Montfort that he did not rest content with a victory by the barons over the Crown. The "apprentice" or bachelor knights, who may be taken as voicing the wishes of the country gentry, formed a virile association of their own entitled "the Community of the Bachelors of England." Simon de Montfort became their champion. Very soon he began to rebuke great lords for abuse of their privileges. At Easter in 1261 Henry, freed by the Pope from his oath to accept the Provisions of Oxford and Westminster, deposed the officials and Ministers appointed by the barons. Both parties competed for popular support. In the civil war that followed the feudal party more or less supported the King. The people, especially the towns, and the party of ecclesiastical reform, especially the Franciscans, rallied to de Montfort.

At Lewes a fierce battle was fought. In some ways it was a forerunner of Edgehill. Edward, like Rupert four hundred years later, conquered all before him, pursued incontinently, and returned to the battlefield only to find that all was lost. The King and all his Court and principal supporters were taken prisoner by de Montfort, and the energetic Prince returned only to share their plight. Simon made a treaty with the captive King and the beaten party, whereby the rights of the Crown were in theory respected, though in practice the King and his son were to be subjected to strict controls. For the moment de Montfort was content that the necessary steps should be taken by a Council of nine who controlled expenditure and appointed officials. In January 1265 a Parliament met in London to which Simon summoned representatives both from the shires and from the towns. Its purpose was to give an appearance of legality to the revolutionary settlement, and this, under the guidance of de Montfort, it proceeded to do. Its importance lay, however, more in its character as a representative assembly than in its work. The practical reason for summoning the strong popular element was de Montfort's desire to weight the Parliament with his own supporters: among the magnates only five earls and eighteen barons received writs of summons. Again he fell back upon the support of the country gentry and the burgesses against the hostility or indifference of the magnates. In this lay his message and his tactics.

Throughout these struggles of lasting significance the English barons never deviated from their own self-interest. At Runnymede they had served national freedom when they thought they were defending their own privilege. They had now no doubt that Simon was its enemy. He was certainly a despot, with a king in his wallet and the forces of social revolution at his back. The barons formed a hard confederacy among themselves, and with all the forces of the Court not in Simon's hands schemed night and day to overthrow him. By promising to uphold the Charters, to remedy grievances, and to expel the foreigners Edward succeeded in uniting the baronial party and in cutting away the ground from under de Montfort's feet. Outmaneuvered politically by Edward, he also placed himself at a serious military disadvantage. The Earl was caught in turn at Evesham; and here on August 4 the final battle took place. De Montfort died a hero on the field.

In the last years of his life, with de Montfort dead and Edward away on Crusade, the feeble King enjoyed comparative peace; he could turn back to the things of beauty that interested him far more than political struggles. The new Abbey of Westminster, a masterpiece of Gothic architecture, was now dedicated; its consecration had long been the dearest object of Henry III's life. And here in the last weeks of 1272 he was buried. The quiet of these last few years should not lead us to suppose that de Montfort's struggle and the civil war had been in vain. Among the common people he was for many years worshipped as a saint, and miracles were worked at his tomb. Though a prince among administrators, he suffered as a politician from over-confidence and impatience. He trampled upon vested interests, broke with all traditions, did violence to all forms, and needlessly created suspicion and distrust. Yet de Montfort had lighted a fire never to be quenched in English history. Already in 1267 the Statute of Marlborough had re-enacted the chief of the Provisions of Westminster. Not less important was his influence upon his nephew, Edward, the new King, who was to draw deeply upon the ideas of the man he had slain. In this way de Montfort's purposes survived both the field of Evesham and the reaction which succeeded it, and in Edward I the great Earl found his true heir.

Few princes had received so thorough an education in the art of rulership as Edward I when at the age of thirty-three his father's death brought him to the Crown. He was of elegant build and lofty stature, a head and shoulders above the height of the ordinary man. He was an experienced leader and a skilful general. He presents us with qualities which are a mixture of the administrative capacity of Henry II and the personal prowess and magnanimity of Cœur de Lion. No English king more fully lived up to the maxim he chose for himself: "To each his own." He was animated by a passionate regard for justice and law, as he interpreted them, and for the rights of all groups within the community. Injuries and hostility roused, even to his last breath, a passionate torrent of resistance. But submission, or a generous act, on many occasions earned a swift response and laid the foundation of future friendship.

Proportion is the keynote of his greatest years. He saw in the proud, turbulent baronage and a rapacious Church checks upon the royal authority; but he also recognized them as oppressors of the mass of his subjects; and it was by taking into account to a larger extent than had occurred before the interests of the middle class, and the needs of the people as a whole, that he succeeded in producing a broad, well-ordered foundation upon which an active monarchy could function in the general interest. Here was a time of setting in

order. In this period we see a knightly and *bourgeois* stage of society increasingly replacing pure feudalism. The organs of government, land tenure, the military and financial systems, the relations of Church and State, all reach definitions which last nearly till the Tudors.

The first eighteen years of the reign witnessed an outburst of legislative activity for which there was to be no parallel for centuries. Nearly every year was marked by an important statute. Few of these were original, most were conservative in tone, but their cumulative effect was revolutionary. The First Statute of Westminster in the Parliament of 1275 dealt with administrative abuses. The Statute of Goucester in 1278 directed the justices to inquire by writs of *Quo Warranto* into the rights of feudal magnates to administer the law by their own courts and officials within their demesnes, and ordained that those rights should be strictly defined. In 1279 the Statute of Mortmain, *De Religiosis,* forbade gifts of land to be made to the Church, though the practice was allowed to continue under royal license. In 1285 the Statute of Winchester attacked local disorder, and in the same year was issued the Second Statute of Westminster, *De Donis Conditionalibus,* which strengthened the system of entailed estates. The Third Statute of Westminster, *Quia Emptores,* dealt with land held, not upon condition, but in fee simple.

In those days, when the greatest princes were pitifully starved in cash, there was already in England one spring of credit bubbling feebly. The Jews had unseen and noiselessly lodged themselves in the social fabric of that fierce age. Land began to pass into the hand of Israel, either by direct sale or more often by mortgage. For some time past there had been growing a wrathful reaction. Edward saw himself able to conciliate powerful elements and escape from awkward debts, by the simple and well-trodden path of anti-Semitism. The Jews, held up to universal hatred, were pillaged, maltreated, and finally expelled the realm. Not until four centuries had elapsed was Oliver Cromwell by contracts with a moneyed Israelite to open again the coasts of England to the enterprise of the Jewish race. It was left to a Calvinist dictator to remove the ban which a Catholic king had imposed.

Edward I was remarkable among medieval kings for the seriousness with which he regarded the work of administration and good government. By the end of the thirteenth century three departments of specialized administration were already at work. One was the Exchequer, established at Westminster, where most of the revenue was received and the accounts kept. The second was the Chancery, a general secretariat responsible for the writing and drafting of innumerable royal charters, writs, and letters. The third was the Wardrobe, with its separate secretariat, the Privy Seal, attached to the ever-moving royal Household, and combining financial and secretarial functions, which might range from financing a Continental war to buying a pennyworth of pepper for the royal cook.

Though the most orthodox of Churchmen, Edward I did not escape conflict with the Church. Anxious though he was to pay his dues to God, he had a far livelier sense than his father of what was due to Cæsar, and circumstances more than once forced him to protest. The leader of the Church party was John Pecham, a Franciscan friar, Archbishop of Canterbury from 1279 to 1292. With great courage and skill Pecham defended what he regarded as the just rights of the Church and its independence against the Crown. Yet moderation was observed, and in 1286 by a famous writ Edward wisely ordered his itinerant justices to act circumspectly in matters of ecclesiastical jurisdiction, and listed the kinds of case which should be left to Church courts.

At the beginning of the reign relations between England and France were governed by the Treaty of Paris, which the baronial party had concluded in 1259. For more than thirty years peace reigned between the two countries, though often with an undercurrent of hostility. Finally however the Parlement of Paris declared the Duchy of Gascony forfeit. Edward now realized that he must either fight, or lose his French possessions. The war itself had no important features. Any enthusiasm which had been expressed at the outset wore off speedily under the inevitable increases of taxation. In the winter of 1294 the Welsh revolted, and when the King had suppressed them he returned to find that Scotland had allied itself with France. From 1296 onward war with Scotland was either smoldering or flaring. After October 1297 the French War degenerated into a series of truces which lasted until 1303. Such conditions involved expense little less than actual fighting. The position of the clergy was made more difficult by the publication in 1296 of the Papal Bull *Clericis Laicos,* which forbade the payment of extraordinary taxation without Papal authority. For a time passion ran high, but eventually a calmer mood prevailed. Edward was the more prepared to come to terms with the Church because opposition had already broken out in another quarter. He proposed to the barons at Salisbury that a number of them should serve in Gascony while he conducted a campaign in Flanders. This was ill received. Humphrey de Bohun, Earl of Hereford and Constable of England, together with the Marshal, Roger Bigod, Earl of Norfolk, voiced the resentment felt by a large number of the barons who for the past twenty years had steadily seen the authority of the Crown increased to their own detriment. The time was ripe for a revival of the baronial opposition which a generation before had defied Edward's father.

For the moment the King ignored the challenge. The opposition saw their long-awaited opportunity. They demanded the confirmation of those two instruments, Magna Carta and its extension, the Charter of the Forest, which were the final version of the terms extorted from John, together with six additional articles. The Regency, unable to resist, submitted. The articles were confirmed, and in November at Ghent the King ratified them, reserving however certain financial rights of the Crown. By this crisis and its manner of resolution two principles had been established from which important consequences flowed. One was that the King had no right to dispatch the feudal host wherever he might choose. This limitation sounded the death-knell of the feudal levy, and inexorably led in the following century to the rise of indentured armies serving for pay. The second point of principle now recognized was that the King could not plead "urgent necessity" as a reason for imposing taxation without consent. Other English monarchs as late as the seventeenth century were to make the attempt. But by Edward's failure a precedent had been set up, and a long stride had been taken toward the dependence of the Crown upon Parliamentary grants.

Edward I was the first of the English kings to put the whole weight of the Crown's resources behind the effort of national expansion in the West and North, and to him is due the conquest of the independent areas of Wales and the securing of the Western frontier. He took the first great step towards the unification of the Island. All assertions of Welsh independence were a vexation to Edward; but scarcely less obnoxious was a system of guarding the frontiers of England by a confederacy of robber barons who had

more than once presumed to challenge the authority of the Crown. Edward I, utilizing all the local resources which the barons of the Welsh Marches had developed in the chronic strife of many generations, conquered Wales in several years of persistent warfare, coldly and carefully devised, by land and sea. The land of Llewellyn's Wales was transferred to the King's dominions and organized into the shires of Anglesey, Carnarvon, Merioneth, Cardigan, and Carmarthen. The King's son Edward, born in Carnarvon, was proclaimed the first English Prince of Wales.

The Welsh wars of Edward reveal to us the process by which the military system of England was transformed from the age-long Saxon and feudal basis of occasional service to that of paid regular troops. Instead of liege service Governments now required trustworthy mercenaries, and for this purpose money was the solvent. At the same time a counter-revolution in the balance of warfare was afoot. The mailed cavalry which from the fifth century had eclipsed the ordered ranks of the legion were wearing out their long day. A new type of infantry raised from the common people began to prove its dominating quality. This infantry operated, not by club or sword or spear, or even by hand-flung missiles, but by an archery which, after a long development, concealed from Europe, was very soon to make an astonishing entrance upon the military scene and gain a dramatic ascendancy upon the battle-fields of the Continent. Here was a prize taken by the conquerors from their victims. In South Wales the practice of drawing the long-bow had already attained an astonishing efficiency. This was a new fact in the history of war, which is also a part of the history of civilization, deserving to be mentioned with the triumph of bronze over flint, or iron over bronze. Thus the Welsh wars, from two separate points of departure, destroyed the physical basis of feudalism, which had already, in its moral aspect, been outsped and outclassed by the extension and refinement of administration.

The great quarrel of Edward's reign was with Scotland. Since the days of Henry II the English monarchy had intermittently claimed an overlordship of Scotland, based on the still earlier acknowledgment of Saxon overlordship by Scottish kings. King Edward now imposed himself with considerable acceptance as arbitrator in the Scottish succession. But the national feeling of Scotland was pent up behind these barriers of legal affirmation. To resist Edward the Scots allied themselves with the French. Since Edward was at war with France he regarded this as an act of hostility. Edward struck with ruthless severity. He advanced on Berwick. The city, then the great emporium of Northern trade, was unprepared, after a hundred years of peace, to resist attack, and sank in a few hours from one of the active centers of European commerce to the minor seaport which exists today. This act of terror quelled the resistance of the ruling classes in Scotland. But, as in Wales, the conqueror introduced not only an alien rule, but law and order, all of which were equally unpopular. It has often been said that Joan of Arc first raised the standard of nationalism in the Western World. But over a century before she appeared an outlaw knight, William Wallace, arising from the recesses of South-West Scotland which had been his refuge, embodied, commanded, and led to victory the Scottish nation. He had few cavalry and few archers; but his confidence lay in the solid "schiltrons" (or circles) of spearmen, who were invincible except by actual physical destruction. It was not until 1305 that Wallace was captured, tried with full ceremonial in Westminster

Hall, and hanged, drawn, and quartered at Tyburn. But the Scottish War was one in which, as a chronicler said, "every winter undid every summer's work." Wallace was to pass the torch to Robert Bruce.

King Edward was old, but his willpower was unbroken. He launched a campaign in the summer of 1306 in which Bruce was defeated and driven to take refuge on Rathlin Island, off the coast of Antrim. Here, according to the tale, Bruce was heartened by the persistent efforts of the most celebrated spider known to history. Next spring he returned to Scotland. Edward was now too ill to march or ride. Like the Emperor Severus a thousand years before, he was carried in a litter against this stern people, and like him he died upon the road.

Edward I was the last great figure in the formative period of English law. His statutes, which settled questions of public order, assigned limits to the powers of the seigneurial courts, and restrained the sprawling and luxurious growth of judge-made law, laid down principles that remained fundamental to the law of property until the mid nineteenth century. In the constitutional sphere the work of Edward I was not less durable. He had made Parliament—that is to say, certain selected magnates and representatives of the shires and boroughs—the associate of the Crown, in place of the old Court of Tenants-in-Chief. By the end of his reign this conception had been established. Dark constitutional problems loomed in the future. Idle weaklings, dreamers, and adventurous boys disrupted the nascent unity of the Island. Long years of civil war, and despotism in reaction from anarchy, marred and delayed the development of its institutions. But when the traveler gazes upon the plain marble tomb at Westminster on which is inscribed, "Here lies Edward I, the Hammer of the Scots. Keep troth," he stands before the resting-place of a master-builder of British life, character, and fame.

Edward II's reign may fairly be regarded as a melancholy appendix to his father's and the prelude to his son's. A strong, capable King had with difficulty upborne the load. He was succeeded by a perverted weakling, of whom some amiable traits are recorded. He was addicted to rowing, swimming, and baths. He carried his friendship for his advisers beyond dignity and decency.

In default of a dominating Parliamentary institution, the Curia Regis seemed to be the center from which the business of Government could be controlled. On the death of Edward I the barons succeeded in gaining control of this mixed body of powerful magnates and competent Household officials. They set up a committee called "the Lords Ordainers." Piers Gaveston, a young, handsome Gascon, enjoyed the King's fullest confidence. His decisions made or marred. The barons' party attacked Piers Gaveston. Edward and his favorite tried to stave off opposition by harrying the Scots. They failed, and in 1311 Gaveston was exiled to Flanders. Thence he was so imprudent as to return, in defiance of the Lords Ordainers. Besieged in the Castle of Scarborough, Gaveston made terms with his foes. His life was to be spared; and on this they took him under guard. But other nobles overpowered the escort, seized the favorite at Deddington in Oxfordshire, and hewed off his head on Blacklow Hill, near Warwick.

Edward was still in control of Government, although he was under restraint. To wipe out his setbacks at home he resolved upon the conquest of the Northern kingdom. A great army crossed the Tweed in the summer of 1314. Twenty-five thousand men, hard to gather, harder

still to feed in those days, with at least three thousand armored knights and men-at-arms, moved against the champion of Scotland, Robert Bruce. The Scottish army, of perhaps ten thousand men, was composed mainly of the hard, unyielding spearmen. Bruce, who had pondered deeply upon the impotence of pikemen, however faithful, with a foresight and skill which proves his military quality, took three precautions. First, he chose a position where his flanks were secured by impenetrable woods; secondly, he dug upon his front a large number of small round holes and covered them with branches and turfs as a trap for charging cavalry; thirdly, he kept in his own hand his small but highly trained force of mounted knights to break up any attempt at planting archers upon his flank. These dispositions made, he awaited the English onslaught. On the morning of June 24 the English advanced, and a dense wave of steelclad horsemen descended the slope, splashed and scrambled through the Bannock Burn, and charged uphill upon the schiltrons. No more grievous slaughter of English chivalry ever took place in a single day. Even Towton in the Wars of the Roses was less destructive. The Scots claimed to have slain or captured thirty thousand men, more than the whole English army, but their feat in virtually destroying an army of cavalry and archers mainly by the agency of spearmen must nevertheless be deemed a prodigy of war.

The feudal baronage had striven successfully against kings. They now saw in the royal officials agents who stood in their way, yet at the same time were obviously indispensable to the widening aspects of national life. The whole tendency of their movement was therefore in this generation to acquire control of an invaluable machine. One of the main charges brought against Edward II at his deposition was that he had failed in his task of government. From early in his reign he left too much to his Household officials. Outside this select, secluded circle the rugged, arrogant, virile barons prowled morosely. It is the nature of supreme executive power to withdraw itself into the smallest compass; and without such contraction there is no executive power. But when this exclusionary process was tainted by unnatural vice and stained by shameful defeat in the field it was clear that those who beat upon the doors had found a prosperous occasion. The forces were not unequally balanced. The barons might have a blasting case against the King at Westminster, but if he appeared in Shropshire or Westmorland with his handful of guards and the royal insignia he could tell his own tale, and men, both knight and archer, would rally to him. Thus we see in this ill-starred reign both sides operating in and through Parliament, and in this process enhancing its power. Parliament was called together no fewer than twenty-five times under King Edward II. In the long story of a nation we often see that capable rulers by their very virtues sow the seeds of future evil and weak or degenerate princes open the pathway of progress.

Thomas of Lancaster, nephew to Edward I, was the forefront of the baronial opposition. Little is known to his credit. Into the hands of Thomas and his fellow Ordainers Edward was now thrown by the disaster of Bannockburn, and Thomas for a while became the most important man in the land. Within a few years however the moderates among the Ordainers became so disgusted with Lancaster's incompetence and with the weakness into which the process of government had sunk that they joined with the royalists to edge him from power. Edward, for his part, began to build up a royalist party, at the head of which were the Despensers, father and son, both named Hugh. They were especially unpopular among the Marcher lords, who were disturbed by their restless ambitions in South Wales. In 1321 the Welsh Marcher lords and the Lancastrian party joined hands with intent to procure the exile of the Despensers. Edward soon recalled them, and for once showed energy and resolution. By speed of movement he defeated first the Marcher lords and then in the next year the Northern barons under Lancaster at Boroughbridge in Yorkshire. Lancaster was beheaded by the King.

But a tragedy with every feature of classical ruthlessness was to follow. One of the chief Marcher lords, Roger Mortimer, though captured by the King, contrived to escape to France. In 1324 Charles IV of France took advantage of a dispute in Gascony to seize the Duchy, except for a coastal strip. Edward's wife, Isabella, "the she-wolf of France," who was disgusted by his passion for Hugh Despenser, suggested that she should go over to France to negotiate with her brother Charles about the restoration of Gascony. As soon as the fourteen-year-old Prince Edward, who as heir to the throne could be used to legitimatize opposition to King Edward, was in her possession she and Mortimer staged an invasion of England at the head of a large band of exiles. So unpopular and precarious was Edward's government that Isabella's triumph was swift and complete, and she and Mortimer were emboldened to depose him. The end was a holocaust. In the furious rage which in those days led all who swayed the government of England to a bloody fate the Despensers were seized and hanged. For the King a more terrible death was reserved. He was imprisoned in Berkeley Castle, and there by hideous methods, which left no mark upon his skin, was slaughtered. His screams as his bowels were burned out by red-hot irons passed into his body were heard outside the prison walls, and awoke grim echoes which were long unstilled.

The failures of the reign of Edward II had permanent effects on the unity of the British Isles. Bannockburn ended the possibility of uniting the English and Scottish Crowns by force. Hatred of the English was the mark of a good Scot. Though discontented nobles might accept English help and English pay, the common people were resolute in their refusal to bow to English rule in any form. The memory of Bannockburn kept a series of notable defeats at the hands of the English from breeding despair or thought of surrender.

The disunity of the kingdom, fostered by English policy and perpetuated by the tragedies that befell the Scottish sovereigns, was not the only source of Scotland's weakness. The land was divided in race, in speech, and in culture. The rift between Highlands and Lowlands was more than a geographical distinction. The Lowlands formed part of the feudal world, and, except in the South-West, in Galloway, English was spoken. The Highlands preserved a social order much older than feudalism. In the Lowlands the King of Scots was a feudal magnate; in the Highlands he was the chief of a loose federation of clans. Meanwhile, the Scots peasant farmer and the thrifty burgess, throughout these two hundred years of political strife, pursued their ways and built up the country's real strength in spite of the numerous disputes among their lords and masters. The Church devoted itself to its healing mission, and many good bishops and divines adorn the annals of medieval Scotland. In the fifteenth century three Scottish universities were founded, St. Andrew's, Glasgow, and Aberdeen—one more than England had until the nineteenth century.

When the long, sorrowful story began of English intervention in Ireland the country had already endured the shock and torment of Scandinavian invasion. In 1169 there arrived in the country the first progenitors of the Anglo-Norman ascendancy, but there was no organized colonization and settlement. English authority was accepted in the Norse towns on the southern and eastern coasts, and the King's writ ran over a varying area of country surrounding Dublin. Immediately outside lay the big feudal lordships, and beyond there were the "wild" unconquered Irish of the West. Within a few generations of the coming of the Anglo-Normans the Irish chieftains began to recover from the shock of new methods of warfare. They regained for the Gaelic-speaking peoples wide regions of Ireland, and might have won more, had they not incessantly quarreled among themselves. Meanwhile, a change of spirit had overtaken many of the Anglo-Norman Irish barons. Their stock was seldom reinforced from England, except by English lords who wedded Irish heiresses, and then became absentee landlords. Gradually a group of Anglo-Irish nobles grew up, largely assimilated to their adopted land, and as impatient as their Gaelic peasants of rule from London. If English kings had regularly visited Ireland, or regularly appointed royal princes as resident lieutenants, the ties between the two countries might have been closely and honorably woven together. As it was, when the English king was strong English laws generally made headway; otherwise a loose Celtic anarchy prevailed. King John, in his furious fitful energy, twice went to Ireland, and twice brought the quarrelsome Norman barons and Irish chiefs under his suzerainty. Although Edward I never landed in Ireland English authority was then in the ascendant. Thereafter the Gaels revived.

It seemed that the strong blood of Edward I had but slumbered in his degenerate son, for in Edward III England once more found leadership equal to her steadily growing strength. Beneath the squalid surface of Edward II's reign there had none the less proceeded in England a marked growth of national power and prosperity. The English people stood at this time possessed of a commanding weapon, the qualities of which were utterly unsuspected abroad. The long-bow, handled by the well-trained archer class, brought into the field a yeoman type of soldier with whom there was nothing on the Continent to compare. The power of the long-bow and the skill of the bowmen had developed to a point where at two hundred and fifty yards the arrow hail produced effects never reached again by infantry missiles at such a range until the American Civil War. The skilled archer was a professional soldier, earning and deserving high pay. The protracted wars of the two Edwards in the mountains of Wales and Scotland had taught the English many hard lessons, and although European warriors had from time to time shared in them they had neither measured nor imparted the secret of the new army. It was with a sense of unmeasured superiority that the English looked out upon Europe at the end of the first quarter of the fourteenth century.

The reign of King Edward III passed through several distinct phases. In the first he was a minor, and the land was ruled by his mother and her lover, Roger Mortimer. This government, founded upon unnatural murder and representing only a faction in the nobility, was condemned to weakness at home and abroad. Its rule of nearly four years was marked by concession and surrender both in France and in Scotland. In May 1328 the "Shameful Treaty of Northampton," as it was called at the time, recognized Bruce as King north of the Tweed, and implied the abandonment of all the claims of Edward I in Scotland. All eyes were therefore turned to the young King. When fifteen, in 1328, he had been married to Philippa of Hainault. In June 1330 a son was born to him; he felt himself now a grown man who must do his duty by the realm. In October Parliament sat at Nottingham. Mortimer and Isabella, guarded by ample force, were lodged in the castle. An underground passage led into its heart. Through this on an October night a small band of resolute men entered, surprised Mortimer in his chamber, which as usual was next to the Queen's, and, dragging them both along the subterranean way, delivered them to the King's officers. Mortimer, conducted to London, was brought before the peers, accused of the murder in Berkeley Castle and other crimes, and, after condemnation by the lords, hanged on November 29. Isabella was consigned by her son to perpetual captivity.

The guiding spirit of the new King was to revive the policy, assert the claims, and restore the glories of his grandfather. The quarrel with Scotland was resumed. The contacts between Scotland and France and the constant aid given by the French Court to the Scottish enemies of England roused a deep antagonism. Thus the war in Scotland pointed the path to Flanders. Here a new set of grievances formed a substantial basis for a conflict. The loss of all the French possessions, except Gascony, and the constant bickering on the Gascon frontiers, had been endured perforce since the days of John. But in 1328 the death of Charles IV without a direct heir opened a further issue. Philip of Valois assumed the royal power and demanded homage from

Edward, who made difficulties. King Edward III, in his mother's right—if indeed the female line was valid—had a remote claim to the throne of France. This claim, by and with the assent and advice of the Lords Spiritual and Temporal, and of the Commons of England, he was later to advance in support of his campaigns. He was conscious moreover from the first of the advantage to be gained by diverting the restless energies of his nobles from internal intrigues and rivalries to the unifying purpose of a foreign war. This was also in harmony with the temper of his people. Now we see the picture of the Estates of the Realm becoming themselves ardently desirous of foreign conquests.

The wool trade with the Low Countries was the staple of English exports, and almost the sole form of wealth which rose above the resources of agriculture. Repeated obstructions were placed by the counts of Flanders upon the wool trade, and each aroused the anger of those concerned on both sides of the Narrow Sea. In 1336 Edward was moved to retaliate in a decisive manner. He decreed an embargo on all exports of English wool, thus producing a furious crisis in the Netherlands. The townspeople rose against the feudal aristocracy, and under Jacques Van Arteveldt, a warlike merchant of Ghent, gained control, after a struggle of much severity, over a large part of the country. The victorious burghers, threatened by aristocratic and French revenge, looked to England for aid, and their appeals met with a hearty and deeply interested response.

Thus all streams of profit and ambition flowed into a common channel at a moment when the flood-waters of conscious military strength ran high, and in 1337, when Edward repudiated his grudging homage to Philip VI, the Hundred Years War began. It was never to be concluded; no general peace treaty was signed, and

not until the Peace of Amiens in 1802, when France was a republic and the French royal heir a refugee within these isles, did the English sovereign formally renounce his claims to the throne of the Valois and the Bourbons.

Edward slowly assembled the expeditionary army of England. This was not a feudal levy, but a paid force of picked men. Philip VI looked first to the sea. But Edward had not neglected the sea-power. His interest in the Navy won him from Parliament early in his reign the title of "King of the Sea." In the summer of 1340 the hostile navies met off Sluys, and a struggle of nine hours ensued. The French admirals had been ordered, under pain of death, to prevent the invasion, and both sides fought well; but the French fleet was decisively beaten and the command of the Channel passed into the hands of the invading Power. Joined with the revolted Flemings, Edward's numbers were greatly augmented, and this combined force, which may have exceeded twenty thousand, undertook the first Anglo-Flemish siege of Tournai. But the capture of this fortress was beyond Edward's resources in money and supplies; the first campaign of what was a great European war yielded no results, and a prolonged truce supervened. The French wreaked their vengeance on the burghers of the Netherlands, whom they crushed utterly, and Van Arteveldt met his death in a popular tumult at Ghent. The English retaliated as best they could. There was a disputed succession in Brittany, which they fomented with substantial aids. The chronic warfare on the frontiers of Gascony continued.

By the spring of 1346 Parliament had at length brought itself to the point of facing the taxation necessary to finance a new invasion. In one wave two thousand four hundred cavalry, twelve thousand archers, and other infantry sailed, and landed unopposed at St. Vaast in Normandy on July 12, 1346. Their object this time was no less than the capture of Paris by a sudden dash. A huge force which comprised all the chivalry of France and was probably three times as big as Edward's army assembled in the neighborhood of St. Denis. Against such opposition, added to the walls of a fortified city, Edward's resources could not attempt to prevail. The thrust had failed and retreat imposed itself upon the army. They must now make for the Somme, and hope to cross between Amiens and the sea.

Philip, at the head of a host between thirty and forty thousand strong, was hard upon the track. He had every hope of bringing the insolent Islanders to bay with their backs to the river, or catching them in transit. When he learned that they were already over he called a council of war. His generals advised that, since the tide was now in, there was no choice but to ascend to Abbeville and cross by the bridge which the French held there. To Abbeville they accordingly moved, and lay there for the night. Edward gathered his chiefs to supper and afterwards to prayer. It was certain that they could not gain the coast without a battle. No other resolve was open than to fight at enormous odds. The King and the Prince of Wales, afterwards famous as the Black Prince, received all the offices of religion, and Edward prayed that the impending battle should at least leave him unstripped of honor.

King Philip at sunrise on Saturday, August 26, 1346, heard Mass in the Monastery of Abbeville, and his whole army, gigantic for those times, rolled forward in their long pursuit. About midday the King, having arrived with large masses on the farther bank of the Somme, received their reports. The English were in battle array and meant to fight. He gave the sage counsel to halt for the day, bring up the rear, form the

battleline, and attack on the morrow. While many great bodies halted obediently, still larger masses poured forward, forcing their way through the stationary or withdrawing troops, and at about five in the afternoon came face to face with the English army lying in full view on the broad slopes of Crécy. King Philip, arriving on the scene, was carried away by the ardor of the throng around him. The sun was already low; nevertheless, all were determined to engage.

There was a corps of six thousand Genoese crossbowmen in the van of the army. These were ordered to make their way through the masses of horsemen, and with their missiles break up the hostile array in preparation for the cavalry attacks. At this moment, while the crossbowmen were threading their way to the front, dark clouds swept across the sun and a short, drenching storm beat upon the hosts. After wetting the bow-strings of the Genoese, it passed as quickly as it had come, and the setting sun shone brightly in their eyes and on the backs of the English. The Genoese, drawing out their array, gave a loud shout, advanced a few steps, shouted again, and a third time advanced, "hooted," and discharged their bolts. Unbroken silence had wrapped the English lines, but at this the archers, six or seven thousand strong, ranged on both flanks in "portcullis" formation, who had hitherto stood motionless, advanced one step, drew their bows to the ear, and came into action. They "shot their arrows with such force and quickness," says Froissart, "that it seemed as if it snowed." The effect upon the Genoese was annihilating; at a range which their own weapons could not attain they were in a few minutes killed by thousands. The front line of the French cavalry rode among the retreating Genoese, cutting them down with their swords. In doing so they came within the deadly distance. The arrow snow-storm beat upon them, piercing their mail and smiting horse and man. Valiant squadrons from behind rode forward into the welter, and the main attack of the French now developed. Evading the archers as far as possible, they sought the men-at-arms, and French, German, and Savoyard squadrons actually reached the Prince of Wales's division. The enemy's numbers were so great that those who fought about the Prince were sent to the windmill, whence King Edward directed the battle, for reinforcements. But the King would not part with his reserves, saying, "Let the boy win his spurs"—which in fact he did. Continuous cavalry charges were launched upon the English front, until utter darkness fell upon the field. And all through the night fresh troops of brave men, resolved not to quit the field without striking their blow, struggled forward, groping their way. All these were slain, for "No quarter" was the mood of the English, though by no means the wish of their King. "When on this Saturday night the English heard no more hooting or shouting, nor any more crying out to particular lords, or their banners, they looked upon the field as their own and their enemies as beaten." On the Sunday morning fog enshrouded the battlefield, and the King sent a strong force of five hundred lancers and two thousand archers to learn what lay upon his front. "It has been assured to me for fact," says Froissart, "that of foot-soldiers sent from the cities, towns, and municipalities, there were slain, this Sunday morning four times as many as in the battle of the Saturday." This astounding victory of Crécy ranks with Blenheim, Waterloo, and the final advance in the last summer of the Great War as one of the four supreme achievements of the British Army.[1]

Edward marched through Montreuil

and Etaples to Boulogne, passed through the Forest of Hardelot, and opened the siege of Calais. Calais presented itself to English eyes as the hive of that swarm of privateers who were the endless curse of the Channel. Calais held out for eleven months, and yet this did not suffice. Famine at length left no choice to the besieged. They sued for terms. Calais then, was the fruit, and the sole territorial fruit so far, of the exertions, prodigious in quality of the whole power of England in the war with France. But Crécy had a longer tale to tell.

Christendom has no catastrophe equal to the Black Death. We read of lawsuits where all parties died before the cases could be heard; of monasteries where half the inmates perished; of dioceses where the surviving clergy could scarcely perform the last offices for their flocks and for their brethren; of the Goldsmiths' Company, which had four Masters in a year. These are detailed indications. But far more convincing is the gap which opens in all the local annals of the nation. A whole generation is slashed through by a hideous severance.

Philosophers might suggest that there was no need for the use of the destructive mechanism of plague to procure the changes deemed necessary among men. The early fifteenth century was to see the end of the rule of the armored men. Gunpowder, which we have seen used in the puny bombards which, according to some authorities, Edward had fired at Crécy and against Calais, was soon decisively to establish itself as a practical factor in war and in human affairs based on war. If cannon had not been invented the English mastery of the long-bow might have carried them even farther in their Continental domination.

The war between England and France continued in a broken fashion, and the Black Prince, the most renowned warrior

[1] Written in 1939.

in Europe, became a freebooter. In 1355 King Edward obtained from Parliament substantial grants for the renewal of active war. The Black Prince would advance northward from the English territories of Gascony and Aquitaine toward the Loire. His younger brother, John of Gaunt, Duke of Lancaster, struck in from Brittany. But all this miscarried, and the Black Prince found himself, with forces shrunk to about four thousand men, of whom however nearly a half were the dreaded archers, forced to retire with growing urgency before the advance of a French royal army twenty thousand strong. Terms were rejected by the French, who once again saw their deeply hated foe in their grasp. At Poitiers the Prince was brought to bay. But King John of France was resolved to avenge Crécy and finish the war at a stroke.

Ten years had passed since Crécy, and French chivalry and high command alike had brooded upon the tyranny of that event. They had been forced to accept the fact that horses could not face the arrow storm. King John was certain that all must attack on foot, and he trusted to overwhelming numbers. But the great merit of the Black Prince is that he did not rest upon the lessons of the past or prepare himself to repeat the triumphs of a former battle. The French nobility left their horses in the rear. The Black Prince had all his knights mounted. The French chivalry, encumbered by their mail, plodded ponderously forward amid vineyards and scrub. Many fell before the arrows, but the arrows would not have been enough at the crisis. It was the English spear- and axe-men who charged in the old style upon ranks disordered by their fatigue of movement and the accidents of the ground. At the same time, in admirable concert, a strong detachment of mounted knights, riding around the French left flank, struck in upon the harassed and already disordered attack.

The result was a slaughter as large and a victory as complete as Crécy, but with even greater gains. The whole French army was driven into ruin. King John and the flower of his nobility were captured or slain.

King John was carried to London. In May 1360, the Treaty of Brétigny was concluded. By this England acquired, in addition to her old possession of Gascony, the whole of Henry II's possessions in Aquitaine in full sovereignty, Edward I's inheritance of Ponthieu, and the famous port and city of Calais, which last was held for nearly two hundred years. A ransom was fixed for King John at three million gold crowns, the equivalent of £500,000 sterling. This was eight times the annual revenue of the English Crown in time of peace. The triumph and the exhaustion of England were simultaneously complete. A great French hero appeared in Bertrand du Guesclin, who, like Fabius Cunctator against Hannibal, by refusing battle and acting through sieges and surprises, rallied the factor of time to the home side. It was proved that the French army could not beat the English, and at the same time that England could not conquer France. The main effort of Edward III, though crowned with all the military laurels, had failed.

The years of the war with France are important in the history of Parliament. The need for money drove the Crown and its officials to summoning it frequently. Under Edward I the Commons were not an essential element in a Parliament, but under Edward III they assumed a position distinct, vital, and permanent. They had their own clerk, who drafted their petitions, and their rejoinders to the Crown's replies. The separation of the Houses now appears. The concessions made by Edward III to the Commons mark a decisive stage. He consented that all aids should be granted only in Parliament. He accepted the formal drafts of the Commons' collective petitions as the preliminary bases for future statutes, and by the time of his death it was recognized that the Commons had assumed a leading part in the granting of taxes and the presentation of petitions.

Against Papal agents feeling was strong. The war with France had stimulated and embittered national sentiment, which resented the influence of an external institution whose great days were already passing. Morover, this declining power had perforce abandoned its sacred traditional seat in Rome, and was now installed under French influence in enemy territory at Avignon. The renewal in 1369 of serious fighting in Aquitaine found England exhausted and disillusioned. Churchmen were ousting the nobility from public office and anti-clerical feeling grew in Parliament. The King was old and failing and a resurgence of baronial power was due. John of Gaunt set himself to redress the balance in favor of the Lords by a carefully planned political campaign against the Church. The arguments for reform set forth by a distinguished Oxford scholar named Wyclif attracted attention. Wyclif's doctrine could not remain the speculation of a harmless schoolman. It involved reducing the powers of the Church temporal in order to purify the Church spiritual. John of Gaunt was interested in the first, Wyclif in the second. They entered into alliance. Both suffered from their union. The bishops, recognizing in Wyclif Gaunt's most dangerous supporter, arraigned him on charges of heresy at St. Paul's. Gaunt, coming to his aid, encountered the hostility of the London mob. The ill-matched partnership fell to pieces and Wyclif ceased to count in high politics.

It was at this same point that his enduring influence began. He resolved to appeal to the people. Church abuses and his own reforming doctrines had attracted many young students around him. He wrote English tracts, of which the most famous was *The Wicket,* which were passed from hand to hand. Finally, with his students he took the tremendous step of having the Bible translated into English.

The long reign had reached its dusk. The glories of Crécy and Poitiers had faded. A few coastal towns alone attested the splendor of victories long to be cherished in the memories of the Island race. The old King had fallen under the consoling thrall of Alice Perrers, a lady of indifferent extraction, but of remarkable wit and capacity, untrammeled by scruple or by prudence. In 1376 the Black Prince expired, leaving a son not ten years old as heir apparent to the throne. King Edward III's large share of life narrowed sharply at its end. Mortally stricken, he retired to Sheen Lodge, where Alice, after the modern fashion, encouraged him to dwell on tournaments, the chase, and wide plans when he should recover. But hostile chroniclers have it that when the stupor preceding death engulfed the King she took the rings from his fingers and other movable property in the house and departed for some time to extreme privacy. The Black Prince's son was recognized as King by general assent on the very day his grandfather died, no question of election being raised, and the Crown of England passed to a minor, Richard II.

CHAPTER THREE

The End of the Feudal Age

John of Gaunt, Duke of Lancaster, younger brother of the Black Prince, uncle of the King, was head of the Council of Regency and ruled the land. Both the impact and the shadow of the Black Death dominated the scene. In the economic and social sphere there arose a vast tumult. Nearly one-third of the population being suddenly dead, a large part of the land passed out of cultivation. The survivors turned their plows to the richest soils and quartered their flocks and herds on the fairest pastures. Many landowners abandoned plows and enclosed, often by encroachment, the best grazing. Plowmen and laborers found themselves in high demand, and were competed for on all sides. They in their turn sought to better themselves, or at least to keep their living equal with the rising prices. But their masters saw matters differently. They repulsed fiercely demands for increased wages; they revived ancient claims to forced or tied labor. Assertions of long-lapsed authority, however good in law, were violently resisted by the country folk. They formed unions of laborers to guard their interests. There were escapes of villeins from the estates, like those of the slaves from the Southern States of America in the 1850's. On some manors the serfs were enfranchised in a body and a class of free tenants came into being. But this feature was rare. The turmoil through which all England passed affected the daily life of the mass of the people in a manner not seen again in our social history till the Industrial Revolution of the nineteenth century. Many vehement agitators, among whom John Ball is the best known, gave forth a stream of subversive doctrine. The country was full of broken soldiers, disbanded from the war, and all knew about the long-bow and its power to kill nobles, however exalted and well armed. The preaching of revolutionary ideas was widespread, and a popular ballad expressed the response of the masses:

When Adam delved and Eve span,
Who was then a gentleman?

This was a novel question for the fourteenth century, and awkward at any time. The rigid, time-enforced framework of medieval England trembled to its foundations.

Throughout the summer of 1381 there was a general ferment. Beneath it all lay organization. The royal Council was bewildered and inactive. Early in June the main body of rebels from Essex and Kent moved on London. Here they found support. For three days the city was in confusion. Foreigners were murdered; two members of the Council, Simon Sudbury, the Archbishop of Canterbury and Chancellor, and Sir Robert Hales, the Treasurer, were dragged from the Tower and beheaded on Tower Hill; the Savoy Palace of John of Gaunt was burnt; Lambeth and Southwark were sacked. But the loyal citizen body rallied around the Mayor, and at Smithfield the young King faced the rebel leaders. Wat Tyler, a military adventurer with gifts and experience of leadership, was first wounded by Mayor Walworth and then smitten to death by one of the King's esquires. As the rebel leader rolled off his horse, dead in the sight of the great assembly, the King met the crisis by riding forward alone with the cry, "I will be your leader. You shall have from me all you seek. Only follow me to the fields outside." But the death of Tyler proved a signal for the wave of reaction. The leaderless bands wandered home and spread a vulgar lawlessness through their counties. They were pursued by reconstructed authority. Vengeance was wreaked. The rising had spread throughout the South-West. In Hertfordshire the peasants rose against the powerful and hated Abbey of St. Albans, and marched on London under Jack Straw. There was a general revolt in Cambridgeshire, accompanied by burning of rolls and attacks on episcopal manors. In Norfolk and Suffolk, where

[249]

the peasants were richer and more independent, the irritation against legal villeinage was stronger. Waves of revolt rippled on as far North as Yorkshire and Cheshire, and to the West in Wiltshire and Somerset.

But after Tyler's death the resistance of the ruling classes was organized. Letters were sent out from Chancery to the royal officials commanding the restoration of order, and justices under Chief Justice Tresilian gave swift judgment upon insurgents. Nevertheless, the reaction was, according to modern examples, very restrained. Not more than a hundred and fifty executions are recorded in the rolls. Even in this furious class reaction no men were hanged except after trial by jury. Yet for generations the upper classes lived in fear of a popular rising and the laborers continued to combine. Servile labor ceased to be the basis of the system. The legal aspect of serfdom became of little importance, and the development of commutation went on, speaking broadly, at an accelerated pace after 1349.

In the charged, sullen atmosphere of the England of the 1380's Wyclif's doctrines gathered wide momentum. But, faced by social revolution, English society was in no mood for Church reform. The landed classes gave silent assent to the ultimate suppression of the preacher by the Church. Cruel days lay ahead. The political tradition was to be burned out in the misery of Sir John Oldcastle's rebellion under Henry V. But a vital element of resistance to the formation of a militant and triumphant Church survived in the English people.

It was not till he was twenty that Richard determined to be complete master of his Council, and in particular to escape from the control of his uncles. A group of younger nobles threw in their fortunes with the Court. Of these the head was Robert de Vere, Earl of Oxford, who now played a part resembling that of Gaveston under Edward II. The accumulation of Household and Government offices by the clique around the King and his effeminate favorite affronted the feudal party, and to some extent the national spirit. As so often happens, the opposition found in foreign affairs a vehicle of attack. Parliament was led to appoint a Commission of five Ministers and nine lords, of whom the former Councillors of Regency were the chiefs. When the Commissioners presently compelled the King to dismiss his personal friends Richard in deep distress withdrew from London. He sought to marshal his forces for civil war at the very same spot where Charles I would one day unfurl the royal standard. Upon this basis of force Tresilian and four other royal judges pronounced that the pressure put upon him by the Lords Appellant, as they were now styled, and the Parliament was contrary to the laws and Constitution of England. The King's uncle, Gloucester, together with other heads of the baronial oligarchy, denounced the Chief Justice and those who had acted with him, including de Vere and the other royal advisers, as traitors to the realm. Gloucester, with an armed power, approached London. In Westminster Hall the three principal Lords Appellant, Gloucester, Arundel, and Warwick, with an escort outside of three hundred horsemen, bullied the King into submission. De Vere retired to Chester and raised an armed force to secure the royal rights. But now appeared in arms the Lords Appellant, and also Gaunt's son Henry. At Radcot Bridge, in Oxfordshire, Henry and they defeated and broke de Vere. The favorite fled overseas. The King was now at the mercy of the proud faction which had usurped the rights of the monarchy. "The Merciless Parliament" opened its session. Only the per-

ENGLISH POSSESSIONS
in FRANCE, 15th Century

IRISH SEA

York
Lincoln
Chester
Stamford
Hereford
Cambridge
Norwich
ENGLAND
London
Bristol
Southampton
Hastings Dover Calais
Wareham
Arundel

NORTH SEA

Amsterdam
Antwerp
Cologne
BURGUNDIAN
NETHERLANDS

ARTOIS
Agincourt
Amiens

ENGLISH CHANNEL

Harfleur
Rouen
Bayeux
NORMANDY
Verneuil
Brest
BRITTANY
MAINE Orleans

Paris
CHAMPAGNE
Troyes
Arc
Verdun

Tours
ANJOU
Poitiers
POITOU
BERRY
BURGUNDY
Macon
Bourbon
BOURBON
DAUPHINE

BAY OF BISCAY

F R A N C E
LIMOUSIN

Castillon
Bordeaux
GUIENNE
ARMAGNAC
Vienne
Avignon
Marseilles

0 Miles 100

Bayonne
Toulouse
Narbonne

SPAIN

MEDITERRANEAN SEA

N

son of the King was respected, and that by the narrowest of margins. Richard, forced not only to submit but to assent to the slaughter of his friends, buried himself as low as he could in retirement. He laid his plans for revenge and for his own rights with far more craft than before.

On May 3, 1389, Richard took action which none of them had foreseen. Taking his seat at the Council, he asked blandly to be told how old he was. On being answered that he was three-and-twenty he declared that he had certainly come of age, and that he would no longer submit to restrictions upon his rights. He would manage the realm himself; he would choose his own advisers; he would be King indeed. Richard used his victory with prudence and mercy. The terrible combination of 1388 had dissolved. The machinery of royal government, triumphant over faction, resumed its sway, and for the next eight years Richard governed England in the guise of a constitutional and popular King. The patience and skill with which Richard accomplished his revenge are most striking. While the lords were at variance the King sought to strengthen himself by gathering Irish resources. In 1394 he went with all the formality of a royal Progress to Ireland, and for this purpose created an army dependent upon himself, which was to be useful later in overawing opposition in England. To free himself from the burden of war, which would make him directly dependent upon the favors of Parliament, he made a settlement with France. He wished beyond doubt to gain absolute power over the nobility and Parliament. Whether he also purposed to use this dictatorship in the interests of the humble masses of his subjects is one of the mysteries, but also the legend, long linked with his name. The King next devoted himself to the construction of a compact, efficient Court party. Both Gaunt and his son and Mowbray, Earl of Norfolk, one of the former Appellants, were now rallied to his side, partly in loyalty to him and partly in hostility to Arundel and Gloucester.

In January 1397 the Estates were summoned to Westminster, where under deft and at the same time resolute management they showed all due submission. Thus assured, Richard decided at last to strike. Arundel and some others of his associates were declared traitors and accorded only the courtesy of decapitation. Warwick was exiled to the Isle of Man. Gloucester, arrested and taken to Calais, was there murdered by Richard's agents; and this deed, not being covered by constitutional forms, bred in its turn new retributions. Parliament was called only to legalize these events. Never has there been such a Parliament. With ardor pushed to suicidal lengths, it suspended almost every constitutional right and privilege gained in the preceding century. The relations between Gaunt's son, Henry, the King's cousin and contemporary, passed through drama into tragedy. A quarrel arose between Henry and Thomas Mowbray, now Duke of Norfolk. Henry accused Mowbray of treasonable language. Trial by battle appeared the correct solution. The famous scene took place in September 1398. The lists were drawn; the English world assembled; the champions presented themselves; but the King, exasperating the spectators of all classes who had gathered in high expectation to see the sport, cast down his warder, forbade the combat, and exiled Mowbray for life and Henry for a decade. During 1398 there were many in the nation who awoke to the fact that a servile Parliament had in a few weeks suspended many of the fundamental rights and liberties of the realm. Not only the old nobility, who in the former crisis had been defeated, but all the gentry and merchant classes were aghast at the triumph of absolute rule.

In February of 1399 died old John of Gaunt, "time-honored Lancaster." Richard, pressed for money, could not refrain from a technically legal seizure of the Lancaster estates in spite of his promises. He declared his cousin disinherited. This challenged the position of every property-holder. And forthwith, by a fatal misjudgment of his strength and of what was stirring in the land, the King set forth in May upon a punitive expedition, which was long overdue, to assert the royal authority in Ireland. In July Henry of Lancaster, as he had now become, landed in Yorkshire, declaring that he had only come to claim his lawful rights as heir to his venerated father. The course of his revolt followed exactly that of Isabella and Mortimer against Edward II seventy-two years before. It took some time for the news of Henry's apparition and all that followed so swiftly from it to reach King Richard in the depths of Ireland. Having landed in England on July 27, he made a rapid three weeks' march through North Wales in an attempt to gather forces. The Welsh, who would have stood by him, could not face the advancing power of what was now all England. At Flint Castle he submitted to Henry, into whose hands the whole administration had now passed. His abdication was extorted; his death had become inevitable. The last of all English kings whose hereditary right was indisputable disappeared for ever beneath the portcullis of Pontefract Castle. Henry, by and with the consent of the Estates of the Realm and the Lords Spiritual and Temporal, ascended the throne as Henry IV.

From the outset Henry depended upon Parliament to make good by its weight the defects in his title, and rested on the theory of the elective, limited kingship rather than on that of absolute monarchy. He was therefore alike by mood and need a constitutional King. During this time therefore Parliamentary power over finance was greatly strengthened. Not only did the Estates supply the money by voting the taxes, but they began to follow its expenditure, and to require and to receive accounts from the high officers of the State. Nothing like this had been tolerated by any of the Kings before.

On one issue indeed, half social, half religious, King and Parliament were heartily agreed. The Lollards' advocacy of a Church purified by being relieved of all worldly goods did not command the assent of the clergy. The lords saw that their own estates stood on no better title than those of the Church. They therefore joined with the clergy in defense of their property. Thus did orthodoxy and property make common cause and march together.

The Welsh, already discontented, under the leadership of Owen Glendower, presently espoused Richard's cause. Armed risings appeared in several parts of the country, but the conspiracy received no genuine support and was fatal to the former King. Richard's death was announced in February 1400. But far and wide throughout England spread the tale that he had escaped, and that in concealment he awaited his hour to bring the common people of the time to the enjoyment of their own. All this welled up against Henry Bolingbroke. The trouble with the Welsh deepened into a national insurrection. Owen Glendower, who was a remarkable man, of considerable education, carried on a war which was the constant background of English affairs till 1409. The King was also forced to fight continually against the Scots. After six years of this harassment we are told that his natural magnanimity was worn out, and that he yielded himself to the temper of his supporters and of his Parliament in cruel deeds.

His most serious conflict was with the Percys. These lords of the Northern Marches, the old Earl of Northumberland and his fiery son Hotspur, had for nearly three years carried on the defense of England against the Scots unaided and almost entirely at their own expense. The Percys had played a great part in placing Henry on the throne. They held a great independent power, and an antagonism was perhaps inevitable. Hotspur raised the standard of revolt. But at Shrewsbury on July 21, 1403, Henry overcame and slew him in a small, fierce battle. The old Earl, who was marching to his aid, was forced to submit, and pardon was freely extended to him. But two years later, with his son's death at heart, he rebelled again, and this time the conspiracy was far-reaching. Once again Henry marched north, and once again he was successful. At the same time the King's health failed. He still managed to triumph in the Welsh War, and Owen Glendower was forced back into his mountains. But Parliament took all advantages from the King's necessities. Henry saw safety only in surrender. A Council must be nominated by the King which included the Parliamentary leaders. The accounts of Government expenses were subjected to a Parliamentary audit. By these submissions Henry became the least of kings.

Henry's eldest son, the Prince of Wales, showed already an extraordinary force and quality. As his father's health declined he was everywhere drawn into State business. But there can be no doubt that the dying sovereign still gripped convulsively the reins of power. In 1412, when the King could no longer walk and scarcely ride, he was with difficulty dissuaded by his Council from attempting to command the troops in Aquitaine. He lingered through the winter, talked of a Crusade, summoned Parliament in February, but could do no business with it. In March, when praying in Westminster Abbey, he had a prolonged fit, from which he rallied only to die in the Jerusalem Chamber on March 20, 1413. Thus the life and reign of King Henry IV exhibit to us another instance of the vanities of ambition and the harsh guerdon which rewards its success.

Henry V was King at twenty-five. His face, we are told, was oval, with a long, straight nose, ruddy complexion, dark, smooth hair, and bright eyes, mild as a dove's when unprovoked, but lion-like in wrath; his frame was slender, yet well-knit, strong, and active. His disposition was orthodox, chivalrous, and just. The romantic stories of his riotous youth and sudden conversion to gravity and virtue when charged with the supreme responsibility must not be pressed too far. He led the nation away from internal discord to foreign conquest; and he had the dream, and perhaps the prospect, of leading all Western Europe into the high championship of a Crusade. The Commons were thereupon liberal with supply. A wave of reconciliation swept the land. The King declared a general pardon. He sought to assuage the past.

At Henry V's accession the Orleanists had gained the preponderance in France, and unfurled the Oriflamme against the Duke of Burgundy. Henry naturally allied himself with the weaker party, the Burgundians, who, in their distress, were prepared to acknowledge him as King of France.

During the whole of 1414 Henry V was absorbed in warlike preparations by land and sea. He reorganized the Fleet. Instead of mainly taking over and arming private ships, as was the custom, he, like Alfred, built many vessels for the Royal

Navy. The English army of about ten thousand fighting men sailed to France on August 11, 1415, in a fleet of small ships, and landed without opposition at the mouth of the Seine. Harfleur was besieged and taken by the middle of September. The King was foremost in prowess:

Once more unto the breach, dear friends, once more;
Or close the wall up with our English dead.

Leaving a garrison in Harfleur, and sending home several thousand sick and wounded, the King resolved, with about a thousand knights and men-at-arms and four thousand archers, to traverse the French coast in a hundred-mile march to his fortress at Calais, where his ships were to await him. All the circumstances of this decision show that his design was to tempt the enemy to battle. This was not denied him. He had to ascend the Somme to above Amiens by Boves and Corbie, and could only cross at the ford of Béthencourt. All these names are well known to our generation. On October 20 he camped near Péronne. The French heralds came to the English camp and inquired, for mutual convenience, by which route His Majesty would desire to proceed. "Our path lies straight to Calais," was Henry's answer. This was not telling them much, for he had no other choice. The French army, which was already interposing itself, by a right-handed movement across his front fell back before his advance-guard behind the Canche River. Henry, moving by Albert, Frévent, and Blangy, learned that they were before him in apparently overwhelming numbers. He must now cut his way through, perish, or surrender. When one of his officers, Sir Walter Hungerford, deplored the fact "that they had not but one ten thousand of those men in England

that do not work today," the King rebuked him and revived his spirits in a speech to which Shakespeare has given an immortal form:

If we are marked to die, we are enough
To do our country loss; and if to live,
The fewer men, the greater share of honour.

"Wot you not," he actually said, "that the Lord with these few can overthrow the pride of the French?" He and the "few" lay for the night at the village of Maisoncelles, maintaining utter silence and the strictest discipline. The French headquarters were at Agincourt, and it is said that they kept high revel and diced for the captives they should take.

The English victory of Crécy was gained against great odds upon the defensive. Poitiers was a counter-stroke. Agincourt ranks as the most heroic of all the land battles England has ever fought. It was a vehement assault. The French, whose numbers have been estimated at about twenty thousand, were drawn up in three lines of battle, of which a proportion remained mounted. With justifiable confidence they awaited the attack of less than a third their number, who, far from home and many marches from the sea, must win or die. The whole English army, even the King himself, dismounted and sent their horses to the rear; and shortly after eleven o'clock on St. Crispin's Day, October 25, he gave the order, "In the name of Almighty God and of Saint George, Avaunt Banner in the best time of the year, and Saint George this day be thine help." The archers kissed the soil in reconciliation to God, and, crying loudly, "Hurrah! Hurrah! Saint George and Merrie England!" advanced to within three hundred yards of the heavy masses in their front. They planted their stakes and loosed their arrows. The

French were once again unduly crowded upon the field. They stood in three dense lines, and neither their crossbowmen nor their battery of cannon could fire effectively. Under the arrow storm they in their turn moved forward down the slope, plodding heavily through a plowed field already trampled into a quagmire. But once again the long-bow destroyed all before it. Horse and foot alike went down; a long heap of armored dead and wounded lay upon the ground, over which the reinforcements struggled bravely, but in vain. Now occurred a terrible episode. The King, believing himself attacked from behind, while a superior force still remained unbroken on his front, issued the dread order to slaughter the prisoners. Then perished the flower of the French nobility, many of whom had yielded themselves to easy hopes of ransom. The alarm in the rear was soon relieved; but not before the massacre was almost finished. The French third line quitted the field without attempting to renew the battle in any serious manner. Henry, who had declared at daybreak, "For me this day shall never England ransom pay," now saw his path to Calais clear before him. But far more than that: the victory of Agincourt made him the supreme figure in Europe. When in 1416 the Holy Roman Emperor Sigismund visited London in an effort to effect a peace he recognized Henry as King of France. But there followed long, costly campaigns and sieges which outran the financial resources of the Island and gradually cooled its martial ardor. After hideous massacres in Paris, led by the Burgundians, hot-headed supporters of the Dauphin murdered the Duke of Burgundy at Montereau in 1419, and by this deed sealed the alliance of Burgundy with England. In May 1420, by the Treaty of Troyes, Charles VI recognized Henry as heir to the French kingdom upon his death and as Regent during his

life. To implement and consolidate these triumphs Henry married Charles's daughter Catherine, a comely princess, who bore him a son long to reign over impending English miseries.

This was the boldest bid the Island ever made in Europe. Henry V was no feudal sovereign of the old type with a class interest which overrode social and territorial barriers. He was entirely national in his outlook: he was the first King to use the English language in his letters and his messages home from the Front; his triumphs were gained by English troops; his policy was sustained by a Parliament that could claim to speak for the English people. For it was the union of the country gentry and the rising middle class of the towns, working with the Common Lawyers, that gave the English Parliament thus early a character and a destiny that the States-General of France and the Cortes of Castile were not to know. Henry stood, and with him his country, at the summit of the world.

But glory was, as always, dearly bought. When Henry V revived the English claims to France he opened the greatest tragedy in our medieval history. Agincourt was a glittering victory, but the wasteful and useless campaigns that followed more than outweighed its military and moral value, and the miserable, destroying century that ensued casts its black shadow upon Henry's heroic triumph. If Henry V united the nation against France he set it also upon the Lollards. This degradation lies about him and his times, and our contacts with his personal nobleness and prowess, though imperishable, are marred. Fortune, which had bestowed upon the King all that could be dreamed of, could not afford to risk her handiwork in a long life. In the full tide of power and success he died at the end of August 1422 of a malady contracted in the field, probably dysentery, against which the medicine of those times could not make head. He was more deeply loved by his subjects of all classes than any King has been in England.

At the time of the great King's death the ascendancy of the English arms in France was established. In 1421 the French and their Scottish allies under the Earl of Buchan defeated the English at Baugé, but three other considerable actions ended in English victories. At Cravant, in August 1423, the French were again aided by a strong Scots contingent. But the English archers, with their Burgundian allies, shot most of them down. At Verneuil a year later this decision was repeated. The English attempt to conquer all vast France with a few thousand archers led by warrior-nobles, with hardly any money from home, and little food to be found in the ruined regions, reached its climax in the triumph of Verneuil. There seemed to the French to be no discoverable way to contend against these rugged, lusty, violent Islanders, with their archery, their flexible tactics, and their audacity. At this time the loves and the acquisitiveness of the Duke of Gloucester, who in Bedford's absence in France became Protector of the English child-King, drove a wedge between England and Burgundy. Jacqueline, Princess of Hainault, Holland, and Zeeland, and heir to these provinces, had been married for reasons of Burgundian policy to the Duke of Brabant, a sickly lout fifteen years of age. She revolted from this infliction, took refuge in England, and appealed to Gloucester for protection. This was accorded in full measure. Gloucester resolved to marry her, enjoy her company, and acquire her inheritance. This questionable romance gave deep offense to the Duke of Burgundy, whose major interests in the Low Countries were injured. Although both Bedford in France

and the English Council at home completely disclaimed Gloucester's action, and were prodigal in their efforts to repair the damage, the rift between England and Burgundy dates from this event.

There now appeared upon the ravaged scene an Angel of Deliverance, the noblest patriot of France, the most splendid of her heroes, the most beloved of her saints, the most inspiring of all her memories, the peasant Maid, the ever-shining, ever-glorious Joan of Arc. In the poor, remote hamlet of Domrémy, on the fringe of the Vosges Forest, she served at the inn. She rode the horses of travelers, bareback, to water. She wandered on Sundays into the woods, where there were shrines, and a legend that some day from these oaks would arise one to save France. In the fields where she tended her sheep the saints of God, who grieved for France, rose before her in visions. St. Michael himself appointed her, by right divine, to command the armies of liberation. Joan shrank at first from the awful duty, but when he returned attended by St. Margaret and St. Catherine, patronesses of the village church, she obeyed their command. She convinced Baudricourt, Governor of the neighboring town, that she was inspired. He recommended her to a Court ready to clutch at straws. There, among the nobles and courtiers, she at once picked out the King, who had purposely mingled with the crowd. "Most noble Lord Dauphin," she said, "I am Joan the Maid, sent on the part of God to aid you and the kingdom, and by His order I announce that you will be crowned in the city of Rheims."

Orleans in 1429 lay under the extremities of siege. The Maid now claimed to lead a convoy to the rescue. Upon her invocation the spirit of victory changed sides, and the French began an offensive which never rested till the English invaders were driven out of France. The siege was broken, Orleans saved and the Earl of Suffolk later captured.

Joan told Charles he must march on Rheims to be crowned upon the throne of his ancestors. The idea seemed fantastic: Rheims lay deep in enemy country. But under her spell he obeyed, and everywhere the towns opened their gates before them and the people crowded to his aid. With all the pomp of victory and faith, with the most sacred ceremonies of ancient days, Charles was crowned at Rheims.

When in May 1430 the town of Compiègne revolted against the decision of the King that it should yield to the English, Joan with only six hundred men attempted its succor. The enemy, at first surprised, rallied, and a panic among the French ensued. Flavy, the Governor, whose duty it was to save the town, felt obliged to pull up the drawbridge in her face and leave her to the Burgundians. She was sold to the rejoicing English for a moderate sum.

Joan of Arc perished on May 30, 1431. Amid an immense concourse she was dragged to the stake in the marketplace of Rouen. High upon the pyramid of faggots the flames rose toward her, and the smoke of doom wreathed and curled. She raised a cross made of firewood, and her last word was "Jesus!" History has recorded the comment of an English soldier who witnessed the scene. "We are lost," he said. "We have burnt a saint." All this proved true. The tides of war flowed remorselessly against the English. The boy Henry was crowned in Paris in December amid chilly throngs. Burgundy became definitely hostile in 1435. The French gained a series of battles. Their artillery now became the finest in the world. All Northern France, except Calais, was reconquered. Even Guienne, dowry of Eleanor of Aquitaine, for three hundred years a loyal, contented fief of the English Crown, was overrun.

A baby was King of England, and two months later, on the death of Charles VI, was proclaimed without dispute the King of France. Bedford and Gloucester, his uncles, became Protectors, and with a Council comprising the heads of the most powerful families attempted to sustain the work of Henry V. As Henry VI grew up his virtues and simpleness became equally apparent. At the hour when a strong king alone could re-create the balance between the nation and the nobility, when all demanded the restraint of faction at home and the waging of victorious war without undue expense abroad, the throne was known to be occupied by a devout simpleton suited alike by his qualities and defects to be a puppet.

The princes of the House of Lancaster disputed among themselves. After Bedford's death in 1435 the tension grew between Gloucester and the Beauforts. At twenty-three it was high time that King Henry should marry. Each of the Lancastrian factions was anxious to provide him with a queen; but Cardinal Beaufort and his brothers, with their ally, Suffolk, whose ancestors, the de la Poles of Hull, had founded their fortunes upon trade, prevailed over the Duke of Gloucester, weakened as he was by maladministration and ill-success. Suffolk was sent to France to arrange a further truce, and it was implied in his mission that he should treat for a marriage between the King of England and Margaret of Anjou, niece of the King of France. This remarkable woman added to rare beauty and charm a masterly intellect and a dauntless spirit. Like Joan the Maid, though without her inspiration or her cause, she knew how to make men fight. Even from the seclusion of her family her qualities became well known. Was she not then the mate for this feeble-minded King? Would she not give him the force that he lacked? And would not those who placed her at his side secure a large and sure future for themselves? Suffolk was enthralled by Margaret. He made the match; and in his eagerness, by a secret article, agreed without formal authority that Maine should be the reward of France. The marriage was solemnized in 1445 with such splendor as the age could afford.

It soon appeared that immense forces of retribution were on foot. It was generally believed, though wrongly, that Gloucester, arrested when he came to a Parliament summoned at St. Edmonsbury, had been murdered by the express direction of Suffolk and Edmund Beaufort. It has, however, been suggested that his death was induced by choler and amazement at the ruin of his fortunes. When in 1448 the secret article for the cession of Maine became public through its occupation by the French anger was expressed on all sides. Suffolk was impeached. Straining his Prerogative, Henry burked the proceedings by sending him in 1450 into a five years' exile. When the banished Duke was crossing the Channel with his attendants and treasure in two small vessels, the *Nicholas of the Tower,* the largest warship in the Royal Navy, bore down upon him and carried him on board. It is a revealing sign of the times that a royal ship should seize and execute a royal Minister who was traveling under the King's special protection. In June and July a rising took place in Kent, which the Lancastrians claimed to bear the marks of Yorkist support. Jack Cade, a soldier of capacity and bad character, home from the wars, gathered several thousand men, all summoned in due form by the constables of the districts, and marched on London. He was admitted to the City, but on his executing Lord Say, the Treasurer, in Cheapside, after a mob trial, the magistrates and citizens turned against him, his followers dispersed under terms of pardon, and he himself was pursued and killed.

As the process of expelling the English from France continued fortresses fell, towns and districts were lost, and their garrisons for the most part came home. The nobles, in the increasing disorder, were glad to gather these hardened fighters to their local defense. They gave them pay or land, or both, and uniforms or liveries bearing the family crest. Cash and ambition ruled and the land sank rapidly toward anarchy. The celebrated Paston Letters show that England, enormously advanced as it was in comprehension, character, and civilization, was relapsing from peace and security into barbaric confusion. A statute of 1429 had fixed the county franchise at the forty-shilling freeholder. It is hard to realize that this arbitrarily contracted franchise ruled in England for four hundred years, and that all the wars and quarrels, the decision of the greatest causes, the grandest events at home and abroad, proceeded upon this basis until the Reform Bill of 1832.

The claims and hopes of the opposition to the House of Lancaster were embodied in Richard, Duke of York. He was a virtuous, law-respecting, slow-moving, and highly competent prince. He had given good service. He had accepted the government of Ireland and won the goodwill of the Irish people. According to established usage he had a prior right to the Crown. York was the son of Richard, Earl of Cambridge, and grandson of Edmund, Duke of York, a younger brother of John of Gaunt. As the great-grandson of Edward III he was the only other person besides Henry VI with an unbroken male descent from Edward III, but in the female line he had also a superior claim through his descent from Gaunt's elder brother, Lionel of

Clarence. By the Act of 1407 the Beauforts—Gaunt's legitimatized bastards—had been barred from the succession. If Henry VI should succeed in annulling the Act of 1407 then Edmund Beaufort (Somerset) would have a better male claim with York. It was this that York feared. York had taken Gloucester's place as first Prince of the Blood. Around York and beneath him there gathered an immense party of discontent, which drove him hesitantly to demand a place in the government, and eventually, through Queen Margaret's increasing hostility, the throne itself.

Although the Yorkists predominated in the rich South, and the Lancastrians were supreme in the warlike North, there were many interlacements and overlaps. We are, however, in the presence of the most ferocious and implacable quarrel of which there is factual record. The individual actors were bred by generations of privilege and war, into which the feudal theme had brought its peculiar sense of honor, and to which the Papacy contributed such spiritual sanction as emerged from its rivalries and intrigues. It was a conflict in which personal hatreds reached their maximum, and from which mass effects were happily excluded. The attitude and feeling of the public, in all parts and at all times, weighed heavily with both contending factions. Thus Europe witnessed the amazing spectacle of nearly thirty years of ferocious war, conducted with hardly the sack of a single town, and with the mass of the common people little affected and the functions of local government very largely maintained.

In 1450 the ferment of discontent and rivalries drew the Duke of York into his first overt act. He quitted his government in Ireland and landed unbidden in Wales. Prayers and protests had failed; there remained the resort to arms. Accordingly, on February 3, 1452, York sent an address to the citizens of Shrewsbury, accusing Somerset of the disgrace in France and of "laboring continually about the King's Highness for my undoing." Civil war seemed about to begin. In the event York dispersed his forces and presented himself unarmed and bareheaded before King Henry, protesting his loyalty, but demanding redress. Since he was supported by the Commons and evidently at the head of a great party, the King promised that "a sad and substantial Council" should be formed, of which he should be a member. The Court had still to choose between Somerset and York. The Queen, always working with Somerset, decided the issue in his favor.

The disasters culminated in France. Somerset, the chief commander, bore the burden of defeat. In this situation the King went mad. He recognized no one, not even the Queen. He could eat and drink, but his speech was childish or incoherent. He could not walk. For another fifteen months he remained entirely without comprehension. The pious Henry had been withdrawn from the worry of existence to an island of merciful oblivion. When these terrible facts became known Queen Margaret aspired to be Protector. On October 13 she gave birth to a son. How far this event was expected is not clear, but, as long afterwards with James II, it inevitably hardened the hearts of all men. It seemed to shut out for ever the Yorkist claim.

But the insanity of the King defeated Somerset: he could no longer withstand York. The strength of York's position bore him to the Protectorate. His party was astounded at his tolerance. When the Government was in his hands, when his future was marred by the new heir to the Crown, when his power or his life might be destroyed at any moment by the

King's recovery, he kept absolute faith with right and justice. Here then is his monument and justification.

Surprises continued. When it was generally believed that Henry's line was extinct he had produced an heir. At Christmas 1454 he regained all his faculties. York ceased legally to be Protector from the moment that the King's mental recovery was known; he made no effort to retain the power. Queen Margaret took the helm. Somerset was not only released but restored to his key position.

York's lords agreed upon a resort to arms. St. Albans was the first shedding of blood in strife. The Yorkist triumph was complete. They gained possession of the King. Somerset was dead. Margaret and her child had taken sanctuary. But soon we see the inherent power of Lancaster. They had the majority of the nobles on their side, and the majesty of the Crown. The four years from 1456 to 1459 were a period of uneasy truce. There were intense efforts at reconciliation. The spectacle was displayed to the Londoners of the King being escorted to Westminster by a procession in which the Duke of York and Queen Margaret walked side by side, followed by the Yorkist and Lancastrian lords, the most opposed in pairs. In 1459 fighting broke out again.

War began in earnest in July 1460. York was still in Ireland; but the Yorkist lords under Warwick, holding bases in Wales and at Calais, with all their connections and partisans, supported by the Papal Legate and some of the bishops, and, on the whole, by the Commons, confronted the Lancastrians and the Crown at Northampton. The royal forces fled in panic. The so-called compromise in which all the Estates of the Realm concurred was then attempted. Henry was to be King for life; York was to conduct the government and succeed him at his death. The Queen fought on. At

Wakefield on December 30, 1460, the first considerable battle of the war was fought. The Lancastrians, with superior forces, caught the Yorkists by surprise, when many were foraging, and a frightful rout and massacre ensued. No quarter was given. The Duke of York was killed; his son, the Earl of Rutland, seventeen years old, was flying, but the new Lord Clifford, remembering St. Albans, slaughtered him with joy, exclaiming, "By God's blood, thy father slew mine; and so will I do thee, and all thy kin." The old Earl of Salisbury, caught during the night, was beheaded immediately by Lord Exeter, a natural son of the Duke of Buckingham. The heads of the three Yorkist nobles were exposed over the gates and walls of York. The great Duke's head, with a paper crown, grinned upon the landscape, summoning the avengers.

Now a new generation took charge. There was a new Lord Clifford, a new Duke of Somerset, above all a new Duke of York, all in their twenties, sword in hand, with fathers to avenge and England as the prize. When York's son, hitherto Earl of March, learned that his father's cause had devolved upon him he did not shrink. He fell upon the Earl of Wiltshire and the Welsh Lancastrians, and on February 2, 1461, at the Battle of Mortimer's Cross, near Hereford, he beat and broke them up. He made haste to repay the cruelties of Wakefield. The victorious Yorkists under their young Duke now marched to help the Earl of Warwick, who had returned from Calais and was being hard pressed in London; but Queen Margaret forestalled him, and on February 17, at the Second Battle of St. Albans, she inflicted upon Warwick a bloody defeat. Margaret now had her husband safe back in her hands and with him the full authority of the Crown. The road to London was open, but she did not choose to advance upon it. This was the turning-point in the struggle. Nine days after the Second Battle of St. Albans Edward of York entered London. He declared himself King, and on March 4, 1461, was proclaimed at Westminster with such formalities as were possible.

King Edward IV marched north to settle once and for all with King Henry VI. Near York the Queen, with the whole power of Lancaster, confronted him not far from Tadcaster, by the villages of Saxton and Towton. On March 28 the Yorkist advance-guard was beaten back at Ferry Bridge by the young Lord Clifford, and Warwick himself was wounded; but as heavier forces arrived the bridge was carried. The next day one of the most ruthless battles on English soil began in a blinding snowstorm, which drove in the faces of the Lancastrians. For six hours the two sides grappled furiously, with varying success. But all hung in the balance until late in the afternoon, when the arrival of the Duke of Norfolk's corps upon the exposed flank of the Lancastrians drove the whole mass into retreat, which soon became a rout. Margaret and her son escaped to York, where King Henry had been observing the rites of Palm Sunday. Gathering him up, the imperious Queen set out with her child and a cluster of spears for the Scottish border. The bodies of thousands of Englishmen and the flower of the Lancastrian nobility and knighthood fell upon the field. When Edward reached the town of York his first task was to remove the heads of his father and others of Margaret's victims and to replace them with those of his noblest captives. Three months later, on June 28, he was crowned King at Westminster, and the Yorkist triumph seemed complete. It was followed by wholesale proscriptions and confiscations. Not only the throne but one-third of the estates in England changed hands.

After Towton the Lancastrian cause was sustained by the unconquerable will of Queen Margaret. Never has her tenacity and rarely have her vicissitudes been surpassed in any woman. In 1462 Margaret, after much personal appeal to the Courts of France, Burgundy, and Scotland, found herself able to land with a power, and whether by treachery or weakness the three strongest Northern castles, Bamburgh, Alnwick, and Dunstanburgh, opened their gates to her. In the winter of 1462 therefore King Edward gathered his Yorkist powers, and, carrying his new train of artillery by sea to Newcastle, began the sieges of these lost strongholds. All three fortresses fell in a month.

The behavior of Edward at this moment constitutes a solid defense for his character. This voluptuous young King, sure of his position, now showed a clemency unheard of in the Wars of the Roses. His magnanimity and forgiveness were ill repaid by Somerset and Percy. When Margaret returned with fresh succors from France and Scotland in 1463 Percy opened the gates of Bamburgh to the Scots, and Alnwick was betrayed about the same time by a soured Yorkist officer, Sir Ralph Grey. Once again Edward and the Yorkists took the field, and the redoubtable new artillery, at that time esteemed as much among the leading nations as atomic weapons are today, was carried to the North. Margaret fled to France, while Henry buried himself amid the valleys and the pious foundations of Cumberland.

At Christmas 1463 Somerset deserted Edward and returned to the Lancastrian side. Again the banner of Lancaster was raised. Somerset joined King Henry. Alnwick and Bamburgh still held out. Norham and Skipton had been captured, but now Warwick's brother Montagu with a substantial army was in the field. On April 25, 1464, at Hedgeley Moor, near Alnwick, he broke and destroyed the Lancastrian revolt. Edward's experiment of mercy in this quarrel was now at an end, and the former rigors were renewed in their extreme degree. Somerset, defeated with a small following at Hexham on May 15, 1464, was beheaded the next morning. Before the month was out in every Yorkist camp Lancastrian nobles and knights by dozens and half-dozens were put to death. Poor King Henry was at length tracked down near Clitheroe, in Lancashire, and conveyed to London. This time there was no ceremonial entry. With his feet tied by leather thongs to the stirrups, and with a straw hat on his head, the futile but saintly figure around whom such storms had beaten was led three times around the pillory, and finally hustled to the Tower, whose gates closed on him—yet not, this time, for ever.

The Castle of Harlech, on the Western sea, alone flaunted the Red Rose. When it surrendered in 1468 there were found to be but fifty effective men in the garrison. Among them was a child of twelve, who had survived the rigors of the long blockade. His name was Richmond, later to become King Henry VII.

The successes of these difficult years had been gained for King Edward by the Neville family. Warwick, and Montagu, now Earl of Northumberland, with George Neville, Archbishop of York, had the whole machinery of government in their hands. Thus some years slipped by, while the King, although gripping from time to time the reins of authority, led in the main his life of ease. His marriage in 1464 with Elizabeth Woodville was a secret guarded in deadly earnest. The statesmen at the head of the Government, while they smiled at what seemed an amorous frolic, never dreamed it was a solemn union, which must shake the land to its depths. Here was the occasion which sundered him from the valiant

King-maker, fourteen years older, but also in the prime of life. Eight new peerages came into existence in the Queen's family: her father, five brothers-in-law, her son, and her brother Anthony. This was generally thought excessive. The arrival of a new nobility who had done nothing notable in the war and now surrounded the indolent King was not merely offensive, but politically dangerous to Warwick and his proud associates. But the clash came over foreign policy. Margaret with her retinue of shadows was welcomed in her pauper stateliness both in Burgundy and in France. It was the policy of Warwick and his connection to make friends with France, by far the stronger Power, and thus obtain effectual security. Edward took the opposite line. With the instinct which afterwards ruled our Island for so many centuries, he sought to base English policy upon the second strongest State in Western Europe. The King therefore, to Warwick's chagrin and alarm, in 1468 married his sister Margaret to Charles the Bold, who had in 1467 succeeded as Duke of Burgundy.

The offended chiefs took deep counsel together. Warwick's plan was singular in its skill. He had gained the King's brother, Clarence, to his side by whispering that but for this upstart brood of the Woodvilles he might succeed Edward as King. When all was ready Warwick struck. A rising took place in the North. At the same time in London the House of Commons petitioned against lax and profuse administration. As soon as the King had been enticed northwards by the rebellion Warwick and Clarence, who had hitherto crouched at Calais, came to England with the Calais garrison. But before he and Clarence could bring their forces against the King's rear the event was decided. The Northern rebels, under "Robin of Redesdale," intercepted Pembroke and Devon, and at Edgcott, near

Banbury, defeated them with a merciless slaughter. The King, trying to rally his scattered forces at Olney, in Buckinghamshire, found himself in the power of his great nobles. At this moment therefore Warwick the King-maker had actually the two rival Kings, Henry VI and Edward IV, both his prisoners, one in the Tower and the other at Middleham. This was a remarkable achievement for any subject. The King found it convenient in his turn to dissemble. Thus was a settlement reached between Warwick and the Crown. But all this was on the surface.

In March 1470, under the pretense of suppressing a Lancastrian rebellion in Lincolnshire, the King called his forces to arms. At Losecoat Field he defeated the insurgents, who fled; and in the series of executions which had now become customary after every engagement he obtained a confession from Sir Robert Welles which accused both Warwick and Clarence of treason. The King, with troops fresh from victory, turned on them all of a sudden. The King-maker found himself by one sharp twist of fortune deprived of almost every resource he had counted upon as sure. He in his turn presented himself at the French Court as a suppliant.

This was the best luck Louis XI had ever known. At Angers he confronted Margaret and her son, now a fine youth of seventeen, with Warwick and Clarence, and proposed brutally to them that they should join together with his support to overthrow Edward. They agreed to forgive and unite. The confederacy was sealed by the betrothal of Margaret's son, the Prince of Wales, to Warwick's youngest daughter, Anne. A son born of this union would have had a great hope of uniting torn, tormented England. But Clarence had been swayed in his desertion of his brother by thoughts of the Crown, and although he

was now named as the next in succession after Margaret's son the value of his chance was no longer high. He must have been a great dissembler; for Warwick was no more able to forecast his actions in the future than his brother had been in the past.

Warwick and Clarence landed at Dartmouth in September 1470. Kent and other Southern counties rose in his behalf. He brought the miserable Henry VI from his prison in the Tower, placed a crown on his head, paraded him through the capital, and seated him upon the throne. At Nottingham Edward received alarming news. Suddenly he learned that while the Northern rebels were moving down upon him and cutting him from his Welsh succors, and while Warwick was moving northward with strong forces, the Marquis of Montagu, Warwick's brother, hitherto faithful, had made his men throw up their caps for King Henry. He had but one refuge—the Court of Burgundy; and with a handful of followers he cast himself upon his brother-in-law. Meanwhile, the King-maker ruled England, and it seemed that he might long continue to do so. He had King Henry VI a puppet in his hand. Statutes were passed in his name which annihilated all the disinheritances and attainders of the Yorkist Parliament. A third of the land of England returned to its old possessors.

In March 1471 Edward landed with his small expedition at Ravenspur, a port in Yorkshire now washed away by the North Sea, but then still famous for the descent of Henry of Bolingbroke in 1399. The King, fighting for his life, was, as usual, at his best. Montagu, with four times his numbers, approached to intercept him. Edward, by extraordinary marches, maneuvered past him. At Warwick he was strong enough to proclaim himself King again.

Edward had a resource unsuspected by Warwick. He knew Clarence was his man. Edward entered London, and was cordially received by the bewildered citizens. Henry VI, who had actually been made to ride about the streets at the head of six hundred horsemen, was relieved from these exertions and taken back to his prison in the Tower.

The decisive battle impended on the North Road, and at Barnet on April 14, 1471, Edward and the Yorkists faced Warwick and the House of Neville, with the new Duke of Somerset, second son of Edmund Beaufort, and important Lancastrian allies. Throughout England no one could see clearly what was happening, and the Battle of Barnet, which resolved their doubts, was itself fought in a fog. The lines of battle overlapped; Warwick's right turned Edward's left flank, and vice versa. The King-maker, stung perhaps by imputations upon his physical courage, fought on foot. The badge of a star and rays on Lord Oxford's banners was mistaken by Warwick's troops for the sun and rays of King Edward. The cry of treason ran through Warwick's hosts. North of the town near which the main struggle was fought the King-maker, just as he was about to reach the necessary horse, was overtaken by the Yorkists and battered to death. By his depraved abandonment of all the causes for which he had sent so many men to their doom he had deserved death; and for his virtues, which were distinguished, it was fitting that it should come to him in honorable guise.

On the very day of Barnet Margaret at last landed in England. On learning that Warwick was slain and his army beaten and dispersed the hitherto indomitable Queen had her hour of despair. Her only hope was to reach the Welsh border, where strong traditional Lancastrian forces were already in arms. Edward, near London, strove to cut Margaret off from Wales. Both armies marched incessantly. The Lancastrians succeeded in reaching the goal first, but only with their troops in a state of extreme exhaustion. Edward, close behind, pressed on, and on the 4th of May brought them to battle at Tewkesbury. The Lancastrians were scattered or destroyed. Margaret was captured. The Prince of Wales, fighting valiantly, was slain on the field, according to one chronicler, crying in vain for succor to his brother-in-law, the treacherous Clarence. Margaret was kept for a show, and also because women, especially when they happened to be queens, were not slaughtered in this fierce age. Eleven years after Tewkesbury she died in poverty in her father's Anjou.

After the battle Richard of Gloucester, known to legend as "Crookback" because of his alleged deformity, had hastened to London. He had a task to do at the Tower. As long as the Prince of Wales lived King Henry's life had been safe, but with the death of the last hope of Lancaster his fate was sealed. On the night of May 21 the Duke of Gloucester visited the Tower with full authority from the King, where he probably supervised the murder of the melancholy spectator who had been the center of fifty years of cruel contention.

The King was now supreme. He was now a matured and disillusioned statesman. Edward was resolved to have as little to do with Parliament as possible, and even as a boy of twenty in the stress of war he had tried hard and faithfully to "live of his own." He had a new source of revenue in the estates of the attainted Lancastrians. Thus so long as there was peace the King could pay his way. But the nobility and the nation sought more. They wanted to reconquer France. He had never liked war, and had had enough of it. Nevertheless, he obtained from the Parliament considerable grants for a war in alliance with Burgundy against France.

In 1475 he invaded France, but advanced only as far as Picquigny, near Amiens. Louis XI shared his outlook. He too saw that kings might grow strong and safe in peace, and would be the prey and tool of their subjects in war. Louis XI offered Edward IV a lump sum of seventy-five thousand crowns, and a yearly tribute of fifty thousand. Edward closed on the bargain, and signed the Treaty of Picquigny. He went back home and drew for seven successive years this substantial payment for not harrying France, and at the same time he pocketed most of the moneys which Parliament had voted for harrying her. At this date the interest of these transactions centers mainly upon the character of Edward IV, and we can see that though he had to strive through fierce deeds and slaughter to his throne he was at heart a Little-Englander and a lover of ease. It by no means follows that his policy was injurious to the realm. He made his administration live thriftily, and on his death he was the first King since Henry II to leave not debts but a fortune.

There came a day when he had to call Parliament together. Nothing could burn out from his mind the sense that Clarence was a traitor who had betrayed his cause and his family at one decisive moment and had been rebought at another. Clarence for his part knew that the wound although skinned over was unhealed; but he was a magnificent prince, and he sprawled buoyantly over the land. When in January 1478 Edward's patience was exhausted he called the Parliament with no other business but to condemn Clarence. Clarence was already in the Tower. How he died is much disputed. According to Shakespeare the Duke was drowned in a butt of Malmsey wine. This was certainly the popular legend believed by the sixteenth century. Why should it not be true? At any rate no one has attempted to prove any different tale.

Queen Elizabeth over the course of years had produced not only five daughters, but two fine boys, who were growing up. The King himself was only forty. His main thought was set on securing the Crown to his son, the unfledged Edward V; but in April 1483 death came so suddenly upon him that he had no time to take the necessary precautions.

All were caught by surprise. The King's eldest son, Edward, dwelt at Ludlow, on the Welsh border, under the care of his uncle, the second Lord Rivers. A Protectorate was inevitable. Richard of Gloucester, the King's faithful brother renowned in war, grave and competent in administration, enriched by Warwick's inheritance and many other great estates, in possession of all the chief military offices, stood forth without compare, and had been nominated by the late King himself. Around him gathered most of the old nobility. One thing at least they would not brook: Queen Elizabeth and her low-born relations should no longer have the ascendancy. For three weeks both parties eyed one another and parleyed.

It was agreed in April that the King should be crowned at the earliest moment, but that he should come to London attended by not more than two thousand horsemen. Accordingly this cavalcade, headed by Lord Rivers and his nephew, Grey, rode through Shrewsbury and Northampton. They had reached Stony Stratford when they learned that Gloucester and his ally, the Duke of Buckingham, coming to London from Yorkshire, were only ten miles behind them. Richard received them amicably; they dined together. But with the morning there was a change. When he awoke Rivers found the doors of the inn locked.

Gloucester and Buckingham met him with scowling gaze and accused him of "trying to set distance" between the King and them. He and Grey were immediately made prisoners. Richard then rode with his power to Stony Stratford, forced his way to the young King, and told him he had discovered a design on the part of Lord Rivers and others to seize the Government and oppress the old nobility. On this declaration Edward V took the only positive action recorded of his reign. He wept. Well he might. The next morning Duke Richard presented himself again to Edward. He embraced him as an uncle; he bowed to him as a subject. He announced himself as Protector. He dismissed the two thousand horsemen to their homes; their services would not be needed. To London then! To the Coronation! Thus this melancholy procession set out.

The Queen, who was already in London, had no illusions. She took sanctuary at once with her other children at Westminster, making a hole through the wall between the church and the palace to transport such personal belongings as she could gather. The report that the King was in duress caused a commotion in the capital. But Lord Hastings reassured the Council that all was well and that any disturbance would only delay the Coronation, upon which the peace of the realm depended. The King arrived in London only on May 4, and the Coronation, which had been fixed for that date, was necessarily postponed. He was lodged at the Bishop of London's palace, but Richard argued that it would be more fitting to the royal dignity to dwell in one of his own castles and on his own ground. With much ceremony and protestations of devotion the child of twelve was conducted to the Tower, and its gates closed behind him. The next step in the tragedy concerned Lord Hastings. He

had played a leading part in the closing years of Edward IV. After the King's death he had been strong against the Woodvilles; but he was the first to detach himself from Richard's proceedings. Of what happened next all we really know is that Hastings was abruptly arrested in council at the Tower on June 13 and beheaded without trial on the same day. Meanwhile, the Queen and her remaining son still sheltered in sanctuary. Richard felt that it would be more natural that the two brothers should be together under his care. Having no choice, the Queen submitted, and the little prince of nine was handed over in Westminster Hall to the Protector, who embraced him affectionately and conducted him to the Tower, which neither he nor his brother was ever to leave again.

The Coronation of Edward V had been postponed several times. Now a preacher named Shaw, brother of the Lord Mayor of London, one of Richard's partisans, was engaged to preach a sermon at St. Paul's Cross. He argued that Edward's children were illegitimate and that the Crown rightly belonged to Richard. On June 25 Parliament met, and after receiving a roll declaring that the late King's marriage with Elizabeth was no marriage at all and that Edward's children were bastard it petitioned Richard to assume the Crown. With becoming modesty Richard persistently refused; but when Buckingham assured him that if he would not serve the country they would be forced to choose some other noble, he overcame his conscientious scruples at the call of public duty.

The Coronation of King Richard III was fixed for July 6, and pageants and processions diverted the uneasy public. Yet from this very moment there began that marked distrust and hostility of all classes towards King Richard III which all his arts and competence could not allay. It is contended by the defenders of King Richard that the Tudor version of these events has prevailed. But the English people who lived at the time and learned of the events day by day formed their convictions two years before the Tudors gained power, or were indeed a prominent factor. Richard III held the authority of Government. He told his own story with what facilities were available, and he was spontaneously and almost universally disbelieved.

No man had done more to place Richard upon the throne than the Duke of Buckingham, and upon no one had the King bestowed greater gifts and favors. Yet during these first three months of Richard's reign Buckingham from being his chief supporter became his mortal foe. Meanwhile, King Richard began a Progress from Oxford through the Midlands. At every city he labored to make the best impression, righting wrongs, settling disputes, granting favors, and courting popularity. Yet he could not escape the sense that behind the displays of gratitude and loyalty which naturally surrounded him there lay an unspoken challenge to his Kingship. In London, Kent, Essex, and throughout the Home Counties feeling already ran high against him, and on all men's lips was the demand that the princes should be liberated. So we come to the principal crime ever afterwards associated with Richard's name. It is certain that the helpless children in the Tower were not seen again after the month of July 1483. Yet we are invited by some to believe that they languished in captivity, unnoticed and unrecorded, for another two years, only to be done to death by Henry Tudor.

Buckingham had now become the center of a conspiracy throughout the West and South of England against the King. He met at this time Margaret, Countess of Richmond, survivor of the Beaufort line, and recognized that even if the House of York were altogether set aside both she and her son Henry Tudor, Earl of Richmond, stood between him and the Crown. The Countess of Richmond, presuming him to be still Richard's right-hand man, asked him to win the King's consent to a marriage between her son Henry of Richmond and one of King Edward's daughters, Elizabeth, still in sanctuary with their mother at Westminster. All Buckingham's preparations were for a general rising on October 18. But the anger of the people at the rumored murder of the princes deranged this elaborate plan. King Richard acted with the utmost vigor. He had an army and he marched against rebellion. The sporadic risings in the South were suppressed. Buckingham, with a high price on his head, was betrayed to Richard, who lost not an hour in having him slaughtered. The usual crop of executions followed. Order was restored throughout the land, and the King seemed to have established himself securely upon his throne.

He proceeded in the new year to inaugurate a series of enlightened reforms in every sphere of Government. He revived the power of Parliament, which it had been the policy of Edward IV to reduce to nullity. He declared the practice of raising revenue by "benevolences" illegal. Parliament again legislated copiously after a long interval. But all counted for nothing. The hatred which Richard's crime had roused against him throughout the land remained sullen and quenchless, and no benefits bestowed, no sagacious measures adopted, no administrative successes achieved could avail the guilty monarch. In April 1484 his only son, the Prince of Wales, died at Middleham, and his wife, Anne, the daughter of the King-maker, whose health was broken, could bear no more children. Henry Tudor, Earl of Richmond, now became obviously the rival claimant and successor to the throne.

All hopes in England were now turned towards Richmond, and it was apparent that the marriage which had been projected between him and Edward IV's eldest daughter Elizabeth offered a prospect of ending for ever the cruel dynastic strife of which the land was unutterably weary. In March 1485 Queen Anne died, probably from natural causes. Rumors were circulating that Richard intended to marry his niece himself, in order to keep her out of Richmond's way. All through the summer Richmond's expedition was preparing at the mouth of the Seine, and the exodus from England of substantial people to join him was unceasing. The suspense was wearing to Richard. He felt he was surrounded by hatred and distrust, and that none served him but from fear or hope of favor. His dogged, indomitable nature had determined him to make for his Crown the greatest of all his fights. He fixed his headquarters in a good central position at Nottingham. He set forth his cause in a vehement proclamation, denouncing ". . . one, Henry Tydder, son of Edmund Tydder, son of Owen Tydder." But this fell cold.

On August 1 Richmond embarked at Harfleur with his Englishmen, Yorkist as well as Lancastrian, and a body of French troops. He evaded the squadrons of "Lovell our dogge," doubled Land's End, and landed at Milford Haven on the 7th. The Welsh were gratified by the prospect of one of their race succeeding to the Crown of mighty England. Appearances favored the King. He had ten thousand disciplined men under the royal authority against Richmond's hastily gathered five thousand rebels. And when on Sunday, the 21st, this whole array came out of Leicester to meet Richmond near the village of Market Bosworth it

was certain that a decisive battle impended on the morrow. At some distance from the flanks of the main army, on opposite hill-tops, stood the respective forces, mainly from Lancashire and Cheshire, of Sir William Stanley and Lord Stanley, the whole situation resembling, as has been said, four players in a game of cards. But even now Richmond was not sure what part Lord Stanley and his forces would play. When, after archery and cannonade, the lines were locked in battle all doubts were removed. The Earl of Northumberland, commanding Richard's left, stood idle at a distance. Lord Stanley's force joined Richmond. The King saw that all was lost, and shouting "Treason! Treason!" hurled himself into the thickest of the fray in the desperate purpose of striking down Richmond with his own hand. Richmond was preserved, and the King, refusing to fly, was borne down and slaughtered as he deserved.

> One foot I will never flee, while
> the breath is my breast within.
> As he said, so did it he—if he lost
> his life he died a king.

Richard's crown, which he wore to the last, was picked out of a bush and placed upon the victor's head. His corpse, naked, and torn by wounds, was bound across a horse, with his head and long hair hanging down, bloody and hideous, and in this condition borne into Leicester for all men to see.

Bosworth Field may be taken as closing a long chapter in English history. Richard's death also ended the Plantagenet line. For over three hundred years this strong race of warrior- and statesmen-kings, whose gifts and vices were upon the highest scale, whose sense of authority and Empire had been persistently maintained, now vanished from the fortunes of the Island. The Plantagenets and the proud, exclusive nobility which their system evolved had torn themselves to pieces. As Cœur de Lion said of his House, "From the Devil we sprang and to the Devil we shall go."

CHAPTER FOUR

Renaissance and Reformation

For two hundred years or more the Renaissance had been stirring the thought and spirit of Italy, and now came forth in the vivid revival of the traditions of ancient Greece and Rome, in so far as these did not affect the foundations of the Christian faith.

The urge to inquire, to debate, and seek new explanations spread from the field of classical learning into that of religious studies. Greek and even Hebrew texts, as well as Latin, were scrutinized afresh. Inevitably this led to the questioning of accepted religious beliefs. The Renaissance bred the Reformation.

While the forces of Renaissance and Reformation were gathering strength in Europe the world beyond was yielding its secrets to European explorers, traders, and missionaries. From the days of the ancient Greeks some men had known in theory that the world was round and global. Now in the sixteenth century navigations were to prove it so. The scattered civilizations of the world were being drawn together, and the new discoveries were to give the little kingdom in the Northern sea a fresh importance. Here was to be the successor both of Portugal and Spain, though the time for entering into the inheritance was not yet. The whole course of trade was shifted and revolutionized. The primacy of the Italian cities was eclipsed by North-West Europe; and the future lay not in the Mediterranean, but on the shores of the Atlantic, where the new Powers, England, France, and Holland, had ports and harbors which gave easy access to the oceans.

Henry VII's first task was to induce magnates, Church, and gentry to accept the decision of Bosworth and to establish himself upon the throne. He was careful to be crowned before facing the representatives of the nation, thus resting his title first upon conquest, and only secondly on the approbation of Parliament. Then he married, as had long been planned, the heiress of the rival House, Elizabeth of York. Lack of money had long weakened the English throne, but military victory now restored to Henry most of the Crown lands alienated during the fifteenth century by confiscation and attainder, and many other great estates besides. Henry was thus assured of a settled income. Legislation was passed stating that all who gave their allegiance to the King for the time being—that is, to the King upon the throne—should be secure in their lives and property. This idea of an actual King as distinct from a rightful King was characteristic of the new ruler.

Henry had to keep ceaseless watch for the invasion of pretenders supported by foreign aid. The first was Lambert Simnel, who finished ingloriously as a scullion in the royal kitchens. The second and more formidable was Perkin Warbeck, the son of a boatman and collector of taxes at Tournai, put forward as the younger of the princes murdered in the Tower. But the classes who had backed the King since Bosworth were staunch.

Throughout the history of medieval England there runs a deep division between North and South. In the South a more fully advanced society dwelt in a rich countryside, with well-developed towns and a prosperous wool trade with Flanders and Italy. The Wars of the Roses had been a serious threat to this organized life, and it was in the South that Henry found his chief support. The North was very different. Great feudal Houses like the Percys dominated the scene. Councils were accordingly established to administer the Northern parts and Welsh Marches. The Wars of the Roses had weakened English authority in Wales, but it was in Ireland that their effects were most manifest. Lords Deputy from England found it profitless to assert their legal powers in face of the dominating local position and island-wide alliances of Kildare, who was called "Garret More," or Great Earl. Sir Edward Poynings, appointed Lord Deputy of Ireland in 1494, tried to limit his powers of mischief. He persuaded the Irish Parliament at Drogheda to pass the celebrated Poynings' Law, subordinating the Irish Parliament to the English, which was not repealed for three hundred years and remained a grievance till the twentieth century.

Henry's dealings with Scotland are characteristic of his shrewd judgment. Although not obviously a man of imagination, he had his dreams. At any rate, Henry took the first steps to unite England and Scotland by marrying his daughter Margaret to James IV in 1502, and there was peace in the North until after his death. Like the other princes of his age, his main interest, apart from an absorbing passion for administration, was foreign policy. He maintained the first permanent English envoys abroad. He realized that more could be gained by the threat of war than by war itself. Like Edward IV, he pocketed not only a considerable subsidy from France, which was punctually paid, but also the taxes collected in England for war.

Henry VII as a statesman was imbued with the new, ruthless political ideas of Renaissance Europe. He strove to establish a strong monarchy in England, molded out of native institutions. The King's Council was strengthened. It was given Parliamentary authority to examine persons with or without oath, and condemn them, on written evidence alone, in a manner foreign to the practice of the Common Law. The Court of Star Chamber met regularly at Westminster, with the two Chief Justices in attendance. It was originally a judicial committee of the King's Council, trying cases which needed special treatment because of the excessive might of one of the parties or the novelty or enormity of the offense. But the main function of the King's Council was to govern rather than to judge. A small inner committee conducted foreign affairs. Another managed the finances, hacking a new path through the cumbrous practices of the medieval Exchequer; treasurers were now appointed who were answerable personally to the King.

Henry VII was probably the best business man to sit upon the English throne. He was also a remarkably shrewd picker of men. How far he was a conscious innovator, turning his back on ancient ways, is in dispute among historians, but his skill and wisdom in transmuting medieval institutions into the organs of modern rule has not been questioned. His achievement was indeed massive and durable. He built his power amid the ruins and ashes of his predecessors. He thriftily and carefully gathered what seemed in those days a vast reserve of liquid wealth. He trained a body of efficient servants. He magnified the Crown without losing the co-operation of the Commons. He identified prosperity with monarchy. Among the princes of Renaissance Europe he is not surpassed in achievement and fame by Louis XI of France or Ferdinand of Spain. Such was the architect of the Tudor monarchy, which was to lead England out of medieval disorder into greater strength and broader times.

Until the death of his elder brother, Prince Arthur, Henry VIII had been intended for the Church. He had therefore been brought up by his father in an atmosphere of learning. Henry in his maturity was a tall, red-headed man who preserved the vigor and energy of ancestors accustomed for centuries to the warfare of the Welsh Marches. Bursts of restless energy and ferocity were combined with extraordinary patience and diligence. Although Henry appeared to strangers open, jovial, and trustworthy, with a bluff good-humor which appealed at once to the crowd, even those who knew him most intimately seldom penetrated the inward secrecy and reserve which allowed him to confide freely in no one. As time passed his willfulness hardened and his temper worsened. The only secret of managing him, both Wolsey and Cromwell disclosed after they had fallen, was to see that dangerous ideas were not permitted to reach him. Almost his first act, six weeks after the death of his father in 1509, was to marry his brother Arthur's widow, Princess Catherine of Aragon. Catherine was at Henry's side during the first twenty-two years of his reign, while England was becoming a force in European affairs, perilous for foreign rulers to ignore.

Henry VII had only once sent English levies abroad, preferring to hire mercenaries who fought alongside foreign armies. Henry VIII now determined that this policy should be reversed. France was preoccupied with Italian adventures, and Henry planned to reconquer Bordeaux, lost sixty years before, while King Ferdinand invaded Navarre, an independent kingdom lying athwart the Pyrenees, and the Pope and the republic of Venice operated against the French armies in Italy. The year was 1512, and this was the first time since the Hundred Years War that an English army had campaigned in Europe.

The English expedition to Gascony failed. After negotiations lasting throughout the winter of 1512–13 Ferdinand and the Venetians deserted Henry and the Pope and made peace with France. In England the responsibility for these failures was cast on Henry's adviser, Thomas Wolsey. In fact it was in the hard work of administration necessitated by the war that he had first shown his abilities and immense energy. But Henry VIII and the Pope never wavered. Under Henry's command, the English, with Austrian mercenaries, routed the French in August 1513 at the Battle of the Spurs, so called because of the rapidity of the French retreat. To aid their French ally the Scots in the King's absence had crossed the Tweed in September and invaded England with an army of fifty thousand men. At Flodden Field a bloody battle was fought on September 9, 1513. The whole of Scotland, Highland and Lowland alike, drew out with their retainers in the traditional schiltrons, or circles of spearmen, and around the standard of their King. The English archers once again directed upon these redoubtable masses a long, intense, and murderous arrow storm. When night fell the flower of the Scottish chivalry lay in their ranks where they had fought, and among them King James IV. This was the last great victory gained by the longbow.

Henry had every intention of renewing his campaign in France in 1514, but his successes had not been to the liking of Ferdinand of Spain. Faced with the defection of his allies, Henry was quick to launch a counter-stroke. The crowning event of the peace was the marriage between Henry's young sister, Mary, and Louis XII himself.

For fourteen years Wolsey in the King's name was the effective ruler of the realm. He owed his position not only to his great capacity for business, but to his considerable personal charm. In the King's company he was brilliant, convivial, and "a gay seeker out of new pastimes." Other would-be counselors of Henry's saw a different side of the Cardinal's character. They resented being scornfully overborne by him in debate; they detested his arrogance, and envied his ever-growing wealth and extensive patronage. He kept a thousand servants, and his palaces surpassed the King's in splendor. Successes abroad enabled Wolsey to develop Henry VII's principles of centralized government. During the twelve years that he was Lord Chancellor Parliament met only once, for two sessions spreading over three months in all. The Court of Star Chamber grew more active. It evolved new and simple methods copied from Roman law, by which the Common Law rules of evidence were dispensed with, and persons who could give evidence were simply brought in for interrogation, one by one, often without even the formality of an oath. This system of arbitrary government, however despotic in theory, however contrary to the principles believed to lie behind Magna Carta, in fact rested tacitly on the real will of the people. Henry VIII, like his father, found an institution ready to his hand in the unpaid Justice of the Peace, the local squire or landlord, and taught him to govern.

Within a few years of his accession Henry embarked upon a program of naval expansion, while Wolsey concerned himself with diplomatic maneuver. For some years at least Wolsey was a powerful factor and balancing weight in Europe. The zenith of this brilliant period was reached at the Field of the Cloth of Gold in June 1520, when Henry crossed the Channel to meet his rival, Francis I of France, for the first time. It was the last display of medieval chivalry. Many noblemen, it was said, carried on

their shoulders their mills, their forests, and their meadows. But Henry and Francis failed to become personal friends. Henry, indeed, was already negotiating with Francis's enemy, the new Emperor Charles V, who had lately succeeded his grandfather, Maximilian. When the Emperor declared war on Francis English wealth was squandered feverishly on an expedition to Boulogne and subsidies to mercenary contingents serving with the Emperor. Wolsey had to find the money. The Government had to beat a retreat, the campaign was abandoned, and Wolsey got the King's consent to make secret overtures for peace to Francis. These overtures were Wolsey's fatal miscalculation; only six weeks later the Imperial armies won an overwhelming victory over the French at Pavia, in Northern Italy. Henry could no longer turn the scales in Europe.

Then there was Queen Catherine. A typical Spanish princess, she had matured and aged rapidly; it was clear that she would bear Henry no male heir. Either the King's illegitimate son, the Duke of Richmond, now aged six, would have to be appointed by Act of Parliament, or perhaps England might accept Catherine's child, Mary, now aged nine, as the first Queen of England in her own right since Matilda. Would England tolerate being ruled by a woman? The first step, clearly, was to get rid of Catherine. We first hear of Anne Boleyn at Court in a dispatch of the Imperial Ambassador dated August 16, 1527, four months after Henry had begun proceedings for the annulment of his marriage.

The Papal Legate, Cardinal Campeggio, who was sent to England to hear the case, used all possible pretexts to postpone a decision. The Pope was now practically a prisoner of Charles V, who was determined that Henry should not divorce his aunt. This broke Wolsey. New counselors were called in. At the same time the King had the writs sent out for a Parliament, the first for six years, to strengthen his hand in the great changes he was planning. Wolsey's high offices of State were conferred on a new administration: Gardiner secured the Bishopric of Winchester, the richest see in England; Norfolk became President of the Council, and Suffolk the Vice-President. During the few days that elapsed until Wolsey was replaced by Sir Thomas More as Lord Chancellor the King applied the Great Seal himself to documents of State. With the death of the Cardinal political interests hitherto submerged made their bid for power.

Thomas Cranmer's idea of an appeal to the universities about Henry's marriage to Catherine proved a great success, and the young lecturer was rewarded with an appointment as Ambassador to the Emperor. The King had known all along that he was right, and here, it seemed, was final proof. He determined to mark his displeasure with the Pope by some striking measure against the power of the Church of England. The House of Lords, where the bishops and abbots still had more votes than the lay peers, agreed to the Bills reforming sanctuaries and abolishing mortuary fees, which affected the lower clergy only, but when the Probate Bill came up to the Lords the Archbishop of Canterbury "in especial," and all the other bishops in general, both frowned and grunted. Thus from the outset the Reformation House of Commons acquired a corporate spirit, and during its long life, longer than any previous Parliament, eagerly pursued any measure which promised revenge against the bishops for what it deemed their evasion and duplicity over the Probate Bill. Hostility to the Episcopate smoldered, and marked the Commons for more than a hundred years.

During December 1530 the Attorney-General charged the whole body of the clergy with breaking the fourteenth-century Statutes of Præmunire and Provisors which had been passed to limit the powers of the Pope. This they had done by acquiescing in Wolsey's many high-handed actions in his role as Papal Legate. In return for a pardon the King extracted large sums from Convocation, £100,000 from the province of Canterbury and £19,000 from York, which was much more than at first they were prepared to pay. After further negotiation he also obtained a new title. On February 7, 1531, the clergy acknowledged that the King was "their especial Protector, one and supreme lord, and, as far as the law of Christ allows, even supreme head." Parliament, which had been prorogued from month to month since the great doings about probate in 1529, was now recalled to hear and disseminate the royal view on the divorce.

The winter of 1531–2 was marked by the tensest crisis of Henry's reign. The Annates Bill armed the King for a greater struggle with the Papacy than had preceded Magna Carta. If the Court of Rome, its preamble ran, endeavored to wield excommunication, interdict, or process compulsory in England, then all manner of sacraments and divine service should continue to be administered, and the interdict should not by any prelate or minister be executed or divulged. If any one named by the King to a bishopric were restrained by Bulls from Rome from accepting office he should be consecrated by the Archbishop, or any one named to an archbishopric. And the Annates, a mainstay of the Papal finances, were limited to five per cent of their former amount. This was the most difficult Bill which Henry ever had to steer through Parliament. The next step was to make the clergy submit to the royal supremacy. Henry got the Commons to prepare a document called the Supplication against the Ordinaries, directed against the authority of Church courts. On the very afternoon these articles were submitted for the royal consent, May 16, 1532, Sir Thomas More resigned the Lord Chancellorship as a protest against royal supremacy in spiritual affairs. Thus the English Reformation was a slow process. An opportunist King measured his steps as he went, until England was wholly independent of administration from Rome.

The death in August of old William Warham, Archbishop of Canterbury and principal opponent of the King's divorce, opened further possibilities and problems. Cranmer took leave of the Emperor at Mantua on November 1, 1532, and left the following day, arriving in London in the middle of December. A week later he was offered the Archbishopric of Canterbury. He accepted. A month later Henry secretly married Anne Boleyn. Cranmer became Archbishop in the traditional manner. At the King's request Bulls had been obtained from Rome by threatening the Papacy with a rigorous application of the Act of Annates. This was important: the man who was to carry through the ecclesiastical revolution had thus been accepted by the Pope and endowed with full authority. Two days afterwards, however, a Bill was introduced into Parliament vesting in the Archbishop of Canterbury the power, formerly possessed by the Pope, to hear and determine all appeals from the ecclesiastical courts in England. This momentous Bill, the work of Thomas Cromwell, which abolished what still remained of Papal authority in England, passed through Parliament in due course, and became known as the Act of Appeals. The following month Henry himself wrote a letter describing his position as "King and Sovereign, recognizing no superior in earth but only God, and not subject to the laws of any earthly crea-

ture." The breach between England and Rome was complete.

The Duke of Norfolk with royal commissioners waited on Queen Catherine at Ampthill. She refused to resign. A fortnight later Cranmer opened a court at Dunstable, and sent a Proctor to Ampthill citing Catherine to appear. She refused. In her absence the Archbishop pronounced judgment. Catherine's marriage with Henry had existed in fact but not in law; it was void from the beginning; and five days afterwards the marriage with Anne was declared valid. Queen Anne Boleyn was crowned on June 1 in Westminster Abbey.

The following month it became clear that the new Queen was expecting a child. A magnificent and valuable bed, which had lain in the Treasury since it had formed part of a French nobleman's ransom, was brought forth, and in it on September 7, 1533, the future Queen Elizabeth was born. Although bonfires were lighted there was no rejoicing in Henry's heart. A male heir had been his desire. An Act was passed vesting the succession in Elizabeth. In March 1534 every person of legal age, male or female, throughout the kingdom was forced to swear allegiance to this Act and renounce allegiance to all foreign authority in England. Bishop Fisher and Sir Thomas More, who both refused the oath, were confined in the Tower for many months. Fisher was executed in June 1535 and More in July.

Sir John Seymour, a worthy old courtier, had a pretty daughter, a former Maid of Honor to Queen Catherine. Jane Seymour was about twenty-five, and although she was attractive no one considered her a great beauty. But she was gay, and generally liked, and Henry fell in love with her. The King was still paying court to Jane when it became known that Anne was expecting another baby.

But this time Henry refused to have anything to do with her. Soon afterwards her uncle, the Duke of Norfolk, strode into the room and told her that Henry had had a serious accident out hunting. In her grief and alarm she nearly fainted. Five days later she miscarried.

In January 1536 Queen Catherine died. If the King was minded to marry again he could now repudiate Queen Anne without raising awkward questions about his earlier union. The Queen had accordingly been watched, and one Sunday two young courtiers, Henry Norris and Sir Francis Weston, were seen to enter the Queen's room, and were, it was said, overheard making love to her. The following Sunday a certain Smeaton, a gentleman of the King's Chamber, who played with great skill on the lute, was arrested as the Queen's lover. On Monday Norris was among the challengers at the May Day tournament at Greenwich, and as the King rode to London after the jousting he called Norris to his side and told him what was suspected. That night Anne learned that Smeaton and Norris were in the Tower. The following morning she was requested to come before the Council. At the conclusion of the proceedings she was placed under arrest, and kept under guard until the tide turned to take her up-river to the Tower. On Friday morning the special commissioners of treason appointed the previous week, including Anne Boleyn's father, the Earl of Wiltshire, and the entire bench of judges except one, formed the court for the trial of Anne's lovers. They were sentenced to be hanged, drawn, and quartered, but execution was deferred until after the trial of the Queen. This opened the following Monday in the Great Hall of the Tower. The Queen denied the charges vigorously, and replied to each one in detail. The peers retired, and soon returned with a verdict of guilty. Norfolk pronounced sentence: the Queen was to be burned or beheaded, at the King's pleasure.

On May 19, 1536, the headsman was already waiting, leaning on his heavy two-handed sword, when the Constable of the Tower appeared, followed by Anne in a beautiful night robe of heavy grey damask trimmed with fur, showing a crimson kirtle beneath. "Pray for me," she said, and knelt down while one of the ladies-in-waiting bandaged her eyes. "God have pity on my soul." "God have mercy on my soul," she repeated, as the executioner stepped forward and slowly took his aim. Then the great blade hissed through the air, and with a single stroke his work was done.

As soon as the execution was known Henry appeared in yellow, with a feather in his cap, and ten days later was privately married to Jane Seymour at York Place. She was the only Queen whom Henry regretted and mourned, and when she died, still aged only twenty-seven, immediately after the birth of her first child, the future Edward VI, Henry had her buried with royal honors in St. George's Chapel at Windsor. He himself lies near her.

The King had now a new chief adviser. Thomas Cromwell, in turn mercenary soldier in Italy, cloth agent, and money-lender, had served his apprenticeship in Statecraft under Wolsey, but he had also learned the lessons of his master's downfall. Ruthless, cynical, Machiavellian, Cromwell was a man of the New Age. Before his day Government policy had for centuries been both made and implemented in the royal Household. Though Henry VII had improved the system he had remained in a sense a medieval king. Thomas Cromwell thoroughly reformed it during his ten years of power, and when he fell in 1540 policy was already carried out by Government departments, operating outside the Household.

The religious Orders had for some time been in decline, and parents were becoming more and more averse to handing over their sons to the cloisters. The idea of suppression was not altogether new: Wolsey had suppressed several small houses to finance his college at Oxford, and the King had since suppressed over twenty more for his own benefit. During the summer of 1536 royal commissioners toured the country, completing the dissolution as swiftly as possible. As First Minister Cromwell handled the dissolution of the monasteries with conspicuous, cold-blooded efficiency. It was a step which appealed to the well-to-do. The high nobility and country gentry acquired on favorable terms all kinds of fine estates. The main result of this transaction was in effect, if not in intention, to commit the landed and mercantile classes to the Reformation settlement and the Tudor dynasty. The immediate impact on the masses is more difficult to judge. In the North, where the old traditions died hard, the new order aroused stiffer resistance than in the South, and the new lay landlord could be harsher than his clerical predecessor.

The older generation considered that Holy Writ was dangerous in the hands of the unlearned and should only be read by priests. But complete printed Bibles, translated into English by Tyndale and Coverdale, had appeared for the first time late in the autumn of 1535, and were now running through several editions. In the autumn of 1536, when the new taxes came to be assessed after Michaelmas, farmers and yokels collected in large numbers throughout the North of England and Lincolnshire, swearing to resist the taxes and maintain the old order in the Church. The revolt,

which took the name of "the Pilgrimage of Grace," was spontaneous. Its leader, a lawyer named Robert Aske, had his position thrust upon him. The nobles and higher clergy took no part. In early 1537 the rebellion collapsed as quickly as it had arisen, but Henry determined to make examples of the ringleaders. Altogether some two hundred and fifty of the insurgents were put to death.

Up to this point Thomas Cromwell had consistently walked with success. But he now began to encounter the conservatism of the older nobility. The Duke of Norfolk headed the reaction, and the King, who was rigidly orthodox, except where his lusts or interests were stirred, agreed with it. Stephen Gardiner, Bishop of Winchester and later Queen Mary's adviser, was the brain behind the Norfolk party.

An alliance with the princes of Northern Germany against the two Catholic monarchs now seemed imperative, and negotiations for a marriage between Henry and Anne, the eldest Princess of Cleves, were hurried on. Anne spent Christmas at Calais, waiting for storms to abate, and on the last day of the year 1539 arrived at Rochester. Henry had sailed down in his private barge, in disguise, bearing a fine sable fur among the presents. On New Year's Day he hurried to visit her. But on seeing her he was astonished and abashed. Privately he dubbed her "the Flanders Mare." But the threat from abroad compelled the King to fulfill his contract. Since he now knew as much about the Canon Law on marriage as anyone in Europe, he turned himself into the perfect legal example of a man whose marriage might be annulled. Norfolk and Gardiner now saw their chance to break Cromwell, as Wolsey had been broken, with the help of a new lady. Yet another of Norfolk's nieces, Catherine Howard, was presented to Henry at Gardiner's house, and captured his affections at first sight. In June 1540 the King was persuaded to get rid of Cromwell and Anne together. Cromwell was condemned under a Bill of Attainder charging him principally with heresy and "broadcasting" erroneous books and implicitly with treason. Anne agreed to have her marriage annulled, and Convocation pronounced it invalid. She lived on in England, pensioned and in retirement, for another seventeen years.

A few days after Cromwell was executed on July 28 Henry was privately married to his fifth wife, Catherine Howard. Aged about twenty-two, with auburn hair and hazel eyes, she was the prettiest of Henry's wives. But wild, tempestuous Catherine was not long content with a husband nearly thirty years older than herself. Her reckless love for her cousin, Thomas Culpeper, was discovered, and she was executed in the Tower in February 1542 on the same spot as Anne Boleyn.

Henry's sixth wife, Catherine Parr, was a serious little widow from the Lake District, thirty-one years of age, learned, and interested in theological questions, who had had two husbands before the King. She married Henry at Hampton Court on July 12, 1543, and until his death three years later made him an admirable wife, nursing his ulcerated leg, which grew steadily worse and in the end killed him.

The brilliant young Renaissance prince had grown old and wrathful. Reviving the obsolete claim to suzerainty, Henry denounced the Scots as rebels, and pressed them to relinquish their alliance with France. The Scots successfully defeated an English raid at Halidon Rig. Then in the autumn of 1542 an expedition under Norfolk had to turn back at Kelso, principally through the failure of the commissariat, which, besides its other shortcomings, left the English army without its beer, and the Scots proceeded to carry the war into the enemy's country. Their decision proved disastrous. Badly led and imperfectly organized, they lost more than half their army of ten thousand men in Solway Moss and were utterly routed. The news of this second Flodden killed James V, who died leaving the kingdom to an infant of one week, Mary, the famous Queen of Scots.

Once again England and the Holy Roman Empire made common cause against the French, and in May 1543 a secret treaty was ratified between Charles V and Henry. While Scotland was left to Edward Seymour, brother of Queen Jane, and now Earl of Hertford, the King himself was to cross the Channel and lead an army against Francis in co-operation with an Imperial force from the north-east. The plan was excellent, but the execution failed. Meanwhile, the English in Scotland, after burning Edinburgh and laying waste much country, ceased to make headway, and in February 1545 were defeated at Ancrum Moor. Without a single ally, the nation faced the possibility of invasion from both France and Scotland. The crisis called for unexampled sacrifices from the English people; never had they been called upon to pay so many loans, subsidies, and benevolences. Next year a peace treaty was signed, which left Boulogne in English hands for eight years, at the end of which time France was to buy it back at a heavy price. Henry completely failed in Scotland. He would make no generous settlement with his neighbors, yet he lacked the force to coerce them.

In these last few months one question dominated all minds: the heir to the kingdom was known, a child of nine, but who would be the power behind the throne? Norfolk or Hertford? The party of reaction or the party of reform? The

King remembered that years before Norfolk had been put forward as a possible heir to the throne, and his son Surrey had been suggested as a husband for Princess Mary. His suspicions aroused, he acted swiftly; in mid-January Surrey was executed. Parliament assembled to pass a Bill of Attainder against Norfolk. On Thursday the 27th the royal assent was given and Norfolk was condemned to death. But that same evening the King himself was dying.

The English Reformation under Henry VIII had received its guiding impulse from the King's passions and his desire for power. He still deemed himself a good Catholic. With the new reign a deeper and more powerful tide began to flow. The guardian and chief counselor of the child-king was his uncle, Edward Seymour, now Duke of Somerset. He and Cranmer proceeded to transform the political reformation of Henry VIII into a religious revolution. The Book of Common Prayer, in shining English prose, was drawn up by Cranmer and accepted by Parliament in 1549. Then followed, after Somerset's fall, the Forty-two Articles of Religion, and a second Prayer Book, until, on paper at least, England became a Protestant State.

Somerset himself was merely one of the regents appointed under Henry's will, and his position as Protector, at once dazzling and dangerous, had little foundation in law or precedent. His brother, Thomas Seymour, Lord High Admiral, had his own ambitions. Proofs were discovered of Thomas Seymour's plots against his brother, and the Protector was forced in January 1549 to dispose of him by Act of Attainder and the block on Tower Hill.

The life and economy of medieval England were fast dissolving. Landlords saw that vast fortunes could be made from wool, and the village communal strips barred their profits. Common land was seized, enclosed, and turned to pasture for flocks. In some counties as much as one-third of the arable land was turned over to grass, and the people looked in anger upon the new nobility, fat with sacrilegious spoil, but greedy still. Somerset had thus to face one of the worst economic crises that England has endured. The popular preachers were loud in denunciation. The Sermon of the Plough, preached by Hugh Latimer at Paul's Cross in 1548, is a notable piece of Tudor invective. Somerset himself sympathized with the yeomen and peasantry, and appointed commissions to inquire into the enclosures. But this increased the discontent, and encouraged the oppressed to take matters into their own hands. The Catholic peasantry in the South-West rose against the Prayer Book, and the yokels of the Eastern Counties against the enclosing landlords. Foreign mercenaries suppressed the Western rebellion. But in Norfolk the trouble was more serious. A tannery-owner named Robert Ket took the lead. The disorders spread to Yorkshire, and presently reverberated in the Midlands. John Dudley, Earl of Warwick, son of the man who had been Henry VII's agent, now seized his opportunity. Warwick's best troops were German mercenaries, whose precise fire-drill shattered the peasant array. Three thousand five hundred were killed.

Somerset's enemies claimed the credit for restoring order. Warwick became the leader of the Opposition. "The Lords in London," as Warwick's party were called, met to take measures against the Protector. They quietly took over the Government. After a spell in the Tower, Somerset, now powerless, was for some months allowed to sit in the Council, but as conditions got worse so the danger grew of a reaction in his favor. In January 1552, splendidly garbed as for a State banquet, he was executed on Tower Hill. This handsome, well-meaning man had failed completely to heal the dislocation of Henry's reign and fell a victim to the fierce interests he had offended. Nevertheless, the people of England remembered him for years as "the Good Duke." The nominal King of England, Edward VI, was a cold, priggish invalid of fifteen. In his diary he noted his uncle's death without a comment.

The Government of Warwick, now become Duke of Northumberland, was held together by class resistance to social unrest. His three years of power displayed to the full the rapacity of the ruling classes. Doctrinal reformation was a pretense for confiscating yet more Church lands, and new bishops paid for their consecration with portions of the episcopal estates. One gleam of enterprise distinguishes this period. It saw the opening of relations between England and a growing new Power in Eastern Europe, hitherto known as Muscovy, but soon to be called Russia.

Under the Succession Act of 1543 the next heir to the throne was Princess Mary, the Catholic daughter of Catherine of Aragon. Northumberland might well tremble for the future. A desperate scheme was evolved. The younger daughter of Henry VII had married the Duke of Suffolk, and their heirs had been named in Henry VIII's will as next in line of succession after his own children. The eldest grandchild in this Suffolk line was Lady Jane Grey, a girl of sixteen. Northumberland married this girl to his son, Guildford Dudley. Nothing remained but to effect a military *coup* when the young King died. On July 6, 1553, Edward VI expired, and Lady Jane Grey was proclaimed Queen in London. The common people flocked to Mary's support. The Privy Councillors and the City authorities swam with the tide. Northumberland was left without an ally.

He asserted that he had always been a Catholic, with shattering effect on the Protestant party. But nothing could save him from an ignominious death.

The woman who now became Queen was probably the most unhappy and unsuccessful of England's sovereigns. Her accession portended a renewal of the Roman connection and a political alliance with the Empire. The religious legislation of the Reformation Parliament was repealed. But one thing Mary could not do. She could not restore to the Church the lands parceled out among the nobility.

The most urgent question was whom Mary should marry. The Commons supported an English candidate, Edward Courtenay, Earl of Devon, a descendant of the House of York. But Mary's eyes were fixed overseas. Renard, envoy of the Emperor Charles V, worked fast, and she promised to wed the Emperor's son, the future Philip II of Spain. In the West Courtenay precipitated a rising. Sir Thomas Wyatt raised his standard in Kent and marched slowly towards London, gathering men as he came. Mary, bitter and disappointed with her people, and knowing she had failed to win their hearts, showed she was not afraid. In a stirring speech at Guildhall she summoned the Londoners to her defense. There was division among the rebels. Wyatt was disappointed by Courtenay, whose rising was a pitiable failure. Straggled fighting took place in the streets, and the Queen's men cut up the intruders. Wyatt was executed. This sealed the fate of Lady Jane Grey and her husband. In February 1554 the two walked calmly to their death on Tower Green. Elizabeth's life was now in great danger. But Mary had shed blood enough and Renard could not persuade her to sign away the life of her half-sister.

Mary journeyed to Winchester to greet her bridegroom. With all the pomp of sixteenth-century royalty the marriage was solemnized in July 1554 according to the rites of the Catholic Church. Gardiner was now dead; but a successor was found in the English cardinal Reginald Pole. Pole had been in exile throughout the reign of Henry VIII, his family having been lopped and shorn in Henry's judicial murders. Mary has been forever odious in the minds of a Protestant nation as the Bloody Queen who martyred her noblest subjects. Generations of Englishmen in childhood learned the somber tale of their sacrifice from Foxe's *Book of Martyrs,* with its gruesome illustrations. These stories have become part of the common memory of the people—the famous scenes at Oxford in 1555, the faggots which consumed the Protestant bishops, Latimer and Ridley, the pitiful recantation and final heroic end in March 1556 of the frail, aged Archbishop, Cranmer. Their martyrdom rallied to the Protestant faith many who till now had shown indifference. These martyrs saw in vision that their deaths were not in vain, and, standing at the stake, pronounced immortal words. "Be of good comfort, Master Ridley," Latimer cried at the crackling of the flames. "Play the man. We shall this day light such a candle, by God's grace, in England as I trust shall never be put out."

In vain the Queen strove to join English interests to those of the Spanish State. As the wife of the King of Spain, against the interests of her kingdom, and against the advice of prudent counselors, among them Cardinal Pole, she allowed herself to be dragged into war with France, and Calais, the last possession of the English upon the Continent, fell without resistance. Hope of a child to secure the Catholic succession was unfulfilled. Philip retired to the Netherlands and then to Spain, aloof and disappointed at the barrenness of the whole political scheme. Surrounded by dis-

loyalty and discontent, Mary's health gave way. In November 1558 she died, and a few hours later, in Lambeth Palace, her coadjutor, Cardinal Pole, followed her. The tragic interlude of her reign was over. It had sealed the conversion of the English people to the Reformed faith. Until the reign of Henry VIII there lay beneath the quarrels of the nobility, the conflicts between King and Church, between the ruling classes and the people, a certain broad unity of acceptance. The evils and sorrows of the medieval ages had lasted so long that they seemed to be the inseparable conditions of existence in a world of woe. With the Reformation there came a new influence cutting to the very roots of English life. The old framework, which, in spite of its many jars, had held together for centuries, was now torn by a division in which all other antagonisms of class and interest were henceforward to be ranged and ruled.

Elizabeth was twenty-five years old when, untried in the affairs of State, she succeeded her half-sister on November 17, 1558. A commanding carriage, auburn hair, eloquence of speech, and natural dignity proclaimed her King Henry's daughter. Other similarities were soon observed: high courage in moments of crisis, a fiery and imperious resolution when defied, and an almost inexhaustible fund of physical energy. She could speak six languages, and was well read in Latin and Greek. Always subtle of intellect, she was often brazen and even coarse in manners and expression. Nevertheless, she had a capacity for inspiring devotion that is perhaps unparalleled among British sovereigns.

The times demanded a politic, calculating, devious spirit at the head of the State, and this Elizabeth possessed. She had, too, a high gift for picking able men to do the country's work. She was a paragon of the New Learning. Around her had gathered some of the ablest Protestant minds: Matthew Parker, who was to be her Archbishop of Canterbury; Nicholas Bacon, whom she appointed Lord Keeper of the Great Seal; Roger Ascham, the foremost scholar of the day; and, most important of all, William Cecil, the adaptable civil servant who had already held office as Secretary under Somerset and Northumberland. Of sixteenth-century English statesmen Cecil was undoubtedly the greatest.

England became Protestant by law, Queen Mary's Catholic legislation was repealed, and the sovereign was declared supreme Governor of the English Church. But this was not the end of Elizabeth's difficulties. With the Reformation the notion that it might be a duty to disobey the established order on the grounds of private conviction became for the first time since the conversion to Christianity of the Roman Empire the belief of great numbers. It is at this point that the party known as the Puritans, who were to play so great a role in the next hundred years, first enter English history. Democratic in theory and organization, intolerant in practice of all who differed from their views, the Puritans challenged the Queen's authority in Church and State. The gentry in Parliament were themselves divided. It was the future distinction of Cavalier and Puritan, Churchman and Dissenter, Tory and Whig.

The security of the English State depended in the last resort on an assured succession. In vain the Houses of Parliament begged their Virgin Queen to marry and produce an heir. Elizabeth was angry. She would admit no discussion. Her policy was to spend her life in saving her people from such a commitment, and using her potential value as a match to divide a European combination against her.

French troops supported the French Queen Mother in Scotland. A powerful Puritan party among the Scottish nobility were in arms against them, while John Knox raised his harsh voice from exile in Geneva. Arms and supplies were smuggled across the Border to the Protestant party. Knox was permitted to return to his native land and his preachings had a powerful effect. By the Treaty of Leith in 1560 the Protestant cause in Scotland was assured forever. Meanwhile, there was Mary Stuart, Queen of Scots. Her young husband, King Francis II, had died shortly after his accession, and in December 1560 she returned to her own kingdom. Her presence in Scotland disturbed the delicate balance which Elizabeth had achieved by the Treaty of Leith. The Catholic English nobility, particularly in the North, were not indifferent to Mary's claims. But Elizabeth knew her rival. The Queen of Scots lacked the vigilant self-control which Elizabeth had learned in the bitter years of childhood. Mary's power melted slowly and steadily away. Defeat and imprisonment followed, and in 1568 she escaped into England and threw herself upon the mercy of the waiting Elizabeth.

Mary in England proved even more dangerous than Mary in Scotland. She became the focus of plots and conspiracies against Elizabeth's life. The whole force of the Counter-Reformation was unloosed against the one united Protestant country in Europe. The idea was now advanced that Mary should marry the Duke of Norfolk, senior of the pre-Tudor nobility, and his somewhat feeble head was turned at the prospect of gambling for a throne. He repented in time. But in 1569 the Earls of Northumberland and Westmorland led a rising in the North. In the South the Catholic lords made no move. There seems to have been no common plan of action, and the rebel force scattered into small parties in the Northern hills. After twelve years of very patient rule Elizabeth was unchallenged Queen of all England.

In February 1570 Pope Pius V, a former Inquisitor-General, issued a Bull of excommunication against Elizabeth. She entered into negotiations with Catherine de Médicis, and a political alliance was concluded at Blois in April 1572. By a sudden massacre of the Huguenots on the eve of the Feast of St. Bartholomew, August 23, 1572, the Guises, pro-Spanish and ultra-Catholic, recaptured the political power they had lost ten years earlier. Elizabeth's alliance with the French Court had clearly failed, and she was now driven to giving secret subsidies and support to the French Huguenots and the Dutch. Francis Walsingham, Cecil's assistant and later his rival in the Government, tracked down Spanish agents and English traitors. Exile in Mary's reign and service as Ambassador in Paris had convinced him that Protestantism would only survive in Europe if England gave it unlimited encouragement and aid. Opposed to all this was Cecil, now Lord Burghley. Aware of the slender resources of the State, deeply concerned for the loss of trade with Spain and the Netherlands, he maintained that Walsingham's policy would founder in bankruptcy and disaster. Elizabeth was inclined to agree.

Most of the Puritans had at first been willing to conform to Elizabeth's Church Settlement in the hope of transforming it from within, but they now strove to drive the Government into an aggressive Protestant foreign policy, and at the same time secure their own freedom of religious organization. Their aim and object was nothing less than the establishment of a theocratic despotism. The Lutheran Church fitted well enough with monarchy, even with absolutism, but Calvinism, as it spread out over Europe, was a dissolving agency, and a violent interruption of historic continuity. Elizabeth's Council therefore struck back. The censorship of the Press was entrusted to a body of ecclesiastical commissioners, known as the Court of High Commission, which had been constituted in 1559 to deal with offenses against the Church Settlement. This combining of the functions of bishop and censor infuriated the Puritan party. They set up a secret, itinerant Press which poured forth over the years a stream of virulent and anonymous pamphlets, culminating in 1588 with those issued under the name of "Martin Marprelate," attacking the persons and office of "the wainscot-faced bishops." Their sturdy and youthful invective shows a robust and relishing consciousness of the possibilities of English prose.

Elizabeth was slow to believe that any of her Catholic subjects were traitors, and the failure of the 1569 rising had strengthened her confidence in their loyalty. But about the year 1579 missionaries of a new and formidable type began to slip into the country. These were the Jesuits, the heralds and missionaries of the Counter-Reformation. By their enemies they were accused of using assassination to achieve their aims. Queen Mary had burnt some three hundred Protestant martyrs in the last three years of her reign. In the last thirty years of Elizabeth's reign about the same number of Catholics were executed for treason. The conspiracies naturally focused upon the person of Mary Queen of Scots, long captive. A voluntary association of Protestant gentry was formed in 1585 for the defense of Elizabeth's life. In the following year evidence of a conspiracy, engineered by one Anthony Babington, an English Catholic, was laid before the Council by Walsingham. Mary's connivance was undeniable. Elizabeth was at last persuaded that her death was a political necessity. Within twenty-four hours she regretted it and tried, too late, to stop the execution.

The scene of Mary's death has caught the imagination of history. In the early morning of February 8, 1587, she was summoned to the great hall of Fotheringay Castle. Accompanied by six of her attendants, Mary appeared at the appointed hour soberly clad in black satin. In the quietness of the hall she walked with stately movements to the cloth-covered scaffold erected by the fireplace. As she disrobed for the headsman's act, her garments of black satin, removed by the weeping handmaids, revealed a bodice and petticoat of crimson velvet. One of her ladies handed her a pair of crimson sleeves, which she put on. Thus the unhappy Queen halted, for one last moment, standing blood-red from head to foot against the black background of the scaffold. There was a deathly hush throughout the hall. She knelt, and at the second stroke the fatal blow was delivered. In death the majestic illusion was shattered. The head of an aging woman with false hair was held up by the executioner. A lapdog crept out from beneath the clothes of the bleeding trunk.

As the news reached London, Elizabeth sat alone in her room, weeping more for the fate of a Queen than a woman.

In the hope of strengthening her own finances and harassing the enemy's preparations against the Netherlands and ultimately against herself, Elizabeth had sanctioned a number of unofficial expeditions against the Spanish coasts and colonies in South America. Gradually these expeditions had assumed an official character, and the Royal Navy surviving from the days of Henry VIII was rebuilt and reorganized by John Hawkins, son of a Plymouth merchant, who had formerly traded with the Portuguese possessions in Brazil. In 1573 he was appointed Treasurer and Controller of the Navy. He had moreover educated an apt pupil, a young adventurer from Devon, Francis Drake. This "Master Thief of the unknown world," as his Spanish contemporaries called Drake, became the terror of their ports and crews.

Spain was deliberately blocking the commercial enterprise of other nations in the New World so far as it was then known. A Devon gentleman, Humphrey Gilbert, began to look elsewhere, and was the first to interest the Queen in finding a route to China, or Cathay, as it was called, by the North-West. He was the first Englishman who realized that the value of these voyages did not lie only in finding precious metals. The idea of planting colonies in America now began to take hold of men's imaginations. In 1583 Gilbert took possession of Newfoundland in the Queen's name, but no permanent settlement was made. Walter Raleigh tried to continue Gilbert's work. In 1585 a small colony was established on Roanoke Island, off the American continent, and christened Virginia in honor of the Queen. This venture also foundered, as did a second attempt two years later. Colonial efforts were postponed for another twenty years by the Spanish War.

The Spaniards had long contemplated an enterprise against England. Preparations were delayed for a year by Drake's famous raid on Cadiz in 1587, "singeing of the King of Spain's beard." Nevertheless, in May 1588 the Armada was ready. A hundred and thirty ships were assembled, carrying twenty-five hundred guns and more than thirty thousand men, two-thirds of them soldiers. The renowned Spanish Admiral Santa Cruz was now dead, and the command was entrusted to the Duke of Medina-Sidonia, who had many misgivings about the enterprise.

The nation was united in the face of

the Spanish preparations. An army was assembled at Tilbury which reached twenty thousand men, under the command of Lord Leicester. This, with the muster in the adjacent counties, constituted a force which should not be underrated. While the Armada was still off the coasts of England Queen Elizabeth reviewed the army at Tilbury and addressed them in these stirring words:

My loving people, we have been persuaded by some that are careful for our safety to take heed how we commit ourselves to armed multitudes, for fear of treachery. But I assure you I do not desire to live to distrust my faithful and loving people. Let tyrants fear. I have always so behaved myself that, under God, I have placed my chiefest strength and safeguard in the loyal hearts and goodwill of my subjects; and therefore I am come amongst you, as you see, resolved, in the midst and heat of the battle, to live or die amongst you all, to lay down for my God, and for my kingdom, and for my people, my honor and my blood, even in the dust. I know I have the body of a weak and feeble woman, but I have the heart and stomach of a king, and of a king of England too, and think foul scorn that Parma or Spain or any prince of Europe should dare to invade the borders of my realm; to which, rather than any dishonor shall grow by me, I myself will take up arms, I myself will be your general, judge and rewarder of every one of your virtues in the field. I know already for your forwardness you have deserved rewards and crowns; and we do assure you, in the word of a prince, they shall be duly paid you.

Hawkins's work for the Navy was now to be tested. He had begun over the years to revise the design of English ships from his experience of buccaneering raids in colonial waters. The castles which towered above the galleon decks had been cut down; keels were deepened, and design was concentrated on sea-worthiness and speed. Most notable of all, heavier long-range guns were mounted. In spite of Hawkins's efforts only thirty-four of the Queen's ships, carrying six thousand men, could put to sea in 1588. As was the custom, however, all available privately owned vessels were hastily collected and armed for the service of the Government, and a total of a hundred and ninety-seven ships was mustered; but at least half of them were too small to be of much service.

The Armada left the Tagus on May 20, but smitten by storms, put in to refit at Corunna, and did not set sail again until July 12. News of their approach off the Lizard was brought into Plymouth harbor on the evening of July 19. The English fleet had to put out of the Sound the same night against light adverse winds which freshened the following day. If Medina-Sidonia had attacked the English vessels to leeward of his ships as they struggled to clear the land on the Saturday there would have been a disaster. But his instructions bound him to sail up the Channel, unite with Parma, and help transport to England the veteran troops assembled near Dunkirk. His report to Madrid shows how little he realized his opportunity. By difficult, patient, precarious tacking the English fleet got to windward of him, and for nine days hung upon the Armada as it ran before the westerly wind up the Channel, pounding away with their long-range guns at the lumbering galleons. On July 23 the wind sank and both fleets lay becalmed off Portland Bill. A further engagement followed on the 25th off the Isle of Wight. The Channel passage was a torment to the Spaniards. Medina then made a fatal mistake. He anchored in Calais Roads.

The Queen's ships which had been stationed in the eastern end of the Channel joined the main fleet in the Straits, and the whole sea-power of England was now combined. The decisive engagement opened. After darkness had fallen eight ships from the eastern squadron which had been filled with explosives and prepared as fire-ships—the torpedoes of those days—were sent against the crowded Spanish fleet at anchor in the Roads. The Spanish captains cut their cables and made for the open sea. Collisions without number followed. The rest of the fleet, with a south-south-west wind behind it, made eastwards to Gravelines. The army and the transports were not at their rendezvous. The Spaniards turned to face their pursuers. A long and desperate fight raged for eight hours, a confused conflict of ships engaging at close quarters. The English had completely exhausted their ammunition, and but for this hardly a Spanish ship would have got away.

The tormented Armada now sailed northwards out of the fight. The horrors of the long voyage round the north of Scotland began. Sailing southwards, they were forced to make for the western coast of Ireland to replenish their supplies of water. The search for water cost more than five thousand Spanish lives. Nevertheless, over sixty-five ships, about half of the fleet that had put to sea, reached Spanish ports during the month of October.

The English had not lost a single ship, and scarcely a hundred men. But their captains were disappointed; half the enemy's fleet had got away. For the last thirty years they had believed themselves superior to their opponents. But to the English people as a whole the defeat of the Armada came as a miracle. One of the medals struck to commemorate the victory bears the inscription *Flavit Deus et dissipati sunt"*—"God blew and they were scattered." Elizabeth and her seamen knew how true this was. Yet the event was decisive. The nation was transported with relief and pride. Shakespeare was writing *King John* a few years later. His words struck into the hearts of his audiences:

Come the three corners of the world in
 arms,
And we shall shock them. Nought shall
 make us rue
If England to itself do rest but true.

England had emerged from the Armada year as a first-class Power. Poets and courtiers alike paid their homage to the sovereign who symbolized the great achievement. Hakluyt speaks for the thrusting spirit of the age when he proclaims that the English nation, "in searching the most opposite corners and quarters of the world, and, to speak plainly, in compassing the vast globe of the earth more than once, have excelled all the nations and peoples of the earth." Before the reign came to a close another significant enterprise took its beginning. The British Empire in India, which was to be painfully built up in the course of the next three centuries, owes its origins to the Charter granted by Queen Elizabeth to a group of London merchants and financiers in the year 1600. The coming years resound with attacks upon the forces and allies of Spain throughout the world—expeditions to Cadiz, to the Azores, into the Caribbean Sea, to the Low Countries, and, in support of the Huguenots, to the northern coasts of France. But there was no way of delivering a decisive stroke against Spain. The English Government had no money for further efforts. The lights of enthusiasm slowly faded out.

One epic moment has survived in the annals of the English race—the last fight of the *Revenge* at Flores, in the Azores.

"In the year 1591," says Bacon, "was that memorable fight of an English ship called the *Revenge,* under the command of Sir Richard Grenville . . . for the space of fifteen hours, sate like a stag amongst hounds at bay, and was sieged and fought with, in turn, by fifteen great ships of Spain. . . . This brave ship the *Revenge,* being manned only with two hundred soldiers and marines, whereof eighty lay sick, yet nevertheless after a fight maintained (as was said) of fifteen hours, and two ships of the enemy sunk by her side, besides many more torn and battered and great slaughter of men, never came to be entered, but was taken by composition; the enemies themselves having in admiration the virtue of the commander and the whole tragedy of that ship." It is well to remember the ordinary seamen. These men faced death in many forms—death by disease, death by drowning, death from Spanish pikes and guns, death by starvation and cold on uninhabited coasts, death in the Spanish prisons. The Admiral of the English fleet, Lord Howard of Effingham, spoke their epitaph: "God send us to sea in such a company together again, when need is."

Victory over Spain was the most shining achievement of Elizabeth's reign, but by no means the only one. The repulse of the Armada had subdued religious dissension at home. The Church she had nursed to strength was a very different body from the half-hearted and distracted community of her early years: more confident, more learned, far less inclined to compromise with dissidents within or separatists without; strong in the attachment of thousands to whom its liturgy had become dear by habit and who thought of it as the Church into which they had been baptized.

War with Spain had set a premium on martial virtues. Young and eager men like Walter Raleigh and Robert Devereux, Earl of Essex, quarreled for permission to lead enterprises against the Spaniards. Essex was Leicester's stepson, and Leicester brought him into the circle of the Court. He found the Government in the hands of the cautious Cecils, William, Lord Burghley, and his son Robert. Essex soon headed the war party in the Council. In 1596 an expedition was sent against Cadiz under the joint command of Essex and Raleigh. The fleet returned home triumphant, but, to Elizabeth's regret, little the richer. Essex was made Master of the Ordnance. He was given command of an expedition to intercept a further Armada now gathering in the ports of western Spain. The English ships headed south-west and made for the Azores; the Spanish Treasure Fleet eluded them; the Armada put out into the Bay of Biscay with the seas clear of defending ships to the north. Once again the winds saved the Island. The muddle and quarreling which had marred the Azores expedition enraged Elizabeth. Essex retired from Court, and thunderous days followed.

Henry VIII had assumed the title of King of Ireland, but this involved no real extension of his authority. The Counter-Reformation revived and reanimated opposition to Protestant England. In April 1599 Essex was allowed to go to Ireland, at the head of the largest army that England had ever sent there. He accomplished nothing and was on the verge of ruin. Disobeying the express orders of the Queen, he deserted his command and rode in haste to London unannounced. Weeks dragged by, and a desperate plot was made by Essex and his younger companions, including Shakespeare's patron, the Earl of Southampton. The scheme failed, and the end came in February 1601 with Essex's death within the Tower. The spoils of office, power, and influence were at stake, and victorious Essex would have dispensed appointments throughout England, and perhaps even have dictated terms to the Queen. She struck back; and in destroying Essex she saved England from the consumption of civil war.

Throughout the reign the weight and authority of Parliament had been steadily growing. Now the issue turned on monopolies. In 1601 grievances flared up into a full-dress debate in the House of Commons. The uproar in the House brought a stinging rebuke from Mr. Secretary Cecil. But the Queen preferred subtler methods. Some monopolies were abolished forthwith. All, she promised, would be investigated. It was to be her last appearance in their midst. The immense vitality displayed by the Queen throughout the troublous years of her rule in England ebbed slowly and relentlessly away. She lay for days upon a heap of cushions in her room. For hours the soundless agony was prolonged. At last Robert Cecil dared to speak. "Your Majesty, to content the people you must go to bed." "Little man," came the answer, "is 'must' a word to use to princes?" In the early hours of the morning of March 24, 1603, Queen Elizabeth died.

Thus ended the Tudor dynasty. For over a hundred years, with a handful of bodyguards, it had maintained its sovereignty, kept the peace, baffled the diplomacy and onslaughts of Europe, and guided the country through changes which might well have wrecked it.

CHAPTER FIVE

The Civil War

King James VI of Scotland was the only son of Mary Queen of Scots. He had fixed ideas about kingship and the divine right of monarchs to rule. He was a scholar with pretensions to being a philosopher, and in the course of his life published numerous tracts and treatises, ranging from denunciations of witchcraft and tobacco to abstract political theory. He came to England with a closed mind, and a weakness for lecturing.

England was secure, free to attend to her own concerns, and a powerful class was now eager to take a hand in their management. Who was to have the last word in the matter of taxation? Was the King beneath the law or was he not? And who was to say what the law was? The greater part of the seventeenth century was to be spent in trying to find answers, historical, legal, theoretical, and practical, to such questions. Over these deep-cutting issues there loomed a fiscal crisis of the first magnitude. To his surprise James very soon found himself pressed for money. This meant frequent Parliaments. Frequent Parliaments gave Members the opportunity to organize themselves, and James neglected to control Parliamentary sessions through his Privy Councillors, as Elizabeth had done. It was an ancient and obstinate belief that the King should "live of his own," and that the traditional revenues from the Crown lands and from the customs should suffice for the upkeep of the public services. Parliament normally voted customs duties to each monarch for life, and did not expect to have to provide more money except in emergencies. Fortunately, the judges ruled that the ports were under the King's exclusive jurisdiction and that he could issue a "book of rates"—that is, impose extra customs duties—as he thought fit. Here, but only for a time, the matter rested.

The King had decided views on religion. He realized that Calvinism and monarchy would quarrel in the long run and that if men could decide for themselves about religion they could also decide for themselves on politics. James made it clear there would be no changes in the Elizabethan Church Settlement. His slogan was "No Bishop, no King."

The Catholics were also anxious and hopeful. But the Pope would not yield. He forbade allegiance to a heretical sovereign. James, although inclined to toleration, was forced to act. Disappointment and despair led a small group of Catholic gentry to an infernal design for blowing up James and his whole Parliament by gunpowder while they were in session at Westminster. One of their followers warned a relative who was a Catholic peer. The story reached Robert Cecil, Earl of Salisbury, and the cellars of Parliament were searched. Guy Fawkes, a veteran of the Spanish Wars against the Dutch, was taken on the spot, and there was a storm of excitement in the City. So novel and so wholesale a treason exposed the Catholic community to immediate and severe persecution and a more persistent and widespread detestation.

At this time a splendid and lasting monument was created to the genius of the English-speaking peoples. In 1611 the Authorized Version of the Bible was produced by the King's Printer. This may be deemed James's greatest achievement, for the impulse was largely his. The Scottish pedant built better than he knew. The scholars who produced this masterpiece are mostly unknown and unremembered. But they forged an enduring link, literary and religious, between the English-speaking peoples of the world.

The Tudors had been discreet in their use of the Royal Prerogative and had never put forward any general theory of government, but James saw himself as the schoolmaster of the whole Island. He found a brilliant supporter in the person of Francis Bacon, the ambitious lawyer who had dabbled in politics with Essex, and crept back to obedience when his patron fell. The subsequent conflict centered on the nature of the Royal Prerogative and the powers of an Act of Parliament. Chief Justice Coke, one of the most learned of English judges, gave a blunt answer to these controversies. He declared that conflicts between Prerogative and statute should be resolved not by the Crown but by the judges. James had a very different view of the function of judges. Their business, as Bacon put it, was to be "lions under the throne." James first tried to muzzle Coke by promoting him from the Court of Common Pleas to the King's Bench. Unsuccessful in this, he dismissed him in 1616. Five years later Coke entered the House of Commons and found that the most active lawyers of the day were in agreement with him. Learned in the law, and not always too scrupulous in the interpretations they twisted from it, they gradually built up a case on which Parliament could claim with conviction that it was fighting, not for something new, but for the traditional and lawful heritage of the English people.

James's foreign policy perhaps met the needs of the age for peace, but often clashed with its temper. When he came to the throne England was still technically at war with Spain. With Cecil's support hostilities were concluded and diplomatic relations renewed. The Princess Elizabeth had married one of the Protestant champions of Europe, Frederick, the Elector Palatine of the Rhine, and Frederick was soon projected into violent revolt against the Habsburg Emperor Ferdinand. The Elector Frederick was soon driven out of Bohemia, and his hereditary lands were occupied by Habsburg troops. The House of Commons clamored for war. James contented himself with academic discussions upon Bohemian rights with the Spanish Ambassador. To pose as Protestant champion in the great war now begun might gain a fleeting popularity with his subjects, but would also deliver him into the hands of the House of Commons.

In the midst of these turmoils Sir Walter Raleigh was executed in Palace Yard to please the Spanish Government. Raleigh had been imprisoned at the beginning of the reign for conspiring to supplant James by his cousin. This charge was probably unjust, and the trial was certainly so. Raleigh's last expedition, for which he was specially released from the Tower, had merely affronted the Spanish Governors of South America. His death on October 29, 1618, was intended to mark the new policy of appeasement and prepare the way for good relations with Spain. This deed of shame sets a barrier forever between King James and the English people. There are others.

James was much addicted to favorites, and his attention to handsome young men resulted in a noticeable loss of respect for the monarchy. One of his favorites, Robert Carr, created Earl of Somerset by the King's caprice, was implicated in a murder by poison, of which his wife was undoubtedly guilty. Carr was succeeded in the King's regard by a good-looking, quick-witted, extravagant youth, George Villiers, soon ennobled as Duke of Buckingham. This young man quickly became all-powerful at Court, and in the affections of James. He formed a deep and honorable friendship with Charles, Prince of Wales. He accepted unhesitatingly the royal policy of a Spanish marriage, and in 1623 staged a romantic journey to Madrid for the Prince and himself to view the bride.

The negotiations with Spain foundered. In this sharp pinch Buckingham with remarkable agility turned himself from a royal favorite into a national, if short-lived, statesman. Whereas all interference by Parliament in foreign affairs had been repelled by the Tudors, and hitherto by James, the Minister-Favourite now invited Lords and Commons to give their opinion. The answer of both Houses was prompt and plain. It was contrary, they said, to the honor of the King, to the welfare of his people, to the interest of his children, and to the terms of his former alliances to continue the negotiations with Spain. But now came the question of raising funds for the war that was to follow. Parliament urged a purely naval war with Spain, in which great profits from the Indies might be won. Suspicious of the King's intentions, the Commons voted less than half the sum for which he asked, and laid down stringent conditions as to how it should be spent.

No sooner was the Spanish match broken off than Buckingham turned to France for a bride for Charles. The old King wanted to see his son married. He ratified the marriage treaty in December 1624. Three months later the first King of Great Britain was dead.

For a while little was heard of the New World. The change came in 1604, when James I made his treaty of peace with Spain. Raleigh's attempts had demonstrated the ill-success of individual effort, but a new method of financing large-scale trading enterprises was evolving in the shape of the joint stock company. In 1606 a group of speculators acquired a royal Charter creating the Virginia Company. The objects of the directors were mixed and ill-defined. A settlement was made at Jamestown, in the Chesapeake Bay, on the Virginian coast, in May 1607. By chance a crop of tobacco was planted, and the soil proved benevolent. Small-holders were bought out, big estates were formed, and the colony began to stand on its own feet.

The Elizabethan bishops had driven the nobler and tougher Puritan spirits out of the Established Church. A congregation at Scrooby, in Nottinghamshire, led by one of their pastors, John Robinson, and by William Brewster, the Puritan bailiff of the manor of the Archbishop of York, resolved to seek freedom of worship abroad. In 1607 they left England and settled at Leyden, hoping to find asylum among the tolerant and industrious Dutch. They were persistent and persevering, but a bleak future faced them in Holland. Emigration to the New World presented itself as an escape from a sinful generation. Their first plan was to settle in Guiana, but then they realized it was impossible to venture out upon their own. They accordingly sent agents to London to negotiate with the only body interested in emigration, the Virginia Company. Thirty-five members of the Leyden congregation left Holland and joined sixty-six West Country adventurers at Plymouth, and in September 1620 they set sail in the *Mayflower,* a vessel of 180 tons.

After two and a half months of voyaging across the winter ocean they reached the shores of Cape Cod, and thus, by an accident, landed outside the jurisdiction of the Virginia Company. This invalidated their patent from London. Before they landed there was trouble among the group about who was to enforce discipline. Those who had joined the ship at Plymouth were no picked band of saints, and had no intention of submitting to the Leyden set. There was no possibility of appealing to England. Yet, if they were not all to starve, some agreement must be reached. Forty-one of the more responsible members thereupon drew up a solemn compact which is one of the remarkable documents in history, a spontaneous covenant for political organization. "In the name of God, Amen. We whose names are under-written, the loyal subjects of our dread sovereign Lord, King James, by the grace of God, of Great Britain, France, and Ireland King, Defender of the Faith, etc. Having undertaken, for the glory of God, and advancement of the Christian faith, and

honor of our King and country, a voyage to plant the first colony in the northern parts of Virginia, do by these presents solemnly and mutually in the presence of God, and one of another, covenant and combine ourselves together into a civil body politic, for our better ordering and preservation and furtherance of the ends aforesaid; and by virtue hereof to enact, constitute, and frame such just and equal laws, ordinances, acts, constitutions, and offices, from time to time, as shall be thought most meet and convenient for the general good of the colony, unto which we promise all due submission and obedience." In December on the American coast in Cape Cod Bay these men founded the town of Plymouth. The financial supporters in London reaped no profits. In 1627 they sold out and the Plymouth colony was left to its own resources. Such was the founding of New England.

After the precedent of Virginia a chartered company was formed, eventually named "The Company of the Massachusetts Bay in New England." An advance-party founded the settlement of Salem, to the north of Plymouth. In 1630 the Governor of the Company, John Winthrop, followed with a thousand settlers. Some of the Puritan stockholders realized that there was no obstacle to transferring the Company, directors and all, to New England. From the joint stock company was born the self-governing colony of Massachusetts.

The leaders and ministers who ruled in Massachusetts, however, had views of their own about freedom. By no means all were rigid Calvinists, and recalcitrant bodies split off from the parent colony when quarrels became strident. In 1635 and 1636 some of them moved to the valley of the Connecticut River, and founded the town of Hartford near its banks. Religious strife drove others beyond the bounds of the parent colony. A scholar from Cambridge, Roger Williams, had been forced to leave the University by Archbishop Laud. He followed the now known way to the New World, and settled in Massachusetts. The magistrates considered him a promoter of disorder, and resolved to send him back to England. Warned in time, he fled beyond their reach, and, followed at intervals by others, founded the town of Providence, to the south of Massachusetts. Other exiles from Massachusetts, some of them forcibly banished, joined his settlement in 1636, which became the colony of Rhode Island.

Two other ventures, both essentially commercial, established the English-speaking peoples in the New World. By the 1640's Barbados, St. Christopher, Nevis, Montserrat, and Antigua were in English hands and several thousand colonists had arrived. Sugar assured their prosperity, and the Spanish grip on the West Indies was shaken. There was much competition and warfare in the succeeding years, but for a long time these island settlements were commercially much more valuable to England than the colonies in North America. In 1632 George Calvert, Lord Baltimore, a Roman Catholic courtier who had long been interested in colonization, applied for a patent for settling in the neighborhood of Virginia. Courtiers and merchants subscribed to the venture, and the new colony was named Maryland in honor of Charles's Queen, Henrietta Maria.

In these first decades of the great emigration over eighty thousand English-speaking people crossed the Atlantic. Never since the days of the Germanic invasions of Britain had such a national movement been seen. Saxon and Viking had colonized England. Now, one thousand years later, their descendants were taking possession of America. Many different streams of migrants were to make their confluence in the New World

and contribute to the manifold character of the future United States. But the British stream flowed first and remained foremost.

A great political and religious crisis was overhanging England. Already in King James's time Parliament had begun to take the lead, not only in levying taxes but increasingly in the conduct of affairs, and especially in foreign policy. An intense desire for England to lead and champion the Protestant cause wherever it was assailed drove forward the Parliamentary movement with a force far greater than would ever have sprung merely from the issues which were now opening at home. The secular issues were nevertheless themselves of enormous weight. Tudor authority had been accepted as a relief from the anarchy of the Wars of the Roses, and had now ceased to fit either the needs or the temper of a continually growing society. Coke had taught the later Parliaments of James I the arguments upon which they could rest and the methods by which they might prevail. Two country gentlemen stand with him; one from the West, Sir John Eliot, a Cornishman; the other, Thomas Wentworth, a Yorkshire squire. Behind them, lacking nothing in grit, were leaders of the Puritan gentry, Denzil Holles, Arthur Hazelrigg, John Pym. Pym was eventually to go far and to carry the cause still farther. Here was a man who understood every move in the political game, and would play it out remorselessly.

The King was affronted by the manner in which his father's overtures for a Spanish match, and he himself, had been slighted in Madrid. He at once carried through his marriage with the French Princess, Henrietta Maria. The new Parliament granted supplies against Spain; but their purpose to review the whole question of indirect taxation was plain when they resolved that the customs duties of tonnage and poundage without which the King could not live, even in peace, should for the first time for many reigns be voted, not for the King's life, but only for one year. The war with Spain went badly. Buckingham was impeached, and to save his friend the King hastily dissolved Parliament. A new complication was now added to the scene. The new, powerful French Minister, Cardinal Richelieu, was determined to curb the independence of the Huguenots in France, and in particular to reduce their maritime stronghold of La Rochelle. In 1627 a considerable force was dispatched under Buckingham to help the Rochelais. It landed off the coast in the Île de Ré, failed to storm the citadel, and withdrew in disorder. Forced loans could not suffice to replenish the Treasury, and having secured a promise that the impeachment of Buckingham would not be pursued the King agreed to summon Parliament. They offered no fewer than five subsidies, amounting to £300,000, all to be paid within twelve months; but before they would confirm this in a Bill they demanded their price.

The following four Resolutions were passed unanimously: that no freeman ought to be restrained or imprisoned unless some lawful cause was expressed; that the writ of *habeas corpus* ought to be granted to every man imprisoned or restrained, even though it might be at the command of the King or of the Privy Council; that if no legal cause for imprisonment were shown the party ought to be set free or bailed; that it was the ancient and undoubted right of every freeman to have a full and absolute property in his goods and estate, and that no tax, loan, or benevolence ought to be levied by the King or his Ministers without common consent by Act of Parliament. At Coke's prompting the Commons now went on to frame the Petition of Right. Its object was to curtail the

King's Prerogative. The Petition complained against forced loans, imprisonment without trial, billeting, and martial law. Charles, resorting to maneuver, secretly consulted the judges, who assured him that even his consent to these liberties would not affect his ultimate Prerogative. We reach here, amid much confusion, the main foundation of English freedom.

Both sides pressed farther along their paths. The Commons came forward with further complaints against the growth of Popery. The King and Buckingham hoped that a second and successful expedition would relieve the Huguenots in La Rochelle and present a military or diplomatic result in which all could rejoice. Far better to rescue Protestants abroad than to persecute Catholics at home. This was not a discreditable position to take up; but Fate moved differently.

The death of Buckingham was a devastating blow to the young King. The murderer, John Felton, seems to have been impaled by nature upon all those prongs of dark resolve which make such deeds possible. He had the private sting of being passed over for promotion. But the documents which he left behind him proved him a slave of larger thoughts. Parliament's remonstrations to the King against Buckingham's lush splendor and corrupt methods had sunk into his soul.

Though the Commons had granted the five subsidies, they held tonnage and poundage in reserve. When the year lapsed for which this had been voted the Parliamentary party throughout the country were angered to find that the King continued to collect the tax by his officers, as had been the custom for so many reigns. The expedition to La Rochelle, which had sailed under another commander, miscarried. Thus when Parliament met again at the beginning of 1629 there was no lack of grievances both in foreign and domestic policy. Yet it was upon questions of religion that the attack began. All was embodied in a single Remonstrance. The Speaker, who had been gained to the King's side, announced on March 2 that the King adjourned the House till the 10th, thus frustrating the carrying of the Remonstrance. When the Speaker rose to leave he was forced back and held down on his chair by two resolute and muscular Members, Holles and Valentine. The doors were barred against Black Rod, and the Remonstrance, recited from memory by Holles, was declared carried by acclamation. It had become plain to all that King and Commons could not work together on any terms.

The Personal Rule of King Charles was not set up covertly or by degrees. First, there must be peace with France and Spain. Without the support of Parliament Charles had not the strength to carry on foreign wars. The second condition was the gaining of some at least of the Parliamentary leaders. Wentworth was more than willing. He knew he judged better than most other men; he was a born administrator; all he wanted was scope for his endeavors. In December 1628 he became Lord President of the Council of the North and a member of the Privy Council. From this moment he not only abandoned all the ideas of which he had been the ablest exponent, but all the friends who had fought at his side. He was "the Satan of the Apostasy," "the lost Archangel," "the suborned traitor to the cause of Parliament." But the third and least sentimental condition of the Personal Rule was dominant —money. The Crown had to make shift with what it could scrape from old taxes. No large question could be stirred. The King, with his elegant, dignified Court, whose figures are portrayed by the pencil of Van Dyck, whose manners and whose morals were an example to all, reigned on the smallest scale. He was a despot, but an unarmed despot. The Prerogative of the Crown offered a wide and vaguely defined field within which taxes could be raised. The King, supported by his judges, strained all expedients to the limit. Hungry forces still lay in shadow. All the ideas which they cherished and championed stirred in their minds, but they had no focus, no expression. The Poor Law was administered with exceptional humanity. Ordinary gentlefolk might have no share in national government, but they were still lords on their own estates. The malcontents looked about for points which would inflame the inert forces of the nation.

Meanwhile, Wentworth, now Lord-Lieutenant of Ireland, had, by a combination of tact and authority, reduced that kingdom to a greater submission to the British Crown than ever before or since. His repute in history must rest upon his Irish administration.

According to the immemorial laws of England, perhaps of Alfred the Great, the whole land should pay for the upkeep of the Fleet. Why should not all pay where all benefited? The project commended itself to the King. In August 1635 he levied "Ship Money" upon the whole country. Forthwith a Buckinghamshire gentleman, a former Member of Parliament, solidly active against the Crown, stood forth among many others and refused to pay upon the principle that even the best of taxes could be levied only with the consent of Parliament. John Hampden's refusal was selected by both sides as a test case. The Crown prevailed. But the grievance ran far and wide.

Here emerges the figure of the man who of all others was Charles's evil genius—William Laud, Archbishop of Canterbury. The Elizabethan Settlement was dependent on the State. By itself the Church had not the strength to bear the strain. An informal compact therefore grew up between the secular and spiritual aspects of government, whereby the State sustained the Church in its property and the Church preached the duty of obedience and the Divine Right of Kings. Laud by no means initiated this compact, but he set himself with untimely vigor to enforce it. Among his innovations was the railing off of the altar, and a new emphasis on ceremony and the dignity of the clergy. Laud now found a new source of revenue for the Crown. All over England men and women found themselves haled before the justices for not attending church, and fined one shilling a time. Here indeed was something that ordinary men and women could understand. The Parliamentary agitation which had been conducted during all these years with so much difficulty gained a widespread accession of strength at a time when the King's difficulties had already massed themselves into a stack.

It was in Scotland, the home of the Stuarts and Charles's birthplace, that the torch was lighted which began the vast conflagration. The Scots must adopt the English Prayer Book, and enter broadly into communion with their English brethren. Charles and his advisers had no thought of challenging doctrine, still less of taking any step towards Popery. They desired to assert the Protestant High Church view. The Scottish people believed, and were told by their native leaders to believe, that they were to be forced by the royal authority to take the first fatal steps towards Roman Catholicism. When in July 1637 the dignitaries of Scottish Church and State were gathered in St. Giles's Church in Edinburgh for the first solemn reading of the new Prayer Book, an outburst of fury and insult overwhelmed the Dean when he sought to read the new dispensation. Edinburgh defied the Crown. A surge of passion swept the ancient capital before which the episcopal and royal authorities trembled. At length the whole original policy of the King was withdrawn.

Meanwhile, the Scottish nation was forming a union which challenged existing conditions both in Church and State. On February 28, 1638, the Covenant was read in Greyfriars churchyard in Edinburgh. It embodied the unalterable resolve of a whole people to perish rather than submit to Popery.

Force was now to be invoked. The Covenanters had resources overseas. The famous part played by the Scots brigades and by Scottish generals under Gustavus Adolphus in Germany had left Scotland with an incomparable military reserve. Alexander Leslie had risen in the Thirty Years War to the rank of Field-Marshal. In a few months, and long before any effective preparations could be made in the South, Scotland had the strongest armed force in the Island. Wentworth was now summoned from Ireland to strengthen the Council. "Thorough" was his maxim; and we have no means of judging how far he would have pushed on in success. He dreamed of a new Flodden; and he was fully prepared to use his Irish army in Scotland whenever it might be necessary.

At this decisive moment England's monarchy might well have conformed to the absolutism which was becoming general throughout Europe. Wentworth saw clearly enough that the royal revenues were not sufficient to support the cost of the campaign. He concluded therefore that Parliament must be summoned. In his over-confidence he thought that the Commons would prove manageable. Parliament met on April 13, 1640. Only a quarter of the former Members reappeared. Eliot was dead in the Tower; Wentworth was now Earl of Strafford, and the King's First Minister. Charles and his chief counselors, Strafford and Laud, found no comfort from the new assembly. On the contrary, they were met by such a temper that by an act of extreme imprudence it was dissolved on May 5 after a few days.

Strafford wished to bring over his Irish troops, but fear of the reactions which this step might provoke paralyzed the Council. Presently the Scots crossed the Tweed in good order. They met with no opposition until they reached the Tyne. Then, as once before, the two hosts faced one another. Someone pulled a trigger; the shot went home; all the Scots cannon fired and all the English army fled. A contemporary wrote that "Never so many ran from so few with less ado." The King could not defend the country himself. He had plumbed the depths of personal failure.

The Privy Council addressed itself to making a truce with the Scots, who demanded £40,000 a month to maintain their army on English soil until their claims should be met. By haggling this was reduced to £850 a day. The so-called "Bishops' War" was over; the real war had yet to begin. There now arose from all quarters a cry that Parliament should be summoned. Thus on November 3, 1640, was installed the second longest and most memorable Parliament that ever sat in England. It derived its force from a blending of political and religious ideas. It was upborne by the need of a growing society to base itself upon a wider foundation than Tudor paternal rule. All the rage of the Parliamentary party, all the rancor of old comradeship forsworn, all that self-preservation dictated, concentrated upon "the wicked Earl," Strafford, a blast of fury such as was never recorded in England before or since. Such a downfall recalls, in its swiftness at least, the fate of Sejanus, the hated Minister of Tiberius. The proscription extended to all the Ministers, as they would now be called, of the King. Re-

spect for law and for human life nevertheless prevailed. In this mortal struggle physical violence was long held in check, and even when it broke into civil war all those conventions were observed which protect even the sternest exercise of the human will from the animal barbarism of earlier and of later times.

The aggressive tendencies of the majority in the Commons shaped themselves into a demand for the abolition of Episcopacy. The Scots, now so influential in London and masters in the North, sought to establish the Presbyterian system of Church government. But now for the first time effective counterforces appeared. A second petition proposed the restriction of the bishops' power to spiritual matters. It was known that the King regarded the Episcopate, based upon the Apostolic Succession, as inseparable from the Christian faith, but whereas in politics the opposition to Personal Rule was at this moment overwhelming, on the Church question the balance was far more even. Pym realized this and decided to delay a full debate.

Meanwhile, the trial of Strafford had begun. Proceeding as they did upon admittedly rival interpretations of law and justice, the Commons at once found difficulty in establishing a case against the hated Minister. They would dispense with a trial and have him declared guilty by Act of Parliament. The cry for "Justice!" rang through London streets. This was the agony of Charles's life, to which none of his other sufferings compared. The question was not whether he could save Strafford, but whether the royal authority would perish with him. He gave his assent to the Bill of Attainder. Strafford died with fortitude and dignity. The circumstances of his trial and of the Attainder threw odium upon his pursuers. They slaughtered a man they could not convict. But that man, if given his full career, would have closed perhaps for generations the windows of civic freedom upon the English people.

The Triennial Bill providing for the summoning of Parliament at least once in three years, if necessary in spite of the Crown, put a final end to the system of Personal Rule over which Charles had so far presided. The grant of tonnage and poundage for one year only was accompanied by a censure upon the exaction of Ship Money, and reparation to all who had suffered for their resistance to it. The King perforce subscribed to all this. But he must have been completely broken for the moment when he assented to a measure designed "to prevent inconvenience that may happen by the untimely prorogation or dissolving of this present Parliament" except by its own consent. The judges, whose tenure had hitherto been dependent upon the pleasure of the Crown, now held office on good behavior. The Court of Star Chamber, which, as we have seen, Henry VII had used to curb the baronage, but which had in the lapse of time become oppressive to the people, was abolished. So was the Court of High Commission, which had striven to impose religious uniformity. The whole Tudor system which the Stuarts had inherited was shaken from its base.

Charles now felt that his hope lay in a reconciliation with Scotland. But all was in vain. The Scots were confirmed in their obduracy, and the King returned to England crestfallen. Upon this melancholy scene a hideous apparition now appeared. The execution of Strafford liberated all the elemental forces in Ireland which his system had so successfully held in restraint. The passions of the original inhabitants and of the hungry, downtrodden masses, bursting from all control, were directed upon the gentry, the landowners, and the Protestants, both within and without the Pale. The mere fact of his absence from London, which had left the Parliamentary forces to their full play, had served the King's interests better than the closest attention to English affairs. Englishmen, irrespective of religious and constitutional convictions, were ill disposed to be taxed for the upkeep of invading Scottish troops. The House of Commons at the end of 1641 had traveled far. From being the servants of the national cause the Puritans had become an aggressive faction. It was in this stormy weather that Pym and Hampden sought to rally their forces by bringing forward what was called the "Grand Remonstrance." It was intended to advertise all that had so far been accomplished by Parliament in remedying old grievances, and to proclaim the future policy of the Parliamentary leaders. Nevertheless, the growing body of Conservatives, or "Episcopalian Party," as they were sometimes named, were affronted by the Remonstrance and determined to oppose it. When Parliament had met a year earlier the King's party could not count on a third of its Members. Now the Grand Remonstrance was carried only by eleven votes.

The King, who, in spite of his failure in Scotland and the Irish catastrophe, had been conscious of ever-gathering support, was now drawn into various contradictory blunders. Still seeking desperately for a foothold, he invited Pym himself to become Chancellor of the Exchequer. Such a plan had no contact with reality. Colepeper took the post instead, and Falkland became Secretary of State. Next, in violent revulsion, Charles resolved to prosecute five of his principal opponents in the Commons for high treason. He certainly convinced himself that Pym meant to impeach the Queen. Thus goaded, Charles, accompanied by three or four hundred swordsmen—"Cavaliers" we may now call them—went down to the House of Commons. It was January 4, 1642. Never before had a king set foot in the Chamber. But a treacherous message from a lady of the Queen's Bedchamber had given Pym a timely warning. The accused Members had already embarked at Westminster Steps and were safe amid the train-bands and magistrates of the City. Speaker Lenthall could give no information. "I have neither eyes to see, nor tongue to speak in this place, but as the House is pleased to direct me, whose servant I am here," he pleaded. The King, already conscious of his mistake, cast his eyes around the quivering assembly. "I see that the birds are flown," he said lamely, and after some civil reassurances he departed at the head of his disappointed, growling adherents. But as he left the Chamber a low, long murmur of "Privilege" pursued him. Henceforth London was irretrievably lost to the King. By stages he withdrew to Newmarket, to Nottingham, and to York. There were now two centers of government.

The negotiations between King and Parliament which occupied the early months of 1642 served only to emphasize their differences while both were gathering their forces. On June 1, 1642, Parliament presented nineteen Propositions to the King. In brief, the King was invited to surrender his whole effective sovereignty over Church and State.

The arrogant tone and ever-growing demands of the Parliamentary party shaped the lines of the struggle and recruited the forces of the King. The greater part of the nobility gradually rallied to the Royalist cause; the tradesmen and merchants generally inclined to the Parliament; but a substantial section of the aristocracy were behind Pym, and many boroughs were devotedly Royalist. The gentry and yeomen in the counties were deeply divided. Those nearer London generally inclined to Parliament, while the North and West remained largely Royalist. Both sides fought in the name of the King, and both upheld the Parliamentary institution. Behind all class and political issues the religious quarrel was the driving power. At Nottingham, where town and county alike had proclaimed devotion, Charles set up his standard on August 22 and called his loyal subjects to his aid. This was the ancient signal for feudal duty, and its message awoke ancestral memories throughout the land.

At Nottingham the King had only eight hundred horse and three hundred foot, and at first it seemed doubtful whether any royal army could be raised. But the violence of Parliament served him well. By the end of September he had with him two thousand horse and six thousand foot. A few weeks later their numbers were more than doubled, and other forces were raised for him all over the country. Meanwhile, the Roundheads, sustained by ample funds from the wealth and regular taxation of London, levied and trained an army of twenty-five thousand men under Essex. As on the Royalist side, most of the regiments were raised personally by prominent people. But whereas the King could give only a commission to raise a regiment or a troop Parliament could provide the equipment as well.

The King, skillfully avoiding Essex's army, now moved west to join his Welsh reinforcements, and then struck south for the Thames valley and London. At Edgehill, in Warwickshire, on October 23 the royal army turned on its pursuers and attacked them before their rearguard, which was approaching the village of Kineton, had come in. The battle was marked by abundant ignorance and zeal on both sides. Edgehill, which might so easily have ended the war in the King's favor, was judged a drawn battle. At least five thousand Englishmen lay upon the field; twelve hundred were buried by the vicar of Kineton. It has often been asked whether Charles could have reached

London before Essex, and what would have happened when he got there. But now the advance was made from Oxford and the King contented himself with disarming and dispersing the local forces that stood in the way. A few days later, at Turnham Green, a few miles west of London, the King found himself confronted with the combined forces of Essex's field army and the London garrison. After a cannonade he withdrew towards Oxford, being, as some held, lucky in getting clear. Thus closed the fighting of the year 1642.

From the beginning of 1643 the war became general. The ports and towns, the manufacturing centers, mostly adhered to the Parliament; what might be called Old England rallied to Charles. At first the decisive action was not in the North. Parliament was already in some doubts about the capacity of Essex as a general. The peace party favored him, but the fancy of those who wanted all-out war was Sir William Waller, now sent to command the Parliamentary army in the West. Here also the most sagacious and skillful of the Royalist generals, Sir Ralph Hopton, commanded. Three fierce battles on a small scale were fought by Hopton and Waller. King Charles was master in the West. His cause had also prevailed in Yorkshire. Here Lord Fairfax and his son, Sir Thomas, led the Parliamentary forces. Sir Thomas besieged York; but the Marquis of Newcastle, a man of no military aptitude, rich, corpulent, proud, but entirely devoted, led his territorial retainers, the valiant "white-coats," to its relief, and later in the summer overwhelmed the Fairfaxes at Adwalton Moor.

Charles possessed a certain strategic comprehension. From the beginning of 1643 his design was for a general advance on London. On the other hand, Gloucester was the sole stronghold remaining to the Parliament between Bris-

tol and York. Its fall would open the Severn to the Royalist flotillas and supply-barges, as well as uniting Oxford and the West to Royalist Wales. Accordingly on August 10 the city was invested. The Earl of Essex had fallen into just disrepute as a general, and was suspected of political lukewarmness. Now, however, he was ordered and conjured to relieve Gloucester. He entered the city in triumph, but found himself immediately short of supplies and food, with a formidable enemy between him and home. Both armies headed for London, and on September 20 they clashed at Newbury, in Berkshire. A third of the troops were casualties, and on the Royalist side many nobles fell. The battle was undecided when darkness fell. Essex had no choice but to renew it at dawn; but the King withdrew, stricken by the loss of so many personal friends, and short of powder, and the London road lay open to the Roundheads.

The King's large plan for 1643 had failed. Nevertheless, the campaign had been very favorable to him. His troops were still, on the whole, better fighting men than the Roundheads. Then on December 8 Pym died, uncheered by success, but unwearied by misfortune. He remains the most famous of the old Parliamentarians, and the man who more than any other saved England from absolute monarchy and set her upon the path she has since pursued.

There was a lull during the winter. Declaring that the Parliament at Westminster was no longer a free Parliament, Charles summoned all who had been expelled or who had fled from it to a Counter-Assembly. The response was remarkable. Eighty-three peers and a hundred and seventy-five Members met in Oxford on January 22, 1644. But these advantages were overwhelmed by the arrival in England of a Scottish army of eighteen thousand foot and three thousand horse, who crossed the Tweed in January. For this succor the London Parliament paid £31,000 a month and the cost of equipment. But the Scots, though in a sense hired, had other objects besides money. They now aspired to out-root the Episcopacy and impose by armed force the Presbyterian system of Church government upon England.

It was now that Oliver Cromwell came into prominence. The Member for Cambridge was deemed the best officer on the Parliamentary side, though he had not yet held a supreme command. The rise of Cromwell to the first rank of power during 1644 sprang both from his triumphs on the battlefield and his resistance to the Presbyterians and the Scots at Westminster. All the obscurer Protestant sects saw in him their champion.

In the North the Marquis of Newcastle had now to contend with the Scottish army on one side and the two Fairfaxes on the other. The loss of York would ruin the King's cause in the North. Charles therefore sent Prince Rupert with a strong cavalry force, which gathered strength as it marched, to relieve the city and sustain the harassed and faithful Marquis. The Scots and Roundheads withdrew together westwards, covering Leeds and joining the forces from East Anglia under Lord Manchester and Cromwell. The three Puritan armies were thus combined, and numbered twenty thousand foot and seven thousand horse. Their outposts lay upon a ridge at Marston Moor. Rupert met the Marquis of Newcastle, and their united forces reached eleven thousand foot and seven thousand horse. Accordingly the Royalist army followed the enemy to Marston Moor, and on July 2 found themselves near their encampments. Marston Moor was the largest and also the bloodiest battle of the war. For the first time the heroic, dreaded Cavaliers met their match, and their master. "We drove the entire cavalry of the Prince off the field," wrote Cromwell. "God made them as stubble to our swords. Then we took their regiments of foot with our cavalry, and overthrew all that we encountered." Newcastle's "white-coats" fought to the death, and fell where they stood. The prestige of Rupert's cavalry was broken. A disaster of the first magnitude had smitten the King's cause.

The success of the King's campaign in the South veiled, at least for a time, the disaster at Marston Moor. It was expected, not only by the Parliament, but in his own circles, that the King would be caught in Oxford and compelled to surrender. However, after providing for the defense of the city, Charles, with great skill, eluded both of the converging armies and reached Worcester. Waller maneuvered against the King, who gradually moved northwards, while Essex broke into the Royalist West. Then, turning east, the King inflicted a severe check on Waller at Cropredy Bridge, in Oxfordshire, on June 6, capturing all his artillery. Outmarching and outwitting Waller, he suddenly during August began to march westward, with the intention of taking Essex in the rear. Essex was outnumbered, his supplies were cut off, and after rejecting a proposal for surrender he sailed with his officers to Plymouth, ordered his cavalry to cut their way out of the trap, and left the rest of his army to its fate. All the infantry and artillery, to the number of eight thousand men, surrendered at Lostwithiel, in Cornwall, on September 2.

The main forces of the Parliament were now thrown against the King. Once again, on October 27, the armies met at Newbury and once again there was a drawn battle, followed by a Royalist retirement. It was late in November before active warfare paused. Charles re-entered Oxford in triumph. In the teeth of ad-

[299]

versity he had maintained himself with little money or supplies against odds of two or three to one.

Cromwell rode in from the Army to his duties as a Member of Parliament. He made a vehement and organized attack on the conduct of the war, and its mismanagement by lukewarm generals of noble rank, namely Essex and Manchester. While he urged the complete reconstitution of the Parliamentary army, his friends in the House of Commons proposed a so-called "Self-denying Ordinance," which would exclude Members of either House from military employment. The handful of lords who still remained at Westminster realized well enough that this was an attack on their prominence in the conduct of the war, if not on their social order. During the winter months the Army was reconstituted in accordance with Cromwell's ideas. The old personally raised regiments of the Parliamentary nobles were broken up and their officers and men incorporated in entirely new formations. These, the New Model, comprised eleven regiments of horse, each six hundred strong, twelve regiments of foot, twelve hundred strong, and a thousand dragoons, in all twenty-two thousand men. Compulsion was freely used to fill the ranks. Sir Thomas Fairfax was appointed Commander-in-Chief. Cromwell, as Member for Cambridge, was at first debarred from serving. However, it soon appeared that his Self-denying Ordinance applied only to his rivals. In June 1645 he was appointed General of the Horse, and was thus the only man who combined high military command with an outstanding Parliamentary position. From this moment he became the dominant figure in both spheres. Amid these stresses Archbishop Laud, who languished ailing in the Tower, was brought to the scaffold.

Largely to please the Scots, a parley for a peace settlement was set on foot at Uxbridge, near London, and on this many hopes were reposed, though not by the die-hards in Parliament. But neither King Charles nor the Roundhead executive had the slightest intention of giving way upon the two main points—Episcopacy and the control of the armed forces. At the same time the Marquis of Montrose sprang upon the scene. He wrote to Charles assuring him that he would bring all Scotland to his rescue if he could hold out. But a decisive battle impended in the South. On June 14, 1645, the last trial of strength was made. Charles, having taken Leicester, which was sacked, met Fairfax and Cromwell in the fine hunting country about Naseby. Rupert shattered the Parliamentary left, and though, as at Edgehill, his troopers were attracted by the Parliamentary baggage column, he returned to strike heavily at the central Roundhead infantry. But Cromwell on the other flank drove all before him, and also took control of the Roundhead reserves. The Royalist foot, beset on all sides by overwhelming numbers, were killed or captured. Naseby was the expiring effort of the Cavaliers in the open field. There still remained many sieges, with reliefs and maneuverings, but the final military decision of the Civil War had been given.

By the spring of 1646 all armed resistance to the Parliamentary army was beaten down. In the main the middle class, being more solid for Parliament, had beaten the aristocracy and gentry, who were divided. Montrose had been defeated in the autumn of 1645 at Philiphaugh, near the Border, by detachments from the regular Scottish army in England. Yet it was to the Scots government that Charles thought of turning. Kept at Newcastle in hard circumstances, he entered upon nearly a year's tenacious bargainings on the national issues at stake. The King naturally hoped to profit by the differences between Parliament and the Army and between the English and Scottish governments. He delayed so long that the Governments came to terms without him. In February 1647 the Scots, having been paid an installment of half the sum due to them for their services in England, handed over Charles under guarantee for his safety to Parliamentary Commissioners and returned to their own country. This transaction, though highly practical, wore and still wears a sorry look.

Now that the war was won most Members of Parliament and their leaders had no more need of the Army. But here a matter very awkward on such occasions obtruded itself. The pay of the Army was in arrear. In the first phase of the dispute Parliament assumed it had the power to give orders. Cromwell, as Member for Cambridge, assured them in the name of Almighty God that the Army would disband when ordered. The reply of the Army was to concentrate at Newmarket. The Presbyterians in Parliament looked to the Scots and the Army leaders looked to the King. Even after Marston Moor and Naseby the victorious Ironsides did not feel sure that anything counted without the royal authority. Here is the salient fact which distinguishes the English Revolution from all others: that those who wielded irresistible physical force were throughout convinced that it could give them no security. Nothing is more characteristic of the English people than their instinctive reverence even in rebellion for law and tradition.

Cromwell and Ireton felt that if they could get hold of the King physically, and before Parliament did so, it would be much. If they could gain him morally it would be all. Ireton was already secretly in touch with the King. Now in early June on his and Cromwell's orders

Cornet Joyce, with near four hundred Ironside troopers, rode to Holmby House, where the King, surrounded by his Household and attended by the Parliamentary Commissioners, was agreeably residing. In the morning Cornet Joyce intimated with due respect that he had come to remove the King. Charles made no protest. Off they all rode together, a jingling and not unhappy company, feeling they had English history in their hands. At this moment there was at finger-tips a settlement in the power of the English people and near to their hearts' desire. But of course it was too good to be true. Charles was never wholly sincere in his dealings with the Army leaders; he still pinned his hopes on help from the Scots. Parliament for their part rejected the military and royal proposals. Here were checks. But another came from the Army itself.

The soldiers were deep in the Old Testament. They particularly admired the conduct of Samuel when before the Lord he hewed to pieces Agag, delicately though he walked. The only chance for the arrangement between Charles and Cromwell was that it should be carried swiftly into effect. Instead there was delay. The mood of the soldiers became increasingly morose; and the generals saw themselves in danger of losing their control over them. On August 6, the Army marched on London, occupied Westminster, entered the City, and everything except their problems fell prostrate before them.

At Putney in the autumn of 1647 the Army held keen debate. The regiments had elected their delegates. These were called by them the "agents," or "agitators." Their ideas were soon abreast of those of the Chartists in the nineteenth century—manhood suffrage at twenty-one, equal electoral districts, biennial Parliaments, and much more in prospect. Cromwell heard all this and brooded over it. Clearly this was dangerous nonsense. He replaced the General Council of the Army by a General Council of his officers.

Late in this autumn of 1647 Cromwell and Ireton came to the conclusion that even with the pay and indemnity settled they could not unite King and Army. In November the King, convinced that he would be murdered by the soldiery, whom their officers could no longer restrain, rode off in the night, and by easy stages made his way to Carisbrooke Castle, in the Isle of Wight. There remained the Scots. With them he signed a secret Engagement by which Royalism and Presbyterianism were to be allied. From this conjunction there shortly sprang the Second Civil War. The King and his Prerogative were now seen, not as obstacles to Parliamentary right, but as the repository of ordinary English freedom. Prisoner at Carisbrooke, Charles was now more truly King than he had ever been in the palmiest days of the Personal Rule.

The story of the Second Civil War is short and simple. King, Lords and Commons, landlords and merchants, the City and the countryside, bishops and presbyters, the Scottish army, the Welsh people, and the English Fleet, all now turned against the New Model Army. The Army beat the lot. And at their head was Cromwell. By the end of 1648 all was over. Cromwell was Dictator.

Plainly the fruit of the victory that could most easily be gathered was the head of the King. The Army meant to have his blood in the manner which would most effectively vindicate their power and their faith. London lay locked under the guard and countersign of the Army. Some Parliamentary time-server had stood by Colonel Pride, when the Members sought to take their seats in the House of Commons, and had ticked off all those not likely to obey the Army's will. Forty-five Members who tried to enter were arrested, and out of a total of over five hundred three hundred did not take their seats again. This was "Pride's Purge." The great trial of "the Man of Blood" was to be presented to the nation and to the world. No English jurist could be found to frame the indictment or invent the tribunal. An Ordinance passed by the docile remnant of the Commons created a court of a hundred and thirty-five Commissioners, of whom barely sixty would serve, to try the King. The carpenters fitted Westminster Hall for its most memorable scene. The King, basing himself upon the law and Constitution he had strained and exploited in his years of prosperity, confronted his enemies with an unbreakable defense. He refused to acknowledge the tribunal. Cromwell and the Army could however cut off the King's head, and this at all costs they meant to do. On the morning of January 30, 1649, Charles was conducted from St. James's, whither he had been removed from his comfortable lodgings by the river, to Whitehall. At one o'clock in the afternoon Charles was informed that his hour had come. He walked through a window of the Banqueting House on to the scaffold. Masses of soldiers, many ranks deep, held an immense multitude afar. He resigned himself to death, and assisted the executioner in arranging his hair under a small white satin cap. He laid himself upon the block, and upon his own signal his head was struck off at a single stroke.

A strange destiny had engulfed this King of England. None had resisted with more untimely stubbornness the movement of his age. He was not a martyr in the sense of one who dies for a spiritual ideal. His own kingly interests were mingled at every stage with the larger issues. Some have sought to represent him as the champion of the small or humble man against the rising money-power. This is fanciful. He cannot be claimed as the defender of English liberties, nor wholly of the English Church, but none the less he died for them, and by his death preserved them not only to his son and heir, but to our own day.

CHAPTER SIX

The Restoration

The English Republic had come into existence even before the execution of the King. On February 5 it was declared that the House of Lords "is useless and dangerous and ought to be abolished." The country was now to be governed by a Council of State chosen annually by Parliament. The highly conservative elements at the head of the Army held firmly to the maintenance of the Common Law and the unbroken administration of justice in all non-political issues. Mutinies broke out. Many hundreds of veteran soldiers appeared in bands in support of "the sovereignty of the people," manhood suffrage, and annual Parliaments. This mood was not confined to the soldiers. Behind these broad principles the idea of equal rights in property as well as in citizenship was boldly announced by a group led by Gerard Winstanley, which came to be known as "the Diggers." It was essential to divide and disperse the Army, and Cromwell was willing to lead the larger part of it to a war of retribution in the name of the Lord Jehovah against the idolatrous and bloodstained Papists of Ireland.

The spirit and peril of the Irish race might have prompted them to unite upon Catholic toleration and monarchy, and on this they could have made a firm alliance with the Protestant Royalists, who, under the Marquess of Ormonde, had an organized army of twelve thousand men. Ormonde would have done better to have kept the open field with his regulars and allowed the severities of the Puritan invaders to rally the Irish nation behind him, but he had occupied the towns of Drogheda and Wexford and was resolved to defend them. He hoped that Cromwell would break his teeth upon a long siege of Drogheda, in which he placed a garrison of three thousand men, comprising the flower of the Irish Royalists, and English volunteers. Cromwell saw that the destruction of these men would not only ruin Ormonde's military power, but spread a helpful terror throughout the island. Having unsuccessfully summoned the garrison to surrender, he breached the ramparts with his cannon, and at the third assault, which he led himself, stormed the town. There followed a massacre so all-effacing as to startle even the opinion of those fierce times. A similar atrocity was perpetrated a few weeks later at the storm of Wexford. "I am persuaded," Cromwell wrote, "that this is a righteous judgment of God upon these barbarous wretches, who have imbrued their hands in so much innocent blood."[1]

In the safe and comfortable days of Queen Victoria, when Liberals and Conservatives, Gladstone and Disraeli, contended about the past, and when Irish Nationalists and Radical Nonconformists championed their old causes, a school grew up to gape in awe and some in furtive admiration at these savage crimes. The twentieth century has sharply recalled its intellectuals from such vain indulgences. We have seen the technique of "frightfulness" applied in our own time with Cromwellian brutality and upon a far larger scale. It is necessary to recur to the simpler principle that the wholesale slaughter of unarmed or dis-

[1] Thomas Carlyle, *Oliver Cromwell's Letters and Speeches* (1846), vol. ii, pp. 59–62.

armed men marks with a mordant and eternal brand the memory of conquerors, however they may have prospered. In Oliver's smoky soul there were evident misgivings. He writes of the "remorse and regret" which are inseparable from such crimes. The consequences of Cromwell's rule in Ireland have distressed and at times distracted English politics down even to the present day. They became for a time a potent obstacle to the harmony of the English-speaking peoples throughout the world.

At the moment when the axe severed the head of Charles the First from his body his eldest son became, in the opinion of most of his subjects and of Europe, King Charles the Second. Montrose, when his army fell to pieces, had on the advice of the late King quitted Scotland, believing at first that the Whitehall execution robbed his life of all purpose. His spirit was revived by a priest who preached to him a duty of revenge. With a handful of followers he landed in Caithness, was defeated by the Government forces and betrayed for a paltry bribe into their power. He was dragged through many Scottish towns, and hanged at Edinburgh on a specially high gallows amid an immense agitated concourse. Yet at the same time that Argyll and the Covenanters inflicted this savage punishment upon an unorthodox Royalist they themselves prepared for war with England in the cause of monarchy and entered into urgent treaty with the young King.

Charles II must bind himself to destroy the Episcopacy and enforce upon England a religious system odious to all who had fought for his father. He hesitated long before taking the grim decision of selling his soul to the Devil, as he conceived it, for the interest of the Crown and betraying the cause to save its life. Still there was again an army to fight for the Crown, and both Cardinal Mazarin in France and Prince William of Orange in Holland lent their aid to Scotland.

The menace in the North brought Cromwell back from Ireland. The armies maneuvered against each other. Cromwell was forced back upon Dunbar, dependent on wind and weather for his daily bread. The pious Scottish army descended from their blockading heights and closed down upon Cromwell and his Saints to prevent their embarkation. Both sides confidently appealed to Jehovah; and the Most High, finding so little to choose between them in faith and zeal, must have allowed purely military factors to prevail. Once the battle was joined among these politico-religious warriors the end was speedy. The Scots fled, leaving three thousand dead on the field. Nine thousand were prisoners in Oliver's hungry camp, and the Army of the Presbyters was broken. A Scottish army now invaded England in 1651 upon a Royalist rather than a Presbyterian enterprise. It is proof of Cromwell's political and military sagacity that he allowed them to pass. On his day of fate, September 3, sixteen thousand Scots were brought to battle at Worcester, not only by the twenty thousand veterans of the New Model, but by the English militia, who rallied in large numbers against this fresh inroad of the hated and interfering Scots. The struggle was one of the stiffest contests of the civil wars, but it was forlorn, and the Scots and their Royalist comrades were destroyed as a military force.

To Cromwell this was "the crowning mercy." To Charles II it afforded the most romantic adventure of his life. He escaped with difficulty from the stricken field. The land was scoured for him. He hid for a whole day in the famous oak tree at Boscobel, while his pursuers passed by. On every side were men who would have rejoiced to win the price of catching him. But also on every side were friends, if they could be found, secret, silent, unflinching. Nearly fifty persons recognized him, and thus became privy to his escape and liable to grave penalties. The magic of the words "the King, our master," cast its spell upon all classes. "The King of England, my master, your master, and the master of all good Englishmen, is near you and in great distress: can you help us to a boat?" "Is he well? Is he safe?" "Yes." "God be blessed." This was the temper of all who were trusted with or discovered the secret. Thus after six weeks of desperate peril did the King find himself again in exile. This was the end of the Civil War or Great Rebellion. The three kingdoms were united under a government in London which wielded autocratic power.

The monarchy had gone; the Lords had gone; the Church of England was prostrate; of the Commons there remained nothing but the few survivors contemptuously named the Rump. It was a nationalistic Rump, at once protectionist and bellicose. While Cromwell was fighting in Ireland and Scotland these Puritan grandees through their chosen Council of State ruled with efficiency. When he returned victorious he was struck by their unpopularity. The Lord General's outlook was clear and his language plain. "These men," Oliver had said, "will never leave till the Army pull them down by the ears." He called in his musketeers to clear the House and lock the doors. While the indignant politicians, most of whom were men of force and fire, were being hustled into the street the General's eye fell on the Mace, symbol of the Speaker's authority. "What shall we do with this bauble?" he asked. "Take it away!" Here sank for the moment all the constitutional safeguards

and processes built and treasured across the centuries, from Simon de Montfort to the Petition of Right.

Cromwell's successes and failures in foreign policy bore consequences throughout the reign of Charles II. In 1654 he ended the sea war against the Dutch which had begun two years earlier. In spite of grave arguments to the contrary urged by the Council, he sent a naval expedition to the West Indies in September 1654 and Jamaica was occupied. This act of aggression led slowly but inevitably to war between England and Spain, and a consequent alliance between England and France.

Cromwell sought the right kind of Parliament to limit his own dictatorship without crossing his will, and he boxed the compass in his search. He had expelled the Rump in the cause of an overdue popular election. He replaced it not by an elected but by a handpicked body of Puritan notables, who became known to history as "Barebone's Parliament," after one of their members, Praise-God Barebone. The political behavior of the Saints was a sad disappointment to their convoker. With breath-taking speed they proceeded to sweep the board clear of encumbrances in order to create a new Heaven and earth. With a temerity justified only by spiritual promptings, they reformed taxation in a manner which seemed to weaken the security for the soldiers' pay. The Army leaders, wishing to avoid the scandal of another forcible ejection, persuaded or compelled the more moderate Saints to get up very early one morning before the others were awake and pass a resolution yielding back their power to the Lord General from whom it had come.

Ireton had died in Ireland, but Lambert and other Army leaders of various ranks drew up an "Instrument of Government," which was in fact the first and last written English Constitution. The executive office of Lord Protector conferred upon Cromwell was checked and balanced by a Council of State, nominated for life, consisting of seven Army leaders and eight civilians. A single Chamber was also set up, elected upon a new property qualification in the country. It was probably not a narrower franchise, but all those who had fought against Parliament were disqualified from voting. Cromwell gratefully accepted the Instrument and assumed the title of Lord Protector. But once again all went wrong with the Parliament. It no sooner met in September 1654 than it was seen to contain a fierce and lively Republican group, which, without the slighest gratitude to the Army leaders or to the Protector for their apparent deference to Republican ideas, set themselves to tear the new Constitution to pieces. At the earliest moment allowed by the Instrument Cromwell dissolved the Commons.

Military dictatorship supervened, naked if not wholly unashamed. Cromwell now proceeded to divide England and Wales into eleven districts, over each of which a Major-General was placed, with the command of a troop of horse and a reorganized militia. The Major-Generals assured him of their ability to pack a compliant House. But Levelers, Republicans, and Royalists were able to exploit the discontent against the military dictatorship, and a large number of Members who were known enemies of the Protector were returned. It was at this stage that a group of lawyers and gentry decided to offer Cromwell the Crown. The "Humble Petition and Advice" in 1657 which embodied the proposed Constitution provided not only for the restoration of kingship, but also for the firm re-establishment of Parliament, including a nominated Upper House and a substantial reduction in the powers of the Council of State. But the Army leaders and still more the soldiers showed at once their inveterate hostility to the trappings of monarchy, and Cromwell had to content himself with the right to nominate his successor to the Protectoral throne. In May 1657 he accepted the main provisions of the new Constitution without the title of King. Cromwell, in the exaggerated belief that a hostile design was on foot against him, suddenly, in January 1658, dissolved the most friendly Parliament which he had ever had. He ended his speech of dissolution with the words, "Let God judge between you and me." "Amen," answered the unrepentant Republicans.

The maintenance of all privilege and authority in their own hands at home and a policy of aggression and conquest abroad absorbed the main energies of Cromwell and his Council. They were singularly barren in social legislation. The English Puritans, like their brethren in Massachusetts, concerned themselves actively with the repression of vice. The feast days of the Church, regarded as superstitious indulgences, were replaced by a monthly fast day. Christmas excited the most fervent hostility of these fanatics. Parliament was deeply concerned at the liberty which it gave to carnal and sensual delights. Soldiers were sent round London on Christmas Day before dinnertime to enter private houses without warrants and seize meat cooking in all kitchens and ovens. Everywhere was prying and spying. To the mass of the nation the rule of Cromwell manifested itself in the form of numberless and miserable petty tyrannies, and thus became hated as no government has ever been hated in England before or since. For the first time the English people felt themselves governed from a center in the control of which they had no say.

The repulsive features fade from the picture and are replaced by color and even charm as the summit of power is reached. We see the Lord Protector in his glory, the champion of Protestantism, the arbiter of Europe, the patron of learning and the arts. We feel the dignity of his bearing to all men, and his tenderness toward young people. We feel his passion for England, as fervent as Chatham's and in some ways more intimate and emotional. Cromwell, although crafty and ruthless as occasion claimed, was at all times a reluctant and apologetic dictator. Liberty of conscience as conceived by Cromwell did not extend to the public profession of Roman Catholicism, Prelacy, or Quakerism. Believing the Jews to be a useful element in the civil community, he opened again to them the gates of England, which Edward I had closed nearly four hundred years before. There was in practice comparatively little persecution on purely religious grounds, and even Roman Catholics were not seriously molested. Religious toleration challenged all the beliefs of Cromwell's day and found its best friend in the Lord Protector himself.

On September 3, 1658, the anniversary of the Battles of Dunbar and Worcester and of the siege of Drogheda, in the crash and howling of a mighty storm, death came to the Lord Protector. If in a tremendous crisis Cromwell's sword had saved the cause of Parliament, he must stand before history as a representative of dictatorship and military rule who, with all his qualities as a soldier and a statesman, is in lasting discord with the genius of the English race.

In his last hours Cromwell had in terms "very dark and imperfect" nominated his eldest son, Richard, to succeed him. He was at first accepted by the Army and duly installed in his father's seat; but when he attempted to exercise authority he found he had but the form. Within four months of succeeding to his august office Richard Cromwell found himself deserted even by his personal guard. The Army was master, with Fleetwood and Lambert rivals at its head. Even in this hour of bloodless and absolute triumph the soldiery felt the need of some civil sanction for their acts. Thus was the Rump of the Long Parliament exhumed and exhibited to a bewildered land. In the summer of 1659 Cavaliers, strangely consorting with Presbyterian allies, appeared in arms in several counties. The revolt was so swiftly crushed that Charles II, fortunately for himself, had no chance of putting himself at its head. At this moment Lambert became the most prominent figure. He seems to have believed that he could satisfy the Army, both in politics and religion, better under a restored monarchy than under either the Rump or a Protectorate. His course was secret, tortuous, and full of danger. At Christmas the Army resolved to be reconciled with Parliament. But obviously this could not last. Someone must set in train the movement which would produce in England a government which stood for something old or new.

The Cromwellian commander in Scotland, though very different in temperament from Lambert, was also a man of mark. He ranged himself from the first against the violence of the Army in London. Monk was one of those Englishmen who understand to perfection the use of time and circumstance. It is a type which has thriven in our Island. The General received the emissaries of every interest and party in his camp. He listened patiently, as every great Englishman should, to all they had to urge, and with that simple honesty of character on which we flatter ourselves as a race he kept them all guessing for a long time what he would do. Informed of events in London, he crossed the Tweed from Coldstream on the cold, clear New Year's Day of 1660. At York he received what he had long hoped for, the invitation of the House of Commons, the desperate Rump, to come to London. He marched south through towns and counties in which there was but one cry—"A free Parliament!" When Monk and his troops reached London he was soon angered by the peremptory orders given him by the Rump. Unlike Cromwell and Lambert, Monk decided to tame the Rump by diluting, not by dissolving, it. In February he recalled the Members who had been excluded by Pride's Purge. They declared Monk Commander-in-Chief of all the forces. The Rump of the Long Parliament was dissolved by its own consent. Monk was satisfied that a free Parliament should be summoned, and that such a Parliament would certainly recall Charles II.

The King might "enjoy his own again," but not all the Cavaliers. There must be a full recognition that men should keep what they had got or still had left. There must be no reprisals. Monk's advice was accepted by Charles's faithful Chancellor, Hyde, who had shared his master's exile and was soon to be rewarded with the Earldom of Clarendon. The Lords and Commons were restored. It remained only to complete the three Estates of the Realm by the recall of the King. The Fleet, once so hostile, was sent to conduct him to his native shores. Immense crowds awaited him at Dover. There on May 25, 1660, General Monk received him with profound reverence as he landed. The journey to London was triumphal.

The wheel had not however swung a full circle, as many might have thought. Indeed, it was the greatest hour in Parliamentary history. All the laws of the Long Parliament since Charles I quitted London at the beginning of 1642, all the statutes of the Commonwealth or of the Protectorate, now fell to the ground. But there remained the potent limitations of the Prerogative to which Charles I had

agreed. The King relinquished his feudal dues from wardships, knight service, and other medieval survivals. Parliament granted him instead revenues for life which, with his hereditary property, were calculated to yield about £1,200,000. For all extraordinary expenditure the King was dependent upon Parliament, and both he and Clarendon accepted this. The Crown was not to be free of Parliament. The Cavaliers were mortified that the vindication of their cause brought them no relief from the mulctings of which they had been the victims. Everyone however, except the soldiers, was agreed about getting rid of the Army; and that this could be done, and done without bloodshed, seemed a miracle. The Ironside soldiers were abashed by public opinion. They were paid their dues. They returned to their homes and their former callings, and within a few months this omnipotent, invincible machine, which might at any moment have devoured the whole realm and society of Britain, vanished in the civil population, leaving scarcely a trace behind.

In all, through Charles's exertions, and at some expense to his popularity, less than a dozen persons were put to death in this intense Counter-Revolution. Leading figures of the Parliamentary party, peers and commoners, high officers under the Republic or Cromwell, made ready shift to sit upon the tribunals which slaughtered the regicides; and it is upon these that history may justly cast whatever odium belongs to these melancholy but limited reprisals.

The Parliament which recalled the King was a balanced assembly, and represented both sides of the nation. The House could not claim to be a Parliament, but only a Convention. At the end of 1660 it was thought necessary to dissolve it. The longest Parliament in English history now began. It lasted eighteen years. It has been called the Cavalier Parliament—or, more significantly, the Pension Parliament. From the moment when it first met it showed itself more Royalist in theory than in practice. It did not mean to part with any of the Parliamentary rights which had been gained in the struggle. It was ready to make provision for the defense of the country by means of militia; but the militia must be controlled by the Lord-Lieutenants of the counties. The repository of force had now become the county families and gentry.

Since Clarendon as Lord Chancellor was the chief Minister, and preponderant in the government, his name is identified with the group of Acts which re-established the Anglican Church and drove the Protestant sects into enduring opposition. In so doing it consolidated Nonconformity as a political force with clear objectives: first, toleration, which was secured at the Revolution of 1688; and thereafter the abolition of the privileged status of the Church. The Clarendon Code of 1662 went some way beyond the ideas of Clarendon himself. Neither did Charles will this great separation. He walked by the easy path of indifference to the uplands of toleration. The Cavalier Parliament sternly corrected this deplorable laxity. The Code embodied the triumph of those who had been beaten in the field and who had played little part in the Restoration. Its echoes divide the present-day religious life of England. It potently assisted the foundation of parties. Thus from the Restoration there emerged no national settlement, but rather two Englands, each with its different background, interests, culture, and outlook. As Macaulay wrote, and later writers have confirmed his view, "there was a great line which separated the official men and their friends and dependants, who were sometimes called the Court party, from those who were sometimes honored with the appellation of the Country party." We enter the era of conflict between broad party groups which shaped the destinies of the British Empire till all was melted in the fires of the Great War of 1914.

For these far-reaching fissures Charles II had no responsibility. Throughout his reign he consistently strove for toleration. But Charles II had need of an Act of Indulgence for himself. Court life was one unceasing flagrant and brazen scandal. The King's example spread its demoralization far and wide, and the sense of relief from the tyranny of the Puritans spurred forward every amorous adventure. Nature, affronted, reclaimed her rights with usury. The people of England did not wish to be the people of God in the sense of the Puritan God. They descended with thankfulness from the superhuman levels to which they had been painfully hoisted.

Two personalities of force and capacity, vividly contrasted in character, Clarendon and Ashley, afterwards Earl of Shaftesbury, swayed the Privy Council. Shaftesbury was the most powerful representative of the vanished domination. Throughout the reign he stood by the City of London, and the City stood by him. For the first seven years of the reign Clarendon continued First Minister. This wise, venerable statesman wrestled stoutly with the licentiousness of the King and Court, with the intrigues of the royal mistresses, with the inadequacy of the revenue, and with the intolerance of the House of Commons. The Chief Minister was now father-in-law to the King's brother. His grandchildren might succeed to the throne.

The acquisition of Tangier as part of the dowry of Catherine of Braganza turned the eyes of the Government to Mediterranean and Oriental trade. Cromwell's capture of Dunkirk imposed upon the royal Exchequer an annual cost of no less than £120,000 a year, or one-tenth of the normal revenue. The Tory policy already looked to "trade and plantations" in the outer seas rather than to action in Europe. Charles, on Clarendon's advice, sold Dunkirk to the French for £400,000. The rivalry of England and Holland upon the seas in fishery and in trade had become intense, and the strength of the Dutch had revived since Cromwell's war. The King was roused to patriotic ardor, the Duke of York thirsted for naval glory. The great sum of over two and a half millions was voted. More than a hundred new ships were built, armed with new and heavier cannon. Former Cavalier and Cromwellian officers joined hands and received commissions from the King. Rupert and Monk commanded divisions of the Fleet. War at sea began off the West African coast in 1664, and spread to home waters in the following year. In June the English fleet of more than one hundred and fifty ships, manned by twenty-five thousand men and mounting five thousand guns, met the Dutch in equal strength off Lowestoft, and a long, fierce battle was fought, in which many of the leaders on both sides perished. The English artillery was markedly superior in weight and skill, and the Dutch withdrew worsted though undismayed. The return of Admiral De Ruyter from the West Indies restored the fortunes of the Republic. An even greater battle than Lowestoft was fought in June 1666. For four days the English and Dutch fleets battled off the North Foreland. At the close of the second day's cannonading the English were outmatched; then Rupert, arriving on the third day, restored the balance. But the fourth day was adverse, and Monk and Rupert, with heavy losses, retired into the Thames. De Ruyter had triumphed.

Both sides bent beneath the financial strain. But other calamities drained the strength of the Island. From the spring of 1665 the Great Plague had raged in London. Never since the Black Death in 1348 had pestilence spread such ravages. In London at the climax about seven thousand people died in a single week. The worst of the plague was over when in September 1666 the Great Fire engulfed the tormented capital. It broke out near London Bridge, in a narrow street of wooden houses, and, driven by a strong east wind, the flames spread with resistless fury for four whole days. When the fire was at length stopped outside the City walls by blowing up whole streets more than thirteen thousand dwelling-houses, eighty-nine churches, and St. Paul's Cathedral had been devoured.

Want of money prevented the English battle fleet from keeping the sea, and while the negotiations lingered the Dutch, to spur them, sailed up the Medway under Admiral De Witt, brother of the famous John, Grand Pensionary of Holland, broke the boom which guarded Chatham harbor, burn four ships of the line, and towed away the battleship *Royal Charles,* which had destroyed Admiral Opdam in the Battle of Lowestoft. Peace, of which both sides had equal need, was made on indifferent terms. England's chief gain in the war was New Amsterdam, now renamed New York.

Clarendon, expostulating with all sides, was assailed by all. An impeachment was launched against him, and he went into exile, there to complete his noble *History of the Rebellion,* which casts its broad and lasting illumination on the times through which he lived. The growing discontents of the Cavalier Parliament at the morals and expense of the Court made it necessary to broaden the basis of the government, and from 1668 five principal personages began to be recognized as the responsible Ministers. There had been much talk of Cabinets and Cabals; and now, by chance, the initials of these five men, Clifford, Arlington, Buckingham, Ashley, and Lauderdale, actually spelled the word "CABAL."

The dominant fact on the continent of Europe, never realized by Cromwell, was the rise of France at the expense of Spain and Austria. Charles and the Cabal, aided by their envoy Sir William Temple at The Hague, concluded a triple alliance with Holland and Sweden against France. The Protestant combination was hailed with delight by the whole counrty. This, the first of the long series of coalitions against France, checked Louis XIV for a while. He addressed himself to England and in 1670 began secret negotiations with Charles II. Above all things Charles needed money. He pointed out to Louis that Parliament would give him ample funds to oppose France; how much would Louis pay him not to do so? Here was the basis of the shameful Treaty of Dover. Besides the clauses which were eventually made public, there was a secret clause upon which Arlington and Clifford were Charles's only confidants. "The King of Great Britain being convinced of the truth of the Catholic Faith is determined to declare himself a Catholic . . . as soon as the welfare of his realm will permit." The King was also to receive a subvention of £166,000 a year.

The Treaty of Dover contemplated a third Dutch War, in which France and England would combine when Louis XIV felt the moment opportune. In March 1672 Louis claimed fulfillment of the pact. War began. In a great battle at Sole Bay on May 28, 1672, De Ruyter surprised the English and French, who were ten ships stronger, as they lay at anchor. Grievous and cruel was the long battle. The Suffolk shores were crowded with frantic spectators, and the cannonade was heard many miles away. The French squadron put out to sea, but the wind prevented them from engaging. The Duke of York's flagship, the *Prince,* was beset on every side. Upon her decks stood the First Company of the Guards, in which Ensign Churchill was serving. She became such a wreck that the Duke, who fought with his usual courage, was forced to shift his flag to the *St. Michael,* and, when this ship was in turn disabled, to the *London.* Nevertheless, the Dutch drew off with very heavy losses of their own.

On land Louis struck with terrible force at the hard-pressed Republic. The Dutch people, faced with extermination, turned in their peril to William of Orange. The great-grandson of William the Silent, now Captain-General, did not fail them. He uttered the famous defiance, "We can die in the last ditch." The sluices in the dykes were opened; the bitter waters rolled in a deluge over the fertile land, and Holland was saved.

Resentment of the Dutch affronts at sea and jealousy of their trade were overridden by fear and hatred of Papist France and her ever-growing dominance in Europe. The secret article in the Dover Treaty had only to be known to create a political explosion of measureless violence. Shaftesbury, though not privy to it, must have had his suspicions. Early in 1673 Arlington seems to have confessed the facts to him. With dexterity and promptitude Shaftesbury withdrew himself from the Government, and became the leader of an Opposition which was ultimately as violent as that of Pym. A bill was forced upon the King for a Test. No man could hold office or a King's commission afloat or ashore who would not solemnly declare his disbelief in the doctrine of Transubstantiation. This purge destroyed the Cabal. All eyes were now fixed upon James, Duke of York, a convert to Rome. Very soon it was known that the heir to the throne had laid down his post of Lord High Admiral rather than submit to the Test. The strength of the forces now moving against the King and his policy rose from the virtual unanimity which prevailed between the Anglicans and the Dissenters, between the swords which had followed Rupert and the swords which had followed Cromwell. They were all on the same side now, and at their head was the second great Parliamentary tactician of the century, Shaftesbury.

Sir Thomas Osborne, a Yorkshire landowner, had gathered great influence in the Commons, and was to a large extent forced upon the King for his own salvation. He was very soon raised to the peerage as Earl of Danby, and began an administration which was based on a party organization possessing a small but effective majority in the House of Commons. Economy, Anglicanism, and independence from France were the principal ideals of this party. In foreign affairs the new Minister publicly differed from his master. The height of his precarious popularity was reached when he contrived a marriage between Mary, the Duke of York's daughter by his first wife, and the now famous Protestant hero, William of Orange.

It was at this moment that Louis XIV, dissatisfied with his English investments and indignant at a marriage which threatened to carry England into the Dutch system and was a strong assertion of Protestant interests, resolved to ruin Danby. He revealed to the Opposition, most of whom took his bribes while opposing his interests, that the English Minister had been asking for French money. A renegade priest of disreputable character, Dr. Titus Oates, presented himself as the Protestant champion. He accused the Duchess of York's private secretary, Coleman, of a conspiracy to murder the King, bring about a French invasion, and cause a general massacre of Protestants. Coleman was examined in October 1668 before a magistrate, Sir Edmund Berry Godfrey, and while the case was proceeding Godfrey was found dead one night at the foot of Greenberry Hill, now Primrose Hill. This cumulative sensation drove English society into madness. Oates rose in a few months to be a popular hero; and being as wicked as any man who ever lived, he exploited his advantage to the full. Charles, wishing to stay the capital proceedings instituted against his Minister, partly unjustly, and anyhow for actions which Danby had taken only to please the King, at length, in December 1678, dissolved the Cavalier Parliament.

As happened after the Short Parliament of Charles I, all the prominent opponents of the King were returned. The situation was not unlike that of 1640; but with one decisive difference. Both the King and the country had gone through an experience which neither wished to repeat. Charles II yielded to the wish of the nation; he bowed to the hostile Parliament. Danby, threatened by attainder, was glad to be forgotten for five years in the Tower. He had still a part to play. The brunt fell upon James, Duke of York. The King had already asked him not to attend the Privy Council, and now advised him to leave the country. Charles, thus relieved at home, faced the fury of the anti-Popish hurricane. The last five years of his reign are those most honorable to his memory. His mortal duel with Shaftesbury was a stirring episode. The struggle centered upon the Exclusion Bill. To keep the Papist heir from the throne was the main object of the majority of the nation. Shaftesbury looked to William of Orange; but he also looked, with more favor, upon the Duke of Monmouth, Charles's illegitimate son by Lucy Walters. Nothing would induce the King to betray the succession. He labored to present a compromise. But in the prevailing temper no one would believe that any restrictions could be imposed upon a Popish King. The Exclusion Bill passed its second reading by an overwhelming vote, and the King descended upon the Parliament with another dissolution. Nevertheless this short-lived legislature left behind it a monument. It passed a Habeas Corpus Act which confirmed and strengthened the freedom of the individual against arbitrary arrest by the executive government. The descent into despotism which has engulfed so many leading nations in the present age has made the virtue of this enactment, sprung from English political genius, apparent even to the most thoughtless, the most ignorant, the most base.

As soon as the King saw that the election gave him no relief he prorogued the meeting of the resulting Parliament for almost another year. And it is in this interval that we first discern the use of those names Whig and Tory which were to divide the British Island for nearly two hundred years. The term "Whig" had described a sour, bigoted, canting, money-grubbing Scots Presbyterian. Irish Papist bandits ravaging estates and manor-houses had been called "Tories." One can see from these expressions of scorn and hatred how narrowly England escaped another cruel purging of the sword.

Charles was now in full breach with Louis XIV, who scattered his bribes widely among the Opposition. A glorified Privy Council assembled. Shaftesbury, the leader of the Opposition, was appointed its President by the King. When Parliament met in October 1680 Shaftesbury again championed the Exclusion Bill, and at this moment he reached his zenith. The Exclusion Bill was carried through the Commons, and the struggle was fought out in the Lords. That it ended bloodlessly was largely due to the statesman who had rendered the word "Trimmer" illustrious. George Savile, Marquis of Halifax, was the opponent alike of Popery and of France. He was one of those rare beings in whom cool moderation and width of judgment are combined with resolute action. Halifax, who had been so hot against Danby, broke the Exclusion Bill in the House of Lords. In the immortal pen-pictures which Dryden has drawn of the personalities of these turbulent days none is more pleasing than that of Jotham, who

> only tried
> The worse awhile, then chose the
> better side,
> Nor chose alone, but changed the balance too.
> So much the weight of one brave man
> can do.

The fury against the Popish Plot was gradually slaked in the blood of its victims. Charles saw in this new temper the chance of a more favorable Parliament. Halifax, fresh from rendering him the highest service, opposed the dissolution. But for the third time in three years there was an electoral trial of strength. Again there was no decisive change in the character of the majority returned. Presently it was learned that Parliament was to meet in Oxford, where the King could not be bullied by the City of London and Shaftesbury's gangs of apprentices called "White Boys." He had caused Lawrence Hyde, Clarendon's son, the Duke of York's brother-in-law, a competent financier, to examine precisely the state of the normal revenue granted to the Crown for life. Hyde was next employed in negotiating with Louis XIV, and eventually £100,000 a year was obtained upon the understanding that England would not act contrary to French ambitions on the Continent. With this aid it was thought the King could manage independently of the ferocious Parliament. A private Member of importance unfolded to the House the kind of plan for a Protestant Protectorate during James's reign which the King had in mind. James, when he succeeded, should be King only in name. The kingdom would be governed by a Protector and the Privy Council. The administration should rest in Protestant hands. But Oxford was a camp in which two armed factions jostled one another. At any moment there might be an outbreak. The Commons passed a resolution for excluding the Duke of York. On the Monday following Black Rod knocked at the door and summoned them to the Peers. Most Members thought that this portended some compliance by the King with their wishes. They were surprised to see him robed, upon his throne, and astounded when the Lord Chancellor declared in his name that Parliament was again dissolved. Shaftesbury made a bid to convert the elements of the vanished Parliament into a revolutionary Convention. But the dose of the Civil War still worked in the Englishmen of 1681. Charles had hazarded rightly.

Within two months the King felt strong enough to indict Shaftesbury for fomenting rebellion. The Middlesex Grand Jury, faithful to his cause, wrote "Ignoramus" across the bill presented against him. This meant that they found the evidence insufficient. He was liberated according to law. He counseled insurrection; and it seemed that a royal murder would be one of its preliminaries. Shaftesbury at this point fled to Holland, hoping perhaps for Dutch support, and died at The Hague in a few weeks. He cannot be ranked with the chief architects of the Parliamentary system. He sought above all the triumph of his party and his tenets. His life's work left no inheritance for England. He was as for-

midable as Pym, but his fame sinks to a different level.

The absorbing question now was whether there would be civil war. Fifty zealous Ironsides could easily overpower the small traveling escort of the King and the Duke of York on their return from their pastime of horse-racing. Above this dark design, and unwitting of it, was a general conspiracy for armed action. The lucky accident of a fire in Newmarket, by which much of the town was destroyed, led Charles and James to return some days before the expected date. They passed the Rye House in safety, and a few weeks later the secret of the plot was betrayed. When the news spread through the land it caught the Royalist reaction upon its strong upturn. Two famous men were engulfed. Neither William, Lord Russell, nor Algernon Sidney had sought the King's life; but Russell had been privy to preparations for revolt, and Sidney had been found with an unpublished paper, scholarly in character, justifying resistance to the royal authority. After public trial both went to the scaffold. Martyrs for religion there had been in plenty. But here were the first martyrs for the sake of Party.

The power of Charles at home remained henceforth unchallenged. By pressure and manipulation Tory sheriffs were elected in London, and henceforth through that agency City juries could be trusted to deal severely with Whig delinquents. The Whig corporations were asked by writs of *Quo Warranto* to prove their title to their long-used liberties. Under these pressures large numbers of hitherto hostile corporations threw themselves on the mercy of the Crown and begged for new charters in accordance with the royal pleasure. Talk of excluding James from the throne died away. He resumed his functions. The King was only fifty-six, and in appearance lively and robust, but his exorbitant pleasures had undermined his constitution. Halifax, now more than ever trusted, still urged him to the adventure of a new Parliament, and Charles might have consented, when suddenly in February 1685 an apoplectic stroke laid him low. With that air of superiority to death for which all mortals should be grateful he apologized for being "so unconscionable a time in dying." James was at hand to save his soul. Apart from hereditary monarchy, there was not much in which Charles believed in this world or another. He wanted to be King, as was his right, and have a pleasant life. He was cynical rather than cruel, and indifferent rather than tolerant. His care for the Royal Navy is his chief claim upon the gratitude of his countrymen.

Eighty years of fearful events and the sharpest ups and downs of fortune had brought the monarchy, in appearance and for the practical purposes of the moment, to almost Tudor absolutism. For the last two years of his brother's reign James had played a leading part in the realm. All he thought he needed to make him a real king, on the model now established in Europe by Louis XIV, was a loyal Fleet and a standing Army, well trained and equipped. Behind this there swelled in the King's breast the hope that he might reconcile all his people to the old faith and heal the schism which had rent Christendom for so many generations. He was resolved that there should at least be toleration among all English Christians. It is one of the disputes of history whether toleration was all he sought. James ascended the throne with all the ease of Richard Cromwell. He tried to dispel the belief that he was vindictive or inclined to arbitrary rule. The electors returned a House of Commons loyal and friendly to the new King. They voted him a revenue for life which,

with the growth of trade, amounted to nearly £2,000,000 a year.

It was at this moment, on June 11, 1685, that Monmouth landed. He entered the harbor of Lyme Regis, not far from Portland Bill. He was at once welcomed by the populace. He issued a proclamation asserting the validity of his mother's marriage and denouncing James as a usurper who had murdered Charles II. All the ruling forces rallied round the Crown. One last chance remained—a sudden night attack upon the royal army. Feversham was surprised in his camp at Sedgemoor; but an unforeseen deep ditch, called the Bussex Rhine, prevented a hand-to-hand struggle. Lord Churchill, James's long-trusted officer and agent, vigilant and active, took control. The West Country peasantry and miners, though assailed by sixteen pieces of artillery and charged in flank and rear by the Household troops, fought with Ironside tenacity. They were slaughtered where they stood, and a merciless pursuit, with wholesale executions, ended their forlorn endeavor. Monmouth escaped the field only to be hunted down a few days later. He could claim no mercy, and none did he receive.

Chief Justice Jeffreys was sent into the West to deal with the large number of prisoners. This cruel, able, unscrupulous judge made his name forever odious by "the Bloody Assize." Between two and three hundred persons were hanged, and about eight hundred transported to Barbados, where their descendants still survive.

James was now at the height of his power. As soon as Jeffreys's "campaign," as James called it, was ended he proposed to his Council the repeal of the Test Act and the Habeas Corpus Act. Halifax was removed, not only from the Presidency of the Council, but from the Privy Council altogether; and when North died soon after, Chief Justice

Jeffreys, red-handed from "the Bloody Assize," was made Lord Chancellor in his stead. Robert Spencer, Earl of Sunderland, later in the year became Lord President in the place of Halifax, as well as Secretary of State, and was henceforth James's Chief Minister. Parliament met for its second session on November 9, and the King laid his immediate purpose before it. A strong standing Army was indispensable to the peace and order of the realm. He also made it plain that he would not dismiss his Catholic officers on the morrow of their faithful services. These two demands shook the friendly Parliament to its foundations. Its most hideous nightmare was a standing Army, its dearest treasure the Established Church.

During the whole of 1686 and 1687 James held Parliament in abeyance, and used his dispensing power to introduce Roman Catholics into key positions. The Church, the bulwark of legitimacy, the champion of non-resistance, seethed with suppressed alarms, and only the powerful influence of Lawrence Hyde, now Earl of Rochester, upon the bishops and clergy prevented a vehement outburst. It was plain that the King, with all the downright resolution of his nature, was actively and of set purpose subverting the faith and Constitution of the land. He now embarked upon a political maneuver at once audacious, crafty, and miscalculated. If Whigs and Tories were combined he would match them by a coalition of Papists and Nonconformists under the armed power of the Crown. In January 1687 came the fall of the Hydes. Clarendon, the elder brother, in Ireland, had been overawed by James's faithful follower, the Roman Catholic Earl of Tyrconnel; Rochester, in Whitehall, was subdued by Sunderland. With the dismissal of Rochester began the revolutionary conspiracy. Meanwhile, James was raising and preparing his Army.

Every summer a great camp was formed at Hounslow to impress the Londoners. In August 1686 this contained about ten thousand men. A year later Feversham could assemble fifteen thousand men and twenty-eight guns.

The provocations of the royal policy continued. The first Declaration of Indulgence was issued. It did precisely what James's Parliament had objected to in advance: it set aside statutory Act by Royal Prerogative. Meanwhile, an attempt to force a Catholic President upon Magdalen College, Oxford, and the expulsion of the Fellows for their resistance, added to the stir. In July James planned the public reception of the Papal Nuncio, d'Adda. The King had, in modern parlance, set up his political platform. The second step was to create a party machine, and the third to secure by its agency a Parliament with a mandate for the repeal of the Tests. The narrow franchise could be manipulated in the country to a very large extent by the Lord-Lieutenants and by the magistrates, and in the towns and cities by the corporations. Upon these therefore the royal energies were now directed. The process of setting Papists and Dissenters over or in place of Anglicans and Cavaliers ruptured and recast the whole social structure of English life as established at the Restoration. The rich and powerful, in resisting the Crown, felt themselves upborne by the feelings of the voteless masses.

In England during the autumn of 1688 everything pointed, as in 1642, to the outbreak of civil war. At the end of April James had issued a second Declaration of Indulgence. On May 18 seven bishops, headed by the Primate, the venerable William Sancroft, protested against this use of the dispensing power. James, furious at disobedience, and apparently scandalized at this departure, by the

Church he was seeking to undermine, from its doctrine of non-resistance, demanded that the bishops should be put on trial for seditious libel. As they stepped on board the barge for the Tower they were hailed by immense crowds with greetings in which reverence and political sympathy were combined. The same scenes were repeated when they were brought back to Westminster Hall on June 15, and at their trial on June 29. When on the following day the bishops were declared "Not Guilty" the verdict was acclaimed with universal joy. But the attitude of the Army was more important. The King had visited them at Hounslow, and as he departed heard loud cheering. "What is that clamor?" he asked. "Sire, it is nothing; the soldiers are glad that the bishops are acquitted." "Do you call that nothing?" said James. On the same night, while cannon and tumults proclaimed the public joy, the seven leaders of the party of action met at Shrewsbury's town-house, and there and then dispatched their famous letter to William of Orange. The signatories were Shrewsbury, Danby, Russell, Bishop Compton, Devonshire, Henry Sidney, and Lumley. But on June 10, while the trial of the bishops was still pending, the Queen had given birth to a son. The legend that a child had been smuggled into St. James's Palace in a warming-pan was afoot even before the ashes of the official bonfires had been cleared from the streets. Up to this moment there always lived the hope that the stresses which racked the nation would die with the King. Now William, stricken in his ambition by the birth of a male Stuart heir, exclaimed, "Now or never!" and began to prepare his expedition.

Louis XIV kept all in suspense till the last moment. Had James been willing to commit himself finally to a French alliance Louis would have invaded Holland. But James had patriotic pride as well as religious bigotry. To the last he wavered so that in Holland they thought he was allied to France, and in France to Holland. Louis therefore decided that the best he could hope for would be an England impotent through civil war. At the end of September he turned his armies towards the Middle Rhine, and from that moment William was free to set forth.

As the autumn weeks slipped by excitement and tension grew throughout the Island, and the vast conspiracy which now comprised the main strength of the nation heaved beneath the strain of affairs. Everyone watched the weathercock. All turned on the wind. Rumor ran riot. The Irish were coming. The French were coming. The Papists were planning a general massacre of Protestants. The kingdom was sold to Louis. Nothing was safe, and no one could be trusted. The laws, the Constitution, the Church—all were in jeopardy. But a deliverer would appear. He would come clad with power from over the seas to rescue England from Popery and slavery—if only the wind would blow from the east. The scale and reality of William's preparations and the alarming state of feeling throughout England had terrified Sunderland and Jeffreys. These two Ministers induced the King to reverse his whole policy. Parliament must be called without delay. But it was too late. On October 19 William set out upon the seas. On November 5 he landed at Torbay, on the coast of Devon.

James was not at first greatly alarmed at the news. At this crisis the King could marshal as large an army as Oliver Cromwell at his height. Nearly forty thousand regular soldiers were in the royal pay. But now successive desertions smote the unhappy prince. Lord Cornbury, eldest son of the Earl of Clarendon, an officer of the Royal Dragoons, endeavored to carry three regiments of horse to William's camp. James, warned from many quarters, meditated Churchill's arrest. On the night of November 23, having failed to carry any large part of the Army with them, Churchill and the Duke of Grafton, with about four hundred officers and troopers, quitted the royal camp. At the same time the Princess Anne, attended by Sarah Churchill, and guided by Bishop Compton, fled from Whitehall and hastened northwards. And now revolt broke out all over the country. Danby was in arms in Yorkshire, Devonshire in Derbyshire, Delamere in Cheshire. Lord Bath delivered Plymouth to William. Byng, later an admiral, representing the captains of the Fleet, arrived at his headquarters to inform him that the Navy and Portsmouth were at his disposal. City after city rose in rebellion. By one spontaneous, tremendous convulsion the English nation repudiated James.

Meanwhile, the invading army moved steadily forward towards London. James sent his wife and son out of the kingdom, and on the night of December 11 stole from the palace at Whitehall, crossed the river, and rode to the coast. The London mob sacked the foreign embassies, and a panic and terror, known as "Irish Night," swept the capital. James in his flight had actually got on board a ship, but, missing the tide, was caught and dragged ashore by the fishermen and townsfolk. He was brought back to London, and after some days of painful suspense was allowed to escape again. This time he succeeded and left English soil forever.

CHAPTER SEVEN

England's Advance to World Power

William of Orange was fatherless and childless. His life was loveless. As a sovereign and commander he was entirely without religious prejudices. The darkest stain upon his memory was to come from Scotland. A Highland clan whose chief had been tardy in making his submission was doomed to destruction by William's signed authority. Troops were sent to Glencoe "to extirpate that den of thieves." But the horror with which this episode has always been regarded arises from the treacherous breach of the laws of hospitality by which it was accomplished. The King had not prescribed the method, but he bears the indelible shame of the deed.

William was cold, but not personally cruel. His sole quarrel was with Louis XIV. For all his experience from a youth spent at the head of armies, and for all his dauntless heart, he was never a great commander. He had not a trace of that second-sight of the battlefield which is the mark of military genius. His inspiration lay in the sphere of diplomacy. He has rarely been surpassed in the sagacity, patience, and discretion of his Statecraft. He required the wealth and power of England by land and sea for the European war. He never was fond of England, nor interested in her domestic affairs.

A Convention Parliament was summoned by the Prince on the advice of the statesmen who had made the Revolution. Loyal Tories were alarmed by the prospect of disturbing the Divine Right in the Stuart succession. Danby got in touch with Princess Mary. An obvious solution which would please many Tories was the accession of Mary in her own right. But other Tories, including Mary's uncle, the Earl of Clarendon, favored the appointment of William as Regent, James remaining titular King. The whole situation turned upon the decision of William. Would he be content with the mere title of honorary consort to his wife? After protracted debates in the Convention Halifax's view was accepted that the Crown should be jointly vested in the persons of William and Mary. His triumph was complete, and it was he who presented the Crown and the Declaration of Rights to the two sovereigns on behalf of both Houses. Many honors and promotions at the time of the Coronation rewarded the Revolutionary leaders. Churchill, though never in William's immediate circle, was confirmed in his rank of Lieutenant-General, and employed virtually as Commander-in-Chief to reconstitute the English Army. He was created Earl of Marlborough, and when in May 1689 war was formally declared against France, and William was detained in England and later embroiled in Ireland, Marlborough led the English contingent in Flanders.

Cracks speedily appeared in the fabric of the original National Government. William felt that Whig principles would ultimately lead to a republic. He was therefore ready to dissolve the Convention Parliament which had given him the Crown while, as the Whigs said, "its work was all unfinished." At the election of February 1690 the Tories won.

It may seem strange that the new King should have turned to the Earl of Sunderland, who had been King James's chief adviser. But James and Sunderland had now irrevocably quarreled, and Sunderland was henceforth bound to William's interests. His knowledge of the European political scene was invaluable to his sovereign's designs. After a brief interval he reappeared in England, and gained a surprising influence. The actual government was entrusted to the statesmen of the middle view—the Duke of Shrewsbury, Sidney Godolphin, and Marlborough, and, though now, as always, he stood slightly aloof from all parties, Halifax.

Ireland presented itself as the obvious immediate center of action. James, sustained by a disciplined French contingent, many French officers, and large supplies of French munitions and money, had landed in Ireland in March. He was welcomed as a deliverer.

The whole island except the Protestant settlements in the North passed under the control of the Jacobites, as they were henceforth called. The loyal defense of Londonderry and its relief from the sea was the one glorious episode of the campaigning season of 1689. Had William used his whole strength in Ireland in 1689 he would have been free to carry it to the Continent in 1690; but in the new year he found himself compelled to go in person with his main force to Ireland. The Prince of Waldeck, William's Commander in the Low Countries, suffered a crushing defeat at the Battle of Fleurus. At the same time the French Fleet gained a victory over the combined fleets of England and Holland off Beachy Head. It was said in London that "the Dutch had the honor, the French had the advantage, and the English the shame." However, on July 11 King William gained a decisive victory at the Boyne and drove King James out of Ireland back to France. By the winter the French Fleet was dismantled, and the English and Dutch Fleets were refitted and again at sea. The end of 1690 therefore saw the Irish War ended and the command of the sea regained.

Thereafter a divergence grew between the King and Marlborough. He was the leading British general, and many officers of various ranks resorted to him and loudly expressed their resentment at the favor shown to the Dutch. Shrewsbury, Halifax, and Marlborough all entered into correspondence with James. There was talk of the substitution of Anne for William and Mary, and at the same time the influence of the Churchills with Princess Anne continued to be dominating. As often happens in disputes among high personages, the brunt fell on a subordinate. The Queen demanded the dismissal of Sarah Churchill from Anne's household. Anne refused with all the obstinate strength of her nature. The next morning the Earl of Nottingham, Secretary of State, delivered to Marlborough a written order to sell at once all the offices he held, civil and military, and consider himself as from that date dismissed from the Army and all public employment and forbidden the Court.

No sooner had King William set out upon the Continental war than the imminent menace of invasion fell upon the Island he had left denuded of troops. It was not until the middle of April 1692 that French designs became known to the English Government. Louis XIV planned a descent upon England. King James was to be given his chance of regaining the throne. On May 19–20, 1692, the English and Dutch Fleets met Tourville with the main French naval power in the English Channel off Cape La Hogue. The whole apparatus of invasion was destroyed under the very eyes of the former King whom it was to have borne to his native shore. The Battle of Cape La Hogue, with its consequential actions, effaced the memories of Beachy Head. It broke decisively for the whole of the wars of William and Anne all French pretensions to naval supremacy. It was the Trafalgar of the seventeenth century.

On land the campaign of 1692 unrolled in the Spanish Netherlands, which we now know as Belgium. Namur fell to the French armies. Worse was to follow. In August William marched by night with his whole army to attack Marshal Luxembourg. The French were surprised near Steinkirk in the early morning. But Luxembourg was equal to the emergency and managed to draw out an ordered line of battle. The British infantry formed the forefront of the Allied attack. Eight splendid regiments, under General Mackay, charged and broke the Swiss in fighting as fierce as had been seen in Europe in living memory. Luxembourg now launched the Household troops of France upon the British division, already strained by its exertions, and after a furious struggle, fought mostly with cold steel, beat it back. From all sides the French advanced and their reinforcements began to reach the field. Count Solms, the Dutch officer and William's relation, who had replaced Marlborough in command of the British contingent, had already earned the cordial dislike of its officers and men. He now refused to send Mackay the help for which he begged. William, who was unable to control the battle, shed bitter tears as he watched the slaughter, and exclaimed, "Oh, my poor English!" By noon the whole of the Allied army was in retreat, and although the losses of seven or eight thousand men on either side were equal the French proclaimed their victory throughout Europe. These events infuriated the English Parliament. Against great opposition supplies were voted for another mismanaged and disastrous year of war. In July 1693 was fought the great Battle of Landen, unmatched in Europe for its slaughter except by Malplaquet and Borodino for over two hundred years. William rallied the remnants of his army, gathered reinforcements, and, since Luxembourg neglected to pursue his victory, was able to maintain himself in the field. In 1694 he planned an expedition upon Brest, and, according to the Jacobites, Marlborough betrayed this design to the enemy.

The Continental ventures of William III now forced English statesmen to a reconstruction of the credit and finances of the country. The first war Government formed from the newly organized Whig Party possessed in the person of Charles Montagu a first-rate financier. The first essential step was the creation of some national organ of credit. In collaboration with the Scottish banker William Paterson, Montagu, now Chancellor of the Exchequer, started the Bank of England in 1694 as a private corporation. With the help of the philosopher John Locke, and William Loundes of the Treasury, he planned a complete overhaul of the coinage. It is perhaps one of the greatest achievements of the Whigs.

At the end of 1694 Queen Mary had been stricken with smallpox, and on December 28 she died, unreconciled to her sister Anne, mourned by her subjects, and lastingly missed by King William. This altered the whole position of the Princess, and with it that of the redoubtable Churchills, who were her devoted intimates and champions.

In 1695 the King gained his only success. He recovered Namur in the teeth of the French armies. This event enabled the war to be brought to an inconclusive end in 1696. In order to achieve lasting peace it was vital that England should be strong and well armed, and thus enabled to confront Louis on equal terms. The Whigs were sensitive to the danger of the French aggression in Europe. But the Tories were now in one of their moods of violent reaction from Continental intervention. Groaning under taxation, impatient of every restraint, the Commons plunged into a campaign of economy and disarmament. In 1697 the Whig administration was driven from office upon such themes, and with such a program Robert Harley, now the rising hope of Toryism, created his power and position in the House of Commons. Harley was supported by Sir Edward Seymour, the pre-eminent "sham good-fellow" of the age, who marshaled the powerful Tories of Cornwall and the West. In the Lords he was aided by Nottingham and the Earl of Rochester. They did all they could to belittle and undermine the strength of their country. No closer

parallel exists in history than that presented by the Tory conduct in the years 1696 to 1699 with their similar conduct in the years 1932 to 1937. In each case short-sighted opinions, agreeable to the party spirit, pernicious to national interests, banished all purpose from the State and prepared a deadly resumption of the main struggle.

William was so smitten by the wave of abject isolationism which swept the governing classes of the Island that he contemplated an abdication and return to Holland. His distress led him to look again to Marlborough, with whom the future already seemed in a great measure to rest. Anne's sole surviving son, the Duke of Gloucester, was now nine years old, and it was thought fitting to provide the future heir apparent to the Crown with a Governor of high consequence and with an establishment of his own. In the summer of 1698 William invited Marlborough to be Governor of the boy-prince. From this time forth William seemed to turn increasingly towards the man of whose aid he had deprived himself during the most critical years of his reign. The untimely death in 1700 of the little Duke of Gloucester, who succumbed to the fatal, prevalent scourge of smallpox, deprived Marlborough of his office. There was now no direct Protestant heir to the English and Scottish thrones. By an Act of Settlement the House of Hanover, descended from the gay and attractive daughter of James I who had briefly been Queen of Bohemia, was declared next in succession after William and Anne. The Act laid down that every sovereign in future must be a member of the Church of England. It also declared that no foreign-born monarch might wage Continental wars without the approval of Parliament; he must not go abroad without consent, and no foreigners should sit in Parliament or on

[321]

the Privy Council. Thus were recorded in statute the English grievances against William III.

No great war was ever entered upon with more reluctance on both sides than the War of the Spanish Succession. Over all Europe hung the long-delayed, long-dreaded, ever-approaching demise of the Spanish Crown. William cast himself upon the policy of partitioning the Spanish Empire. There were three claimants:

The first of the three was France, represented either by the Dauphin, or if the French and Spanish Crowns could not be joined, by his second son, the Duke of Anjou. The next was the Emperor, who was willing to transfer his claims to the Archduke Charles. Thirdly, there was the Emperor's grandson, the Electoral Prince of Bavaria. The essence of the new Partition Treaty of September 24, 1698, was to recognize the Electoral Prince as heir to Charles II of Spain. This plan concerted between Louis XIV and William III was vehemently resented by the Emperor. As it became known it also provoked a fierce reaction in Spain. Spanish society now showed that it cared above all things for the integrity of the Spanish domains.

But now a startling event occurred. In February 1699 the Electoral Prince of Bavaria, the child in whose chubby hands the greatest States had resolved to place the most splendid prize, suddenly died. Why and how he died at this moment did not fail to excite dark suspicions. By great exertions William and Louis arranged a second Treaty of Partition on June 11, 1699, by which the Archduke Charles was made heir-in-chief.

Meanwhile, the feeble life-candle of the childless Spanish King burned low in the socket. Charles had now reached the end of his torments. But within his diseased frame, his clouded mind, his superstitious soul, trembling on the verge of eternity, there glowed one Imperial thought—the unity of the Spanish Empire. In the end he was persuaded to sign a will leaving his throne to the Duke of Anjou, and couriers galloped with the news from the Escorial to Versailles. On November 1 Charles II expired.

Louis XIV had now reached one of the great turning-points in the history of France. Should he reject the will, stand by the treaty, and join with England and Holland in enforcing it? On the other hand, should he repudiate the treaty, endorse the will, and defend his grandson's claims in the field against all comers? It was decided to repudiate the treaty and stand upon the will. On November 16 a famous scene was enacted at Versailles. Louis XIV, at his levee, presented the Spanish Ambassador to the Duke of Anjou, saying, "You may salute him as your King." The Ambassador gave vent to his celebrated indiscretion, "There are no more Pyrenees." Confronted with this event, William felt himself constrained to recognize the Duke of Anjou as Philip V of Spain. The House of Commons was still in a mood far removed from European realities. They eagerly accepted Louis XIV's assurance that, "content with his power, he would not seek to increase it at the expense of his grandson." A Bourbon prince would become King of Spain, but would remain wholly independent of France. But now a series of ugly incidents broke from outside upon the fevered complacency of English politics. A letter from Melfort, the Jacobite Secretary of State at Saint-Germain, was discovered in the English mailbags, disclosing a plan for the immediate French invasion of England in the Jacobite cause. It appeared that the Spaniards had now offered to a French company the sole right of importing Negro slaves into South America. It also became apparent that the freedom of the

British trade in the Mediterranean was in jeopardy. But the supreme event which roused all England to an understanding of what had actually happened in the virtual union of the Crowns of France and Spain was a tremendous military operation effected under the guise of brazen legality. A line of fortresses in Belgium, garrisoned under treaty rights by the Dutch, constituted the main barrier of the Netherlands against a French invasion. During the month of February 1701 strong French forces arrived before all the Belgian cities. The Spanish commanders welcomed them with open gates. The Dutch garrisons, overawed by force, and no one daring to break the peace, were interned. All that the Grand Alliance of 1689 had defended in the Low Countries in seven years of war melted like snow at Easter. Europe was roused, and at last England was staggered.

William felt the tide had set in his favor. On May 31 he proclaimed Marlborough Commander-in-Chief of the English forces assembling in Holland. In June he appointed him Ambassador Extraordinary to the United Provinces. On September 16, 1701, James II died. Louis visited in State his deathbed at Saint-Germain, and announced to the shadow Court that he recognized James's son as King of England and would ever sustain his rights. All England was roused by the insult to her independence. King William was able to sever diplomatic relations with France. The Emperor had already begun the war, and his famous general, Prince Eugene of Savoy, was fighting in the North of Italy.

At this moment death overtook King William. On February 20, 1702, he was riding in the park round Hampton Court on Sorrel, a favorite horse. Sorrel stumbled in the new workings of a mole, and the King was thrown. The broken collar-bone might well have mended, but in his failing health the accident opened the door to a troop of lurking foes. William died at fifty-two, worn out by his labors. Marlborough at the same age strode forward against tremendous odds upon the ten years of unbroken victory which raised the British nation to a height in the world it had never before attained.

There was at that time an extraordinary wealth of capacity in the English governing class. It was also the Augustan Age of English letters. Addison, Defoe, Pope, Steele, Swift, are names which shine today. Art and science flourished. The work of the Royal Society, founded in Charles II's reign, now bore a largesse of fruit. Sir Isaac Newton in mathematics, physics, and astronomy completed the revolution of ideas which had begun with the Renaissance. Architecture was led to noble achievements by Wren, and to massive monuments by Vanbrugh.

In March 1702 Anne ascended the throne. The new reign opened in a blaze of loyalty. It was the "sunshine day" for which the Princess Anne had long waited with placid attention. Marlborough was made Captain-General of her armies at home and abroad. The office of Stadtholder and Commander-in-Chief was allowed to pass into abeyance and Marlborough was appointed Deputy Captain-General of Holland. He was thus in supreme command of the armies of the two Western Powers. But although the highest title and general deference were accorded to the English General his authority could only assert itself at every stage by infinite patience and persuasiveness. Moreover, he was never head of the government in London. The Tories regarded with aversion the sending of large armies to the Continent. They declared that the country gentlemen were being mulcted while the City of London, its bankers and its merchants, established an ever-growing mortgage upon the landed estates. The Whigs, on the other hand, though banished from office, were ardent advocates of the greatest military efforts. The issue was radical, and much to his regret Marlborough found it necessary to use his paramount influence with the Queen against the leaders of the Tory Party.

For the year 1702 Louis had decided to set his strongest army against Holland. The valiant but fruitless efforts of King William were replaced by the spectacle of substantial advances, and the hitherto aggressive French were seen baffled, hesitating, and in retreat. When after the storm of Liège, Marlborough, narrowly escaping an ambuscade upon the Meuse, returned to The Hague he was received with intense public joy by the Dutch, and on his arrival in England he was created Duke by the Queen. A powerful fleet and army sailed for Cadiz at the end of July under the Duke of Ormonde and Admiral Sir George Rooke. The commanders lacked the nerve to force the harbor upon the first surprise, and a prolonged series of desultory operations ensued. After a month it was decided to re-embark the soldiers and sail for home. The ignominy was relieved by a lucky windfall. News was brought that the Spanish Treasure Fleet with millions from the Indies aboard had run into Vigo Bay. It was decided to raid the harbor. The entire enemy fleet was sunk, burned, or captured. Had they shown at Cadiz one-half of the spirit of Vigo Bay the sea-Powers would have been masters of the Mediterranean in 1703.

For the campaign of 1703 Marlborough was able to concentrate the "Grand Army" of the Alliance around Maastricht, eighty miles south of Nimwegen, the starting-point of the previous year. He deferred to Dutch opinion and began the siege of Bonn on the Rhine. When Bonn fell he made the attempt upon Antwerp, and very rapid maneuvering

and hard marching followed. The "great design," as he called it, did not succeed because the Dutch were not willing to consent to the very severe offensive battle which Marlborough wished to fight. Both at home and abroad the fortunes of the Grand Allies sank to a low ebb in the winter of 1703. Queen Anne here rose to her greatest height. "I will never forsake," she wrote to Sarah, "your dear self, Mr. Freeman [Marlborough], nor Mr. Montgomery [Godolphin]." With this support Marlborough during the winter months planned the supreme stroke of strategy which turned the whole fortune of the war. But before he could proceed to the Continent it was essential to reconstitute the government of the High Tories. Rochester was already dismissed and Nottingham was soon to go. The combination became Marlborough, Godolphin, and Harley, with the Queen and Sarah as before.

The annals of the British Army contain no more heroic episode than Marlborough's march from the North Sea to the Danube. Here for the first time began that splendid comradeship of the Duke and Eugene which for seven years continued without jealousy or defeat. The twin captains—"one soul in two bodies" as they were described—fell upon the French and Bavarian armies at Höchstädt, on the Danube, early in the morning of August 13. The battle was fought with the greatest fury on both sides. Eugene commanded the right and Marlborough the left and center. The English attack upon the village of Blindheim—or Blenheim, as it has been called in history —was repulsed, and for several hours the issue hung in the balance; but Marlborough, as dusk fell on this memorable day, was able to write his famous letter to his wife: "I have not time to say more, but to beg you will give my duty to the Queen, and let her know her army has had a glorious victory."

The victory of Blenheim almost destroyed the French and Bavarian armies on the Danube. Over forty thousand men were killed, wounded, captured, or dispersed. Ulm surrendered after a brief siege, and Marlborough marched rapidly westward to the angle of the Rhine, where he was soon able to concentrate nearly a hundred thousand men. Finally, unwearied by these superb exertions, the Duke marched during October from the Rhine to the Moselle, where he closed a campaign ever a classic model of war by the capture of Treves and Trarbach. The whole force of the Grand Alliance was revived and consolidated. England rose with Marlborough to the summit, and the Islanders, who had never known such a triumph since Crécy and Agincourt, four centuries earlier, yielded themselves to transports of joy. The same year had seen remarkable successes at sea. In May a powerful Anglo-Dutch fleet under Admiral Rooke entered the Mediterranean. Reinforced by a squadron under Sir Cloudesley Shovell, Rooke turned his attention in July to the Rock of Gibraltar. After bombardment the Rock was taken on August 4, in the same month as Blenheim, by a combined assault, led on land by Prince George of Hesse-Darmstadt.

Just as the brilliant campaign of 1702 was succeeded by the disappointments of 1703, so the grand recovery of 1704 gave place to disunity in 1705. The Duke, unsupported, was forced to abandon his plan of fighting a decisive battle at the head of a hundred thousand men and advancing towards Paris. The triumph of Blenheim seemed overclouded.

Wearied with the difficulties of co-operating with the Dutch and with the Princes of the Rhine, Marlborough planned through the winter an even more daring repetition of his march to the Danube in 1704. He schemed to march across Europe with about twenty-five thousand British and British-paid troops by Coblenz, Stuttgart, and Ulm, through the passes of the Alps, to join Eugene in Northern Italy. There the two great captains would strike into France from the south. But the earliest events of the campaign of 1706 destroyed the Italian project. The key fortress of Landau was threatened. Marlborough's hopes were dashed. It was with melancholy thoughts that he began his most brilliant campaign. Fortune, whom Marlborough had so ruefully but sternly dismissed, returned importunate, bearing her most dazzling gift.

Louis XIV had convinced himself that a defensive war could not be maintained against such an opponent. At dawn on May 23 the two armies were in presence near the village of Ramillies. Marlborough, having deployed, about noon began a heavy but feigned attack upon the French right with the British troops. Availing himself of the undulations of the ground, he hurled the whole mass of the Dutch, British, and Danish cavalry, over twenty-five thousand strong, upon the finest cavalry of France. After furious fighting, in which forty thousand horsemen were engaged, he broke the French line, drove their right from the field, and compromised their center. His main infantry now broke attack upon the village of Ramillies, while his victorious cavalry, forming at right angles to the original front, swept along the whole rear of the French line. All the Allied troops now advanced, and the French army fled from the field in utter ruin. In this masterpiece of war, fought between armies almost exactly equal in strength and quality, the military genius of the English General, with a loss of less than five thousand men, destroyed and defeated his opponents with great slaughter and thousands of captives.

The consequences of Ramillies were even more spectacular than those which had followed Blenheim. If, as was said,

Blenheim had saved Vienna, Ramillies conquered Belgium. These immense successes were enhanced by the victories of Prince Eugene in Northern Italy. At the same time in Spain the Allies had achieved much to their credit and come near to a striking success. The Earl of Galway, assisted by a Portuguese army two or three times the size of his own small force of about five thousand British and Dutch, reached the Spanish capital from Portugal in June. The "Year of Victory," as it was called in London, may close on this.

Britain's military prowess and the sense of the Island being at the head of mighty Europe now bore more lasting fruit. At last England was prepared to show some financial generosity to the Scots, and they in turn were willing to accept the Hanoverian succession. The Act of Union was finally passed in 1707, and in spite of some friction was generally accepted. The Union has grown in strength the longer it has lasted.

About this time Sarah's relations with the Queen entered on a perilous phase. She had brought a poor relation, Abigail Hill, into the Queen's life as a "dresser" or lady's maid. Abigail, by the beginning of 1707, had acquired an influence of her own with the Queen destined to deflect the course of European history. Abigail was a cousin of Sunderland's. She was at the same time a cousin of Harley's. Harley was much disconcerted by the arrival of the Whig Sunderland in the Cabinet. Anne loathed the Whigs from the bottom of her heart, but her Ministers could not see how it was possible to carry on the war without the Whigs and with only half the Tory Party at their back. One day a gardener handed Harley a secret letter from the Queen. She appealed for his help. Forthwith he set himself to plan an alternative Government based on the favor of the Queen, comprising Tories and moderate Whigs and sheltered by the renown and, he hoped, the services of Marlborough.

Everything went wrong in 1707. Marlborough's design was that Eugene should debouch from Italy into France and capture Toulon. Meanwhile, Marlborough faced and held the superior forces of Marshal Vendôme in a holding campaign in the North. The campaign in the North reduced itself to stalemate. The great enterprise against Toulon, to which Marlborough had subordinated all other interests, ended in failure. The French concentrated powerful forces not only to defend but to relieve Toulon. After several costly assaults the siege failed. Great misfortunes happened in Spain. A bloody defeat was sustained at Almanza by the Allies, and the whole Spanish scene, so nearly triumphant in 1706, was now completely reversed.

Marlborough returned from these tribulations to a furious party storm in England. Harley's designs were now apparent, and his strength nourished itself upon the military misfortunes. Marlborough and Godolphin together resolved to drive him from the Cabinet. But a true Stuart and daughter of James II would not let Harley go. He advised the Queen to accept his resignation. With him went Henry St. John, whom Marlborough had regarded almost as an adopted son.

This struggle gave Marlborough a final lease of power. It was on these perilous foundations that he embarked upon the campaign of 1708. For the only time in the Duke's career he bent and bowed under the convergent strains at home and in the field. Eugene, arriving with only a cavalry escort, found him near Brussels in the deepest depression. Eugene sustained his comrade. Marlborough rose from his sick-bed, mounted his horse, and the Army was set in motion. As the Allies poured across the Scheldt the French army wheeled to their left to face them. The Battle of Oudenarde was in every aspect modern. It more nearly resembled Tannenberg in 1914 than any great action of the eighteenth century. Marlborough, giving Eugene command of the right wing, held the center at heavy odds himself while the rest of the Army was prolonging its line to the left. This long left arm reached out continually, and the battle front flared and flamed as it grew. The operation of crossing the river corps by corps in the face of an army equal in strength was judged most hazardous by the military opinion of that age of strife. The pace of the battle and its changes prevented all set arrangement. The French fought desperately but without any concerted plan, and a large part of their army was never engaged. At length the Dutch, under the veteran Overkirk, traversed the Oudenarde bridges and swung round upon the heights to the north. At the same time Eugene broke through on the right. The opposite wings of the Allies almost met. In furious anger and consternation Vendôme ordered a retreat on Ghent. A quarter of his army was destroyed or dispersed. The Allies had recovered the initiative. It was resolved to attack Lille, the strongest fortress of France. The siege of Lille was not only the largest but the most complicated operation of its kind known to the eighteenth century. In many ways it is unique in military annals. Marshal Boufflers with fifteen thousand men defended the city. Eugene conducted the siege, and Marlborough with the covering army held off the largely superior forces which, both from the neighborhood of Ghent and from France itself, sought to relieve the city or sever the communications of the besiegers. Sixteen thousand horses drew Marlborough's siege-trains from Brussels to the trenches. The heavy batteries played upon the town, and a succession of bloody assaults was delivered week after week upon the breaches. The citadel of Lille fell in December. Bruges was recaptured at the end of December, and Ghent in the first days of January. At the same time the capture of Minorca, with its fine harbor at Mahon, gave to the English Navy at last a secure, permanent base in the Mediterranean.

The power of France was broken. The Great King was humbled.

Meanwhile, in England the Whigs had at last achieved their long purpose. They drove the remaining Tories from the Cabinet, and installed a single-party administration, above which still sat the two super-Ministers, Marlborough and Godolphin. The Whigs, ardent, efficient masters of the Parliamentary arts, arrived in power at the very moment when their energy and war spirit were least needed. When we look upon the long years of terror and spoliation to which the Princes of the Grand Alliance had been subjected by Louis XIV great allowances must be made for their suspicions in the hour of victory. Nevertheless, the offers now made by France were so ample as to satisfy all reasonable demands of the Allies. In Spain alone did French fortunes prosper. The negotiations broke on the article that Louis must himself become responsible for expelling his grandson from Spain on the pain of having the Allies renew the war against him from the bases and fortresses he was to surrender in guarantee. The drums beat in the Allied camps, and the greatest armies those war-worn times had seen rolled forward to the campaign of 1709 and the carnage of Malplaquet.

Justice quite suddenly gathered up her trappings and quitted one cause for the other. From this moment France, and to a lesser degree Spain, presented national fronts against foreign inroad and overlordship. By swift movements Marlborough and Eugene invested Mons, and, advancing south of it, found themselves confronted by Marshal Villars in the gap between the woods in which the village of Malplaquet stands, almost along the line of the present French Frontier. On September 11 a hundred and ten thousand Allied troops assaulted the entrenchments, defended by about ninety thousand French. Marlborough in the main repeated the tactics of Blenheim. At length the French cavalry were mastered. Their infantry were already in retreat. The Allies had lost over twenty thousand men, and the French two-thirds as many. There were hardly any prisoners. Indeed Malplaquet, the largest and bloodiest battle of the eighteenth century, was surpassed only by Napoleon's barren victory at Borodino a hundred years later.

The great armies faced one another for the campaign of 1710. Their actual numbers were larger than ever before, but Marlborough and Eugene could not or did not bring Villars to battle. While Marlborough was at these toils the political crisis of Queen Anne's reign moved steadily to its climax. Dr. Sacheverell, a High Church divine, delivered a sermon in London in violent attack upon the government, the Whigs, and the Lord Treasurer. With great unwisdom the government ordered a State prosecution in the form of an impeachment. By narrow majorities nominal penalties were inflicted upon Sacheverell. He became the hero of the hour. Queen Anne, advised by Harley, now felt strong enough to take her revenge for what she considered the insult inflicted on her by the Whig intrusion into her Council. Whig Ministers were relieved of office. Harley formed a predominantly Tory government, and at his side Henry St. John became Secretary of State. The General Election, aptly launched, produced a substantial Tory majority in the House of Commons.

Yet Marlborough remained the most precious possession of the hostile government and vengeful Queen. Terms were made between the Tory Ministers and Marlborough for the proper upkeep of the armies at the Front, and the Captain-General for the tenth year in succession took the field. During the winter Villars had constructed an enormous system of entrenchments and inundations stretching from the sea through the fortress of Arras and Bouchain to Maubeuge, on the Sambre. He called these lines "Ne Plus Ultra." Marlborough prepared to pierce this formidable barrier. By subtle arts and stratagems he convinced Villars that he intended to make another frontal attack on the scale of Malplaquet south of Arras. On August 4 the Duke in person conducted a reconnaissance along the whole of Villars's front. Villars was filled with hope.

At length tattoo beat and darkness fell. Orders came to strike tents and stand to arms. Soon staff officers arrived to guide the four columns, and in less than half an hour the whole army was on the march to the left. All through the moonlit night they marched eastward. They traversed those broad undulations between the Vimy Ridge and Arras which two centuries later were to be dyed with British and Canadian blood. A sense of excitement filled the troops. It was not after all to be a bloody battle. Before five o'clock on the morning of the 5th they reached the Scarpe near Vitry. Here the Army found a series of pontoon bridges already laid, and as the light grew they saw the long columns of their artillery now marching with them. Marlborough sent his aides-de-camp and staff officers down the whole length of the marching columns with orders to explain to the officers and soldiers of every regiment what he was doing and what had happened, and to tell them that all now depended upon their marching qualities. "My Lord Duke wishes the infantry to step out." As the light broadened and the day advanced the troops could see upon their right, across the marshes and streams of the Sensée, that the French were moving parallel to them within half cannon-shot. But they also saw that the head of the French horse was only abreast of the Allied foot. In the result Marlborough formed a front beyond the lines, and cast his siege-grip on the fortress of Bouchain. The forcing of the "Ne Plus Ultra" lines and the siege and capture of Bouchain were judged by Europe to be outstanding manifestations of the military art. There is no finer example of Marlborough's skill. For ten years he had led the armies of the Grand Alliance, and during all that period he never fought a battle he did not win or besieged a town he did not take. Nothing like this exists in the annals of war.

It was now impossible to conceal any longer the secret peace negotiations which had all this while been in progress. The Tory leaders were sure they could carry the peace if Marlborough would support it. The Duke, who was in close association with the Elector George of Hanover, the heir to the throne, and still enjoyed the support of the King of Prussia and the Princes of the Grand Alliance, would not agree to a separate peace in any circumstance. The Whigs used their majority in the House of Lords. But Harley, strong in the support of the House of Commons, and using to the full the favor of the Queen, met this assault with a decisive rejoinder. He loosed charges of peculation upon Marlborough, and procured from the Queen an extraordinary creation of twelve peers to override the adverse majority in the Lords. Marlborough was dismissed from all his offices and exposed to the censure of the House of Commons.

England was now riven in twain upon the issue of peace. Harley and St. John could not avoid the campaign of 1712. They appointed the Duke of Ormonde, the splendid magnifico who had failed at Cadiz, to the command. St. John sent secret restraining orders to Ormonde not to "partake in any siege in a way to hazard a battle"—as if such tactics were possible. Upon a dark day the British Army, hitherto the most forward in the Allied cause and admired by all, marched away from the camp of the Allies in bitter humiliation and amid the curses of their old comrades. Villars, advancing rapidly, fell upon Eugene's magazines at Denain and inflicted upon him a cruel defeat in which many of his troops were driven into the Scheldt and drowned. After these shattering defeats all the States of the Grand Alliance were compelled to make peace on the best terms possible.

What is called the Treaty of Utrecht was in fact a series of separate agreements between individual Allied States with France and with Spain. In the forefront stood the fact that the Duke of Anjou, recognized as Philip V, held Spain and the Indies, thus flouting the unreasonable declaration to which the English Parliament had so long adhered. With this out of the way the British Government gained their special terms; the French Court recognized the Protestant succession in Britain, and agreed to expel the Pretender from France, to demolish the fortifications of Dunkirk, and to cede various territories in North America and the West Indies, to wit, Hudson Bay, Newfoundland, Nova Scotia, which had been captured by an expedition from Massachusetts, and St. Christopher. With Spain the terms were that England should hold Minorca and Gibraltar, thus securing to her, while she remained the chief sea-Power, the entry and control of the Mediterranean. Commercial advantages, one day to provoke another war, were obtained in Spanish

South America, and in particular the Asiento, or the sole right for thirty years to import African Negroes as slaves into the New World.

Marlborough was so much pursued by the Tory Party and harassed by the State prosecutions against him for his alleged peculation that at the end of 1712 he left the country and lived in self-imposed exile in Holland and Germany till the end of the reign. The final phase of the Tory triumph was squalid. St. John, raised to the peerage as Viscount Bolingbroke, became involved in a mortal quarrel with Harley, Earl of Oxford. Anne was now broken with gout and other ailments. No one knows whether she wished to make her half-brother, the Pretender, her heir or not. The Whigs, strong in the Act of Succession and in the Protestant resolve of the nation, prepared openly to take arms against a Jacobite restoration. The Elector of Hanover, supported by the Dutch and aided by Marlborough, gathered the forces to repeat the descent of William of Orange. The declaration of the "Pretended Prince of Wales" that he would never abandon the Roman Catholic faith made his imposition upon the British throne impracticable.

Many accounts converge upon the conclusion that the final scene in the long duel between Oxford and Bolingbroke at the Cabinet Council of July 27, 1714, brought about the death of Queen Anne. Bolingbroke remained master of the field and of the day—but only for two days. The Privy Council pressed upon the death-bed of the Queen; they urged her to give to Lord Shrewsbury the White Staff of Lord Treasurer, which Oxford had delivered. With fleeting strength Anne, guided by the Lord Chancellor, passed the symbol to him, and then sank into a coma. Vigorous measures were taken to ensure the Hanoverian succession. When Queen Anne breathed her last at half past seven on August 1 it was

certain that there would be no Popery, no disputed succession, no French bayonets, no civil war.

Thus ended one of the greatest reigns in English history. It had been rendered glorious by Marlborough's victories and guidance. The Union and the greatness of the Island had been established. The power of France to dominate Europe was broken, and only Napoleon could revive it. The last of the Stuart sovereigns had presided over a wonderful expansion of British national strength, and in spite of the moral and physical failures of her closing years she deserved to bear in history the title of "the Good Queen Anne."

CHAPTER EIGHT

The First British Empire

During the late summer of 1714 all England awaited the coming of King George I. On September 18 he landed at Greenwich. Here on English soil stood an unprepossessing figure, an obstinate and humdrum German martinet with dull brains and coarse tastes. Yet the rigidity of his mind was relieved by a slow shrewdness and a brooding common sense. He owed his Crown to the luck of circumstance, but he never let it slip from his grasp.

Foremost among those now in acute anxiety was Bolingbroke. His fall was relentless and rapid. The first Parliament of the new reign demanded his impeachment. A few months later he took the plunge and became Secretary of State to the Pretender. His great rival Robert Harley, Earl of Oxford, was meanwhile imprisoned in the Tower of London. No condign punishment was inflicted on him; but when he emerged from the Tower he was a broken man. George I had come peacefully to the throne. The Tory Party was shattered, and England settled down, grumbling but safe, under the long rule of Whiggism. A new generation of statesmen—Walpole, Stanhope, Carteret, and Townshend—were to ensure the peaceful transition from the age of Anne to the age of the Georges.

On September 6 the Earl of Mar raised the Jacobite standard at Perth. But the Whig Ministers, though nervous, took good precautions. In the North of England a small band of gentry, led by Lord Derwentwater, rose in support of the Stuarts. The Duke of Marlborough was consulted by the military authorities. "You will beat them," he said, marking Preston with his thumbnail on the map, "there." And on November 13 beaten there they were. The Government forces in Scotland, led by the Whig Duke of Argyll, met the Jacobite army at Sheriffmuir on the same day. The battle was indecisive, but was followed by desertion and discouragement in the Jacobite ranks. The collapse was followed by a batch of treason trials and about thirty executions. Despite the incompetence of the rising, the Government perceived and feared the unorganized opposition throughout the country to the new régime. A Septennial Act prolonged the life of the existing House of Commons for another four years, and decreed septennial Parliaments henceforth. This was the boldest and most complete assertion of Parliamentary sovereignty that England had yet seen.

Political power was henceforth founded on influence: in the dispensation of Crown patronage; stars, sinecures, pensions; the agile use of the Secret Service fund; jobs in the Customs for humble dependants; commissions or Church livings for younger sons. Thus the Whigs established control of the Parliamentary machine.

In 1710 a Tory Ministry had granted a charter to a company trading with the South Seas, and had arranged for it to take over part of the National Debt. Financial speculation was encouraged. By June 1721 the South Sea stock stood at 1050. At every coffeehouse in London men and women were investing their savings in any enterprise that would take their money. There was no limit to the credulity of the public. Promoters invited subscriptions for making salt water fresh, for constructing a wheel of perpetual motion, for importing large jackasses from Spain to improve the breed of English mules, and the boldest of all was the advertisement for "a company for carrying on an undertaking of Great Advantage, but no one to know what it is." The Government took alarm, and the process of suppressing these minor companies began. The South Sea Company was only too anxious to exterminate its rivals, but the pricking of the minor bubbles quickened and precipitated a slump. The brief hour of dreamed-of riches closed in wide-eyed misery. Bringing order to the chaos that remained was the first task of Britain's first Prime Minister.

One man only amid the crash and panic of 1721 could preserve the Whig monopoly. He was Robert Walpole, now established as the greatest master of figures of his generation. Walpole, on becoming head of the Government, immediately turned to financial reconstruction. The political crisis was quickly ended. A Jacobite plot was swiftly and silently suppressed. At the same time Walpole did not prevent the pardon and return of Bolingbroke.

Walpole's object was to stabilize the Hanoverian régime and the power of the Whig Party within a generation. Taxation was low; the land tax, which was anxiously watched by the Tory squires, was reduced by economy to one shilling. The National Debt decreased steadily, and an overhaul of the tariff and the reduction of many irksome duties stimulated and expanded trade. But men remembered the great age that had passed and scorned the drab days of George I. A policy of security, prosperity, and peace made small appeal to their hearts, and many were ready to attack the degeneration of politics at home and the futility of England abroad.

A high-poised if not sagacious or successful opposition to Walpole persisted throughout the twenty-one years of his administration. It drew its force from the association of those Whigs who either disliked his policy or were estranged by exclusion from office with the Tories in the shades. The younger Whigs, like William Pulteney and John Carteret, were too clever to be allowed to shine in Walpole's orbit. Nor could they weaken his hold on the House of Commons while he exercised the patronage of the Crown. The Parliamentary Opposition gathered round the Prince of Wales. It was the Hanoverian family tradition that father and son should be on the worst of terms, and the future George II was no exception. But for the strong support of Caroline, Princess of Wales, Walpole would have been in serious danger. Indeed, on the accession of George II in 1727 he suffered a brief eclipse. The new King dismissed him. But, secure in the confidence of Queen Caroline, Walpole returned to office and entrenched himself more firmly than before.

He meant to do as little as possible: to keep the peace, to stay in office, to juggle with men, to see the years roll by. But others responded to more lively themes. Walpole was forced to quarrel. His own brother-in-law, Charles Townshend, was dismissed at the end of 1729. He then entered into close co-operation with a man of limited intelligence and fussy nature, but of vast territorial and electoral wealth—Thomas Pelham Holles, Duke of Newcastle. Newcastle became Secretary of State because, as Walpole said, he himself "had experienced the

trouble that a man of parts gave in that office." However, in 1733 a storm broke. Walpole proposed an excise on wines and tobacco, to be gathered by Revenue officers in place of a duty at the ports. Every weapon at their command was used by the Opposition. Defeated by one of the most unscrupulous campaigns in English history, Walpole withdrew his Excise reform. The violence of his critics recoiled upon themselves, and the Opposition snatched no permanent advantage. At long last the Opposition discerned the foundation of Walpole's ascendancy, namely, the avoidance of any controversy which might stir the country as a whole. The country was bored. It rejected a squalid, peaceful prosperity. The crack came from a series of incidents in Spanish America.

Such was the inefficiency of Spanish administration that it was easy to run contraband cargoes of Negroes in defiance of what was called the "Asiento contract," and the illicit trade grew steadily in the years of peace. But when the Spanish Government at last began to reorganize and extend its colonial government English ships trading unlawfully in the Spanish seas were stopped and searched by the Spanish coastguards. Walpole and Newcastle hoped for a peaceful settlement. The preliminary Convention of Prado was settled and negotiated at Madrid in January 1739. But the Opposition would have none of it. On October 19, 1739, war was declared. By sure degrees, in the confusion and mismanagement which followed, Walpole's power, as he had foreseen, slipped from him. The one success, the capture of Portobello, on the isthmus of Panama, was achieved by Admiral Vernon, the hero of the Opposition. Meanwhile, the tide of national feeling ran high.

In February 1741 an Opposition Member, Samuel Sandys, proposed an address to the King for the dismissal of Walpole. To the amazement of all, the Jacobites voted for him. But under the Septennial Act elections were due. The Prince of Wales spent lavishly in buying up seats, and his campaign, managed by Thomas Pitt, brother of William, brought twenty-seven Cornish seats over to the Opposition. The electoral influence of the Scottish earls counted against Walpole, and when the Members returned to Westminster his Government was defeated on an election petition (contested returns were in those days decided by the House on purely party lines) and resigned. It was February 1742. He had kept England at peace for nearly twenty years. Now he went to the House of Lords as Earl of Orford. He was the first Chief Minister to reside at Number Ten, Downing Street. The sovereign had ceased after 1714 to preside in person over the Cabinet, save on exceptional occasions—a most significant event, though it was only the result of an accident. Walpole had created for himself a dominating position in this vital executive committee, now deprived of its titular chairman. But he founded no convention of collective Ministerial responsibility. One of the charges against him after his fall was that he had sought to become "sole and Prime Minister."

The war between Britain and Spain, which the Opposition had forced upon Walpole, was soon merged in a general European struggle. In October 1740 the Habsburg Emperor Charles VI died, leaving his broad domains, though not his Imperial title, to his daughter Maria Theresa. East of the Elbe the rising kingdom of Prussia acquired a new ruler. Frederick II, later called the Great, ascended his father's throne. He attacked and seized the Austrian province of Silesia, which lay to the south of his own territories. France, ever jealous of the Habsburgs, encouraged and supported him.

In London, after Walpole's fall, King George's Government was managed by Henry Pelham, First Lord of the Treasury, and his brother, the Duke of Newcastle, long a Secretary of State. They were skilled in party maneuver, but inexpert in the handling of foreign or military affairs. George II turned for help and advice to the Pelhams' rival, Lord Carteret. Carteret wanted Hanover and England to preserve and promote a balance of power in Europe. To meet the combination of France, Spain, and Frederick the Great, he negotiated a treaty with Maria Theresa and renewed the traditional agreements with the Dutch. Carteret, to his misfortune, lacked both the personal position and the political following to put his decisions to good effect. Foremost among his critics was William Pitt, Member for the ancient but uninhabited borough of Old Sarum. Pitt made a withering speech against the subsidies proposed for raising Hanoverian troops, which gained him the lasting displeasure of the King. These attacks on Carteret were not unwelcome to Pelham and Newcastle.

Thirty thousand British troops, under the command of one of Marlborough's old officers, the Earl of Stair, fought on the Continent. In the spring of 1743 the King himself, accompanied by his younger son, the Duke of Cumberland, left England to take part in the campaign. The Battle of Dettingen raised a brief enthusiasm in London, but opinion slowly hardened against the continuance of a major European war. At the end of 1744 Carteret, now Lord Granville, was driven from office.

For the campaign of 1745 the King made Cumberland Captain-General of the forces on the Continent. He had to face the most celebrated soldier of the day, Marshal Saxe. The French army concentrated against the barrier fortress line, the familiar battleground of Marlborough's wars, now held by the Dutch. Having masked Tournai, Saxe took up a strong position centering upon the village of Fontenoy, near the Mons road. Cumberland drew up his army in battle order, and marched it under fire to within fifty paces of the French army. He was outnumbered by nearly two to one. Lieutenant-Colonel Lord Charles Hey, of the First (Grenadier) Guards, stepped from the front ranks, took out a flask, raised it in salute to the French Household troops, and declared, "We are the English Guards, and hope you will stand till we come up to you, and not swim the Scheldt as you did the Main at Dettingen." Cheers rang out from both sides. The English advanced, and at thirty paces the French fired. The murderous fusillade did not halt the Allied infantry, and they drove the enemy from their positions. For hours the French cavalry tried to break the Allied columns, and, watching the Irish Brigade of the French army sweeping into action, Cumberland exclaimed, "God's curse on the laws that made those men our enemies." It is a more generous remark than is usually recorded of him.

The set battle-pieces of Dettingen and Fontenoy were perhaps useless, but certainly the most creditable engagements in which English troops took part in the middle eighteenth century. At any rate England played no further part in the War of the Austrian Succession. In October 1745 Cumberland withdrew his men to meet the Young Pretender's invasion of England, and our Continental allies were beaten on every front. The only good news came from across the Atlantic. English colonists, supported by a naval squadron, captured the strongest French fortress in the New World, Louisburg, on Cape Breton.

The Pelham régime, built up upon the support of Whig family groups, was artificial, but it had its merits. Henry Pelham was a good administrator, economical and efficient, but he was a lesser Walpole faced with a major European war. Newcastle, in his own whimsical way, looked upon the work of government as the duty of his class, but he had no clear ideas on how to discharge it. For ten years the Pelham brothers made constant and frantic efforts to create a stable Government. Fumbling and out of date in Europe, and unmindful of the great future overseas, the Broad-bottomed Administration of the 1740's was a painful affair.

In the inaccessible Highlands, where the writ of English government hardly ran, there was a persistent loyalty to the House of Stuart and the Jacobite cause. After the failure of the rising in 1715 the Jacobites had stayed quiet, but once England was involved in war upon the Continent their activities revived. The Old Pretender was now living in retirement, and his son, Prince Charles Edward, was the darling of the impecunious exiles who clustered round him in Rome and Paris. Nothing daunted, he sailed from Nantes in June 1745 with a handful of followers and landed in the Western Isles of Scotland. Thus began one of the most audacious and irresponsible enterprises in British history. Twelve hundred men under Lord George Murray raised the Jacobite standard at Glenfinnan. About three thousand Government troops gathered in the Lowlands under Sir John Cope. The rebels marched southwards; Prince Charles entered the palace at Holyrood, and Cope was met and routed on the battlefield of Prestonpans. By the end of September Charles was ruler of most of Scotland in the name of his father, "King James VIII"; but his triumph was fleeting. With five thousand men the Young Pretender crossed the Border. Plundering as they went, they marched due south, occupying Carlisle, Penrith, Lancaster, and Preston. The number of English adherents that came in was depressingly small. Many Highlanders deserted and returned home during the southward march. At Derby Charles gave the signal to retreat. Murray showed great skill in the withdrawal, and in rearguard actions his troops were invariably successful. They turned and mauled their pursuers at Falkirk. But with Teutonic thoroughness the Duke of Cumberland concentrated the English armies for a decision, and in April 1746 on Culloden Moor the last chances of a Stuart restoration were swept into the past forever. Charles Edward escaped over the moors with a few faithful servants. Disguised as a woman, he was smuggled across to the island of Skye by that heroine of romance, Flora Macdonald. Thence he sailed for the Continent, to drink out his life in perpetual exile.

In April 1746 Pitt became Paymaster of the Forces, an office of immense emolument in time of war. Pitt refused to accept a penny beyond his official salary. A born actor, by this gesture he caught the eye of the people, and held it as no statesman had held it before him. The dismal war on the Continent ended with the Treaty of Aix-la-Chapelle in 1748. Nothing was settled between Britain and France by this peace. Pitt now spent many hours in earnest discussion with Newcastle on the need for a new foreign policy. The French menace obsessed his mind. Pitt fretted, impotent to control or to criticize the policy of the administration of which he was a member. But in the interlude of peace between 1748 and 1754 the issues were too confused and the intrigues too virulent for a dramatic move. Hope of a great political career seemed at an end for William Pitt. After a great speech in the Commons he was dismissed from the Pay Office in November 1755. Two months later a diplomatic revolution took place towards which the four main Powers of Europe had for some time been groping. A convention was signed between Britain and Prussia, shortly followed by a treaty between the French and the Austrians. The mismanagement of the early years of the struggle, which had been precipitated by the bellicose Cumberland, gave Pitt his chance. The loss of the island of Minorca raised a national outcry. The Government shifted the blame on to Admiral Byng, whose ill-equipped fleet had failed to relieve the Minorca garrison. By one of the most scandalous evasions of responsibility that an English Government has ever perpetrated Byng was shot for cowardice upon the quarterdeck of his flagship. Pitt pleaded for him with the King. "The House of Commons, Sir, is inclined to mercy." "You have taught me," the King replied, "to look for the sense of my people elsewhere than in the House of Commons."

Pitt's hour had almost come.

We must now survey the scene presented by the American colonies, which had been quietly and steadily growing for the past hundred and fifty years, often on the initiative of the men on the spot rather than by planned direction from London. English commerce was expanding. The Hudson's Bay Company, launched in 1669, had set up its first trading posts and was building up its influence in the northern territories of Canada. On the coasts of Newfoundland English fishermen had revivified the earliest colony of the Crown. On the American mainland the British occupation of the entire eastern seaboard was almost complete. The capture of New York and the settlement of New Jersey had joined in contiguity the two existing groups of colonies that lay to the north and south. Inland the State of Pennsylvania was beginning to take shape as an asylum for the persecuted of all countries under the guidance of its Quaker proprietor, William Penn. To the south the two Carolinas had been founded and named in honor of the King.

While distracted by the Civil War the Mother Country left them alone, and although Cromwell's Commonwealth asserted that Parliament was supreme over the whole of the English world its decree was never put into practice, and was swept away by the Restoration. But after 1660 the home Government had new and definite ideas. For the next fifty years successive English administrations tried to enforce the supremacy of the Crown in the American colonies and to strengthen royal power and patronage in the overseas possessions. The English Revolution of 1688 changed the whole position. Hitherto the colonies had regarded the Parliament in England as their ally against the Crown. But the time was to come when Parliament, victorious over the Crown in the constitutional struggles at home, would attempt to enforce its own sovereignty over America.

The early eighteenth century saw the foundation of the last of the Thirteen Colonies. The philanthropist James Oglethorpe had been painfully moved by the horrible condition of the small debtors in English prisons. After much thought he conceived the idea of allowing these people to emigrate to a new colony. The polyglot community, named Georgia, soon attracted ardent missionaries, and it was here that John Wesley began his ministering work. This colony was the last foundation of the Mother Country in the territories that were later to become the United States.

Emigration from England had now dwindled to a trickle, but new settlers arrived from other parts. Towards the end of the seventeenth century there had been an influx of Scottish-Irish refugees, whose industrial and commercial endeavors at home had been stifled by the legislation of the English Parliament. They formed a strong English-hating element in their new homes. Pennsylvania received a steady flow of immigrants from Germany, soon to number over two hundred thousand souls. Hard-working and prosperous Huguenots arrived from France in flight from religious persecution. There was a teeming diversity of human types. On the Western farms which bordered the Indian country were rugged pioneers and sturdy yeomen farmers, and in the New England colonies assertive merchants, lawyers, and squires, and the sons of traders.

From his office in Cleveland Row Pitt designed and won a war which extended from India in the East to America in the West. The whole struggle depended upon the energies of this one man. Whether Pitt possessed the strategic eye, whether the expeditions he launched were part of a considered combination, may be questioned. Now, as at all times, his policy was a projection on to a vast screen of his own aggressive, dominating personality. But Pitt's success was not immediate. In April 1757 he was dismissed by the King. Nevertheless, he had already made his mark with the nation. For three months there was no effective Government, though Pitt gave all the orders and did the day-to-day work. A stable war Ministry was not formed until June, but for the next four years Pitt was supreme.

Unless France were beaten in Europe as well as in the New World and in the East she would rise again. Both in North America and in Europe she was in the ascendant. At sea she was a formidable enemy. In India it seemed that if ever a European Power established itself on the ruins of the Mogul Empire its banner would be the lilies and not the cross of

St. George. On the Continent Britain had one ally, Frederick of Prussia, facing the combined power of Austria, Russia, and France. Never did a war open with darker prospects. Before the year was out it seemed as if Fortune, recognizing her masters, was changing sides. Frederick, supported by the subsidies which Pitt had spent the eloquence of his youth in denouncing, routed the French at Rossbach and the Austrians at Leuthen.

So the great years opened, years for Pitt and his country of almost intoxicating glory. The French were swept out of Hanover; the Dutch, fishing in the murky waters of Oriental intrigue, were stopped by Clive and made to surrender their ships at Chinsura; Cape Breton was again taken, and the name of the "Great Commoner" stamped on the map at Pittsburgh, Pennsylvania. France's two main fleets, in the Mediterranean and in the Channel, were separately defeated. Between these victories Wolfe had fallen at Quebec, leaving Amherst to complete the conquest of Canada, while Clive and Eyre Coote were uprooting the remnants of French power in India. Even more dazzling prizes seemed to be falling into British hands. Pitt proposed to conquer the Spanish Indies, West and East, and to seize the annual Treasure Fleet. But at this supreme moment in his career, when world peace and world security seemed within his grasp, the Cabinet declined to support him and he resigned.

Pitt's very success contributed to his fall. Just as Marlborough and Godolphin had been faced by a growing war-weariness after Malplaquet, so now Pitt, an isolated figure in his own Government, confronted an increasing dislike of the war after the great victories of 1759. His Imperial war policy had succeeded only too well, leaving him with the detested and costly subsidies to Prussia which he knew were essential to the final destruction of French power. In October 1760 George II died. He had never liked Pitt, but had learned to respect his abilities. The temper of the new ruler was adverse. George III had very clear ideas of what he wanted and where he was going.

Pitt hoped that war with Spain would rouse the same popular upsurge as in 1739. His proposal for the declaration of war was put to the Cabinet. He found himself isolated. He had no choice but resignation. William Pitt ranks with Marlborough as the greatest Englishman in the century between 1689 and 1789. He was not the first English statesman to think in terms of a world policy and to broaden on to a world scale the political conceptions of William III. But he is the first great figure of British Imperialism.

Unsupported by the fame of Pitt, the Duke of Newcastle was an easy victim, and the administration slid easily into the hands of Lord Bute. His sole qualification for office, apart from great wealth and his command of the Scottish vote, was that he had been Groom of the Stole to the King's mother. For the first time since the assassination of the Duke of Buckingham the government of England was committed to a man with no political experience, and whose only connection with Parliament was that he had sat as a representative peer of Scotland for a short time twenty years before. Within three months of Pitt's resignation the Government were compelled to declare war on Spain. This led to further successes in the West Indies and elsewhere. These achievements were largely cast away. Britain's acquisitions under the terms of the Peace of Paris in 1763 were nevertheless considerable. In America she secured Canada, Nova Scotia, Cape Breton, and the adjoining islands, and the right to navigate the Mississippi, important for Red Indian trade. In the West Indies Grenada, St. Vincent, Dominica, and Tobago were acquired. From Spain she received Florida. In Africa she kept Senegal. In India, as will be related, the East India Company preserved its extensive conquests, and although their trading posts were returned the political ambitions of the French in the subcontinent were finally extinguished. In Europe Minorca was restored to England, and the fortifications of Dunkirk were at long last demolished.

Historians have taken a flattering view of a treaty which established Britain as an Imperial Power, but its strategic weakness has been smoothly overlooked. The naval power of France had been left untouched. Spain regained the West Indian port of Havana, which controlled the maritime strategy of the Caribbean. She also received back Manila, an important center for the China trade. In Africa, in spite of Pitt's protests, France got back Goree—a base for privateers on the flank of the East Indian trade routes. Moreover, the treaty took no account of the interests of Frederick the Great. This ally was left to shift for himself. Vain was it that Pitt denounced the treaty and prophesied war. "The peace was insecure, because it restored the enemy to her former greatness. The peace was inadequate, because the places gained were no equivalent for the places surrendered."

The accession of George III caused a profound change in English politics. In theory and in law the monarchy still retained a decisive influence and power in the making of policy, the choice of Ministers, the filling of offices, and the spending of money. Both George I and George II were aliens in language, outlook, upbringing, and sympathy; George III was, or thought he was, an Englishman born and bred. The times were opportune for a revival of the royal influence. In 1761 elections were held throughout England, in which Newcastle was not allowed to control all the royal patronage and many offices in the gift of the Crown were bestowed on supporters of the new monarch. In March Bute was appointed Secretary of State, and Newcastle was shuffled querulously out of office in the following spring. Within two years of his accession the "King's Friends" predominated in the House of Commons.

The first decade of his reign passed in continual and confused maneuvering between the different Parliamentary groups, some of them accepting the new situation, some making passive resistance to the new tactics of the Crown.

Many people shared Dr. Johnson's opinion of the Scots, and Bute, who was much disliked, fell from power early in 1763. His successor, George Grenville, was a mulish lawyer, backed by the enormous electoral power of the Duke of Bedford. On April 23, 1763, a newspaper called *The North Briton* attacked Ministers as "tools of despotism and corruption." George was incensed. A week later his Secretary of State issued a warrant commanding that the authors, printers, and publishers of *"The North Briton, No. 45,"* none of whom was named, should be found and arrested. Searches were made, houses were entered, papers were seized, and nearly fifty suspects were put in prison. Among them was John Wilkes, a rake and a Member of Parliament. He protested that the warrant was illegal and claimed Parliamentary privilege against the arrest. The legality of "general" warrants which named no actual offender became a constitutional question of the first importance. Wilkes was charged with seditious libel and outlawed. But his case became a national issue when he returned to fight his Parliamentary seat. The radical-minded Londoners welcomed this rebuff to the Government, and in March 1768 he was elected for Middlesex. The next February he was expelled from the

House of Commons and there was a by-election. Wilkes stood again, and obtained 1,143 votes against his Government opponent, who polled 296. Finally his opponent in Middlesex was declared duly elected. When Wilkes was released from jail in April 1770 London was illuminated to greet him. After a long struggle he was elected Lord Mayor, and again a Member of Parliament.

The whole machinery of eighteenth-century corruption was thus exposed to the public eye. By refusing to accept Wilkes the Commons had denied the right of electors to choose their Members and held themselves out as a closed corporation of privileged beings. Pitt himself, now Earl of Chatham, in blistering tones attacked the legality of general warrants and the corruption of politics, claiming that more seats in the counties would increase the electorate and diminish the opportunities for corruption, so easy in the small boroughs. His speeches were indeed the first demands for Parliamentary reform in the eighteenth century. Wilkes and the other victims sued the officials who had executed the warrants. The judges ruled that the warrants were illegal. Wilkes obtained £4,000 damages from the Secretary of State himself. Here indeed was a potent weapon against overbearing Ministers and zealous officials. The lesson bit deep. Not until the world wars of the twentieth century was the mere word of a Minister of the Crown enough to legalize the imprisonment of an Englishman. Freedom of the Press and freedom of speech developed by much the same unspectacular, technical, but effective steps. History will not deny some share in the credit for this achievement to Alderman John Wilkes.

The contest with America had meanwhile begun to dominate the British political scene. Vast territories had fallen to the Crown on the conclusion of the Seven Years War. From the Canadian border to the Gulf of Mexico the entire hinterland of the American colonies became British soil, and the parceling out of these new lands led to further trouble with the colonists. George III was also determined that the colonies should pay their share in the expenses of the Empire and in garrisoning the New World. The results were unsatisfactory on both sides of the Atlantic. Indirect taxation of trade being so unfruitful, Grenville and his lieutenant Charles Townshend consulted the Law Officers about levying a direct tax on the colonies. There were no protests, although the colonists had always objected to direct taxation, and in 1765 Parliament passed the Stamp Act. The personality of George III was now exercising a preponderant influence upon events. He was one of the most conscientious sovereigns who ever sat upon the English throne. He possessed great moral courage and an inveterate obstinacy, and his stubbornness lent weight to the stiffening attitude of his Government. His responsibility for the final breach is a high one.

In July 1765 the Marquis of Rockingham, a shy, well-meaning Whig who was disturbed at George's conduct, undertook to form a Government, and brought with him as private secretary a young Irishman named Edmund Burke, already known in literary circles as a clever writer and a brilliant talker. He was much more. He was a great political thinker. He had to overcome the notion, widely prevalent, that party was in itself a rather disreputable thing, a notion which had been strengthened by Pitt's haughty disdain for party business and organization. A consistent program, to be advocated in Opposition and realized in office, was Burke's conception of party policy, and the new issues arising plainly required a program. On Ireland, on

America, on India, Burke's attitude was definite. He stood, and he brought his party to stand, for conciliation of the colonies, relaxation of the restraints on Irish trade, and the government of India on the same moral basis as the government of England. He was perhaps the greatest man that Ireland has produced. The same gifts, with a dash of English indolence and irony—he could have borrowed them from Charles James Fox, Henry Fox's famous son, who had plenty of both to spare—might have made him Britain's greatest statesman.

Rockingham's Government, which lasted thirteen months, passed measures that went far to soothe the animosities raised by Grenville on both sides of the Atlantic. But the King was determined to be rid of them, and Pitt, whose mind was clouded by sickness, was seduced by royal flattery and by his own dislike of party into lending his name to a new administration formed on no political principle whatever. The conduct of affairs slipped into other hands: Charles Townshend, the Duke of Grafton, and Lord Shelburne. In 1767 Townshend, against the opposition of Shelburne, introduced a Bill imposing duties on American imports of paper, glass, lead, and tea. There was rage in America. The Cabinet was not seriously apprehensive, but perturbed. It agreed to drop the duties, except on tea. Suddenly by some mysterious operation of Nature the clouds which had gathered round Chatham's intellect cleared. Ill-health had forced him to resign in 1768, and he had been succeeded in office by Grafton. The scene on which he reopened his eyes was lurid enough to dismay any man. But George III, after twelve years' intrigue, had at last got a docile, biddable Prime Minister. Lord North became First Lord of the Treasury in 1770. A charming man, of good abilities and faultless temper, he presided over the loss of the American colonies.

Here Samuel Adams, fertile organizer of resistance and advocate of separation, saw the struggle was now reaching a crucial stage. In March 1770 the persistent snowballing by Boston urchins of an English sentry outside the custom-house caused a riot. In the confusion and shouting some of the troops opened fire and there were casualties. This "massacre" was just the sort of incident that Adams had hoped for. Virginian agitators, led by the young Patrick Henry, created a standing committee of their Assembly to keep in touch with the other colonies, and a chain of such bodies was quickly formed. Thus the machinery of revolt was quietly and efficiently created. Nevertheless, the Radicals were still in a minority and there was much opposition to an abrupt break with England. In spite of the Boston "massacre," the violence on the high seas, and the commercial squabbles, the agitations of Adams and his friends were beginning to peter out, when Lord North committed a fatal blunder. The East India Company was nearly bankrupt, and the Government had been forced to come to its rescue. An Act was passed through Parliament, attracting little notice among the Members, authorizing the Company to ship tea, of which it had an enormous surplus, direct to the colonies, without paying import duties, and to sell it through its own agents in America. The outcry across the Atlantic was instantaneous. The Radicals, who began to call themselves "Patriots," seized their opportunity to force a crisis. In December 1773 the first cargoes were lying in Boston. Rioters disguised as Red Indians boarded the ships and destroyed the cases. "Last night," wrote John Adams, Samuel's cousin, and later the second President of the United States, "three cargoes of

Bohea tea were emptied into the sea. . . . This is the most magnificent movement of all. There is a dignity, a majesty and sublimity in this last effort of the Patriots that I greatly admire. . . ." When the news reached London the cry went up for coercion and the reactionaries in the British Government became supreme. In September 1774 the colonial assemblies held a Congress at Philadelphia. A Declaration of Rights demanded the rescinding of some thirteen commercial Acts passed by the British Parliament since 1763. The tone of this document, which was dispatched to London, was one of respectful moderation. The petition was rejected with contempt.

Events now moved swiftly. The Patriots had about ten thousand men in the colonial militia. Agents were sent abroad to buy weapons. The Patriots began accumulating these warlike stores at Concord, a village twenty miles from Boston, where the Massachusetts Assembly, which Parliament had declared illegal, was now in session. General Thomas Gage, the Massachusetts Military Governor, decided to seize their ammunition and arrest Samuel Adams and his colleague John Hancock. On April 18, 1775, eight hundred British troops set off in darkness along the Concord road. But the secret was out. Paul Revere, warned by lantern signals from the steeple of the North Church, mounted his horse and rode hard to Lexington, rousing Adams and Hancock from their beds and urging them to flight. At five o'clock in the morning the local militia of Lexington, seventy strong, formed up on the village green. The colonial committees were very anxious not to fire the first shot, and there were strict orders not to provoke open conflict with the British regulars. But in the confusion someone fired. A volley was returned. Brushing aside the survivors, the British column marched on to Concord. The news of Lexington and Concord spread to the other colonies, and Governors and British officials were expelled. The War of Independence had begun.

In May 1775 a Congress of delegates from the American colonies met in the Carpenters' Hall of the quiet Pennsylvanian town of Philadelphia. Many of them still hoped for peace with England. Yet British troops under General Sir William Howe were on their way across the Atlantic, and armed, violent, fratricidal conflict stared them in the face. The center of resistance and the scene of action was Boston, where Gage and the only British force on the continent were hemmed in by sixteen thousand New England merchants and farmers. To the north, across a short tract of water, lay a small peninsula connected by a narrow neck with the mainland. Here Breed's Hill and Bunker Hill dominated the town. If the colonists could occupy and hold these eminences they could cannonade the English out of Boston. On the evening of June 16 Gage determined to forestall them, but next morning a line of entrenchments had appeared upon the heights across the water. Patriot troops, warned by messages from Boston, had dug themselves in during the night. On the hot afternoon of the 17th the redcoats moved slowly towards the summit of Breed's Hill. The whole of Boston was looking on. At the third rush the regulars drove the farmers from their line. Over a thousand Englishmen had fallen on the slopes. Of the three thousand farmers who had held the crest a sixth were killed or wounded. The British had captured the hill, but the Americans had won the glory. On both sides of the Atlantic men perceived that a mortal struggle impended.

It was now imperative for the Patriots to raise an army. Two days before the action at Breed's Hill Congress had agreed. Adams's eye centered upon a figure in uniform, among the dark brown clothes of the delegates. He was Colonel George Washington, of Mount Vernon, Virginia. He was the only man of any military experience at the Congress, and this was limited to a few minor campaigns on the frontier. The colonies contained about two hundred and eighty thousand men capable of bearing arms, but at no time during the war did Washington succeed in gathering together more than twenty-five thousand. Congress nevertheless resolved on an offensive. An expedition was dispatched to Canada under Benedict Arnold, who was to be forever infamous in American history, and Richard Montgomery, who had once served under Wolfe. French Canadians were on the whole content with life under the British Crown. Soon Canada was to harbor many refugees from the United States who were unable to forswear their loyalty to George III.

Meanwhile, Howe was still confined to Boston. He now set himself the task of overawing the Americans. This however needed extensive help from England, and as none arrived, and Boston itself was of no strategic importance, he evacuated the town in the spring of 1776 and moved to the only British base on the Atlantic seaboard, Halifax, in Nova Scotia. Patriot resistance was stiffening, and although the moderate elements in Congress had hitherto opposed any formal Declaration of Independence the evacuation of Boston roused them to a sterner effort. But it was the British Government which took the next step towards dissolving the tie of allegiance between England and America. Early in 1776 it put into force a Prohibitory Act forbidding all intercourse with the rebellious colonies and declaring a blockade of the American coast. A large-scale British invasion was feared. Many of the colonists felt that a formal defiance would wreck their cause and alienate their supporters But at last a committee was appointed, a paper was drafted by Thomas Jefferson, and on July 4, 1776, a Declaration of Independence was unanimously accepted by the Congress of the American colonies. This historic document was in the main a restatement of the principles which had animated the Whig struggle against the later Stuarts and the English Revolution of 1688, and it now became the symbol and rallying center of the Patriot cause.

In June 1776 Howe moved to New York, and began to invest the city, and in July his brother, Admiral Howe, arrived from England with a fleet of over five hundred sail and reinforcements. Howe was now in command of some twenty-five thousand men. From the British camp on Staten Island the American lines could be seen across the bay on the spurs of Long Island, and on the heights of Brooklyn above the East River. In August Howe attacked. Washington was compelled to retreat into New York City. It seemed impossible to make a stand in New York, yet to abandon it would dismay the Patriots. But Congress agreed that he should evacuate the city without fighting, and after skirmishing on the Harlem heights he withdrew slowly northwards. At this juncture victory lay at Howe's finger-tips. If he had pursued Washington with the same skill and vigor as Grant was to pursue Lee eighty-eight years later he might have captured the colonial army. But for nearly a month Washington was unmolested. Howe resolved to move on Philadelphia. He turned south, capturing as he went the forts in the neighborhood of New York, and the delegates at Philadelphia fled. Thousands of Americans flocked to the British camp to declare their loyalty. The only hope for the Patriots seemed a mass trek across the Alleghanies into new lands, a migration away from British rule like that of the Boers in the nineteenth century. The Patriot cause seemed lost. But Washington remained alert and undaunted and fortune rewarded him. With an imprudence which is difficult to understand, and was soon to be punished, outposts from the British army were flung about in careless fashion through the New Jersey towns. The year ended with the British in winter quarters in New Jersey, but confined to the east of the Delaware. Meanwhile, Benjamin Franklin and Silas Deane, first of American diplomats, crossed the Atlantic to seek help from France.

Posterity should not be misled into thinking that war on the American colonies received the unanimous support of the British people. Indeed, but for the violence of the Opposition, which far outran the country's true feelings, it is probable that Lord North's administration would have fallen much sooner. Though technically responsible as First Lord of the Treasury and Chancellor of the Exchequer, he had no grip on the conduct of affairs and allowed the King and the departmental Ministers to control the day-to-day work of government. Rarely has British strategy fallen into such a multitude of errors. Every maxim and principle of war was either violated or disregarded. The objective was to destroy Washington's army and kill or capture Washington. If he could be brought to battle and every man and gun turned against him, British victory was almost certain. But these obvious truths were befogged and bedeviled by multiplicity of counsel. The Government were well aware that Howe intended to move in the opposite direction to General Burgoyne, namely, southwards against Philadelphia, but did nothing to dissuade him.

Washington, from his winter quarters at Morristown, on the borders of New Jersey, moved hastily south-westwards to screen Philadelphia. At the beginning of September Howe advanced with about fourteen thousand men. His tactics went like clockwork. On September 26 his advance-guards entered Philadelphia. Burgoyne, with a few hundred Indians and seven thousand regulars, of whom half were German, was moving through the Canadian forests expecting to join with the British forces from New York. All concerned were confident that after capturing Philadelphia Howe could quickly return to New York and reach out to the expedition from Canada. He failed to do so, and Burgoyne paid the price. As Burgoyne advanced the New England militia gathered against him. General Clinton's garrison there had been halved, since Howe had called upon him for reinforcements. Nevertheless, Clinton marched north and captured two forts below West Point, but as the autumn rains descended Burgoyne was cornered at Saratoga, and the New Englanders, their strength daily increasing, closed in. Days of hard fighting in the woodlands followed. The German mercenaries refused to fight any longer, and on October 17, 1777, Burgoyne surrendered to the American commander, Horatio Gates.

At this point in the struggle the Old World stepped in to aid and comfort the New. Although militarily indecisive in America, Saratoga had an immediate effect in France. There was consternation in London, where the Whig Opposition had long warned the Government against harsh dealings with the colonists, and the British Ministry formulated a generous compromise. It was too late. On February 6, 1778, before the Congress could be apprised of the new offer, Benjamin Franklin signed an alliance with France. Thus began another world war, and Britain was now without a single ally. In the agony all minds except the King's turned to Chatham. On April 7 Chatham dragged himself upon crutches to make his last speech against an Opposition address for recalling the Army in America. He had always stood for conciliation and not for surrender. In whispering sentences, shot through with a sudden gleam of fierce anger, he made his attack "against the dismemberment of this ancient and most noble monarchy." He scourged his countrymen for their inhumanity. "My lords, if I were an American as I am an Englishman, while a foreign troop was landed in my country I never would lay down my arms—never, never, never." Burke's was a fitting memorial: "The means by which Providence raises a nation to greatness are the virtues infused into great men." Such men were very few in the England of Lord North.

While Washington could not count on provisions for his men even a day in advance, Howe danced and gambled in Philadelphia. Unnerved perhaps by the carnage at Bunker Hill, and still hoping for conciliation, he did nothing. Some inkling of his reluctance may have reached the ears of the Government; at any rate, when news of the French alliance with the rebels reached England at the beginning of the New Year his resignation was accepted. Howe's successor was Sir Henry Clinton, the former Commander of New York, who held very different views on the conduct of hostilities. The solution, he thought, was to occupy and settle the whole country. He resolved to abandon the offensive in the North and begin the process of reduction by subduing the South. Much could be said for all this, and much might have been achieved if he had been allowed to try it out, but there now appeared a new force which abruptly checked and in time proved deadly to the realization of these large plans. In April 1778 twelve French ships of the line, mounting, with their attendant frigates, over eight hundred guns, set sail from Toulon. News of their approach reached Clinton and it became his immediate and vital task to stop them seizing his main base at New York. On June 18 he accordingly abandoned Philadelphia and marched rapidly across New Jersey with ten thousand troops. Washington, his army swollen by spring recruiting to about equal strength, set off in parallel line of pursuit. Clinton beat off the Americans, not without heavy loss, and did not reach New York till the beginning of July. He was only just in time. Military operations in America came slowly to a standstill, and although three thousand of Clinton's troops occupied Savannah in Georgia on December 29 his plans for subduing the rebels from a Loyalist base in the South were hampered and curtailed. Stalemate continued throughout 1779, and for a time the main seat of war shifted from the New World. Fear of invasion gripped the British Government and troops intended for Clinton were kept in the British Isles. French diplomacy brought Spain into the war.

In December Clinton decided to try his hand once more at subduing the South. He resolved to capture Charleston, and on the 26th sailed for South Carolina with eight thousand men. For a time he prospered, heartened by news that the French fleet in the West Indies had been beaten by Admiral Rodney. Bad weather delayed him and the main siege did not begin till the end of March, but in May 1780 the town fell and five thousand Patriot troops surrendered in the biggest disaster yet sustained by American arms. Clinton had gained a valuable base, but he was confronted with civil war. It became evident that a huge army would be needed to occupy and subdue the country. But again sea-power intervened. Rumors that French troops were once more crossing the Atlantic made Clinton hasten back to New York, leaving Cornwallis, his second-in-command, to do the best he could in the South. This was little enough. Washington sent a small force against him under Gates. Cornwallis defeated Gates, the victor of Saratoga, at the Battle of Camden and marched into North Carolina, routing the guerrillas as he went, but the countryside rose in arms behind him.

In the North Clinton for the second time found himself in great peril. Over five thousand French troops under the Comte de Rochambeau had disembarked in July at Newport, in Rhode Island. New York, Clinton's base and harbor, seemed lost. But events, in the form of treachery, ran for a time with the British. Benedict Arnold had long been dissatisfied with the conduct of the Patriots, and he had recently married a Loyalist lady. His discontent and his doubts were deepened by the news of Gates's defeat at Camden, and he now offered to surrender West Point to Clinton for the sum of £20,000. Arnold's act of betrayal, though discovered in time, had a marked, if temporary, effect on the sentiment and cohesion of the Patriots.

Strategic divergences between Clinton and Cornwallis now brought disaster to the British and Loyalist cause. Clinton judged that the holding of South Carolina was the main object of the war in the South, and that any inland excursions depended on naval control of the coast. Cornwallis on the other hand was eager to press forward. There is no doubt he was wrong. In spite of the Loyalists' unpromising behavior in the previous campaign, and in spite of the nomination of Washington's ablest general, Nathanael Greene, to command the Patriot forces in the South, Cornwallis resolved to advance. In January 1781 he moved towards the borders of North Carolina. His forward detachments clashed with the Americans at Cowpens on the morning of the 17th. The American commander had placed his ill-organized and ill-disciplined militia with the Broad River behind them to stop them dispersing. But this time, stiffened by Continental troops, they mauled the British. Cornwallis nevertheless pressed on. His only hope was to bring Greene to battle and destroy him. They met at Guilford Court House on March 15. The American militia proved useless, but the trained nucleus of Greene's troops drawn up behind a rail fence wrought havoc among the British regulars. Cornwallis had no choice but to make for the coast and seek reinforcements from the Navy. Greene let him go. He lost the battles, but he won the campaign.

Cornwallis in the meantime, starved of supplies, and with ever-lengthening lines of communication, marched to the coast, where he hoped to make direct contact with Clinton by sea. In August he arrived at Yorktown, on Chesapeake Bay, and began to dig himself in. Nearly nine thousand Americans and eight thousand French assembled before Yorktown, while De Grasse blockaded the coast with thirty ships of the line. At the end of September the investment of Yorktown began, and the bombardment of the French siege artillery shattered the earth redoubts. On October 19, 1781, the whole army, about seven thousand strong, surrendered. On the very same day Clinton and the British squadron sailed from New York, but on hearing of the disaster they turned back. Sea-power had once more decided the issue, and but for the French blockade the British war of attrition might well have succeeded. Two years were to pass before peace came to America, but no further military operations of any consequence took place.

The surrender at Yorktown had immediate and decisive effects in England. In March North informed the Commons that he would resign. Rockingham made his terms with the King: independence for the colonies and some lessening of the Crown's influence in politics. George III was forced to accept, and Rockingham took office. It fell to him and his colleague, Lord Shelburne, to save what they could from the wreckage of the First British Empire.

The eighteenth century saw a revolutionary change in the British position in India. The English East India Company, founded simply as a trading venture, grew with increasing speed into a vast territorial Empire. About the year 1700 probably no more than fifteen hundred English people dwelt in India, including wives, children, and transient seamen. They lived apart in a handful of factories, as their trading stations were called, little concerned with Indian politics. A hundred years later British officials and soldiers in their thousands, under a British Governor-General, were in control of extensive provinces. This remarkable development was in part a result of the struggle between Britain and France, which filled the age and was fought out all over the globe.

The acquisition of territory played little part in the thoughts and plans of either nation, and indeed the Directors of the English East India Company had long been reluctant to own any land or assume any responsibilities beyond the confines of their trading stations. About 1740 events forced them to change their tune. The Mahrattas slaughtered the Nawab, or Imperial Governor, of the Carnatic, the five-hundred-mile-long province on the south-eastern coast. It was becoming impossible for the European traders to stand aside. They must either fight on their own or in alliance with Indian rulers or quit. The Government was never involved as a principal in the Indian conflict, and while Pitt, who justly appreciated the ability of Robert Clive, supported him with all the re-sources at his command, his influence on events was small. Of India it has been well said that the British Empire was acquired in a fit of absence of mind.

CHAPTER NINE

Napoleon

The Marquis of Rockingham had waited long for his opportunity to form a Government, and when at last it came in March 1782 he had but four months to live. He died in July, and Lord Shelburne was entrusted with the new administration. Shelburne sought to form a Government by enlisting politicians of the most diverse views and connection. Of great ability, a brilliant orator, and with the most liberal ideas, he was nevertheless, like Carteret before him, distrusted on all sides. Shelburne himself had the support of those who had followed Chatham, including his son, the young William Pitt, who was appointed Chancellor of the Exchequer. But North still commanded a considerable faction, and, smarting at his sovereign's cold treatment after twelve years of faithful service, coveted a renewal of office. The third group was headed by Charles James Fox, vehement critic of North's régime, brilliant, generous-hearted, and inconsistent. Hostility to Shelburne grew and spread. Nevertheless, by negotiations in which he displayed great skill, the Prime Minister succeeded in bringing the world war to an end on the basis of American independence. The difficulty was the Canadian frontier. After months of negotiation a frontier was agreed upon which ran from the borders of Maine to the St. Lawrence, up the river, and through the Great Lakes to their head. Everything south of this line, east of the Mississippi and north of the borders of Florida, became American territory. This was by

ENGLISH CONFLICTS
in EUROPE
18th Century
Boundaries as of 1713, after Treaty of Utrecht

far the most important result of the treaty. France now made her terms with England. An armistice was declared in January 1783, and the final peace treaty was signed at Versailles later in the year. The French kept their possessions in India and the West Indies. They were guaranteed the right to fish off Newfoundland, and they reoccupied the slave-trade settlements of Senegal on the African coast. The important cotton island of Tobago was ceded to them, but apart from this they gained little that was material. Their main object however was achieved. The Thirteen Colonies had been wrested from the United Kingdom, and England's position in the world seemed to have been gravely weakened. Spain was forced to join in the general settlement. Her American ambitions had melted away, her one gain in this theater being the two English colonies in Florida; but this was at the expense of the English retention of Gibraltar, the main Spanish objective. She had conquered Minorca, the English naval station in the Mediterranean during the war, and she kept that at the peace. Thus ended what some then called the World War.

England's emergence from her ordeal was the work of Shelburne. He resigned after eight months, in February 1783. Shelburne's Government was followed by a machine-made coalition between North and Fox. It was said that this combination was too much even for the agile consciences of the age. Within nine months this Ministry also collapsed. Party and personal issues alike being exhausted by the weight of the disaster, George III saw his opportunity if he could find the man. By what was certainly the most outstanding domestic action of his long reign, in December 1783, the King asked Pitt to form a Government.

The revolt of the American colonies had shattered the complacency of eigh-

teenth-century England. Men began to study the root causes of the disaster and the word "reform" was in the air. England was silently undergoing a revolution in industry and agriculture, which was to have more far-reaching effects than the political tumults of the times. An ever-expanding and assertive industrial community was coming into being. The religious revival of John Wesley had broken the stony surface of the Age of Reason. Demand for some reform of the representation in Parliament began to stir; but the agitation was now mild and respectable. The main aim of the reformers was to increase the number of boroughs which elected Members of Parliament, and thus reduce the possibilities of Government corruption. Many of the early reform schemes were academic attempts to preserve the political power and balance of the rural interest. The individualism of eighteenth-century England assumed no doctrinaire form. The enunciation of first principles has always been obnoxious to the English mind.

The elections which carried Pitt into power were the most carefully planned of the century. His majority rested on a number of elements—Pitt's personal following; the "Party of the Crown," put at his disposal by George III; the independent country gentlemen; the East India interest, alienated by Fox's attempt to curb their political power; and the Scottish Members, marshaled by Dundas. Thus from the outset Pitt was overcome by the dead hand of eighteenth-century politics. He failed to abolish the slave trade. He failed to make a settlement in Ireland. He failed to make Parliament more representative of the nation, and the one achievement in these early months was his India Act, which increased rather than limited the opportunities for political corruption. He saw quite clearly the need and justification for reform, but preferred always to compromise with the forces of resistance. The greatest orators of the age, Fox and Burke, were Pitt's opponents. They dwelt eloquently on the broad themes of reform. Yet it was Pitt, aided by Dundas, who in a quiet, business-like way reconstructed the practical policies of the nation.

It was in the most practical and most urgent problem, the ordering and reconstruction of the country's financial structure, that Pitt achieved his best work, and created that Treasury tradition of wise, incorruptible management which still prevails. It is to Pitt that we owe the modern machinery of the "Budget." By gathering around him able officials he reorganized the collection and disbursement of the revenue. The National Debt stood at two hundred and fifty million pounds, more than two and a half times as great as in the days of Walpole. Pitt resolved to acquire a surplus in the revenue and apply it to the reduction of this swollen burden. In 1786 he brought in a Bill for this purpose. Each year a million pounds would be set aside to buy stock, and the interest would be used to reduce the National Debt. Here was the famous oft-criticized Sinking Fund. In this same year, 1786, the Customs and Excise were amalgamated, and a reconstituted Board of Trade established in its modern form. But perhaps the most striking achievement of Pitt's management was the negotiation of the Eden treaty with France —the first Free Trade treaty according to the new economic principles. In 1776 Adam Smith had published *The Wealth of Nations,* which quickly became famous throughout educated circles. Pitt was deeply influenced by his book. He was the first English statesman to believe in Free Trade, and for a while his Tory followers accepted it.

Fully aware of the economic changes in eighteenth-century England, Pitt was less sensitive to signs of political disturbance abroad. He believed firmly in non-intervention, and the break-up of the Old Régime in France left him unimpressed. The First Minister was deaf to the zealous campaign of the Whig Opposition in favor of the French Revolutionaries, and ignored the warnings of Burke and others who believed that the principles of monarchy, and indeed of civilized society, were endangered by the roar of events across the Channel.

In England the Whigs, and especially the reformers and Radicals, had at first welcomed the French Revolution. They were soon repelled by its excesses. In his Budget speech of 1792 Pitt had announced that he believed in fifteen years of peace for Europe. Non-intervention was his policy. Something more vital to Britain than a massacre of aristocrats or a speech in the Convention, something more concrete than a threat of world revolution, had to happen before he would face the issue of war. The spark, as so often in England's history, came from the Netherlands. On the last day of January 1793 the French Convention, with Danton's defiant speech in their ears, decreed the annexation of the Austrian Netherlands to the French Republic. The next day France declared war on Great Britain and Holland, firm in the belief that an internal revolution in England was imminent. Pitt now had no choice.

If Britain had possessed even a small effective army it would not have been difficult, in concert with allies moving from the Rhine, to strike from the French coast at Paris and overthrow the Government responsible for provoking the conflict. But Pitt was barely able to send five thousand men to help his Dutch allies protect their frontiers from invasion. By 1795 the British forces on the Continent were driven back upon the mouth of the Ems on the German border, whence they were evacuated home. Great hopes had been founded in London upon the French Royalists, who launched daring schemes to arrest the Revolution by civil war in France. In 1793 they seized Toulon, and but for the fact that Dundas had already assigned all available troops to the West Indies a vital base for future invasion might have been secured. Something else happened at Toulon. A young lieutenant of the French Army, sprung from a leading Corsican family, well versed in artillery and other military matters, happening to be on leave from his regiment, looked in on the camp of General Carteaux, who commanded the Jacobin besieging army. Orders arrived from Paris prescribing the method of siege according to customary forms, for which however the necessary material resources were lacking. None dared dispute the instructions of the terrible Committee of Public Safety which was now at the head of French affairs. Nevertheless, at the council of war, held in daylight, on bare ground, the expert lieutenant raised his voice. The orders, he said—or so he claimed later—were foolish, and all knew it. There was however a way of taking Toulon. He placed his finger on the map where Fort l'Aiguillette on its promontory commanded the entrance to the harbor. "There is Toulon," he said, and all, taking their lives in their hands, obeyed him. He organized and led the assault upon Fort l'Aiguillette. After a hot fight it fell. The whole wide front of the Toulon defenses remained intact, but on the morning after Fort l'Aiguillette fell the British Fleet was seen to be leaving the harbor. Once the British Fleet had departed all resisting power perished. The lieutenant had understood not only the military significance of the captured fort, but the whole set of moral and political forces upon which the Royalist defense of Toulon hung. His name was Napoleon Bonaparte. He became the sword of the Revolution, which he was determined to exploit and to destroy.

In England the Government had been forced to take repressive measures of a sternness unknown for generations. Republican lecturers were swept into prison. The Habeas Corpus Act was suspended. The mildest criticism of the Constitution brought the speaker under danger from a new Treason Act. Few victories came to brighten these dark years. In 1794 the French Channel Fleet, ill-equipped and under-officered, was half-heartedly engaged by Admiral Howe. Three years later, off Cape St. Vincent, the Spanish Fleet—Spain being now in alliance with France—was soundly beaten by Jervis and Nelson. But such had been the neglect of conditions of service in the Navy that the ships at Spithead refused to put to sea. Some slight concessions satisfied the mutineers, and they retrieved their honor in a handsome victory off Camperdown over the Dutch, who were now satellites of France. France, dominant in Western Europe, firmly planted in the Mediterranean, safeguarded against attack from Germany by a secret understanding with Austria, had only to consider what she would conquer next. A sober judgment might have said England, by way of Ireland. Bonaparte thought he saw his destiny in a larger field. In the spring of 1798 he sailed for Egypt.

During the afternoon of August 1 a scouting vessel from Nelson's fleet signaled that a number of French battleships were anchored in Aboukir Bay, to the east of Alexandria. The French Admiral Brueys was convinced that not even an English admiral would risk sailing his ship between the shoals and the French line. But Nelson knew his captains. Five British ships passed in succession on the land side of the enemy, while Nelson, in the *Vanguard,* led the rest of his fleet to lie to on the starboard of the French line. Relentlessly the English ships, distinguished by four lanterns hoisted in a horizontal pattern, battered the enemy van, passing from one disabled foe to the next down the line. At ten o'clock Brueys's flagship, the *Orient,* blew up. The five ships ahead of her had already surrendered; the rest, their cables cut by shot, or frantically attempting to avoid the inferno of the burning *Orient,* drifted helplessly. In the morning hours three ran ashore and surrendered, and a fourth was burned by her officers. Of the great fleet that had convoyed Napoleon's army to the adventure in Egypt only two ships of the line and two frigates escaped. Nelson's victory of the Nile cut Napoleon's communications with France and ended his hopes of vast Eastern conquests. In 1799 he escaped back to France, leaving his army behind him. The British Fleet was once again supreme in the Mediterranean Sea. This was a turning-point. With the capture of Malta in 1800 after a prolonged siege Britain had secured a strong naval base in the Mediterranean, and there was no further need to bring the squadrons home for the winter as in the early part of the war. But still the British Government could conceive no coordinated military plan upon the scale demanded by European strategy. Their own resources were few and their allies seldom dependable. Meanwhile, Napoleon again took charge of the French armies in Italy. In June 1800 he beat the Austrians at Marengo, in Piedmont, and France was once more mistress of Europe.

Union with Scotland had been a success. Why not with Ireland too? The shocks and alarms of the previous years determined Pitt to attempt some final settlement in that troubled island. But the prime requisite for any agreement must be the emancipation of Irish Catholics from the disabilities of the penal laws. Pitt had committed himself to the cause of Catholic freedom without extracting a written agreement from the King. When George refused his assent, on March 14, 1801, Pitt felt bound to resign. Catholic emancipation was delayed for nearly thirty years. The Act of Union had meanwhile been carried through the Irish Parliament by wholesale patronage and bribery against vehement opposition. Bitter fruits were to follow from this in the later nineteenth century. Pitt was succeeded by a pinchbeck coalition of King's Friends and rebels from his own party. Masquerading as a Government of National Union, they blundered on for over three years. Their leader was Henry Addington, an amiable former Speaker of the House of Commons whom no one regarded as a statesman. In March 1802 Addington's Government made terms with Napoleon by the Treaty of Amiens, and for a time there was a pause in the fighting. In May 1803 war was renewed, and once more mismanaged.

Pitt was in retirement at Walmer, in Kent. The strain of the past years had broken his health. He was prematurely aged. He had lived a lonely, artificial life, cheered by few friendships. The only time that he ever came in contact with the people was during this brief interval from office, when as Warden of the Cinque Ports he organized the local militia against the threat of invasion. Few things in England's history are more remarkable than this picture of an ex-Prime Minister, riding his horse at the head of a motley company of yokels, drilling on the fields of the South Coast, while a bare twenty miles away across the Channel the Grand Army of Napoleon waited only for a fair wind and a clear passage.

In 1804 Pitt was recalled to power. Since the renewal of war Britain had found herself alone against Napoleon, and for two years she maintained the struggle single-handed during one of the most critical periods in her history.

At the crest of his hopes Napoleon had himself crowned by the Pope as Emperor of the French. One thing alone was lacking to his designs—command of the sea. As before and since in her history, the Royal Navy alone seemed to stand between the Island and national destruction. Day in, day out, winter and summer, British fleets kept blockade of the French naval bases of Brest and Rochefort on the Atlantic coast and Toulon in the Mediterranean. In May 1803 Nelson had returned to the Mediterranean to resume command of his fleet. He kept a screen of frigates watching Toulon, and himself with his battleships lay off Sardinia, alert for interception. Twice in the course of two years the French attempted a sortie, but retired.

In May 1804 the Emperor had confided the Toulon fleet to Admiral Villeneuve, an excellent seaman, who realized that his ships, except for the luck of circumstance, could only play a defensive part. Spain was dragged into his schemes, her Fleet being a necessary adjunct to the main plan. In the early months of 1805 Napoleon made his final arrangements. Over ninety thousand assault troops, picked and trained, lay in the camps round Boulogne. The French Channel ports were not constructed to take battleships, and the French fleets in the Atlantic and Mediterranean harbors must be concentrated elsewhere to gain command of the Channel. The Emperor fixed upon the West Indies. Here, after breaking the Mediterranean and Atlantic blockades, and drawing off the British Fleet, as he thought, into the waters of the Western Atlantic, his ships were ordered to gather. The combined French and Spanish Fleets would then unite with Ganteaume, the Admiral of the Brest Squadron, double back to Europe, sail up the Channel, and assure the crossing from Boulogne.

Nelson was lying in wait off the Sardinian coastline in April 1805 when news reached him that Villeneuve was at sea, having slipped out of Toulon on the dark night of March 30, sailing, as Nelson did not yet know, in a westerly direction with eleven ships of the line and eight frigates. The fox was out and the chase began. Nelson, picking up scattered reports from frigates and merchantmen, pieced together the French design. Villeneuve and his Spanish allies reached Martinique on May 14. Nelson made landfall at Barbados on June 4. Meanwhile, news of his arrival alarmed the French Admiral, who was promptly out again in the Atlantic by June 8, heading east. Before leaving the islands Nelson sent a fast sloop back to England with dispatches, and on June 19 it passed Villeneuve's fleet, noting his course and position. The commander of the sloop saw that Villeneuve was heading northeastwards for the Bay of Biscay, and raced home, reaching Plymouth on July 8. Nelson was sailing rapidly eastwards after Villeneuve, believing he would catch him at Cadiz and head him off the Straits, while the French Fleet was making steadily on a more northerly course in the direction of Cape Finisterre. Villeneuve intended to release the Franco-Spanish squadron blockaded at Ferrol, and, thus reinforced, join with Ganteaume from Brest. But Ganteaume, in spite of peremptory orders from Napoleon, failed to break out. Admiral Cornwallis's fleet in the Western Approaches kept him in port. Meanwhile, on orders from the First Lord of the Admiralty, Lord Barham, Admiral Calder intercepted Villeneuve off Finisterre, and here in late July the campaign of Trafalgar opened. Calder's action was indecisive, and the French took refuge in Ferrol.

Nelson meanwhile had reached Cadiz on July 18. Realizing that Villeneuve must have gone north, he replenished his fleet in Morocco and sailed for home waters on the 23rd. On the same day Napoleon arrived at Boulogne. Calder joined Cornwallis off Brest on August 14, and on the next day Nelson arrived with twelve more ships, bringing the main fleet up to a total of nearly forty ships of the line. Thus was the sea-barrier concentrated against the French. Nelson went on alone with his flagship, the *Victory,* to Portsmouth. In the following days the campaign reached its climax. Villeneuve sailed again from Ferrol on August 13 in an attempt to join Ganteaume and enter the English Channel, for Napoleon still believed that the British fleets were dispersed and that the moment had come for invasion. On August 21 Ganteaume was observed to be leaving harbor, but Cornwallis closed in with his whole force and the French turned back. Meanwhile, Villeneuve, having edged out into the Atlantic, had changed his mind. The threat of invasion was over.

Early in September dispatches reached London telling that Villeneuve had gone south. Nelson, summoned from his home at Merton, was at once ordered to resume his command. Amid scenes of enthusiasm he rejoined the *Victory* at Portsmouth and sailed on September 15. A fortnight later he joined the Fleet off Cadiz, now numbering twenty-seven ships of the line. His object was to starve the enemy Fleet, now concentrated in Cadiz harbor, and force it out into the open sea and to battle. To gain a decisive victory, he was resolved to abandon the old formal line of battle, running parallel to the enemy's Fleet. He would break Villeneuve's line, when it came out of port, by sailing at right angles boldly into it with two main divisions. While the enemy van was thus cut off and out of touch his center and rear would be destroyed. At daybreak on the 21st he saw from the quarterdeck of the *Victory* the

battle line of the enemy, consisting of an advance-squadron of twelve Spanish ships under Admiral Gravina and twenty-one French ships of the line under Villeneuve. Nelson signaled his ships to steer east-north-east for the attack in the two columns he had planned. The enemy turned northwards on seeing the advancing squadrons, and Nelson pressed on with every sail set. The clumsy seamanship of his men convinced Villeneuve that flight was impossible, and he hove to in a long sagging line to await Nelson's attack. Nelson signaled to Collingwood, who was at the head of the southern column in the *Royal Sovereign,* "I intend to pass through the van of the enemy's line, to prevent him getting into Cadiz." Nelson went down to his cabin to compose a prayer. "May the Great God whom I worship grant to my country and for the benefit of Europe in general a great and glorious Victory. . . . For myself individually I commit my life to Him who made me, and may His blessing light upon my endeavors for serving my country faithfully." The Fleets were drawing nearer and nearer. Another signal was run up upon the *Victory,* "England expects every man will do his duty."

A deathly silence fell upon the Fleet as the ships drew nearer. Each captain marked down his adversary, and within a few minutes the two English columns thundered into action. The *Victory* smashed through between Villeneuve's flagship, the *Bucentaure,* and the *Redoutable.* The three ships remained locked together, raking each other with broadsides. Nelson was pacing as if on parade on his quarterdeck when at 1:15 p.m. he was shot from the mast-head of the *Redoutable* by a bullet in the shoulder. His backbone was broken, and he was carried below amid the thunder of the *Victory's* guns. By the afternoon of October 21, 1805, eighteen of the enemy ships had surrendered and the remainder were in full retreat. Eleven entered Cadiz, but four more were captured off the coast of Spain. In the log of the *Victory* occurs the passage, "Partial firing continued until 4:30, when a victory having been reported to the Right Hon. Lord Viscount Nelson, K.B. and Commander-in-Chief, he then died of his wound."

Napoleon meanwhile was attracted to other fields. He determined to strike at the European coalition raised against him by Pitt's diplomacy and subsidies. The campaign that followed wrecked Pitt's hopes and schemes. A personal sorrow now darkened Pitt's life. The House of Commons by the casting vote of the Speaker resolved to impeach his close colleague and lifelong companion, Henry Dundas, now Lord Melville, for maladministration in the Admiralty and for the peculations of certain of his subordinates. The decisive speech against Dundas was made by none other than Wilberforce, the friend of Pitt's Cambridge days, and the only person who enjoyed his confidence. It was this disgrace, rather than the news of Austerlitz, which finally broke the spirit and energy of the Prime Minister. In January 1806 he died.

"In an age," runs the inscription on his monument in Guildhall, "when the contagion of ideals threatened to dissolve the forms of civil society he rallied the loyal, the sober-minded, and the good around the venerable structure of the English monarchy." This is a fitting epitaph.

The three years between the death of Pitt in January 1806 and the rise of Wellington in 1809 were uncheered by fortune. In 1806 and 1807 there was a brief Ministry of "All the Talents" under Lord Grenville. The Government's tenure of office was redeemed by Fox's abolition of the slave trade, a measure which ranks among the greatest of British achievements, and from which Pitt had always shrunk. It was Fox's last effort. For forty years his warm-hearted eloquence had inspired the Whigs. Almost his whole Parliamentary life was spent in Opposition. He died as Secretary of State, nine months after his great rival, Pitt, had gone to the grave. In 1807 the Whigs fell. They were succeeded by a mixed Government of Tory complexion under the nominal leadership of the Duke of Portland. Its object was to hold together the loyalties of as much of the nation as it could command. In this it was remarkably successful.

The Franco-Russian Alliance, signed at Tilsit on July 7, was the culmination of Napoleon's power. Only Britannia remained, unreconciled, unconquered, implacable. There she lay in her Island, mistress of the seas and oceans, ruled by her proud, stubborn aristocracy, facing this immense combination alone, sullen, fierce, and almost unperturbed. Secure throughout the rest of Europe, Napoleon turned his attention to the Spanish Peninsula. Powerless at sea, he realized that to destroy his one outstanding rival he must turn the weapon of blockade against the Island. English goods must be kept out of the markets of Europe by an iron ring of customs guards stretching from the borders of Russia round the coasts of Northern Europe and Western France and sealing the whole Mediterranean coastline as far as the Dardanelles. In reply to Napoleon's Continental System the British Government issued an Order in Council declaring a sea blockade of all French and French-allied ports —in other words, of almost the whole of Europe. Napoleon's decrees and the English Orders wounded the merchant shipping of the neutral countries. The results of this trade war were far-reaching for both sides. The commerce of Europe was paralyzed and the nations stirred beneath the French yoke. Interference by British ships with neutral vessels raised with the United States the question of the freedom of the seas. It was a grievous dispute, not to be settled without recourse to war.

Napoleon, insatiable of power, and seeking always to break England and her intangible blockade, resolved to seize the Spanish Crown. He placed his own brother Joseph on the throne of Spain as a vassal of the French Empire. As soon as the Spaniards realized what had happened and that their country was practically annexed to France they rose everywhere in spontaneous revolt. Nothing like this universal uprising of a numerous, ancient race and nation, all animated by one thought, had been seen before. This country, which Napoleon had expected to incorporate in his Empire by a personal arrangement with a feeble Government, by a trick, by a trap, without bloodshed or expense, suddenly became his main military problem. Canning and his colleagues decided to send an army to the Peninsula to aid the Spanish insurgents. At the head of the first troops to land appeared Sir Arthur Wellesley, whose conduct of the Mahratta War in India had been distinguished. He did not wait for the rest of the army, but immediately took the field. The French columns of assault were broken by the reserved fire of the "thin red line," which now began to attract attention. Junot retreated upon Lisbon. Wellesley's wish to seize the pass of Torres Vedras and thus cut Junot's line of retreat was frustrated by his seniors. But the French commander now offered to evacuate Portugal if the British would carry him back to France. The Convention of Cintra was signed, and punctiliously executed by the British. History has endorsed Byron's line, "Britannia sickens, Cintra! at thy name."

Napoleon now moved a quarter of a million of his best troops into Spain. An avalanche of fire and steel broke upon the Spanish Juntas who, with ninety thousand raw but ardent volunteers, had nursed a brief illusion of freedom regained. The Emperor advanced upon Madrid, driving the Spanish army before him in a series of routs, in which the French cavalry took pitiless vengeance. But the Spanish people were undaunted, and all around the camps of the victorious invaders flickered a horrible guerrilla.

A new English general of high quality had succeeded the commanders involved in the Convention of Cintra. Sir John Moore advanced from Lisbon through Salamanca to Valladolid. His daring thrust cut or threatened the communications of all the French armies, and immediately prevented any French action in the south of Spain or against Portugal. But Napoleon, watching from Madrid, saw him a prey. Moore, warned in time, and invoking amphibious power, dropped his communications with Portugal and ordered his transports to meet him at Corunna, on the north-west tip of Spain. The retreat of the British through the rugged, snow-bound hill country was arduous. The French pressed heavily. It was now resolved to slip away in the night to Corunna, where the army arrived on January 14, 1809. But the harbor was empty. Contrary winds had delayed the Fleet and transports. On the 16th Soult assaulted Moore with twenty thousand against fourteen thousand. He was everywhere repulsed, and indeed counter-attacked. But both Sir John Moore and his second-in-command, Sir David Baird, had fallen on the field. Moore's countrymen may well do him justice. By daring, skill, and luck he had ruptured Napoleon's winter campaign and had drawn the Emperor and his finest army into the least important part of Spain, thus affording protection and time for movements to get on foot in all the rest of the Peninsula. His campaign had restored the military reputation of Britain, which had suffered increasing eclipse since the days of Chatham; he had prepared the way for a new figure, destined to lead the armies of Europe upon the decisive field.

When the British sailed away from Corunna no organized forces remained in Spain to hinder Napoleon's Marshals. Soult now entered Portugal and established himself at Oporto. Few observers were then convinced that effective success could be won in distant Spain and Portugal. These doubts were not shared by Arthur Wellesley. In April he was reappointed to take command in Lisbon. The passage of the Douro, the surprise of Oporto, and the discomfiture of Soult constituted a brilliant achievement for the new British General and paved the way for further action. Wellesley now resolved to penetrate into the center of Spain along the valley of the Tagus, and, joining the Spanish army under Cuesta, to engage Marshal Victor. Wellesley's position at Talavera, a hundred miles south-west of Madrid, became precarious, and his soldiers were near starvation. Marshal Victor conceived himself strong enough to attack without waiting for the arrival of Soult. On the afternoon of July 27, 1809, the armies engaged. Victor's attacks, which began in earnest on the 28th, were ill-concerted, and were repulsed with heavy loss after fierce massfighting with the bayonet. In the afternoon the crisis of the battle was reached. By nightfall Marshal Victor accepted defeat and withdrew towards Madrid. The ferocity of the fighting may be judged from the British losses. Nearly six thousand men out of Wellesley's total of twenty thousand had fallen, killed or wounded; the French had lost seven thousand five hundred and twenty guns. The Spaniards claimed to have lost one thousand two hundred men. Wellesley

was in no condition to pursue. He withdrew unmolested along the Tagus back to Portugal. In England there was unwonted satisfaction. Sir Arthur Wellesley was raised to the peerage as Viscount Wellington, and, in spite of Whig opposition, was granted a pension of £2,000 a year for three years.

The disgrace of the Convention at Cintra had sharpened the rivalry and mutual dislike of Canning and Castlereagh. Now the two Ministers were at loggerheads over the disaster that threatened the expedition to Walcheren. Tempers were sharpened by the ill-defined and over-lapping functions of the Foreign Secretary and the Secretary for War. A duel was fought between them, in which Canning was wounded. Both resigned office, and so did Portland. Spencer Perceval, hitherto Chancellor of the Exchequer, took over the Government. Wellington's cause in Spain was favored by the new administration. In 1810 the King's renewed madness provoked a fresh crisis. George, Prince of Wales, became Regent.

These were testing years for Wellington. He commanded Britain's sole remaining army on the continent of Europe. The French had always bent every effort to driving the British into the sea. In 1810 they were massing for a fresh attempt. The ablest of Napoleon's Marshals, Masséna, now headed the French Army of Portugal. In September there was a stiff battle at Busaco. The French were badly mauled and beaten. Wellington's withdrawal nevertheless continued. Suddenly the forward flow of the French came to a halt. Ahead of them rose the formidable lines of Torres Vedras, manned by the undefeated British, and all around extended a countryside deliberately laid waste. This was the hinge of the whole campaign. The French paused and dug into winter quarters. In the following spring Masséna gave up. He retreated into Spain, leaving behind him seventeen thousand dead and eight thousand prisoners.

Rejoicing in London and Lisbon however was mingled with a certain impatience. Wellington himself was unperturbed by cries for haste. He must have in his hands the frontier fortresses of Badajoz and Ciudad Rodrigo, which guarded the roads to Madrid. Two French armies confronted him. Masséna, later replaced by Marmont, held the northern front in the province of Leon. Soult lay to the south in Andalusia. The Battles of Fuentes and Albuera, which was fought by Wellington's lieutenant, Beresford, were not decisive, but the British remained masters of the field. In fact Wellington was already laying his plans for the day when he would drive the French back over the Pyrenees and carry the conflict into their own country. Amid the snows of January 1812 he was at last able to seize Ciudad Rodrigo. Four months later Badajoz fell to a bloody assault. The cost in life was heavy, but the way was opened for an overpowering thrust into Spain. Wellington and Marmont maneuvered about one another, each watching for the other to make a mistake. It was Marmont who erred, and at Salamanca Wellington achieved his first victory on the offensive in the Peninsular War. King Joseph Bonaparte fled from Madrid, and the British occupied the capital amid the pealing of bells and popular rejoicing. But there was still Soult to be dealt with. He outnumbered the British commander by nearly two to one, and he was careful to offer no opening for promising attack. Wellington fell back once more on the Portuguese frontier. In the year's campaign he had shattered one French army and enabled the whole of Southern Spain to be freed from the French. But meanwhile heavier shadows from the East were falling upon Napoleon's Empire. It was the winter of the retreat from Moscow.

On the southern front Wellington's achievement surpassed all expectations. At the Battle of Vitoria on June 21 he routed Marshal Jourdan and drove his forces over the Pyrenees. News of this victory heartened the Czar and for the first and only time in history the success of British arms was greeted by a *Te Deum* sung in Russian. Tenaciously Wellington pursued his purpose of reducing, as he put it, "the power and influence of the grand disturber of Europe." By spring of 1814 he was on French soil and had occupied Bordeaux. In early April he sought out and defeated his old antagonist, Soult, at Toulouse. For Napoleon the end had already come. In the south the front had crumbled; to the east Prussians, Russians, and Austrians were reaching into the heart of France. Napoleon was never more brilliant in maneuver than during his brief campaign of 1814. But the combined strength of Europe was too much for him. The forces of opposition to his rule in France openly rose against him. On April 3 Napoleon abdicated and retired to the island of Elba. The long, remorseless tides of war rolled back, and at the Congress of Vienna the Powers prepared for the diplomatic struggle of the peace.

The confused and tumultuous issues of European politics reached America in black and white, becoming less theoretical and much more vehement as soon as American commercial interests were affected. Tempers rose as American ships and merchandise endured the commerce-raiding and privateering of France and Britain. But, as the Battle of Trafalgar had proved, the Royal Navy was much more powerful than the French, and it was at the hands of the British that American shipping suffered most. Anglo-American relations grew steadily worse.

The unofficial trade war with the United States was telling heavily upon England. The loss of the American market and the hard winter of 1811–12 had brought widespread unemployment and a business crisis. Petitions were sent to Parliament begging the Government to revoke the Orders in Council. After much hesitation Castlereagh, now at the Foreign Office, announced in the House of Commons that the Government had done so. But it was too late. The Atlantic crossing took too long for the news to reach America in time. On June 18, 1812, two days after Castlereagh's announcement, Congress declared war on Great Britain.

The root of the quarrel, as American historians have pointed out, lay not in rival interpretations of maritime law, but in the problems of the Western frontier. The seaboard States, and especially New England, wanted peace. But on the frontiers, and especially in the North-West, men were hungry for land, and this could be had only from the Indians or from the British Empire. Trouble with the Indians had been brewing for some time. As the Western territories of America filled up, pressure mounted for a farther north-westerly move. In 1811 the Red Indians bordering on the Ohio united under their last great warrior-leader, Tecumseh. It is one of the legends of American history that the resistance of the Indians was encouraged and organized from Canada —a legend created by the war party of 1812. A new generation was entering American politics, headed by Henry Clay from Kentucky and John C. Calhoun from South Carolina. They had no conception of affairs in Europe; they cared nothing about Napoleon's designs, still less about the fate of Russia. Their prime aim and object was to seize Canada and establish American sovereignty throughout the whole Northern continent. A short expedition of pioneers would set

things right, it was thought, and dictate peace in Quebec in a few weeks. Congress adjourned without even voting extra money for the American Army or Navy.

The first American expedition ended in disaster. By August the British were in Detroit, and within a few days Fort Dearborn, where Chicago now stands, had fallen. The remainder of the year was spent on fruitless moves upon the Niagara front, and operations came to an inconclusive end. The British in Canada were forced to remain on the defensive while great events were taking place in Europe. The war at sea was more colorful, and for the Americans more cheering. They had sixteen vessels, of which three surpassed anything afloat. Within a year they had won more successes over the British than the French and Spaniards in two decades of warfare. But retribution was at hand. On June 1, 1813, the American frigate *Chesapeake*, under Captain Laurence, sailed from Boston harbor with a green and mutinous crew to accept a challenge from Captain Broke of H.M.S. *Shannon*. After a fifteen-minute fight the *Chesapeake* surrendered. Other American losses followed, and command of the ocean passed into British hands. American privateers, however, continued to harry British shipping throughout the rest of the war.

The Americans set about revising their strategy. By land they made a number of raids into the province of Upper Canada, now named Ontario. Towns and villages were sacked and burned. In October, the United States were established on the southern shores of the Great Lakes and the Indians could no longer outflank their frontier. But the invasion of Upper Canada on land had been a failure, and the year ended with the Canadians in possession of Fort Niagara.

Hitherto the British in Canada had lacked the means for offensive action.

Troops and ships in Europe were locked in the deadly struggle against Napoleon. But by the spring of 1814 a decision had been reached in Europe. Napoleon abdicated in April and the British could at last send adequate reinforcements.

Peace negotiations had been tried throughout the war, but it was not until January 1814 that the British had agreed to treat. The American Commissioners, among them Henry Clay, reached Ghent in June. The previous November Wellington had been asked to take command in America. He realized that victory depended on naval superiority upon the Lakes. He saw no way of gaining it. He held moreover that it was not in Britain's interest to demand territory from America on the Canadian border. Both sides therefore agreed upon the *status quo* for the long boundary in the North. Other points were left undetermined. Naval forces on the Great Lakes were regulated by a Commission in 1817, and the disputed boundary of Maine was similarly settled later.

Thus ended a futile and unnecessary conflict. The results of the peace were solid and enduring. The British Army and Navy had learned to respect their former colonials. Canadians took pride in the part they had played in defending their country, and their growing national sentiment was strengthened. Henceforward the world was to see a three-thousand-mile international frontier between Canada and the United States undefended by men or guns. On the oceans the British Navy ruled supreme for a century to come, and behind this shield the United States were free to fulfill their continental destiny.

Britain was represented at the Congress of Vienna by Castlereagh. In 1812 the Prime Minister, Perceval, had been shot dead by a madman in the lobby of the House of Commons. His colleague, Lord Liverpool, took over the administration, and remained in power for fifteen years. Castlereagh rejoined the Government as Foreign Secretary, an office he was to hold until his death. Castlereagh believed in the Balance of Power. This is a concept that became unpopular in the twentieth century during the interval between the World Wars. On the Continent the main preoccupation of the Powers was to draw a *cordon sanitaire* around France to protect Central Europe from the infections and dangers of revolution. The British were principally concerned with the colonial settlement. Many conquests were returned, yet the Peace of Paris, which was the outcome of the Congress, marks another stage in the establishment of the new Empire which was replacing the lost American colonies. The captured French colonies were surrendered, with the exception of Mauritius, Tobago and St. Lucia. The Dutch recovered their possessions in the East Indies. At the price of three millions sterling Britain acquired part of Guiana from the Dutch. The Government, however, was most concerned with those possessions which had a strategic value as ports of call. For that reason it held on to Malta, and the key of the route to India, the Cape of Good Hope. From this acquisition in South Africa a troubled saga was to unfold. Dutch Ceylon was kept, and Danish Heligoland, which had proved a fine base for breaking the Continental System and smuggling goods into Germany. These gains were scattered and piecemeal, but, taken together, they represented a powerful consolidation of the Imperial structure.

Napoleon had for nine months been sovereign of Elba. In February 1815 he saw, or thought he saw, that the Congress of Vienna was breaking up. The Allies were at odds, and France, discontented, beckoned to him. On March 1 he landed near Antibes. The drama of the

Hundred Days had begun, and a blood-less march to Paris ensued. The British Government, which had led the country and the world against the Corsican, real-ized that they would have to bear the brunt of a whirlwind campaign. Prussia was the only main ally then in readiness. Within a month of the escape from Elba Wellington took up his command at Brussels.

As the summer drew near Wellington assembled a mixed force of eighty-three thousand men, of whom about a third were British. Napoleon could not afford to waste a day. Nor did he do so. Wel-lington waited patiently in Brussels for a sign of the Emperor's intention. He and his great opponent were to cross swords for the first time. They were both in their forty-sixth year. Quietly on June 15 Napoleon crossed the Sambre at Char-leroi and Marchiennes, driving the Prus-sian forward troops before him to within twenty-five miles of Brussels.

Wellington resolved to concentrate on the strategic point of Quatre-Bras. For the French everything depended upon beating the Prussians before forcing Wellington north-westwards to the coast. Leaving Ney with the French left, the Emperor swung with sixty-three thou-sand men and ninety-two guns to meet the main Prussian army, centered in Ligny. Realizing that so far only a small force held the position at Quatre-Bras, he ordered Ney to attack, and then meet him that evening in Brussels. At two o'clock in the afternoon of the 16th the French went into action on a two-mile front. There was little tactical maneuver in the fierce struggle which swayed back-wards and forwards on that June after-noon at the cross-roads on the way to Brussels. It was a head-on collision in which generalship played no part, though leadership did. Wellington was always at his coolest in the hottest of moments. In this battle of private soldiers the fire-

power of the British infantry prevailed. Out of thirty thousand men engaged by nightfall on their side the Allies lost four thousand six hundred; the French some-what less. But Ney had not gained his objective. Brussels was not in his grasp. Napoleon had gained the advantage at the opening of the campaign, but he had not intended that both wings of his army should be in action at once. At Ligny, however, he won a striking success. Marshal Blücher was out-generaled, his army split in two, battered by the mag-nificent French artillery, and driven back on Wavre. The crisis of the campaign was at hand.

Wellington himself had inspected this Belgian countryside in the autumn of 1814. He had noted the advantages of the ridge at Waterloo. There he would accept battle, and all he asked from the Prussians was the support of one corps. Throughout the night of the 16th and 17th a carefully screened retreat began, and by morning the Waterloo position, a line of defense such as Wellington had already tested in the Peninsula, was oc-cupied. Late in the morning of the 18th of June the French attacked both flanks of the Allied position, of which the key points were the fortified Château of Hougoumont on the right and the farm of La Haye Sainte in the middle. The battle swayed backwards and forwards upon the grass slopes, and intense fight-ing centered in the farm of La Haye Sainte, which eventually fell to the French. At Hougoumont, which held out all day, the fighting was heavier still. In the early afternoon one of the most ter-rific artillery barrages of the time was launched upon Wellington's infantry as preparation for the major cavalry ad-vance of fifteen thousand troopers under Ney. Under the hail of the French guns Wellington moved his infantry farther back over the ridge of Waterloo to give them a little more shelter. On seeing this

Ney launched his squadrons in a series of attacks. Everything now depended upon the British muskets and bayonets. But the French cuirassiers never reached the infantry squares. As one eye-witness wrote: "As to the so-called charges, I do not think that on a single occasion actual collision occurred. I many times saw the cuirassiers come on with boldness to within some twenty or thirty yards of a square, when, seeing the steady firmness of our men, they invariably edged away and retired." No visible decision was achieved. Napoleon, looking through his glasses at the awful *mêlée,* exclaimed, "Will the English never show their backs?" "I fear," replied Soult, "they will be cut to pieces first."

Wellington too had much to disturb him. Although the Prussians had been distantly sighted upon the roads in the early afternoon, they were slow in making their presence felt upon the French right. But by six o'clock in the evening Ney's onslaughts had failed and the Prussians were beating relentlessly upon the wing. They drew off fourteen thousand men from the forces assailing Wellington. The French made a final effort, and desperate fighting with no quarter raged again round the farms. The Imperial Guard itself, with Ney at its head, rolled up the hill, but again the fury of British infantry fire held them. The long-awaited moment to counterattack had come. Wellington had been in the forefront of danger all day. Now he rode along his much-battered line and ordered the advance. "Go on, go on!" he shouted. "They will not stand!" His cavalry swept from the ridge and sabered the French army into a disorganized mass of stragglers. Ney, beside himself with rage, a broken sword in his hand, staggered shouting in vain from one band to another. It was too late.

Wellington handed over the pursuit to the Prussians. The day had been almost too much even for a man of iron. The whole weight of responsibility had fallen on him. Only the power and example of his own personality had kept his motley force together. The strain had been barely tolerable. "By God!" as he justly said, "I don't think it would have been done if I had not been there."

On July 26 the Emperor sailed to his sunset in the South Atlantic. He never permitted himself to understand what had happened at Waterloo. The event was everybody's fault but his own. Six years of life in exile lay before him. He spent them with his small faithful retinue creating the Napoleonic legend of invincibility which was to have so powerful an effect on the France of the future.

It remained for the emissaries of the Powers to assemble in Paris and compose a new peace with France. The Prussians pressed for harsh terms. Castlereagh, representing Britain, saw that mildness would create the least grievance and guard best against a renewal of war. In this he had the hearty support of Wellington, who now exerted a unique authority throughout Europe. In the moderation of the settlement with France the second Treaty of Paris had its greatest success. Castlereagh, with his somber cast of mind, thought the treaty would be justified if it kept the peace for seven years. He had built better than he knew. Peace reigned for forty years between the Great Powers, and the main framework of the settlements at Vienna and Paris endured until the twentieth century.

CHAPTER TEN

Recovery and Reform

After a generation of warfare peace had come to Europe in the summer of 1815. The English political scene succumbed to stagnation. The principal figures in the Government were Lord Liverpool, Lord Castlereagh, and, after 1818, the Duke of Wellington. Castlereagh and Wellington towered above their colleagues. The rest of the Cabinet were Tories of the deepest dye, such as the Lord Chancellor, Eldon; Addington, now Viscount Sidmouth, once Prime Minister and now at the Home Office; and Earl Bathurst, Colonial Secretary, whom Lord Rosebery has described as "one of those strange children of our political system who fill the most dazzling offices with the most complete obscurity." Liverpool was the son of Charles Jenkinson, organizer of Government patronage under George III and close colleague of the younger Pitt. In 1812 he became Prime Minister, and for fifteen years presided over the affairs of the realm with tact, patience, and laxity. Castlereagh was a specialist in foreign and Wellington in military affairs. The others were plain Tory politicians resolved to do as little as possible as well as they could.

Britain was a world-Power whose strength lay in her ranging commerce and in her command of the seas. Her trade flourished and multiplied independently of the reigning ideas in Europe. Moreover, her governing classes, long accustomed to public debate, did not share the absolutist dreams that inspired, and deluded, the Courts of the autocrats. Although Tory opinion even in the day of triumph was fearful of Continental commitments, Castlereagh resolved that Britain should not abandon the position of authority she had won during the war. To him the Quadruple Alliance and the Congress at Vienna were merely pieces of diplomatic machinery for discussing European problems. On the other hand, the Austrian Chancellor Metternich and his colleagues regarded them as instruments for preserving the existing order. In spite of these differences the Congress

of Vienna stands as a monument to the success of classical diplomacy. Castlereagh was pre-eminent as the genius of the conference. He reconciled opposing views, and his modest expectation that peace might be ensured for seven years was fulfilled more than fivefold. He represented, with its faults and virtues, the equable, detached and balanced approach to Continental affairs that was to characterize the best of British foreign policy for nearly a century.

Earlier than her neighbors Britain enjoyed the fruits and endured the rigors of the Industrial Revolution. She gained a new domain of power and prosperity. At the same time the growing masses in her ill-built towns were often plunged into squalor and misery, the source of numerous and well-grounded discontents. Machinery, the rise of population, and extensive changes in employment all presented a formidable social problem. The Government were by their background and upbringing largely unaware of the causes of the ills which they had to cure. They concentrated upon the one issue they understood, the defense of property. Napoleon had closed the Continent to British commerce, and the answering British blockade had made things worse for industry at home. There was much unemployment in the industrial North and the Midlands. Smashing of machinery during the Luddite riots of 1812 and 1813 had exposed the complete absence of means of preserving public order. Bad harvests now added to the prevailing distress. Extremist Radical leaders came out of hiding and kept up a perpetual and growing agitation. Their organizations, which had been suppressed during the French Revolution, now reappeared, and began to take the shape of a political movement, though as yet scarcely represented in the House of Commons. The violence of language used by the Radicals frightened Tories and Whigs alike. It stiffened the resistance of the upper middle classes, both industrial and landed, to all proposals for change. English political tradition centered in Parliament, and men still looked to Parliament to cure the evils of the day. If Parliament did nothing, then the structure of Parliament must be changed. Huge meetings were held, and protests vociferously made. The Cabinet was thoroughly perturbed. Habeas Corpus was suspended, and legislation passed against the holding of seditious meetings. These alarms and excursions revealed the gravity of conditions. Not only was there grinding poverty among the working population, but also a deep-rooted conflict between the manufacturing and agricultural classes. The economy of the country was dangerously out of balance.

In 1819 an incident took place which increased the unpopularity and quickened the fears of the Government. A meeting of protest was held at St. Peter's Fields, in mid-Manchester, attended by over fifty thousand people, including women and children. The local magistrates lost their heads, and, after reading the Riot Act, ordered the yeomanry to charge. Eleven people were killed, two of them women, and four hundred were injured. This "massacre of Peterloo," as it was called in ironic reference to the Battle of Waterloo, aroused widespread indignation, which was swelled still further when the Government took drastic steps to prevent the recurrence of disorder. Soon afterwards a conspiracy was discovered against the whole Cabinet. A small gang of plotters was arrested in Cato Street, a turning off the Edgware Road, where they had met to plan to murder all the Ministers at a dinner-party and seize the Bank of England. Yet compared with most Continental countries, Britain came lightly out of these years of disturbance.

Once again in English history the personal affairs of the royal family now exploded into public view. In 1810 the old King finally sank into incurable imbecility. He lived for another ten years, roaming the corridors of Windsor Castle with long white beard and purple dressing-gown. The Prince of Wales became Regent, with unrestricted royal prerogatives. To the consternation of his old Whig friends, he had kept his Tory advisers in power and prosecuted the war with vigor. Whatever the faults of George IV, his determination as Regent to support Wellington and Castlereagh and to stand up to Napoleon should earn him an honorable place in his country's history.

In 1784 the Prince had fallen in love. The Prince's Whig friends were alarmed when the heir to the most Protestant throne in Europe insisted on marrying a Roman Catholic widow who had already survived two husbands. Under the Royal Marriages Act the union was illegal, and George's behavior was neither creditable to himself nor to his position. Mrs. Fitzherbert, prim and quiet, was not the woman to hold him for long. At the bidding of his parents in 1795 he was wedded to Caroline of Brunswick, a noisy, flighty, and unattractive German princess. A high-spirited, warm-hearted girl was born of their brief union, Princess Charlotte, who found her mother quite as unsatisfactory as her father. In 1814 George banned his wife from Court, and after an unseemly squabble she left England for a European tour, vowing to plague her husband when he should accede to the throne. The Government were perturbed about the problem of the succession. Princess Charlotte married Prince Leopold of Saxe-Coburg, later King of the Belgians, but in 1817 she died in childbirth. Her infant was stillborn. George's brothers, who were all in different ways eccentric, were thoroughly unpopular; as Wellington said, "the damnedest millstone about the necks of any Government." They lacked not only charm, but lawful issue. In 1818 however the obliging Dukes of Clarence and Kent did their royal duty—for a sum. Kent made a German marriage, and retired to Gibraltar to exercise his marital talents upon the Rock. The offspring of this alliance was the future Queen Victoria.

The Prince of Wales had long played with the idea of divorcing his itinerant wife. He got a commission appointed to inquire into the Princess's conduct. It posted to Italy to collect evidence from the unsavory entourage of Caroline. In July 1819 the Government received a report producing considerable circumstantial evidence against her. The Princess's chief legal adviser was Henry Brougham, the ablest of the younger Whigs. He entered into confidential relations with the Government, hoping for a compromise which would bring advancement to himself. But in January 1820 the mad old King died and the position of the new sovereign's consort had to be determined. George IV fell seriously ill, but his hatred of Caroline sustained and promoted his recovery. In April 1820 an open letter appeared in the London Press, signed by her, and recounting her woes. Brougham was sent to intercept the Queen on her journey to England. But nothing would stop the infuriated woman, whose obstinacy was inflamed by Radical advice. In June she landed, and she drove amid stormy scenes of enthusiasm from Dover to London. The Government reluctantly decided that they must go through with the business. A Secret Committee of the Lords was set up, and their report persuaded Liverpool to agree to introduce a Bill of Pains and Penalties if the Queen were proved guilty

of adultery. In July the hearing of the charges was opened in Westminster Hall. In lengthy sessions the Attorney-General put the case for the Government, producing unreliable Italian witnesses from Caroline's vagabond Court. Stories of keyholes, of indecorous costumes and gestures, regaled the public ear. Brougham led the defense. The peers thought the Queen guilty, but doubted the wisdom of divorce, and the Bill passed through their House by only nine votes. The Whigs, when compromise had become impossible, voted against the Government. The Cabinet now decided that there was small chance of forcing the Bill through the Commons. They withdrew it and the affair was dropped. The London mob rioted in joy; the whole city was illuminated. One political result of the crisis was the resignation of George Canning, who had been on friendly terms with the Queen. In July 1821 George IV was crowned in pomp at Westminster Abbey. Caroline attempted to force her way into the Abbey, but was turned away because she had no ticket. A month later she died.

The agitation over the Queen had been essentially the expression of discontent. It marked the highest point of the Radical movement in these post-war years. Towards the end of 1820, however, industry and trade revived and popular disturbances subsided. The mass of the country was instinctively Royalist and the personal defects of the sovereign had little effect upon this deep-rooted tradition.

Modern scholars, delving deeply into family connections and commercial interests, have sought to show that there was no such thing as a two-party system in eighteenth-century Britain. It is not much of a conclusion to come to about a great age of Parliamentary debate. The ins and outs might as well have names, and why not employ the names of Whig and Tory which their supporters cast at one another? At any rate, in the 1820's a Government of Tory complexion had been in power almost without interruption for thirty years. This Government had successfully piloted the country through the longest and most dangerous war in which Britain had yet been engaged. It had also survived, though with tarnishing reputation, five years of peacetime unrest. But the Industrial Revolution posed a set of technical administrative problems which no aristocratic and agricultural party, Whig or Tory, was capable of handling.

The younger Tories, headed by George Canning and supported by William Huskisson, spokesman of the merchants, advocated a return to Pitt's policy of Free Trade and intelligent commercial legislation. But even they were disunited. Meanwhile, Peel became Canning's rival for the future leadership of the Tories. Personalities added their complications. Canning had played a leading part in the conception and launching of the Peninsular War. His chief interest lay in foreign affairs. But this field seemed barred to him by his quarrel with Castlereagh. The older Members distrusted him. Brilliant, witty, effervescent, he had a gift for sarcasm which made him many enemies. Early in 1822 Canning was offered the post of Governor-General of India. His political life seemed at an end. But then Fate took a hand. In August while he was waiting to take up his post in the East, Castlereagh, his mind unhinged by overwork, cut his throat in the dressing-room of his home. Canning's presence in the Government was now essential: he was appointed Foreign Secretary, and in this office he dominated English politics until his death five years later. The Ministry had recently been joined by Peel

at the Home Office and now Huskisson went to the Board of Trade. Canning, Peel, and Huskisson pursued bold policies which in many respects were in advance of those propounded by the Whigs. The penal code was reformed by Peel, and the London police force is his creation. But on one issue Canning was firm. He was a stubborn defender of the existing franchise. He believed that by far-sighted commercial measures and a popular foreign policy the problems of Parliamentary Reform could be evaded. Length of years was not given him in which to perceive himself mistaken.

Up and down the whole length of the Andes campaigns were fought for South American liberation. By Canning's time at the Foreign Office most of the republics that now figure on the map had come into separate if unstable existence. In the meanwhile British commerce with these regions had trebled in value since 1814. Canning urged the United States to join Britain in opposing European interference in the countries across the Atlantic. As he later declared in a triumphant phrase, he had "called the New World into existence to redress the balance of the Old." The New World meanwhile had something of its own to say. The United States had no wish to see European quarrels transferred across the ocean. Hence there was propounded on December 2, 1823, in the President's annual message to Congress a purely American doctrine, the Monroe Doctrine, which has often since been voiced in transatlantic affairs. "The American continents," President Monroe said, "by the free and independent condition they have assumed and maintain, are henceforth not to be considered as subjects for future colonization by any European Powers. . . . We should consider any attempt on their part to extend their [political] system to any portion of this hemisphere as dangerous to our peace and safety." These were resounding claims. Their acceptance by the rest of the world depended on the friendly vigilance of the British man-of-war, but this was a fact seldom openly acknowledged. For the best part of a century the Royal Navy remained the stoutest guarantee of freedom in the Americas. So Canning's view prevailed. His stroke over South America may probably be judged his greatest triumph in foreign policy.

His colleagues had become increasingly critical of the activities of their Foreign Secretary. The two wings of the administration were only held together by the conciliatory character of the Prime Minister, and in February 1827 Liverpool had a stroke. A major political crisis followed. Canning abroad and Huskisson at home had alienated the old Tories in the party. The choice of Prime Minister still lay with the Crown, and George IV hesitated for a month before making his decision. It soon became plain that no Government could be constructed which did not include Canning and his friends, and that Canning would accept all or nothing. His final argument convinced the King. "Sire," he said, "your father broke the domination of the Whigs. I hope your Majesty will not endure that of the Tories." "No," George IV replied, "I'll be damned if I do." In April 1827 Canning became Prime Minister, and for a brief hundred days held supreme political power. Canning's Ministry signaled the coming dissolution of the eighteenth-century political system. He held office by courtesy of a section of the Whigs. The only able Tory leader in the House of Commons whom he had lost was Robert Peel. Peel resigned partly for personal reasons and partly because he knew that Canning was in favor of Catholic Emancipation. Had Canning been granted a longer spell of

life the group he led might have founded a new political allegiance. But on August 8, after a short illness, Canning died. He was killed, like Castlereagh, by overwork.

Canning's death at a critical moment at home and abroad dislocated the political scene. A makeshift administration composed of his followers, his Whig allies, and a group of Tories struggled ineptly with the situation. Its leader was the lachrymose Lord Goderich, formerly Chancellor of the Exchequer. There had been a hitch in carrying out Canning's policy of non-intervention in the Greek revolt against the Turks. Admiral Codrington, one of Nelson's captains, who had fought at Trafalgar and was now in command of the Allied squadron in Greek waters, had on his own initiative destroyed the entire Turkish Fleet in the Bay of Navarino. The Government, rent by Whig intrigues, abruptly disappeared.

Wellington became Prime Minister, with Peel as Home Secretary and Leader of the House of Commons. The old Tories were to fight one more action. Peel was one of the ablest Ministers that Britain has seen. But his was an administrative mind. General ideas moved him only when they had seized the attention of the country and become inescapable political facts. The Government's first retreat was the carrying of an Opposition measure repealing the Test and Corporation Acts which nominally excluded the Noncomformists from office. After a long struggle they at last achieved political rights and equality. Not so the Catholics. The greatest failure of British Government was in Ireland. A main dividing line in politics after 1815 was upon this issue of Catholic Emancipation. But the patience of the Irish was coming to its end. They were organizing under Daniel O'Connell for vehement agitation against England. If the English Government refused to enfranchise the Catholics there

would be revolution in Ireland, and
political disaster at home. As a general
Wellington knew the hopelessness of
attempting to repress a national rising.
The only opponents of Emancipation
were the English bishops, the old-
fashioned Tories, and the King. The
bishops and the Tories could be out-
voted; but the King was a more serious
obstacle. Wellington and Peel had had a
most unsatisfactory interview with him at
Windsor. Peel was growing more and
more uncomfortable, but the attitude of
the King would dictate his own. Wellington could not carry the measure without
Peel, and the Whigs could not carry it
without the King. This determined Peel.
His offer to stand by Wellington finally
persuaded George IV, who dreaded a
Whig administration. Peel himself introduced the Bill for Catholic Emancipation
into the House of Commons, and it was
carried through Parliament in 1829 with
comfortable majorities. Revolution in Ireland was averted.

In June 1830 King George IV died,
with a miniature of Mrs. Fitzherbert
round his neck. His extravagance had
become a mania, and his natural abilities
were clouded by years of self-indulgence.
"The first gentleman of Europe" was not
long mourned by his people.

George IV was succeeded on the
throne by his brother, the Duke of Clarence, the most eccentric and least obnoxious of the sons of George III. He had
been brought up in the Navy, and had
passed a life of total obscurity, except for
a brief and ludicrous interval when Canning had made him Lord High Admiral
in 1827. It had been expected that the
new King might prefer a Whig administration. As Duke of Clarence he had
been dismissed from the Admiralty by
the Duke of Wellington. But on his accession William IV welcomed and retained the Duke. His reputation for fairness proved to be of political value.

"Sailor William" needed every ounce of
fairness. There were heavy seas ahead.

In 1830 the Liberal forces in Europe
stirred again. At the polls the Whigs
made gains, but the result was indecisive.
The Whig leader was Earl Grey, a friend
and disciple of Fox. He and his colleagues perceived that the agitation
which had shaken England since Waterloo issued from two quite separate
sources—the middle classes, unrepresented, prosperous, respectable, influenced by the democratic ideas of the
French Revolution, but deeply law-
abiding in their hunger for political
power; and on the other side a bitter and
more revolutionary section of working
men, smitten by the economic dislocation
of war and its aftermath, prepared to talk
of violence and perhaps even to use it.
Parliament met in November. There were
some who hoped that the Tories would
do again what they had done over Catholic Emancipation and, after a rearguard
action, reform the franchise themselves.
But Wellington was adverse. To the
House of Lords he said, "I have never
read or heard of any measure . . .
which can in any degree satisfy my mind
that the state of the representation can be
improved. . . ." When he sat down he
turned to his Foreign Secretary, the Earl
of Aberdeen. "I have not said too much,
have I?" He received no direct answer,
but in reporting the incident later the
Foreign Secretary described Wellington's
speech briefly. "He said that we were
going out." A fortnight later the Tories
were defeated and King William IV
asked Grey to form a Government.

Only Parliamentary Reform could
maintain the Whig Government, and to
this they now addressed themselves. A secret Cabinet committee was appointed to
draft the scheme, and in March 1831
Lord John Russell rose in the House of
Commons to move the first Reform Bill.

Amid shouting and scornful laughter he read out to their holders a list of over a hundred and fifty "pocket" borough seats which it was proposed to abolish and replace with new constituencies for the unrepresented areas of the Metropolis, the industrial North, and the Midlands. To the Tories this was a violation of all they stood for, an affront to their deepest political convictions, a gross attack on the rights of property. Radical leaders were disappointed by what they conceived to be the moderation of the Bill, but in their various ways they supported it.

The Government was by no means sure of its majority, and although a small block of Irish votes controlled by O'Connell, leader of the emancipated Catholics, was cast for Grey the Bill was defeated. A roar of hatred and disappointment swept the country. Grey asked the King for a dissolution, and William IV had the sense to realize that a refusal might mean revolution. Excited elections were held on the single issue of Reform. It was the first time a mandate of this kind had been asked of the British people. They returned an unmistakable answer. The Tories were annihilated in the country constituencies and the Whigs and their allies gained a majority of 136 in the House of Commons. When Parliament reassembled the battle was shifted to the House of Lords. The Bill was defeated and a new constitutional issue was raised —the Peers against the People. In December Russell introduced the Bill for the third time, and the Commons carried it by a majority of two to one. In the following May it came again before the Lords. It was rejected by thirty-five votes. There was now no question of another dissolution and Grey realized that only extreme remedies would serve. He accordingly drove to Windsor and asked the King to create enough new peers to carry the Bill. The King refused and the

Cabinet resigned. William IV asked Wellington and Peel to form an administration to carry Reform as they had carried Catholic Emancipation, and thus avoid swamping the Lords. But Peel would not comply; he was not prepared to assume Ministerial responsibility for a measure of which he disapproved. Feeling in the country became menacing. Radical leaders declared they would paralyze any Tory Government which came to power, and after a week the Duke admitted defeat. On the afternoon of May 18 Grey and Brougham called at St. James's Palace. The King authorized them to draw up a list of persons who would be made peers and could be counted on to vote for the Whigs. When the Bill was again introduced the Opposition benches were practically empty. It was carried by an overwhelming majority, and became law on June 7, 1832.

The Whigs became more and more uncomfortable, and Grey, feeling he had done enough, retired in 1834. The new leaders were Lord Melbourne and Lord John Russell. Russell was a Whig of the old school, sensitive to any invasion of political liberty and rights. He saw the need for further reforms in the sphere of government, but the broadening paths of democracy did not beckon him. Melbourne in his youth had held advanced opinions, but his lack of any guiding aim and motive, his want of conviction, his cautious scepticism, denied him and his party any theme or inspiration. He accepted the office of Prime Minister with reluctance, genuinely wondering whether the honor was worth while. One of Melbourne's ablest colleagues was Lord Palmerston, who held the Foreign Office for nearly eleven years. Under Melbourne Palmerston did much as he pleased in foreign affairs. His leading beliefs were two: that British interests must everywhere be stoutly upheld, if necessary by a show of force, and that

Liberal movements in the countries of Europe should be encouraged whenever it was within Britain's power to extend them sympathy or even aid.

With the passing of the Reform Bill the Whig Party had done its work. Its leaders neither liked nor understood the middle classes. Some quarter of a million voters had been added by the Reform Bill to the electorate, which now numbered nearly 700,000 persons. However, they by no means gave their undivided support to the Whigs. The strange habit of British electors of voting against Governments which give them the franchise now made itself felt, and it was with great difficulty that the Whig administrations preserved a majority. Nevertheless, the legislation and the commissions of these years were by no means unfruitful. The slaves in the West Indies were finally emancipated in 1833. For the first time in English history the Government made educational grants to religious societies. The Poor Law was reformed on lines that were considered highly advanced in administrative and intellectual circles, though they did not prove popular among those they were supposed to benefit. The first effective Factory Act was passed, though the long hours of work it permitted would horrify the twentieth century and did not satisfy the humanitarians of the time. The whole system of local government was reconstructed and the old local oligarchies abolished. A large mass of the country still remained unenfranchised. The relations of capital and labor had scarcely been touched by the hand of Parliament, and the activities of the early trade unions frightened the Government into oppressive measures. The most celebrated case was that of the Tolpuddle "Martyrs" of 1834, when six laborers from that Dorsetshire village of curious name were sentenced to transportation for the technical offense of "administering unlawful

oaths" to members of their union. Sir Robert Peel, on the other hand, was not slow to adjust the Tories to the new times and a speedy reorganization of their machinery was set on foot. In 1837 King William IV died. Humorous, tactless, pleasant, and unrespected, he had played his part in lowering esteem for the monarchy, and indeed the vices and eccentricities of the sons of George III had by this time almost destroyed its hold upon the hearts of the people. The new sovereign was a maiden of eighteen. The country knew nothing of either her character or her virtues. "Few people," wrote Palmerston, "have had opportunities of forming a correct judgment of the Princess; but I incline to think that she will turn out to be a remarkable person, and gifted with a great deal of strength of character." He was right. On the eve of her accession the new Queen wrote in her diary: "Since it has pleased Providence to place me in this station, I shall do my utmost to fulfill my duty toward my country; I am very young, and perhaps in many, though not in all things, inexperienced, but I am sure that very few have more real good will and more real desire to do what is fit and right than I have." It was a promise she was spaciously to fulfill.

By the time Queen Victoria came to the throne the Whigs had shot their bolt. Conditions in the industrial North soon became as bad as after Waterloo, and in May 1838 a group of working-class leaders published a "People's Charter." Chartism, as it was called, in which some historians discern the beginnings of socialism, was the last despairing cry of poverty against the Machine Age. Agitation revived from time to time in the years that followed, culminating in the revolutionary year of 1848. But in the end the whole muddled, well-intentioned business came to nothing. In 1839 Melbourne offered to resign, but for another two years Victoria kept him in office. His charm had captured her affections. He imparted to her much of his wisdom on men and affairs, without burdening her with his scepticism, and she refused to be separated from her beloved Prime Minister. In February of the following year a new figure entered upon the British scene. The Queen married her cousin, Prince Albert of Saxe-Coburg. The Prince was an upright, conscientious man with far-ranging interests and high ideals. At first the Prince found his presence in England resented by the political magnates of the time. Eventually the party leaders in England learnt to value his advice, especially on foreign affairs, though they did not always pay heed to it. Together the Queen and the Prince set a new standard for the conduct of monarchy which has ever since been honorably observed.

Peel, unlike Melbourne, had given the Queen an impression of awkwardness and coldness of manner; but at last in 1841 a General Election brought him to power. His abilities now came into full play. In 1843 trade began to revive, prosperity returned, and the demand for political reform was stilled. But a storm was gathering in Ireland.

The Tory Party leaned heavily on the votes of the landowners, who had invested much capital in their properties during the Napoleonic wars. Peace had brought cheaper corn from abroad, and the cry for Protection had led in 1815 to a prohibition of the import of foreign grain except when the price in the home market was abnormally high. Hostility to the Corn Laws had grown during the depression of 1838–42. An Anti-Corn Law League was formed at Manchester to press for their abolition. Cobden and Bright's thundering speeches against the landed classes reverberated through the nation. Peel, like Cobden and Bright,

came from the middle class, and their arguments bit deeply into his mind. England's trade and prosperity demanded the abolition of the Corn Laws, but at least half his supporters were landowners, and such a step would wreck the Conservative Party. Then in August 1845 the potato crop failed in Ireland. Famine was imminent and Peel could wait no longer, but when he put his proposals to the Cabinet several of his colleagues revolted and in December he had to resign. The Whig leader Russell refused to form an administration, and Peel returned to office to face and conquer the onslaught of the Tory Protectionists. Their spokesman, the hitherto little-known Benjamin Disraeli, denounced him not so much for seeking to abolish the Corn Laws as for betraying his position as head of a great party.

On June 25, 1846, with the help of Whig and Irish votes, the Corn Laws were repealed. Disraeli immediately had his revenge. Turmoil in Ireland destroyed Peel's Government, and by a vote on the same night the great Ministry, one of the strongest of the century, came to an end. Peel had been the dominating force and personality in English politics since the passing of the great Reform Bill. The age over which he presided was one of formidable industrial advance. It was the Railway Age. By 1848 some five thousand miles of railroads had been built in the United Kingdom. Coal and iron production had doubled. Free trade seemed essential to manufacture, and in manufacture Britain was entering upon her supremacy. All this Peel grasped.

Lord John Russell's Government, with a few upsets, survived for six years. It achieved little of lasting note, but it piloted Britain through a restless period when elsewhere in Europe thrones were overturned and revolutions multiplied. The Tories for their part were irreconcilably split. The faithful followers of

Peel and Free Trade, who included in Aberdeen and Gladstone two future Prime Ministers, were content to let the Whigs bear the heat of the day. The Liberal Party, which would presently arise from the coalition of Whigs, Peelites, and Radicals, was not yet foreseen. The opponents of the Peelites, the old Tories, were led by Lord Stanley, soon to be Lord Derby, whose forebears had played a role in the kingdom for even longer than the Russells. Derby was increasingly assisted in the House of Commons by his lieutenant Disraeli, whose reputation for brilliance was growing rather faster than his capacity for inspiring trust. It was Disraeli's gradual task over these years to persuade the Tories to abandon their fidelity to the Corn Law tariff and to work out a new and more broadly based Conservative policy.

In 1851 the Great Exhibition was opened in Hyde Park. In spite of prophecies of failure, the Exhibition was a triumphant success. The Queen paid many visits to the Crystal Palace, where her presence aroused in the scores of thousands of subjects with whom she mingled a deep loyalty and a sense of national pride. Never had the Throne been so firmly grounded in the affections of the people. The mid-century marks the summit of Britain's preponderance in industry. In another twenty years other nations, among whom industrial progress had started later, had begun to cut down her lead. Critics were not wanting of the age of mass production that was now taking shape. Charles Dickens in his novels revealed the plight of the poor, holding up to pity the conditions in which many of them dwelt and ridiculing the State institutions that crudely encompassed them. John Ruskin was another. His heart lay in the Middle Ages, which he imagined to be peopled by a fraternity of craftsmen harmoniously creating works of art. Peering out upon the Victorian scene, this prophetic figure looked in vain for similar accomplishment.

Foreign affairs and the threat of war now began to darken the scene. Turkey had troubled the statesmen of Europe for many years. The need to resist Russia was plain to most British observers, though Radicals like Cobden strongly opposed this view. At home Lord Derby, after a brief spell in office, had been succeeded by Lord Aberdeen, who presided over a coalition Government of Whigs and Peelites, far from united in their opinions. The Prime Minister himself and his Foreign Secretary, Lord Clarendon, were hesitant and favored appeasement. In early July 1853 Russian troops crossed the River Pruth and entered Turkish Moldavia. On October 4 the Sultan declared war on Russia, and soon afterward attacked the Russians beyond the Danube. Palmerston sent in his resignation in December on a domestic issue, but his action was interpreted as a protest against the Government's Eastern policy and Aberdeen was accused of cowardice. Thus England drifted into war. In February 1854 Nicholas recalled his Ambassadors from London and Paris, and at the end of March the Crimean War began, with France and Britain as the allies of Turkey.

The operations were ill-planned and ill-conducted on both sides. With the exception of two minor naval expeditions to the Baltic and the White Sea, fighting was confined to Southern Russia, where the great naval fort of Sebastopol, in the Black Sea, was selected as the main Allied objective. Unable to complete their investment of the town, the Allies had to beat off fresh Russian field armies which arrived from the interior. At Balaclava in October the British cavalry distinguished themselves by two astonishing charges against overwhelming odds. The second of these was the celebrated charge of the Light Brigade, in which 673 horsemen, led by Lord Cardigan, rode up the valley under heavy fire, imperturbably, as if taking part in a review, to attack the Russian batteries. They captured the guns, but only a third of the brigade answered the first muster after the charge. Lord Cardigan calmly returned to the yacht on which he lived, had a bath, dined, drank a bottle of champagne, and went to bed. His brigade had performed an inspiring feat of gallantry. But it was due, like much else in this war, to the blunders of commanders. Lord Raglan's orders had been badly expressed and were misunderstood by his subordinates. The Light Brigade had charged the wrong guns.

The Battle of Inkerman followed, fought in the mists of a November dawn. It was a desperate infantry action, in which the British soldier proved his courage and endurance. Russian casualties were nearly five times as many as those of the Allies. But Inkerman was not decisive. Amid storms and blizzards the British Army lay, without tents, huts, food, warm clothes, or the most elementary medical care. Cholera, dysentery, and malarial fever took their dreadful toll.

Even the War Office was a little shaken by the incompetence and suffering. *The Times* under its great editor J. T. Delane, sent out the first of all war correspondents, William Russell, and used his reports to start a national agitation against the Government. Aberdeen was assailed from every quarter, and when Parliament reassembled in January a motion was introduced by a private Member to appoint a commission of inquiry into the state of the army before Sebastopol. Aberdeen resigned, and was succeeded by Palmerston, who accepted the commission of inquiry. By the summer of 1855 the Allied armies had been reinforced and were in good heart. In September Sebastopol at last fell. Threatened by an Austrian ultimatum, Russia agreed to terms, and in February 1856 a peace conference opened in Paris. The Treaty of Paris, signed at the end of March, removed the immediate causes of the conflict, but provided no permanent settlement of the Eastern Question. Within twenty years Europe was nearly at war again over Russian ambitions in the Near East. The fundamental situation was unaltered: so long as Turkey was weak so long would her Empire remain a temptation to Russian Imperialists and an embarrassment to Western Europe.

With one exception few of the leading figures emerged from the Crimean War with enhanced reputations. Miss Florence Nightingale had been sent out in an official capacity by the Secretary at War, Sidney Herbert. The Red Cross movement, which started with the Geneva Convention of 1864, was the outcome of her work, as were great administrative reforms in civilian hospitals.

Palmerston, though now in his seventies, presided over the English scene. With one short interval of Tory government, he was Prime Minister throughout the decade that began in 1855. Not long after the signing of peace with Russia he was confronted with another emergency which also arose in the East, but this time in Asia. The scale of the Indian Mutiny should not be exaggerated. It was in no sense a national movement, or, as some later Indian writers have suggested, a patriotic struggle for freedom or a war of independence. But from now on there was an increasing gulf between the rulers and the ruled. The easy-going ways of the eighteenth century were gone for ever, and so were the missionary fervor and reforming zeal of the early Victorians and their predecessors. British administration became detached, impartial, efficient. Great progress was made and many material benefits were secured. The frontiers were guarded and the peace was kept. Starvation was subdued. The population vastly increased. The Indian Army, revived and reorganized, was to play a glorious part on Britain's side in two World Wars. The Indian Mutiny made, in some respects, a more lasting impact on England than the Crimean War. It paved the way for Empire. After it was over Britain gradually and consciously became a world-wide Imperial Power.

While these events unrolled in India the political scene in England remained confused. Palmerston was willing to make improvements in government, but large-scale changes were not to his mind. Russell hankered after a further measure of electoral reform, but that was the limit of his program. The greatest of the European movements in these years was the cause of Italian unity. This long-cherished dream of the Italian peoples was at last realized, though only partially, in 1859 and 1860. The story is well known of how the Italians secured the military aid of Napoleon III for the price of ceding Nice and Savoy to France, and how, after winning Lombardy from the Austrians, the French Emperor left his allies in the lurch. Venice remained unredeemed; still worse, a French army protected the rump of the Papal State in Rome, and for ten years deprived the Italians of their natural capital. But as one small Italian State after another cast out their alien rulers, and merged under a single monarchy, widespread enthusiasm was aroused in England. Garibaldi and his thousand volunteers, who overturned the detested Bourbon Government in Sicily and Naples with singular dash and speed, were acclaimed as heroes in London. These bold events were welcome to

Palmerston and his Foreign Secretary, Russell. At the same time the British leaders were suspicious of Napoleon III's designs and fearful of a wider war. Congratulation but non-intervention was therefore their policy. It is typical of these two old Whigs that they applauded the new Italian Government for putting into practice the principles of the English Revolution of 1688. Russell in the House of Commons compared Garibaldi to King William III. History does not relate what the Italians made of this. Radicalism in these years made little appeal to the voters. The doctrine of industrious self-help, preached by Samuel Smiles, was widely popular in the middle classes and among many artisans as well. Religious preoccupations were probably more widespread and deeply felt than at any time since the days of Cromwell. But the theory of evolution, and its emphasis on the survival of the fittest in the history of life upon the globe, was a powerful adjunct to mid-Victorian optimism. It lent fresh force to the belief in the forward march of mankind.

A sublime complacency enveloped the Government. Disraeli, chafing on the Opposition benches, vented his scorn and irritation on this last of the eighteenth-century politicians. But the Tories were little better off. Disraeli more than once sought an alliance with the Radicals, and promised them that he would oppose armaments and an aggressive foreign policy. But their chief spokesman, John Bright, was under no illusions. "Mr. Disraeli," he said, "is a man who does what may be called the conjuring for his party. He is what among a tribe of Red Indians would be called a mysteryman." Thus foiled, Disraeli returned to his attack on the Whigs. He was convinced that the only way to destroy them was by extending the franchise yet further so as to embrace the respectable artisans and counter the hostility of the middle classes. Standing apart both from the Whigs and Derby's Tories were the Peel-ites, of whom the most notable was William Gladstone. Having started his Parliamentary career in 1832 as a strict Tory, he was to make a long pilgrimage into the Liberal camp. In 1859, aged nearly fifty, Gladstone joined the Whigs and the pilgrimage was over. In 1865, in his eighty-first year, Palmerston died. The eighteenth century died with him. Gladstone, like Disraeli, wanted to ex-tend the franchise to large sections of the working classes: he was anxious to cap-ture the votes of the new electorate. He prevailed upon the Government, now headed by Russell, to put forward a Re-form Bill, but it was defeated on an amendment and the Cabinet resigned. Minority administrations under Derby and Disraeli followed, which lasted two and a half years.

Disraeli now seized his chance. He introduced a fresh Reform Bill in 1867, which he skillfully adapted to meet the wishes of the House, of which he was Leader. There was a redistribution of seats in favor of the large industrial towns, and nearly a million new voters were added to an existing electorate of about the same number. The carrying of the second Reform Bill so soon after the death of Palmerston opened a new era in English politics. In February 1868 Derby resigned from the leadership of the party and Disraeli was at last Prime Minister—as he put it, "at the top of the greasy pole." He had to hold a General Elec-tion. The new voters gave their over-whelming support to his opponents, and Gladstone, who had become leader of the Liberal Party, formed the strongest ad-ministration that England had seen since the days of Peel.

The long struggle against France had stifled or arrested the expansion of the English-speaking peoples, and the ships and the men who might have founded the second British Empire had been con-sumed in twenty years of world war. Once more the New World offered an escape from the hardships and frustra-tions of the Old. The result was the most spectacular migration of human beings of which history has yet had record and a vast enrichment of the trade and indus-try of Great Britain. The increasing population of Great Britain added to the pressure. The numbers grew, and the flow began: in the 1820's a quarter of a million emigrants, in the 1830's half a million, by the middle of the century a million and a half, until sixty-five years after Waterloo no fewer than eight mil-lion people had left the British Isles.

Of the new territories Canada was the most familiar and the nearest in point of distance to the United Kingdom. Pitt in 1791 had sought to solve the racial prob-lems of Canada by dividing her into two parts. In Lower Canada the French were deeply rooted, a compact, alien commu-nity, holding stubbornly to their own traditions and language. Beyond them, to the north-west, lay Upper Canada, the modern Province of Ontario, settled by some of the sixty thousand Englishmen who had left the United States toward the end of the eighteenth century rather than live under the American republic. These proud folk had out of devotion to the British Throne abandoned most of their possessions, and been rewarded with the unremunerative but honorable title of United Empire Loyalists. The Mohawk tribe, inspired by the same sentiments, had journeyed with them. French, English, and Red Indians all fought against the Americans, and re-pulsed them in the three-year struggle between 1812 and 1814. Then trouble began. The French in Lower Canada feared that the immigrants would out-number and dominate them. The Loyal-ists in Upper Canada welcomed new settlers who would increase the price of land but were reluctant to treat them as equals. Moreover, the two Provinces started to quarrel with each other. Differences over religion added to the irritations. From about 1820 the Assembly in Lower Canada began to behave like the Parliaments of the early Stuarts and the legislatures of the American colonies, refusing to vote money for the salaries of royal judges and permanent officials. Liberals wanted to make the executive responsible to the Assembly and talked wildly of leaving the Empire, and in 1836 the Assembly in which they held a majority was dissolved. In the following year both Provinces rebelled, Lower Canada for a month and Upper Canada for a week. The Whig leaders in London were wiser than George III. They perceived that a tiny minority of insurgents could lead to great troubles, and in 1838 Lord Durham was sent to investigate, assisted by Edward Gibbon Wakefield. Durham stayed only a few months. His high-handed conduct aroused much criticism at Westminster. Feeling himself deserted by Lord Melbourne's Government, with which he was personally unpopular, but which should nevertheless have stood by him, Durham resigned and returned to England. He then produced the famous report in which he diagnosed and proclaimed the root causes of the trouble and advocated responsible government, carried on by Ministers commanding the confidence of the popular Assembly, a united Canada, and planned settlement of the unoccupied lands. These recommendations were largely put into effect by the Canada Act of 1840, which was the work of Lord John Russell. Thereafter Canada's progress was swift and peaceful.

The British North America Act of 1867 created the first of the self-governing British Dominions beyond the seas. The Provinces of Ontario, Quebec, New Brunswick, and Nova Scotia were the founding members. Manitoba became a Province of the Dominion in 1870, and in the next year British Columbia was also admitted. The challenging task that faced the Dominion was to settle and develop her empty Western lands before the immigrant tide from America could flood across the 49th parallel. The answer was to build a transcontinental railway. When the Maritime Provinces joined the federation they had done so on condition they were linked with Ontario by rail, and after nine years of labor a line was completed in 1876. British Columbia made the same demand and received the same promise. The Canadian Pacific Railway was opened in 1885. Canada had become a nation, and shining prospects lay before her.

South Africa, unlike America, had scanty attractions for the early colonists and explorers. The establishment of a permanent settlement was discussed, but nothing was done till 1652, when, at the height of their power and in the Golden Age of their civilization, the Dutch sent Jan van Riebeek, a young ship's surgeon, with three ships to take possession of Table Bay. Throughout the eighteenth century the colony prospered and grew. In 1760 the first European crossed the Orange River, and by 1778 the Fish River had been made its eastern boundary. Napoleon's wars ruined the Dutch trade, swept the Dutch ships from the seas, and overthrew the Dutch State. Holland had no longer the power to protect her possessions, and when the Dutch were defeated by the French and the puppet-State of the Batavian Republic was established the British seized Cape Colony as enemy territory. It was finally ceded to them under the peace settlement of 1814 in return for an indemnity of £6,000,000. They decided that the only way to secure the line of the Fish River was to colonize the border with British settlers, and between 1820 and 1821 nearly five thousand of them were brought out from Great Britain. This emigration coincided with a change of policy. Convinced that South Africa was now destined to become a permanent part of the British Empire, the Government resolved to make it as English as they could. Thus was born a division which Canada had surmounted. British methods of government created among the Boers a more bitter antagonism than in any other Imperial country except Ireland. By 1857 there were five separate republics and three colonies within the territory of the present Republic of South Africa. The old colony of the Cape meanwhile prospered, as the production of wool increased by leaps and bounds, and in 1853 an Order in Council established representative institutions in the colony, with a Parliament in Cape Town, though without the grant of full responsible government. Here we may leave South African history for a spell of uneasy peace.

Australia has a long history in the realms of human imagination. The extent of the continent was not accurately known until the middle of the eighteenth century, when Captain James Cook made three voyages between 1768 and 1779, in which he circumnavigated New Zealand, sailed inside the Australian Barrier Reef, sighted the great Antarctic icefields, discovered the Friendly Islands, the New Hebrides, New Caledonia, and Hawaii, and charted the eastern coastline of Australia. English convicts had long been transported to America, but since the War of Independence the Government had nowhere to send them and many were now dying of disease in the hulks and jails of London. The younger Pitt's administration shrank from colonial ventures after the disasters in North America, but delay was deemed impos-

sible, and in January 1788 seven hundred and seventeen convicts, of whom one hundred and ninety-eight were women, were anchored in Botany Bay. The region had been named by Captain Cook after South Wales.

There were of course a few free settlers from the first, but the full migratory wave did not reach Australia until the 1820's. Driven by the post-war distress in Great Britain and attracted by the discovery of rich pasture in the hinterland of New South Wales, English-speaking emigrants began to trickle into the empty sub-continent and rapidly transformed the character and life of the early communities. The population changed from about fifteen thousand convicts and twenty-one thousand free settlers in 1828 to twenty-seven thousand convicts and over a hundred thousand free settlers in 1841. Free men soon demanded, and got, free government. Transportation to New South Wales was finally abolished in 1840, and two years later a Legislative Council was set up, most of whose members were elected by popular vote.

Long before 1850 the settlement of other parts of Australia had begun. The first to be made from the mother-colony of Port Jackson was in the island of Tasmania, or Van Diemen's Land as it was then called; at Hobart in 1804; and two years later at Launceston. The third offspring of New South Wales was Queensland. It grew up around the town of Brisbane, but developed more slowly and did not become a separate colony until 1859. By then two other settlements had arisen on the Australian coasts, both independently of New South Wales and the other colonies. In 1834 a body known as "the Colonization Commissioners for South Australia" had been set up in London, and two years later the first settlers landed near Adelaide. The city was named after William IV's Queen. South Australia was never a convict settlement. The other colony, Western Australia, had a very different history. Founded in 1829, it nearly died at birth. Convicts, which the other colonies deemed an obstacle to progress, seemed the only solution, and the British Government, once again encumbered with prisoners, eagerly accepted an invitation to send some out to Perth. In 1849 a penal settlement was established, with much money to finance it. Thus resuscitated, the population trebled within the next ten years, but Western Australia did not obtain representative institutions until 1870, after the convict settlement had been abolished, nor full self-government till 1890.

Australia, as we now know it, was born in 1901 by the association of the colonies in a Commonwealth, with a new capital at Canberra. Federation came late and slowly to the southern continent, for the lively, various, widely separated settlements cherished their own self-rule. Even today most of the Australian population dwells in the settlements founded in the nineteenth century. The heart of the country, over a million square miles in extent, has attracted delvers after metals and ranchers of cattle, but it remains largely uninhabited. The silence of the bush and the loneliness of the desert are only disturbed by the passing of some transcontinental express, the whirr of a boomerang, or the drone of a pilotless missile.

Twelve hundred miles to the east of Australia lie the islands of New Zealand. Here, long before they were discovered by Europeans, a Polynesian warrior race, the Maoris, had sailed across the Pacific from the northeast and established a civilization notable for the brilliance of its art and the strength of its military system. Soon after Cook's discovery a small English community gained a footing in the Bay of Islands in the far north, but they were mostly whalers and sealers, ship-wrecked mariners, and a few escaped convicts from Australia, enduring a lonely, precarious, and somewhat disreputable existence. They constituted no great threat to Maori life or lands. Resistance to English colonization was fortified by the arrival of Christian missionaries. A move to colonize the islands had nevertheless long been afoot in London, impelled by a group of men around Gibbon Wakefield, who had already so markedly influenced the future of Canada and Australia. But the Government was hostile. Wakefield, however, was resolute, and in 1838 his Association formed a private joint stock company for the colonization of New Zealand, and a year later dispatched an expedition under his younger brother. Over a thousand settlers went with them, and they founded the site of Wellington in the North Island. News that France was contemplating the annexation of New Zealand compelled the British Government to act. Instead of sanctioning Wakefield's expedition they sent out a man-of-war, under the command of Captain Hobson, to treat with the Maoris for the recognition of British sovereignty. In February 1840 Hobson concluded the Treaty of Waitangi with the Maori chiefs. By this the Maoris ceded to Great Britain all the rights and powers of sovereignty in return for confirmation in "the full and exclusive possession of their lands and estates." Two powers were thus established, the Governor at Auckland at the top of the North Island, which Hobson had chosen as the capital, and the Company at Wellington. The Company wanted land, as much and as soon as possible. The treaty and the Colonial Office said it belonged to the Maoris. Nevertheless, by 1859 the settlers had occupied seven million acres in the North Island and over thirty-two million acres in the South, where the Maoris were fewer. The result was the Maori Wars, a series of intermittent local conflicts lasting from 1843 to 1869. But by 1869 the force of the movement was spent and the risings were defeated. Thereafter the enlightened policy of Sir Donald MacLean, the Minister for Native Affairs, produced a great improvement. The Maoris realized that the British had come to stay.

Despite a depression in the eighties, the prosperity of New Zealand has continued to grow ever since. New Zealand's political development was no less rapid. Indeed her political vitality is no less astonishing than her economic vigor. The tradition and prejudices of the past weighed less heavily than in the older countries. Many of the reforms introduced into Great Britain by the Liberal Government of 1906, and then regarded as extreme innovations, had already been accepted by New Zealand. Industrial arbitration, old-age pensions, factory legislation, State insurance and medical service, housing Acts, all achieved between 1890 and the outbreak of the First World War, and State support for co-operative production, testified to the survival and fertility even in the remote and unfamiliar islands of the Pacific, of the British political genius.

CHAPTER ELEVEN

The Victorian Age

We now enter upon a long, connected, and progressive period in British history—the Prime Ministerships of Gladstone and Disraeli. Both men were at the height of their powers, and their skill and oratory in debate gripped and focused public attention on the proceedings of the House of Commons. When Gladstone became Prime Minister in 1868 he was deemed a careful and parsimonious administrator who had become a sound Liberal reformer. But this was only one side of his genius. What gradually made him the most controversial figure of the century was his gift of rousing moral indignation both in himself and in the electorate. Such a demand, strenuously voiced, was open to the charge of hypocrisy when, as so often happened, Gladstone's policy obviously coincided with the well-being of the Liberal Party. But the charge was false; the spirit of the preacher breathed in Gladstone's speeches. To face Gladstone Disraeli needed all the courage and quickness of wit with which he had been so generously endowed. Many Tories disliked and distrusted his reforming views, but he handled his colleagues with a rare skill. He has never been surpassed in the art of party management. In all his attitudes there was a degree of cynicism; in his make-up there was not a trace of moral fervor. He never became wholly assimilated to English ways of life, and preserved to his death the detachment which had led him as a young man to make his own analysis of English society. Nothing created more bitterness between them than Gladstone's conviction that Disraeli had captured the Queen for the Conservative Party and endangered the Constitution by an unscrupulous use of his personal charm. Gladstone, though always respectful, was incapable of infusing any kind of warmth into his relationship with her. She once said, according to report, that he addressed her like a public meeting. Disraeli did not make the same mistake. He wooed her from the loneliness and apathy which engulfed her after Albert's death, and flattered her desire to share in the formulation of policy. She complained that Gladstone, when in office, never told her anything. But in fact little harm was done; Gladstone grumbled that "the Queen is enough to kill any man," but he served her patiently, if not with understanding.

Gladstone came in on the flood; a decisive electoral victory and a country ready for reform gave him his opportunity. He began with Ireland and, in spite of bitter opposition and in defiance of his own early principles, which had been to defend property and the Anglican faith, he carried, in 1869, the disestablishment of the Protestant Church of Ireland. This was followed next year by a Land Act which attempted to protect tenants from unfair eviction. After the Electoral Reform of 1867 Robert Lowe, now Chancellor of the Exchequer, had said that "We must educate our masters." Thus the extension of the franchise and the general Liberal belief in the value of education led to the launching of a national system of primary schools. This was achieved by W. E. Forster's Education Act of 1870, blurred though it was, like all education measures for some decades to come, by sectarian passion and controversy. At the same time patronage was finally destroyed in the home Civil Service. In the following year all religious tests at Oxford and Cambridge were abolished. The Judicature Act marked the culmination of a lengthy process of much-needed reform. A single Supreme Court was set up, with appropriate divisions, and procedure and methods of appeal were made uniform.

Reforms were long overdue at the War Office. They were carried out by Gladstone's Secretary of State, Edward Cardwell, one of the greatest of Army reformers. The Commander-in-Chief, the Duke of Cambridge, was opposed to any reform whatever, and the first step was taken when the Queen, with considerable reluctance, signed an Order in Council subordinating him to the Secretary of State. Flogging was abolished. An Enlistment Act introduced short service, which would create an efficient reserve. In 1871 Cardwell went further, and after a hard fight with Service opinion the

purchase of commissions was prohibited. The infantry were rearmed with the Martini-Henry rifle, and the regimental system was completely reorganized on a county basis. The War Office was overhauled, though a General Staff was not yet established.

All this was achieved in the space of six brilliant, crowded years, and then, as so often happens in English history, the pendulum swung back. Great reforms offend great interests. The working classes were offered little to attract them apart from a Ballot Act which allowed them to exercise the newly won franchise in secret and without intimidation. The settlement for fifteen million dollars of the *Alabama* dispute with the United States, though sensible, was disagreeable to a people long fed on a Palmerstonian diet.[1] An unsuccessful Licensing Bill, prompted by the Temperance wing of the Liberal Party, estranged the drink interest and founded an alliance between the brewer and the Conservative Party. Gladstone fought the election on a proposal to abolish the income tax, which then stood at threepence in the pound, and to the end of his life he always regretted his failure to achieve this object. But the country was now against him and he lost. He went into semi-retirement, believing that the great reforming work of Liberalism had been completed.

Disraeli's campaign began long before Gladstone fell. He concentrated on social reform and on a new conception of the Empire, and both prongs of attack struck Gladstone at his weakest points. Disraeli proclaimed that "the first consideration of a Minister should be the health of the people." Liberals tried to laugh this off as

---

[1] The *Alabama* was a Confederate commerce-raider built in Britain which sailed out of the Mersey under a false name in June 1862, at the height of the American Civil War, in spite of the protests of the American Minister in London.

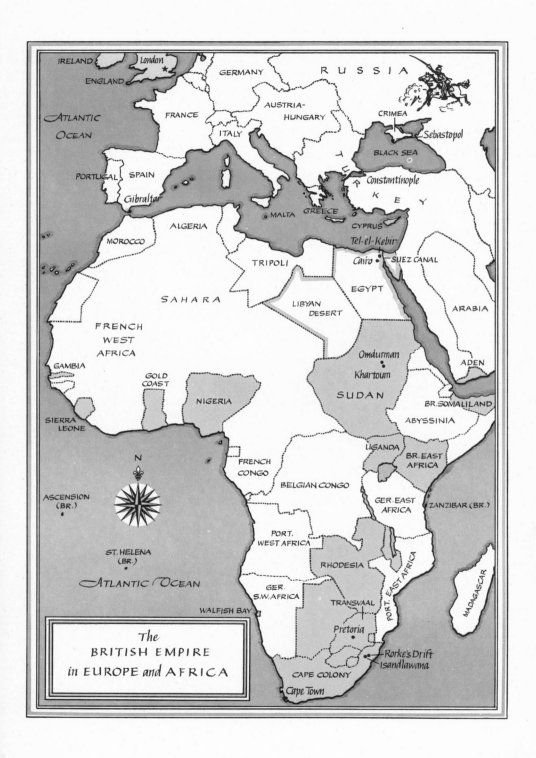

The
BRITISH EMPIRE
in EUROPE and AFRICA

a "policy of sewage." In his first full session after reaching office Disraeli proceeded to redeem his pledge. He was fortunate in his colleagues, among whom the Home Secretary, Richard Cross, was outstanding in ability. A Trade Union Act gave the unions almost complete freedom of action, an Artisan's Dwelling Act was the first measure to tackle the housing problem, a Sale of Food and Drugs Act and a Public Health Act at last established sanitary law on a sound footing. Disraeli succeeded in persuading much of the Conservative Party not only that the real needs of the electorate included healthier conditions of life, better homes, and freedom to organize in the world of industry, but also that the Conservative Party was perfectly well fitted to provide them. The second part of the new Conservative program, Imperialism, had also been launched before Disraeli came to power. At first Disraeli was brilliantly successful. The Suez Canal had been open for six years, and had transformed the strategic position of Great Britain. In 1875, on behalf of the British Government, Disraeli bought, for four million pounds, the shares of the Egyptian Khedive Ismail in the Canal. In the following year Queen Victoria, to her great pleasure, was proclaimed Empress of India. Disraeli's purpose was to make those colonies which he had once condemned as "a millstone around our necks" sparkle like diamonds. New storms in Europe distracted attention from this glittering prospect.

In 1876 the Eastern Question erupted anew. The nice choice appeared to lie between bolstering Turkish power and allowing Russian influence to move through the Balkans and into the Mediterranean by way of Constantinople. In a famous pamphlet, *The Bulgarian Horrors and the Question of the East,* Gladstone delivered his onslaught on the Turks and

Disraeli's Government. After this broadside relations between the two great men became so strained that Lord Beaconsfield (as Disraeli now was) publicly described Gladstone as worse than any Bulgarian horror.

At the end of the year a conference of the Great Powers was held in Constantinople at which Lord Salisbury, as the British representative, displayed for the first time his diplomatic talents. Salisbury's caustic, far-ranging common sense supplemented Disraeli's darting vision. A program of reform for Turkey was drawn up, but the Turks, sustained in part by a belief that Salisbury's zeal for reform did not entirely reflect the views of his Prime Minister and the British Cabinet, rejected it. The delegates returned to their capitals and Europe waited for war to break out between Russia and Turkey. When it came in the summer of 1877 the mood of the country quickly changed. Gladstone, whose onslaught on the Turks had at first carried all before it, was now castigated as a pro-Russian. Public opinion reached fever-point. The music-hall song of the hour was:

> We don't want to fight, but by jingo if
> we do
> We've got the ships, we've got the
> men, we've got the money too!
> We've fought the Bear before, and
> while we're Britons true
> The Russians shall not have Constanti-
> nople.

In February 1878, after considerable prevarication, a fleet of British ironclads steamed into the Golden Horn. They lay in the Sea of Marmora, opposite the Russian army, for six uneasy months of truce.

In March Turkey and Russia signed the Treaty of San Stefano. It gave Russia effective control of the Balkans, and was obviously unacceptable to the other Great Powers. War again seemed likely, and Lord Derby, who objected to any kind of military preparations, resigned. He was replaced at the Foreign Office by Lord Salisbury, who immediately set about summoning a conference of the Great Powers. They met at the Congress of Berlin in June and July. The result was that Russia gave up much of what she had momentarily gained at San Stefano. Beaconsfield returned from Berlin claiming that he had brought "peace with honor."

The following weeks saw the zenith of Beaconsfield's career. But fortune soon ceased to smile upon him. Thrusting policies in South Africa and Afghanistan led, in 1879, to the destruction of a British battalion by the Zulus at Isandhlwana and the massacre of the Legation staff at Kabul. These minor disasters, though promptly avenged, lent fresh point to Gladstone's vehement assault upon the Government, an assault which reached its climax in the autumn of 1879 with the Midlothian Campaign. His constant theme was the need for the nation's policy to conform with the moral law. This appeal to morality infuriated the Conservatives, who based their case on the importance of defending and forwarding British interests and responsibilities wherever they might lie. But the force of Gladstone's oratory was too much for the exhausted Ministry. Moreover, their last years in office coincided with the onset of an economic depression, serious enough for industry but ruinous for agriculture. When Beaconsfield dissolved in March 1880 the electoral result was decisive.

Beaconsfield died a year later. He made the Conservatives a great force in democratic politics. The large-scale two-party system with its "swing of the pendulum" begins with him. Such was the work of Disraeli, for which his name will be duly honored.

The emergence of a mass electorate called for a new kind of politics. Of the two leaders Gladstone was slow to see the implications of the new age. Disraeli, on the other hand, produced both a policy and an organization. The Central Office was established and a network of local associations was set up, combined in a National Union. In the Liberal camp the situation was very different. Gladstone's coolness and Whig hostility prevented the building of a centralized party organization. The impulse and impetus came not from the center, but through the provinces. In 1873 Joseph Chamberlain had become Mayor of Birmingham. Aided by a most able political adviser, Schnadhorst, he built up a party machine which, although based on popular participation, his enemies quickly condemned as a "caucus."

Gladstone and Disraeli had done much to bridge the gap between aristocratic rule and democracy. Elections gradually became a judgment on what the Government of the day had accomplished and an assessment of the promises for the future made by the two parties. By 1880 they were being fought with techniques which differ very little from those used today.

When Gladstone in 1880 became Prime Minister for the second time his position was not the comfortable one he had held twelve years before. In the first Gladstone Government there had been little discord. But the old Whig faction thought that reform had gone far enough, and Gladstone himself had some sympathy with them. He disliked intensely the methods of the Radical "caucus" and scorned their policies of social and economic reform. But the Liberals, or rather the Whigs, were not alone in their troubles and anxieties. Shocked by the onset of democracy and its threat to old, established interests, the Tory leaders proceeded to forget the lessons which Disraeli had tried so long to teach them. Into the breach stepped a small but extremely able group whose prowess at Parliamentary guerrilla fighting has rarely been equaled, the "Fourth Party"—Lord Randolph Churchill, A. J. Balfour, Sir Henry Drummond Wolff, and John Gorst. Conflict was fierce, but often internecine. Chamberlain and Lord Randolph, though sometimes in bitter disagreement, had far more in common than they had with their own leaders.

One of the first troubles sprang from South Africa. There the Boer Republic of the Transvaal had long been in difficulties, threatened by bankruptcy and disorders within and by the Zulu warrior kingdom upon its eastern border. To save it from ruin and possible extinction Disraeli's Government had annexed it, an action which at first met with little protest. As soon as British arms had finally quelled the Zulus in 1879, a fierce desire for renewed independence began to stir among the Transvaal Boers. At the end of 1880 they revolted and a small British force was cut to pieces at Majuba Hill. The outcome was the Pretoria Convention of 1881, which, modified in 1884, gave virtual independence to the Transvaal. This application of Liberal principles provided the foundation of Boer power in South Africa.

As Gladstone had foreseen at the time, Disraeli's purchase of shares in the Suez Canal, brilliant stroke though it was, soon brought all the problems of Egypt in its wake. On June 11, 1882, fifty Europeans were killed in riots in Alexandria. A few days later the Cabinet decided to dispatch an army under Sir Garnet Wolseley to Egypt. The decision was crowned by military success, and Arabi's army was decisively defeated at Tel-el-Kebir on September 13. Intervention in Egypt led to an even more perplexing entanglement in the Sudan. During the same year that the Egyptians revolted against France and Britain the Sudanese rebelled against the Egyptians. Either the Sudan must be reconquered or it must be evacuated, and the Government in London chose evacuation. On January 14, 1884, General Charles Gordon left London charged by the Cabinet with the task. He arrived in Khartoum in February, and once there he judged that it would be wrong to withdraw the garrisons and abandon the country to the mercy of the Mahdi's Dervishes. He was resolved to remain in Khartoum until his self-imposed mission was accomplished. His strength of will, often capricious in its expression, was pitted against Gladstone's determination not to be involved in fresh colonial adventures. Eventually, upon the insistence of Lord Hartington, then Secretary of State for War, who made it a matter of confidence in the Cabinet, the Government were induced to rescue Gordon. In September Wolseley hastened to Cairo, and in less than a month he had assembled a striking force of ten thousand men. In October he set out from the borders of Egypt upon the eight-hundred-mile advance to Khartoum. His main strength must proceed steadily up-river until, all cataracts surmounted, they would be poised for a swoop upon Khartoum. In the meantime he detached the Camel Corps under Sir Herbert Stewart to cut across a hundred and fifty miles of desert and rejoin the Nile to the north of Gordon's capital. On January 21 steamers arrived from Khartoum, sent downriver by Gordon. On the 24th a force of 26 British and 240 Sudanese sailed south on two of the steamers, assailed by Dervish musketry fire from the banks. On the 28th they reached Khartoum. It was too late. Gordon's flag no longer flew over the Residency. He was dead; the city had fallen two days before, after a prodigious display of valor by its defender. He had fallen alone, unsuccored and unsupported by any of his own countrymen. In the eyes of perhaps half the nation Gladstone was a murderer. Thirteen years went by before Gordon was avenged.

While the nation thought only of Gordon the Government was pressing ahead with its one considerable piece of legislation, a Reform Bill which completed the work of democratizing the franchise in the counties. Almost every adult male was given a vote. Another Act abolished the remaining small boroughs and, with a few exceptions, divided the country into single-Member constituencies.

Further speculation about the future of English politics was abruptly cut short by the announcement of Gladstone's conversion to the policy of Home Rule. In the years since the Great Famine of the 1840's Ireland had continued in her misery. In the forty years before 1870 forty-two Coercion Acts were passed. During the same period there was not a single statute to protect the Irish peasant from eviction and rack-renting. This was deliberate; the aim was to make the Irish peasant a day-laborer after the English pattern. But Ireland was not England; the Irish peasant clung to his land; he used every means in his power to defeat the alien landlords. It must not be supposed that the Irish picture can be seen from Britain entirely in black and white. The landlords were mostly colonists from England and of long standing; they believed themselves to be, and in many ways were, a civilizing influence in a primitive country. They had often had to fight for their lives and their property. The deep hold of the Roman Catholic Church on a superstitious peasantry had tended on political as well as religious grounds to be hostile to England. In 1870 Isaac Butt had founded the Home Rule League. Effective leadership of the movement soon passed into the hands of Charles Stewart Parnell. A patrician in the Irish party, he was a born leader, with a power of discipline and a tactical skill that soon converted Home Rule from a debating topic into the supreme question of the hour. The root of Parnell's success was the junction of the Home Rule cause with a fresh outburst of peasant agitation. This process was just beginning when, in 1877, Michael Davitt came out of prison after serving a seven-year sentence for treason. It was Davitt's belief that Home Rule and the land question could not be separated, and, in spite of opposition from the extreme Irish Nationalists, he successfully founded the Land League in 1879. Its objects were the reduction of rack-rents and the promotion of peasant ownership of the land. When Parnell declared his support for the League the land hunger of the peasant, the political demand for Home Rule, and the hatred of American emigrants for their unforgotten oppressors were at last brought together in a formidable alliance.

At the time none of this was immediately clear to Gladstone; his mind was occupied by the great foreign and Imperial issues that had provoked his return to power. His Government's first answer was to promote an interim Compensation for Disturbance Bill. When this was rejected by the House of Lords in August 1880 Ireland was quick to reply with Terror. The Government then decided both to strike at terrorism and to reform the land laws. In March 1881 a sweeping Coercion Act gave to the Irish Viceroy the power, in Morley's phrase, "to lock up anybody he pleased and to detain him for as long as he pleased." The Coercion Act was followed immediately by a Land

Act which conceded almost everything that the Irish had demanded. This was far more generous than anything the Irish had expected, but Parnell, driven by Irish-American extremists and by his belief that even greater concessions could be extracted from Gladstone, set out to obstruct the working of the new land courts. The Government had no alternative, under the Coercion Act, but to arrest him. Crime and murder multiplied, and by the spring of 1882 Gladstone was convinced that the policy of coercion had failed. In April therefore what was called the "Kilmainham Treaty" was concluded, based on the understanding that Parnell would use his influence to end crime and terror in return for an Arrears Bill which would aid those tenants who, because they owed rent, had been unable to take advantage of the Land Act. W. E. Forster, Chief Secretary for Ireland and advocate of coercion, and the Viceroy, Lord Cowper, resigned. They were replaced by Lord Frederick Cavendish and Lord Spencer. On May 6 Lord Frederick Cavendish landed in Dublin. A few hours after his arrival he was walking in Phoenix Park with his under-secretary, Burke, when both men were stabbed to death. Gladstone did what he could to salvage a little from the wreck of his policy.

Thus we return to 1885. On June 8 the Government was defeated on an amendment to the Budget, and Gladstone promptly resigned. After some hesitation and difficulty Lord Salisbury formed a Government which was in a minority in the House of Commons. A most significant appointment was that of the Earl of Carnarvon as Viceroy of Ireland. It was well known that Carnarvon favored a policy of Home Rule, and on August 1 he met Parnell in a house in Grosvenor Square. He left Parnell with the impression that the Government was contemplating a Home Rule measure. When the election came in November Parnell, unable to extract a clear promise of support from Gladstone, ordered the Irish in Britain to vote Conservative. In the new House of Commons the Liberal majority over the Conservatives was eighty-six. But Parnell had realized his dream. His followers, their ranks swollen by the operation of the Reform Act in the Irish counties, also numbered eighty-six. In these circumstances Gladstone continued to hope that the Parnellite-Conservative alliance would hold fast and that Home Rule would pass as an agreed measure without undue opposition from the House of Lords.

It is doubtful whether there had ever been substance in Gladstone's hopes. Carnarvon represented himself and not his party or the Cabinet. His approach to Parnell had been tentative and the Government was uncommitted. Salisbury, for his part, was naturally content to have the Irish vote in a critical election, but his Protestantism, his belief in the Union, his loyalty to the landowners and to the Irish minority who had put their faith in the Conservative Party, were all far too strong for him ever to have seriously considered Home Rule. Carnarvon resigned in the New Year, and on January 26 Salisbury's Government announced that it would introduce a Coercion Bill of the most stringent kind. Without hesitation, almost without consultation with his colleagues, Gladstone brought about its defeat on an amendment to the Queen's speech. There was no doubt that the new Government would be a Home Rule Government, and Hartington and the other leading Whigs refused to join. This was probably inevitable, but Gladstone destroyed any remaining hope of success by his treatment of Chamberlain. In the eyes of the country Chamberlain now stood next to his leader in the Liberal Party. But he was not consulted in the preparation of the Home Rule Bill, and his own scheme for local government reform was ignored. He resigned on March 26, to become Gladstone's most formidable foe. The Home Rule Bill was introduced into the Commons on April 8, 1886, by Gladstone in a speech which lasted for three and a half hours. The Bill was defeated on the second reading two months after its introduction. Ninety-three Liberals voted against the Government. Gladstone had a difficult decision to make. He could resign or dissolve. He chose the latter course and fought the election on the single issue of Home Rule. The new House contained 316 Conservatives and 78 Liberal Unionists, against 191 Gladstonians and 85 Parnellites. Gladstone resigned immediately, and Salisbury again took office.

The long period of Liberal-Whig predominance which had begun in 1830 was over. The turn of the wheel had brought fortune to the Conservatives, whose prospects had seemed so gloomy in 1880. The opponents whom they had feared as the irresistible instruments of democracy had delivered themselves into their hands.

Salisbury's Government depended upon the support of the Liberal Unionists, led by Hartington, though their most formidable figure, both in Parliament and in the country, was Joseph Chamberlain. Inside the Cabinet there was little harmony. Lord Randolph's ideas on Tory Democracy struck no spark in Salisbury's traditional Conservatism. The differences between the two men, both in character and policy, were fundamental. The final collision occurred over a comparatively trivial point, Lord Randolph's demand for a reduction in the Army and Navy Estimates. He resigned on the eve of Christmas 1886 at the wrong time, on the wrong issue, and he made no attempt to rally support. Salisbury made George Goschen, a Liberal Unionist of impeccable Whig views, his Chancellor of the Exchequer, thus proclaiming that Tory Democracy was now deemed an unnecessary encumbrance. Thereafter his Government's record in law-making was meager in the extreme. The main measure was the Local Government Act of 1888, which created county councils and laid the basis for further advance. Three years later school fees were abolished in elementary schools, and a Factory Act made some further attempt to regulate evils in the employment of women and children. It was not an impressive achievement. Even these minor measures were largely carried out as concessions to Chamberlain.

Salisbury's interest and that of a large section of public opinion lay in the world overseas, where the Imperialist movement was reaching its climax of exploration, conquest, and settlement. Livingstone, Stanley, Speke, and other travelers had opened up the interior of darkest Africa. Their feats of exploration paved the way for the acquisition of colonies by the European Powers. It was the most important achievement of the period that this partition of Africa was carried out peacefully. The credit is largely due to Salisbury, who in 1887 became Foreign Secretary as well as Prime Minister, and who never lost sight of the need to preserve peace while the colonial map of Africa was being drawn. His foreign policy was largely swayed by these colonial affairs. When Salisbury took office he himself promoted no great schemes of Imperial expansion, but he was prepared to back up the men on the spot. The key to his success lay in his skillful handling of the innumerable complications that arose between the Powers in an age of intense national rivalries. He once said that "British policy is to drift lazily downstream, occasionally putting out a boat-hook to avoid a collision." No

British Foreign Secretary has wielded his diplomatic boat-hook with greater dexterity.

The relentless question of a sullen and embittered Ireland over-shadowed domestic politics. "What Ireland wants," Salisbury had asserted before the election campaign, "is government—government that does not flinch, that does not vary," and in his nephew, A. J. Balfour, who became Irish Secretary in 1887, he found a man capable of putting into practice the notion that all could be solved by "twenty years of resolute government." Balfour stretched his authority to the limit and acted with a determination that fully matched the ruthlessness of his Irish opponents. Parnell stood aloof from these tumults. But his adherence to cautious and constitutional action was stricken by the publication in *The Times* on April 18, 1887, of a facsimile letter, purporting to bear his signature, in which he was made to condone the Phoenix Park murders. Parnell, while denouncing the letter as a forgery, refused to bring an action in an English court. But in the following year the Government set up a commission of three judges to investigate the whole field of Irish crime. They had been sitting for six months when, in February 1889, they at last began to probe the letters. They discovered that they had been forged by a decrepit Irish journalist named Richard Piggot. For a few months Parnell rode the crest of the wave. A General Election was approaching, the Government was out of favor, and nothing, it seemed, could prevent a victory for Gladstone and Home Rule. But the case was altered. On November 13, 1890, the suit of O'Shea *v.* O'Shea and Parnell opened in the Divorce Court. A decree *nisi* was granted to Captain O'Shea. Parnell, as co-respondent, offered no defense. The Nonconformist conscience, powerful in the Liberal Party, reared its head. Tremendous pressure was put on the Irish leader. As a last measure Gladstone wrote to Parnell that he would cease to lead the Liberal Party unless the Irishman retired. After Parnell had made a bitter attack upon Gladstone the Catholic Church declared against him, and he was disavowed by most of his party. Within a year he died.

Liberal prospects, which had been so bright in 1889, were now badly clouded. They were not improved by the adoption of the comprehensive "Newcastle Program" of 1891. When the election came in the summer of the following year the result was a Home Rule majority of only forty, dependent on the Irish Members. Gladstone was resolute. Work began immediately on a second Home Rule Bill, and in February 1893 he introduced it himself. At the age of eighty-three he piloted the Bill through eighty-two sittings against an Opposition led by debaters as formidable as Chamberlain and Balfour. There have been few more remarkable achievements in the whole history of Parliament. It was all in vain. Passing through the Commons by small majorities, the Bill was rejected on the second reading in the Lords by 419 votes to 41. Thus perished all hope of a united, self-governing Ireland, loyal to the British Crown. After the defeat of the Home Rule Bill Gladstone fell increasingly out of sympathy with his colleagues. He resigned on March 3, 1894, fifty-two and a half years after his swearing in as a Privy Councillor. He died in 1898. His career had been the most noteworthy of the century, leaving behind innumerable marks on the pages of history. Few of his conceptions were unworthy. Gladstone's achievements, like his failures, were on the grand scale.

In January 1893 the Independent Labor Party had been founded at a conference at Bradford, with J. Keir Hardie, the Scottish miners' leader, as its chairman. The aims of the I.L.P., as it was called, were the popularization of Socialist doctrine and the promotion of independent working-class candidates at Parliamentary elections. Of far greater importance in England was the emergence about the same time of the Fabian Society, run by a group of young and obscure but highly gifted men, Sidney Webb and George Bernard Shaw among them. They damned all revolutionary theory and set about the propagation of a practical Socialist doctrine. They were not interested in the organization of a new political party. Most working men knew little of these higher intellectual activities. They were absorbed in efforts to raise their standards of living. During the mid-Victorian years Trade Union organization had been largely confined to the skilled and relatively prosperous members of the working class. But in 1889 the dockers of London, a miserably underpaid group, struck for a wage of sixpence an hour. The dockers' victory, made possible by much public sympathy and support, was followed by a rapid expansion of Trade Union organization among the unskilled workers. Throughout the country small groups of Socialists began to form, but they were politically very weak. Their sole electoral success had been the return for West Ham in 1892 of Keir Hardie, who created a sensation by going to the House for his first time accompanied by a brass band and wearing a cloth cap. Keir Hardie patiently toiled to woo the Unions away from the Liberal connection. The outcome was a meeting sponsored by the Socialist societies and a number of Trade Unions which was held in the Memorial Hall, Farringdon Street, London, on February 27, 1900. It was there decided to set up a Labor Representation Committee, with Ramsay MacDonald as its secretary. The aim of the committee was defined as the establishment of "a distinct Labor group in Parliament who shall have their own Whips and agree upon policy." The Labor Party had been founded. MacDonald in the twentieth century was to become the first Labor Prime Minister. He was to split his party at a moment of national crisis, and die amid the execrations of the Socialists whose political fortunes he had done so much to build.

Gladstone had been succeeded as Prime Minister by Lord Rosebery. His was a bleak, precarious, wasting inheritance. Rosebery had the good luck to win the Derby twice during his sixteen months of office. Not much other fortune befell him. Rosebery had a far-ranging mind, above the shifts and compromises indispensable in political life. He was the Queen's own choice as Prime Minister, and his Imperialist views made him unpopular with his own party. The Lords continued to obstruct him. At this moment the Chancellor of the Exchequer, Sir William Harcourt, included in his Budget proposals a scheme for the payment of substantial death duties. The Cabinet was rent by clashes of personality and the quarrels of Imperialists and "Little Englanders." When the Government was defeated on a snap vote in June 1895 it took the opportunity to resign.

At the General Election the Conservative–Liberal Unionist alliance won a decisive victory. Its majority over the Opposition, including the Irish Nationalists, was 152. Lord Salisbury thereupon formed a powerful administration. His deputy and closest adviser was his nephew, Arthur Balfour, who became First Lord of the Treasury. But the man who in the public eye dominated the Government was the Liberal Unionist leader, Joseph Chamberlain, now at the height of his powers and anxious for the office which had been denied to him for so long by the events of 1886. By his own choice Chamberlain became Colonial Secretary. His instinct was a sure one. Interest in home affairs had languished. In its five years of office the Government passed only one substantial reforming measure, the Workmen's Compensation Act of 1897. The excitement of politics lay in the clash of Imperial forces in the continents of Africa and Asia, and it was there that Chamberlain resolved to make his mark. A great change had taken place in him. The Municipal Socialist and Republican of his Birmingham years was now the architect of Empire. "It is not enough," he declared, "to occupy certain great spaces of the world's surface unless you can make the best of them—unless you are willing to develop them. We are landlords of a great estate; it is the duty of a landlord to develop his estate."

From the moment he took office projects of reform were pushed into the background by the constant eruption of questions inseparable from a policy of expansion. The first was that of the Ashanti, who terrorized much of the Gold Coast; by January 1896 the Ashanti kingdom had been crushed. The situation in Nigeria was much more difficult, since the French were attempting to confine the British to the coastal areas by using their superior military strength. Chamberlain's skillful diplomacy backed resolute action, and the Anglo-French Convention of June 1898 drew boundary lines in West Africa which were entirely satisfactory to the British. A few months later a far more dangerous dispute broke out between Britain and France over the control of the Upper Nile. Since the death of Gordon the Dervishes had held unquestioned sway in the Sudan. In 1896 French moves towards the sources of the Nile were already taking place, and must be forestalled. In March Sir Herbert Kitchener, Sirdar of the Egyptian Army, launched his campaign for the avenging of Gordon and the reconquest of the Sudan. It was largely an engineers' war, enlivened by many short, fierce, gallant actions. After two and a half years the Dervish Army was finally confronted and destroyed outside Khartoum at the Battle of Omdurman on September 2, 1898. This, as described at the time by a young Hussar who took part in the battle, was "the most signal triumph ever gained by the arms of science over barbarians." The French gave way, and by the Convention of March 1899 the watershed of the Congo and the Nile was fixed as the boundary separating British and French interests. The Sudan then entered upon a period of constructive rule.

Britain entered the twentieth century in the grip of war. The Transvaal had been transformed by the exploitation of the extremely rich goldfields on the Witwatersrand. This was the work of foreign capital and labor, most of it British. The Uitlanders—or Outlanders, as foreigners were called—equaled the native Boers in number, but the Transvaal Government refused to grant them political rights, even though they contributed all but one-twentieth of the country's taxation. Paul Kruger, the President of the Republic, who was now past his seventieth year, determined to preserve the character and independence of his country. The political and economic grievances of the Uitlanders made an explosion inevitable, and Chamberlain by the end of 1895 was ready to meet it. Unknown to him however Rhodes had worked out a scheme for an uprising of the British in Johannesburg to be reinforced by the invasion of the Transvaal by a force led by the Administrator of Rhodesia, Dr. Leander Starr Jameson. It was, in Chamberlain's words, "a disgraceful exhibition of filibustering," and it ended in the failure which it deserved. The raid was a turning-point; the entire course of South African history was henceforth violently diverted from peaceful channels.

The next three years were occupied by long-drawn-out and arduous negotiations, Chamberlain's determination being more than matched by Kruger's tortuous obstinacy. In March 1897 Sir Alfred Milner, an outstanding public servant, became High Commissioner in South Africa. He was an administrator of great talents, but he lacked the gift of diplomacy. The climax was reached in April 1899, when a petition, signed by more than 20,000 Uitlanders, arrived in Downing Street. A conference at Bloemfontein in June between Kruger and Milner settled nothing. On October 9 the Boers delivered an ultimatum while the British forces in South Africa were still weak. Three days later their troops moved over the border.

At the outbreak of the war the Boers put 35,000 men, or twice the British number, in the field, and a much superior artillery derived from German sources. Within a few weeks they had invested Ladysmith to the east, and Mafeking and Kimberley to the west. World opinion was uniformly hostile to the British. Meanwhile a British army corps of three divisions was on the way as reinforcement, under the command of Sir Redvers Buller, and volunteer contingents from the Dominions were offered or forthcoming. The British army corps, as it arrived, was distributed by Buller in order to show a front everywhere. One division was sent to defend Natal, another to the relief of Kimberley, and a third to the north-eastern district of Cape Colony. Within a single December week each of them advanced against the rifle and artillery fire of the Boers, and was decisively defeated with, for those days, severe losses in men and guns. Although the losses of under a thousand men in each case may seem small nowadays, they

came as a startling and heavy shock to the public in Britain and throughout the Empire, and indeed to the troops on the spot. But Queen Victoria braced the nation in words which have become justly famous. "Please understand," she replied to Balfour when he tried to discuss "Black Week," as it was called, "that there is no one depressed in *this* house. We are not interested in the possibilities of defeat. They do not exist." Lord Roberts of Kandahar, who had won fame in the Afghan Wars, was made the new Commander-in-Chief, Lord Kitchener of Khartoum was appointed his Chief of Staff, and in a few months the two already illustrious generals with an ever-increasing army transformed the scene.

Piet Cronje at Mafeking was deceived into thinking that the main blow would fall on Kimberley, and he shifted the larger portion of his troops to Magersfontein, a few miles south of the diamond center. Kimberley indeed was one of Roberts' objectives, but he gained it by sending General French on a long encirclement, and French's cavalry relieved it on February 15. The threat from the rear now compelled Cronje to quit his earthworks and fall back to the northeast. Twelve days later, after fierce frontal assaults by Kitchener, he surrendered with four thousand men. Thereafter all went with a rush. On the following day Buller relieved Ladysmith; on March 13 Roberts reached Bloemfontein, on May 31 Johannesburg, and on June 5 Pretoria fell. Mafeking was liberated after a siege which had lasted for two hundred and seventeen days, and its relief provoked unseemly celebrations in London. Kruger fled. The Orange Free State and the Transvaal were annexed, and in the autumn of 1900 Roberts went home to England. At this Lord Salisbury, on Chamberlain's advice, fought a General Election and gained another spell of power with a large majority.

On January 22, 1901, Queen Victoria died. In England during the Queen's years of withdrawal from the outward shows of public life there had once been restiveness against the Crown, and professed republicans had raised their voices. By the end of the century all this had died away. The Sovereign had become the symbol of Empire. At the Queen's Jubilees in 1887 and 1897 India and the colonies had been vividly represented in the State celebrations. The Crown was providing the link between the growing family of nations and races which the former Prime Minister, Lord Rosebery, had with foresight christened the Commonwealth. The Queen herself was seized with the greatness of her role. She represented staunchness and continuity in British traditions, and as she grew in years veneration clustered around her. The Victorian Age closed in 1901, but the sense of purpose and confidence which had inspired it lived on through the ordeals to come.

The War in South Africa meanwhile continued. Botha, Kritzinger, Hertzog, De Wet, De la Rey, to name only five of the more famous commando leaders, soon faced Kitchener with innumerable local battles and reverses which were not to end for another seventeen months. Each of these leaders wanted an amnesty for the Cape rebels; but Milner, the High Commissioner, was adverse, and the Cabinet in London supported him. Thus frustrated, and much against his judgment and personal inclination, Kitchener was driven to what would nowadays be called a "scorched earth" policy. Blockhouses were built along the railway lines; fences were driven across the countryside; then more blockhouses were built along the fences. Movement within the enclosures thus created became impossible for even the most heroic commandos. Then, area by area, every man, woman, and child was swept into concentration camps. Such methods could only be justified by the fact that most of the commandos fought in plain clothes, and could only be subdued by wholesale imprisonment, together with the families who gave them succor. Nothing, not even the incapacity of the military authorities when charged with the novel and distasteful task of herding large bodies of civilians into captivity, could justify the conditions in the camps themselves. By February 1902 more than twenty thousand of the prisoners, or nearly one in every six, had died, mostly of disease. An Englishwoman, Miss Emily Hobhouse, exposed and proclaimed the terrible facts. Chamberlain removed them from military control; conditions thereupon speedily improved, and at last, on March 23, 1902, the Boers sued for peace. Thirty-two commandos remained unbeaten in the field. Two delegates from each met the British envoys, and after much discussion they agreed to lay down their arms and ammunition. None should be punished except for certain specified breaches of the usages of war; self-government would be accorded as soon as possible, and Britain would pay three million pounds in compensation. Upon the conclusion of peace Lord Salisbury resigned. The last Prime Minister to sit in the House of Lords, he had presided over an unparalleled expansion of the British Empire. He died in the following year, and with him a certain aloofness of spirit, now considered old-fashioned, passed from British politics. All the peace terms were kept, and Milner did much to reconstruct South Africa.

We have now reached in this account the end of the nineteenth century. Nearly a hundred years of peace and progress had carried Britain to the leadership of the world. She had striven repeatedly for the maintenance of peace, at any rate for herself, and progress and prosperity had been continuous in all classes. The franchise had been extended almost to the actuarial limit, and yet quiet and order reigned. There was endless work to be done. It did not matter which party ruled: they found fault with one another, as they had a perfect right to do. None of the ancient inhibitions obstructed the adventurous. If mistakes were made they had been made before, and Britons could repair them without serious consequences. Active and vigorous politics should be sustained. To go forward gradually but boldly seemed to be fully justified.

The future is unknowable, but the past should give us hope.

THE LIFE AND WORKS OF

WINSTON CHURCHILL

By HUGH TREVOR-ROPER

SIR WINSTON CHURCHILL is one of the great figures of European history. He is also a great figure in English literature. No statesman in the past had made such a double impact on his generation. The great political orators of history spoke to their nations only, and to a small segment of their own nations at that, but Churchill's great speeches of World War II were delivered, thanks to the radio, live to the world. They roused England, as William Pitt once roused it, "to save herself by her exertions and Europe by her example." Nor has their impact ceased. Read or reiterated today, after a generation has passed, they still retain their compulsive power. The crisis which called them forth, and which made them so vivid at the time, may be a memory, or a detail of history; but that majestic, perfectly constructed, perfectly balanced style preserves them as literature, and it is as a man of letters, not as a statesman, that the Nobel Prize was awarded to him.

But if it was the events of 1939–1945 which gave Winston Churchill the opportunity of greatness, his quality both as a statesman and as a man of letters had been established long before. Even if he had died in 1938, his position in British, though not in world, history was by then secure, and his published works—autobiographical, biographical, political, and

historical—would have guaranteed him a place in the literary pantheon of his nation. To those who think of him as a statesman and orator of the 1940s, it may be difficult to realize that Churchill's political life goes back to 1900; that he had been a minister of the Crown, with interruptions, since 1905; and that his first book was published in 1898. His was a combined political and literary activity that was continuous for sixty years.

As usual with statesmen, the politics and the literature have alternated one with the other. Churchill's books were written during the years of his own political eclipse. Many statesmen, perhaps particularly English statesmen, have taken to literature in those intervals of power happily guaranteed by our two-party system. Among the prime ministers of the past century, Lord Derby translated Homer, Disraeli wrote novels, Gladstone discharged a turgid flood of scriptural and classical scholarship, Arthur Balfour wrote philosophy, Lord Rosebery history, Lloyd George war memoirs. But Sir Winston Churchill combined the subjects of several of these predecessors, and in productivity he outdid them all. If his one novel cannot compete with those of Disraeli, his history is better, as well as more solid, than that of Rosebery; and if he avoided the details of scholarships in which Gladstone made himself ridiculous, he far outdistanced Lloyd George as a writer of war memoirs. Moreover, he had the better of most of his rivals by leaving lasting portraits of them. In his *Great Contemporaries* he depicted them all, Balfour and Curzon, Rosebery and Asquith, Liberal and Conservative alike, impartially, as he justly might, for he was both himself.

It is not strictly true to say that Churchill, like his immediate predecessors, worked within the English two-party system. In that humdrum machinery he was always something of a misfit. When he first entered Parliament, in 1900, it was as a Conservative—but, like his father, a radical Conservative. Three years later he was converted to Liberalism, just in time to be on the right side in the next election: a landslide election which brought the Liberals to power—first alone, then in coalition—for seventeen years. In those seventeen years he was frequently in office. By the end of that time, he was in the throes of a second conversion. He became a Tory again just in time to be made a minister in the first Tory government since his last conversion. From 1900 to 1929—for as long as the political pendulum swung between the Liberal and the Conservative party—it could be said that Churchill always contrived to be on the winning side. Only in 1929, when the Labor party came to power for the first time, did he take his place on the opposition benches. Whatever his party, Churchill was never a supporter of socialism.

Naturally enough, there were many who regarded him as an opportunist. To the Conservatives, after 1903, he was a renegade, and for a long time they hated him as such. When they came into the Liberal government to form a war coalition, they insisted on his exclusion—for a time successfully. Again, in the 1930s,

the years of Baldwin and Chamberlain, he was widely distrusted as "irresponsible." But of course it is absurd to see him as a mere opportunist. For ordinary men, the way to success in British politics may be through the party system, but the greatest of British statesmen have changed their party or their ideas. Peel, Disraeli, Gladstone—the three greatest prime ministers of the nineteenth century—were all regarded as traitors to their parties. Nor did Churchill's "opportunism" lead him to power by the easy way of compliance. In the 1930s, though a Conservative, he stood outside the official Conservative party, an "independent Conservative" distrusted by government and opposition alike. It was then that he delivered the most famous of his prewar speeches: his speeches criticizing the torpid rule of Stanley Baldwin and the "appeasement" of Neville Chamberlain; and it was then that he wrote his great nonpolitical works of literature, *My Early Life, Great Contemporaries,* and *Marlborough.*

Ironically, when the great crisis came, he was the only man who could unite all parties, and Conservatives, Liberals, and Laborites all served under him in his great war ministry. His "independence," his "opportunism," which made him uncomfortable within any party, made him an ideal master of all. But as he himself said to a friend, "It took Armageddon to make me prime minister." That is not the remark of an opportunist.

Why was Churchill so distrusted in the 1930s? A generation has passed, passions have cooled, and we can now look at that disastrous decade more coolly. In doing so, we can afford to be just to the politicians of that time, to the Baldwins and Chamberlains whom history has condemned for their failure. And if we are just, we must admit that they were not totally wrong. It merely happened that the issue on which they were wrong was, at the time, the gravest issue of all: an issue which made all their other aims, however worthy, temporarily unreal.

For basically, these men sought to realize an old ideal, the ideal of their fathers, which had been frustrated by the terrible holocaust of 1914–1918. They wanted peace in Europe, perhaps even isolation from Europe; and, under cover of that peace or that isolation, they wished to concentrate on material improvement, raise the standard of living, soften the tension between the classes and nations of the empire, rationalize and civilize the industrial society which had come to stay and which, since it had made war so terrible, must learn to do without war. Mature politicians themselves, they reckoned that the world was mature too. They did not believe much in history, in traditional attitudes, in romantic gestures. They had no sense of the past: their philosophy did not need it. Consequently, they could not believe that Churchill was a realist. He was a romantic, who lived in the past, in the remote age of Charles I and Cromwell, Louis XIV and Marlborough, when dictators and wars of conquest were real, as they were not now.

Yes, a romantic. Romanticism, I believe, is one of the deep springs, perhaps the deepest spring, in Churchill's character: a spring which even the inevitable cynicism of politics has not dried up. It breaks out, uninhibited, in his early life: in the love of adventure which took him, as soldier or war correspondent, to Cuba, to India, to the Sudan, to South Africa. It appears, in an uncritical extroverted form in his early chronicles of those experiences: his *Story of the Malakand Field Force* (1898) and his *The River War* (1899). It appears in an unsophisticated self-revealing novel which he wrote in India and published in 1900, *Savrola*. It appears, corrected and sophisticated by maturity in his uncomparable

autobiography, written thirty years later, *My Early Life*.

Savrola, Churchill's only novel, his only work of pure imagination, is not an important work. Were it not by him, no one would now read it. It belongs to a literary genre once fashionable, now extinct: the romantic political novel in which high-minded, liberal English or Anglicized gentlemen are involved in the cloak-and-dagger politics of anarchical or anachronistic imaginary states. The fashion was set by Sir Anthony Hope Hawkins who, under the name of Anthony Hope, published his novel, *The Prisoner of Zenda,* and provided the English language with a new word for such an imaginary, comic-opera state: Ruritania. In *Savrola,* Churchill created another Ruritania. It was called Laurania; and Savrola was an enlightened, liberal leader who, as Churchill afterward described it, "overthrew an arbitrary government, only to be swallowed up by a Socialist revolution." Early Churchill identified himself with the defense of liberal traditions against dictatorships of the right or left, and apprehended the necessity, but also the dangers, of radical allies.

It is tempting to dwell on Churchill's most romantic phase, but it is impossible to compete with his own account of it. To write of one's own childhood and adolescence is notoriously a biographer's problem. How can one, at a mature, sophisticated age, find the right tone of voice in which to recall the fumbling idealism, the naïveté, the disproportionate hopes and fears of one's own earlier incarnation? How avoid the opposite excesses of identification and detachment? But Churchill's *My Early Life* is a model. Its warm, olympian style, its gentle irony, its humanity and yet its detachment, place it among the great English autobiographies; and the story it tells is itself an exhilarating story of mere adventure from which few would deduce either the statesman or (but for the style in which it is written) the man of letters who was to emerge at the end of it.

Winston Churchill was born in a kind of historic purple which he has always worn proudly, yet lightly, and at a private angle: of a ducal family, the descendant of one of the greatest of English soldiers; in a ducal house, perhaps the greatest in England. His father, Lord Randolph Churchill, was a brilliant failure in English politics: a "radical Tory" who made life very difficult for his own prime minister, Lord Salisbury, and then made the fatal miscalculation of resigning in the belief that he was indispensable and would have to be reinstated on his own terms. Lord Salisbury was the better politician. "When a man has just got rid of a boil on the neck," he remarked, "does he ever want another?" He did not reinstate Lord Randolph, who then wasted and died.

Winston Churchill never forgot or forgave that injury. Though his contact with his father was slight, he revered him living and honored him dead. Lord Randolph, on the other hand, never recognized any political genius in his son. After a customary English education, which did not however include a university, he placed him in the army. "For years," the son afterward wrote, "I thought my father, with his experience and flair, had discerned in me the qualities of military genius. But I was told later that he had only come to the conclusion that I was not clever enough to go on the bar."

So the young Winston became a cavalry officer. But a cavalry officer—especially if fond of polo—had expensive tastes and slender pay. He also had five months' leave in the year. Churchill used his leave to earn the money to keep his polo ponies and to enjoy extra adventures. So he fought battles on the north-west frontier of India and took part in the famous cavalry charge at Omdurman, whereby Kitchener conquered the Sudan from the fanatical armies of "the Mad Mullah" and he appeared as a newspaper correspondent in Cuba, where the Spaniards were fighting their rebels, and in South Africa, where he was captured and imprisoned by the Boers. Since he was a noncombatant, he resented his imprisonment, which was contrary to the laws of war, and wrote a protest to the Boer State Attorney, one Jan Smuts, who afterward, as Prime Minister of South Africa, was one of Churchill's most intimate friends. "Winston Churchill noncombatant?" replied Smuts curtly. "Impossible." But by that time Churchill had escaped from his prison in Pretoria, jumped on a coal train, and escaped to Portuguese East Africa. He returned to England a popular hero who had foiled the Boers, and was elected to Parliament. He presented himself, like his father, as a radical Tory. Within a year he was preaching "that we should finish the war by force and generosity, and then make haste to return to paths of peace, retrenchment, and reform." These last words show him already halfway to liberalism.

My Early Life, which ends with Churchill's debut in Parliament, describes also how he became a writer. At school at Harrow he could never acquire a taste for Latin or Greek. He was thus condemned to spend a long time in the lowest form where "Mr. Somervell—a most delightful man, to whom my debt is great—was charged with the duty of teaching the stupidest boys the most disregarded thing, namely to write English. He knew how to do it. He taught it as no one else has ever taught it," that is, he taught its structure and articulation. "Thus I got into my bones the essential structure of the ordinary British sentence —which is a noble thing." A few years later, a subaltern at Bangalore, Churchill felt "a desire for learning," and remembering that his father was said to have read Gibbon's *Decline and Fall of the Roman Empire* with delight, to have known whole pages of it by heart, and to have modeled his style of speech and writing on it—he wrote to his mother to send him that majestic work. So entranced was he by it that he went on to Gibbon's *Autobiography*. To every reader of Churchill who has also read Gibbon the debt is obvious. No other master presides so assuredly over all his writing. In the great speeches, or in the memoirs of two wars, we hear the effortless dignity, the noble periods, the disciplined romanticism, the urbane olympian wit of the *Decline and Fall*. And behind *My Early Life* lies, unmistakably, the most perfect English autobiography, with its detached irony, its warm humanity, its elegant style, and yet its natural charm.

In Bangalore, Churchill not only read Gibbon: he also read Macaulay's great *History of England*. Here again he was fascinated; but Macaulay's glittering rhetoric has left few traces on Churchill's subtler oratory. Besides, Macaulay could be very unjust to persons, and one of the persons to whom he was most unjust was Churchill's ancestor, the great Duke of Marlborough. Churchill did not, at that time, know the extent of Macaulay's injustice: "There was no one at hand to tell me that this historian, with his captivating style and devastating self-confidence, was the prince of literary rogues who always preferred the tale to the truth." He was to learn this later and himself to redress the balance.

In 1903, Churchill made his first change of party. In 1905, the Liberal party to which he had transferred his allegiance came to power, and at once he acquired office. But between those two dates, while he sat on the opposition benches, he was not idle. He was not yet ready to defend his ancestor against Macaulay, but he was engaged on another piece of family rehabilitation, closer to his own experience. He was writing his biography, and vindication, of his father.

It is difficult to see Winston Churchill altogether apart from the father to whom he was so devoted and whose work he so consciously sought to continue. Lord Randolph Churchill had been, in his brief political life, the meteor of the Tory party. Like the young Disraeli, he had discharged his impetuous rhetoric on his own established leaders—"the old gang" as he called them—and was accused of splitting the party. But, unlike Disraeli, he never would split the party. In fact, he strengthened it by creating a new party machinery in the country. He also preached retrenchment of public expense and social reform; no Home Rule for Ireland but generous treatment of Irish peasant grievances. Thanks to his brilliance and his popularity, he had become indispensable even to the leaders whom he attacked. At thirty-seven he was the youngest Chancellor of the Exchequer and leader of the House of Commons since Pitt. At thirty-eight, thanks to that fatal resignation, he had fallen, and fallen finally. Less than ten years later he was dead. To the end, though he hated Lord Salisbury and the traditional image which his long reign had imposed on conservatism, he refused to change his party. Now his son, having changed his party, was pursuing the same policy under Liberal colors; and in his biography of his father he sought to show the real consistency of both their beliefs.

The Life of Lord Randolph Churchill is a long history of a short career. But Edwardian biographies were always long. And this is an important biography. It is packed with political wisdom. It is also the first product of Churchill's mature style. That style would develop further, would acquire greater range and complexity, more oratorical magnificence, more irony and humor. But the power and the political understanding is all here. A modern historian has called it "one of the best political biographies ever written." An older historian, who had also been prime minister and would himself write about Lord Randolph Churchill, Lord Rosebery, described it as "one of the dozen best, perhaps one of the half-dozen best biographies in the English language." No statesman could hope for a better monument than this.

But the book is not only a family monument. It is also a family credo. A biographer should be in sympathy with his subject. Throughout this biography we see more than sympathy: we see identity of ideals. In defending his father's policy, Winston Churchill is often also outlining his own; in vindicating his father's consistency, he is asserting his own; and he even suggests that his father, had he lived, would have done what he himself had done: "snapped the tie of sentiment that bound him to his party," and become a Liberal. "For all its sense of incompleteness, of tragic interruption," he summed up, Lord Randolph's life "presents a harmony and unity of purpose and view. Verbal consistency is of small value." Lord Randolph's name, he wrote, would not be recalled on the beadroll of either party; but what of that? "A politician's character and position are measured in his day by party standards. When he is dead, all that he achieved in the name of party is at an end. . . . There is an England which stretches far beyond the well-drilled masses who are assembled by party machinery to salute with appropriate acclamation the utterances of their recognized fugelmen . . . It was to that England that Lord Randolph Churchill appealed; it was that England he so nearly won; it is by that England he will be justly judged."

So Winston Churchill, in saluting his Tory father from his own place in the Liberal party, staked out, in advance, his claim to real consistency. For the next few years he continued, as a Liberal, to advocate firm but generous measures, financial retrenchment, social reform. But as so often, social reform was at the mercy of foreign affairs, and foreign affairs entailed heavy expenditure on defense, draining resources away from social reform. Those Edwardian years, which seem in retrospect so opulent and still, were in fact years of growing tension and fierce passions. At home there was the agitation for women's suffrage, much of which was directed personally at Churchill who provocatively opposed it; there was the long constitutional struggle between the Liberal House of Commons and the Tory House of Lords, culminating in a dramatic frontal clash in 1909–1911; and there was the perpetual problem of Irish Home Rule which had once seemed a simple problem of preserving or maintaining the parliamentary union of the two countries, achieved by Pitt in 1800, but which now assumed far greater complexity as Protestant Ulster declared its absolute repudiation of rule from Catholic Dublin, even to the point of civil war.

Meanwhile, abroad, all problems were gradually eclipsed by the aggressive policy of imperial Germany: an aggressive policy whose successive stages were marked by the Kaiser's visit to Tangier, the building of the new German navy, the Austrian annexation of Bosnia-Herzegovina, and, finally, in 1911, the sudden appearance of the German gunboat *Panther* at Agadir. In those years of tension Churchill had held several offices; he had contributed to the social reforms of the Liberal government; he had seen the social program yielding inexorably to the foreign danger; and in 1911, at the time of the Agadir crisis, he found himself transferred from the Home Office, the office of reform, to the Admiralty, the key post of defense. He was then thirty-seven, the same age at which his father had held his key office.

In retrospect, Churchill saw the year 1911 as the beginning of World War I. When it was over, he published his second great work, the first of his two great series of war memoirs: *The World Crisis.*

The World Crisis was published in six successive volumes from 1923 to 1931. It covers the period from 1911 to 1925, from the sudden appearance of the *Panther* at Agadir, which gave the signal to prepare for war, to the Treaty of Locarno, which could be hailed—while it lasted—as "the end of the crisis." These years, incidentally, coincided with Churchill's years of office. From 1911 to 1915, he was First Lord of the Admiralty. In 1915, after the failure of his bold attempt to force the Dardanelles, he was obliged to retire. At that time, the Liberal government was changed into a coalition government of Liberals and Conservatives; and the Conservatives, who had never forgiven Churchill for his "desertion" in 1903, insisted on his exclusion. But in 1917 he returned, as Minister of Munitions, and in 1918, when the war was over, he became Minister of War and Secretary of State for Air. Three years later he was Colonial Secretary. But within a year he lost his seat in Parliament. Two years later he would abandon the Liberal party. It was in this period of enforced idleness, which was also a period of ill-health, that he wrote *The World Crisis.*

The World Crisis is perhaps the greatest work of war memoirs ever written, infinitely superior to the spiteful and tendentious war memoirs of the great but controversial wartime Prime Minister, David Lloyd George. In the fourteen years since he had written the life of his father, Churchill had been in the thick of politics; and they had been exciting, even violent politics too. For the British people did not go united into the war of 1914, as they would go into that of 1939. The issues were less clear; opinion was less prepared; and the political differences roused by the domestic policy of the Liberal government were deep and fierce. The war itself was accepted as necessary by all parties; but the Conservatives detested the Liberals because of their policy of Irish Home Rule, and even within the Liberal party there were deepening rifts between the supporters of Asquith and those of Lloyd George.

The overthrow of Asquith in 1916, and his replacement by Lloyd George as Prime Minister, was the culmination of a conspiracy whose ruthless methods split the Liberal party from top to bottom and have poisoned its memories ever since. Moreover, there were violent differences of opinions on strategy, between the "westerners," who believed that the whole Allied effort must be made on the western front, and the "easterners," who hoped to end it more quickly by turning the German flank in southeast Europe. Finally, these divisions were sharpened by a further division between generals and politicians. Just as, in France, Catholic conservative generals were distrusted by radical anticlerical politicians, so, in Britain, a deep gulf divided Conservative aristocratic generals from the Liberal politicians who, so recently, had broken the powers of the House of Lords and driven the British army into opposition by its Irish policy.

The overriding necessities of war might mask these differences, but they did not, and could not eliminate them; and when victory had at last been obtained, and the war memoirs came out, they were naturally revealed. Every politician had been a partisan; and inevitably his memoirs revealed him as such. None appeared more desperate in his partisanship than the leader who, by sheer political energy, no less dynamic for being so tortuous, had fought his way to supreme power, silenced his critics, defeated the generals, and, in the view of his enthusiastic supporters won the war: Lloyd George.

But Churchill, though he naturally held strong views and had been the advocate of bold and controversial policies, never ceases, even in his political apologia, to be a historian. *The World Crisis,* though frankly a personal narrative, illustrated throughout by personal documents, has a certain magnificent objectivity. Always sitting loose as regarding party, believing parties and the struggle of parties to be a necessary function of politics, but never confined within the orthodoxy of any party, he was able—far abler than Lloyd George—to see the whole struggle as a great historic drama and the actors in it as being, whether right or wrong in their interpretation of it, equally devoted to the interest of their country. Justice is done to every man's views. The arguments of Lord Fisher, the tyrannical First Sea Lord whom Churchill brought back from retirement to serve him at the Admiralty, and who bitterly opposed his project of piercing the eastern front and knocking Turkey out of the war by the landing at the Dardanelles, are fully and fairly set forth. So are the arguments of General Joffre and Lord Kitchener who advocated great western offensives. And so indeed are the arguments of all. So too are their personalities. Every personality is set forth in vivid, unforgettable prose. But it is also set forth justly, indeed magnanimously. There are no flat, conventional eulogies. All the subtleties of character and situation are brought out.

All the resources of language are used. But the judgment is always generous; nor is any man condemned who has failed. Churchill wrote of his own work,

> These chapters will recount the fall from dazzling situations of many eminent men; and it is perhaps worthwhile at this point to place the reader on his guard against unworthy or uncharitable judgments. The Great War wore out or justly or unjustly cast aside leaders in every sphere as lavishly as it squandered the lives of private soldiers —French, Kitchener, Joffre, Nivelle, Cadorna, Jellicoe, Asquith, Briand, Painlevé, and many others, even in the victorious states. All made their contribution and fell. Whatever the pain at the moment to individuals, there are no circumstances of humiliation in such supersessions. Only those who succeeded, who lived through the convulsion and emerged prosperously at the end, know by what obscure twists and turns of chance they escaped a similar lot. Those two impostors, Triumph and Disaster, never played their pranks more shamelessly than in the Great War. When men have done their duty and done their best, have shirked no labor and flinched from no decision that it was their task to take, there is no disgrace in eventual personal failure. They are but good comrades who fall in the earlier stages of an assault, which others, profiting by their efforts and experiences, ultimately carry to victory. [III 30–31]

The World Crisis is a marvelously readable book. Its five volumes are full of vitality and freshness. The style is terse and buoyant, the command of language effortless and easy. It can be criticized, as any personal history can be criticized; but it will never cease to be read. Few great works, once taken up, are so difficult to put down. The finest intellect which ever criticized it was indubitably that of J. M. Keynes, a man who has exercised hardly less influence on the twentieth-century world than Churchill himself and whose command of language was no less than his. Although critical in detail, Keynes's final judgment was firm: *The World Crisis,* he wrote, was "by far and away the greatest contribution to the history of the war, the only one which combines the gifts of the historian and born writer with the profound experiences and direct knowledge of one of the prime movers of events."

When Churchill lost his seat in Parliament in 1922, he was a Liberal, but a disillusioned Liberal. The politics of the war had split the Liberal party, and split it permanently. In 1916, Lloyd George had driven Asquith from power as Prime Minister of the coalition. He had never reconciled him. In 1918, in the "coupon election," which returned the coalition to office, he had used his prestige as "the man who won the war" to exclude from Parliament all those members who had supported Asquith against him. In 1923, at the next general election, the followers of Asquith had their revenge. They supported the socialists and, by their support, put them into power.

It was at this point that Churchill, in disgust, once again changed his party. He returned to Parliament in 1924 a Conservative; and the next year when the Conservatives returned to power, he became, for the first time, a Conservative minister. He was Chancellor of the Exchequer under the Conservative Prime Minister, Stanley Baldwin. His chancellorship has not been judged a success by historians. The most famous criticism came, once again, from J. M. Keynes. In 1920, Keynes had published *The Economic Consequences of the Peace,* his famous attack on the Allied policy of levying "reparations" payments on Germany. In 1925, after Churchill's first budget, which entailed a return to the gold standard, he published a pamphlet entitled *The Economic Consequences of Mr. Churchill.*

In spite of Keynes's criticism, Churchill remained Chancellor of the Exchequer for five years. He fell only with the Tory government in 1929. That year, the second socialist government came to power. It did not last long. Within two years the socialist party was split as the Liberal party had been, and in 1931 the Conservatives returned effectively to power behind the façade of a coalition. But Churchill did not return with them. In 1929, he had differed fundamentally with Baldwin on the subject of India. Baldwin, with his sense of twentieth-century realities, at least in social matters, sought agreement with Indian nationalism as he sought agreement with the trade unions and with socialism. Churchill, with his aristocratic romanticism, wished to defy them all. He had rejected liberalism because it had opened the way to a socialist government. He had thrown himself, with genial gusto, into the task of breaking the general strike of 1926. And he never recognized either the claims of Indian nationalism or the greatness of Gandhi. So, when Baldwin returned to power in alliance with the relics of the Socialist government, no office was offered to Churchill.

"What I should have done if I had been asked to join," he wrote afterward, "I cannot tell. It is superfluous to discuss doubtful temptations that have never existed." For the ten years from 1929 to 1939, he remained out of office, a conservative critic of the government from the back benches of the House of Commons; and in the leisure thus acquired he laid bricks at his country house in Kent, he painted in the south of France, and he wrote.

His output in those years was steady. At first it was nonpolitical. Politics, it seemed, had left him behind. In the eyes of the government, and of the public, he was a figure from the past, a reactionary politician who refused to recognize the realities of the present, whether in Britain or in the empire. And in his writing of those years, he duly turned from the present to the past. First there appeared his own exquisite autobiography, *My Early Years,* which I have already discussed. It was published in 1930. Meanwhile he was writing the character studies which would afterward be published as *Great Contemporaries* (1937). The majority of these were written in the years 1929–1931. And finally, he was engaged on his second great work of family history and rehabilitation, his monumental *Marlborough, His Life and Times.*

Great Contemporaries, like *My Early Life,* shows Churchill's style at its happiest. Here the historian has put off his majestic, formal robes and has portrayed in genial, conversational style a series of men whom, by the accident of his own life, he can describe both as public figures and as human personalities. Many of these men, Asquith and Balfour, Foch and Clemenceau, French and Haig, had already appeared, or were appearing as leading figures in *The World Crisis,* and inevitably these biographical essays sometimes repeat that great work, of which, in a sense, they are a casual outgrowth. They are none the worse for that. Being detached, they are also more perfectly rounded; and they show, in concentrated form, some of their author's greatest gifts: that mastery of human character, and particularly of political character, which has made him so happy in political society, so uneasy in party discipline; that familiarity with the charmed, illuminated circle of politics, and yet that sharp vision which pierces into the dark penumbra beyond it.

Great Contemporaries is the political portrait shown through some of its personalities. It has the mellowness, the indulgent charm of a restrospective portrait. It has also, one might add, something of the disillusion. In 1930, Churchill had repudiated the Liberal party, and in doing so, he repudiated, implicitly, some of his own past. Those who look for them will find, in *Great Contemporaries,* in the judgments on imperialism and Ireland for instance, a very different tone from that which had been used twenty-five years earlier by the Liberal member of Parliament for Dundee, Winston Churchill.

If *Great Contemporaries* is the last by-product of *The World Crisis, Marlborough* is a completely new major venture. Churchill, we have seen, had always been both captivated and repelled by that "prince of literary rogues," Lord Macaulay. On the one hand, he was captivated by his bold, rhetorical narrative style, his sure political judgment, his capacity to recreate the romantic pageantry of the past. On the other hand, he was pained by Macaulay's constant denigration of his own ancestor, the founder of the greatness of his family, the great Duke of Marlborough. But how could Macaulay be refuted? At first, Churchill despaired of refuting him. But then, lunching one day with Lord Rosebery, he found that the refutation had already been achieved. Lord Rosebery showed him the "unknown, out-of-print masterpiece" in which, during Macaulay's lifetime, John Paget, a Liberal lawyer, had exposed Macaulay's misuse of evidence about Marlborough and indeed on several other topics. Macaulay had never answered Paget, and Paget's work, *The New Examen,* dropped into oblivion. Delighted by this discovery, encouraged by both Rosebery and Balfour, Churchill resolved to begin anew: to write a completely new biography of Marlborough from original sources; and, in so doing, to kill forever the "black legend" created by Macaulay. As an episode in this congenial campaign, he published, in 1934, a new edition of Paget's *New Examen.*

From 1929 onwards, Churchill was engaged on this great historical undertaking. For it, he had great advantages, and he spared himself no effort. To him, alone among historians, the archives of Blenheim Palace—Marlborough's own papers—were opened. He traveled (like Macaulay) over every site and every battlefield, gathering local color, local knowledge. He also had valuable assistance from other, more professional scholars. But above all, he had his own knowledge and understanding both of strategy and politics, his own powerful coordinating energy.

It is sometimes said that Churchill, for his historical work, relied on "ghost writers." The statement is quite untrue. In all his work, whether political or historical, Churchill used without stint the labor of other men. He was an exacting, even a ruthless taskmaster. But if other men supplied him with facts or figures, neither his speeches nor his writings owed their literary form and quality to anyone but himself, and great personal care always went into their composition. His speeches he always wrote out in full and then learned by heart. His books he dictated and then, in type or in proof, corrected again and again. Thus, and only thus, could that sonorous style have been achieved: a style which, like that of Gibbon or Macaulay, is measured by the ear of the writer and enters the understanding through the ear, not the eye, of the reader. Such a style is intensely personal; it is the expression of a personality, a mind; and *Marlborough,* for all the professional assistance on which it rests, is as authentic and original a work of Churchill as *The Life of Lord Randolph Churchill* or *The World Crisis.*

It is also a major work of history. The four stout volumes which began to appear in 1933 may have struck some critics as too large, and others as too apologetic. But when all the qualifications are made, the achievement remains. This is not merely an elaborate exercise in ancestor worship. It is history in the grand style. And its historical conclusions have passed the test of time. By universal consent, Macaulay's Marlborough, that stage villain of his Glorious Revolution, has passed into the world of fiction; Churchill's Marlborough has replaced him. And if Churchill's Marlborough shines, at times, with an almost unnatural brightness, we do not, for that reason, reject him: we merely discount a little of the amiable partiality of a descendant.

Marlborough was begun in a time of international tranquillity, in those few years after the Treaty of Locarno when Churchill himself believed that the world crisis was over at last. This happy illusion did not last long. In 1933, Hitler came to power in Germany. Almost at once all eyes were drawn toward Central Europe and the specter of a new war, a war of revenge, began to haunt the minds of statesmen, casting its shadow even across purely historical work. In 1935, Churchill added a thoughtful essay on Hitler to the essays he was collecting for *Great Contemporaries.* Europe, he suggested, deserved Hitler. "I have always laid down the doctrine that the redress of the grievances of the vanquished should precede the disarmament of the victors." But this had not been done, and now the price was being paid. By "a prodigy in the history of the world, and a prodigy which is inseparable from the personal exertions and life-thrust of a single man," the tables had been "completely turned upon the complacent, feckless and purblind victors."

And what would Hitler do with the

power he had built up? Would he, like some other men who had secured power by "stern, grim and even frightful methods" turn away from violence to constructive policies? Recently, indeed, he had offered "many words of reassurance, eagerly lapped up by those who have been so tragically wrong about Germany in the past." But Churchill clearly was not convinced. He saw the record of crime in the past; he saw the vast rearmament of Germany gaining momentum; and he would accept no easy assurances.

Meanwhile, in his *Marlborough,* he was portraying the figure of Louis XIV, "the curse and pest of Europe," whose insatiable appetite for conquest was resisted only by the Grand Alliance forged by William III and led to victory by Marlborough. *Marlborough,* begun as the vindication of a traduced ancestor, was becoming the program of a new policy for a later Churchill.

So began the greatest period of Churchill's career: the period first as prophet, then as leader, of European resistance to Hitler. The prophet began in the wilderness. In the years from 1933 to 1939, Churchill was absolutely without power. Even his long record of political activity was held against him. To the socialists he was the romantic, aristocratic, backward-looking imperialist, the strikebreaker of 1926; to the Conservative followers of Stanley Baldwin and Neville Chamberlain he was "a man of no judgment," who shifted from party to party and whose initiative in politics, though often spectacular, had never, in their eyes, been right.

As Hitler consolidated his power in Europe, Conservatives and socialists alike were infuriated by the one man who constantly called for resistance, and for the practical methods of resistance, before it was too late. The socialists deplored Hitler but refused to rearm; the Conserva-

tives insisted that, having acquired power, having restored Germany to independence and self-sufficiency, Hitler would be "sated" and could be "appeased." And if he were "appeased," and the economic and human waste of war, or even of effective rearmament, avoided, then Britain could concentrate on domestic and imperial issues.

To a people who longed for peace, Neville Chamberlain promised that his methods would bring peace. Those of Churchill, he insisted, would bring war. And Hitler, who dreaded the advent to power of Churchill, echoed his words. With the peace-loving Chamberlain, he said, he could negotiate; but how could he be sure that England would always be ruled by a Chamberlain? Was not the "warmonger" Churchill always waiting in the wings? Therefore, as a mere precaution, he must rearm, rearm, rearm.

Against this united front Churchill had at first only one weapon: his command of language. From 1933 onward he delivered that great series of speeches which gradually awoke the nation and enabled him, as aggression succeeded aggression in Europe, to stand forth as its predestined deliverer. In vain the "appeasers" sought to justify their policy. On one hand, Hitler's own acts, on the other hand, Churchill's words, were more eloquent than anything the appeasers could say. The crucial moment came in 1938, with the Munich agreement. To enthusiastic crowds, Chamberlain claimed that it meant "peace in our time." But amid the universal relief caused by what seemed an escape from war, the warning voice of Churchill struck a sobering note. "All over Europe," he declared, "the lights are going out."

Hitler had said that the Sudetenland, which had now been given to him, was his "last territorial demand." Chamberlain had believed him. Churchill did not. "Do not suppose," he declared, "that this is the end. This is only the beginning of the reckoning. This is only the first sip, the first foretaste of a bitter cup which will be offered to us year by year unless, by a supreme recovery of moral health and martial vigor, we arise again and take our stand for freedom as in olden time."

Six months later, Churchill was proved right. Hitler suddenly seized the whole of Czechoslovakia. At that moment scales everywhere fell from blinded eyes. There was a growing public demand that Churchill be admitted to the government. Chamberlain resisted to the end. Only when war was actually declared did he offer Churchill his old post of First Lord of the Admiralty. Six months later, when Hitler conquered Norway and invaded France, Chamberlain himself was swept away in the ruins of his policy. Even as he recognized defeat, he hoped to avoid Churchill as his successor. But by now neither Parliament nor the nation would have accepted any other successor. And Churchill himself was confident, even in disaster. After receiving the King's commission, he wrote,

I was conscious of a profound sense of relief. At last I had the authority to give directions over the whole scene. I felt as if I were walking with destiny, and that all my past life had been but a preparation for this hour and for this trial. Ten years in the political wilderness had freed me from ordinary party antagonisms. My warnings over the last six years had been so numerous, so detailed, and were now so terribly vindicated, that no one could gainsay me. I could not be reproached either for making the war or with want of preparation for it. I thought I knew a good deal about it and I was sure I should not fail.

Churchill's great ministry, during 1940–1945, is a chapter of world history.

It is the history of World War II, from the first campaign in the west to the final victory of the allies. When he took over power, that victory seemed impossible, and his first task was to convince the world that, in spite of the avalanche of disasters which had overwhelmed the allies, ultimate victory was not only possible but would be won. In the darkest days of 1940, by the greatest of all his speeches, he inspired and canalized the determination of the British people as no one, perhaps, has ever done before. The people hung on his words, and in the bombed cities which he visited they struggled, in the words of Roosevelt's envoy Harry Hopkins, "to touch the hem of his garment." Nor was it only the British people whom he inspired. The uncommitted world listened and was convinced that British resistance was worth supporting. Around that nucleus a "Grand Alliance" could gradually be built up to destroy the new tyranny which threatened to conquer the world.

But war leadership does not consist only in speeches. Churchill always believed, and he soon convinced others, that he could not only lead the British people but lead them out of disaster to victory. He had, of course, the immense advantage of his experience in World War I. That experience had also left certain abiding convictions. Churchill always believed that his attempt to force the Dardanelles in 1915, in spite of its failure, was basically sound strategy, and in World War II he was always anxious—too anxious, his critics said—to repeat it.

A more fundamental lesson of 1914–1918 concerned the relations between the government and the generals. In World War I, Lloyd George had never felt sure of his generals. Although he himself had lost confidence in Haig, he was afraid to dismiss a general who enjoyed, as he himself did not, the universal respect of the army and of the people. He therefore undermined him, and by doing so, poisoned the relations between the government and army and weakened his own authority. From the beginning of his ministry, Churchill (as he admitted) was determined that no general was to have the ascendancy which Haig had exercised in World War I. The authority of the civil government was to be absolute. And in fact he made it absolute. His own moral authority was, of course, infinitely greater than that of Lloyd George. But he also took his generals into his confidence. The working out of strategy involved some fierce struggles between them; but Churchill knew when to insist, when to yield. To the combined opposition of the Chiefs of Staff he always ultimately yielded; and by his understanding he gained their respect and the authority to impose his view in all other circumstances. World War II is unique in the harmony between government and services, as it is also in the continuity of persons at the center of strategy; and this, as well as the political and strategic success which made it possible, must be ascribed principally to the character of the man who directed policy and strategy alike.

Churchill's speeches, both before and during the war, have all been published. Oratory is always difficult to separate from the occasion which called it forth and the atmosphere in which it was delivered; and no one can feel now quite the same electric impulse which those speeches created at the time. Nevertheless, even in cold print, they retain much of their power. For the speeches of Churchill, unlike those of most of the orators who have moved men, are literary works. The magnificent periods are constructed with consummate art, the result of a lifelong devotion to the English language. Again and again, in casual utterances, Churchill has shown his in-terest in every detail of language: his hatred of "jargon," of "modern vulgarisms," of particular words; his love of clarity, simplicity, brevity ("short words are best and the old words when short are best of all"); and yet, at the same time, he has intense sophistication, perfectly constructed periods, skillful alternation of colloquial with classical forms, sudden elaborate latinisms or ornate polysyllables which interrupt the hammer stroke of short, emphatic, Saxon words.

Churchill's devotion to the language is vividly illustrated by a minute, or memorandum, which he issued in August 1940, in the hour of Britain's greatest danger, when invasion was daily expected. This minute was addressed to his cabinet colleagues and to the heads of departments of the civil service, and it called upon them, in their official papers, to use good, clear, correct English. "Let us have an end of . . . woolly phrases . . . mere padding. . . . Let us not shrink from using the short expressive phrase, even if it is conversational." In 1940, Churchill sought to save not only England but English; and it can be said that he sought to save them both by example as well as by precept.

When the victory was at last won, Churchill, to his own astonishment, fell from power. In 1945, the electorate, while profuse in its demonstrations of gratitude and affection to him personally, calmly declared its preference for a Labor government. To the electorate, Conservatism was still the Conservatism of Baldwin and Chamberlain, and Churchill was the romantic but reactionary genius whom those men had excluded from power until forced by the necessities of war. But now, thanks to him, peace had returned; and peace required different counsels. So, in Churchill's own words, "I was dismissed by the British electorate from all further conduct of affairs." However, this dismissal gave him leisure; and once again, as in 1922–1926, he took up his pen to record the history of which he had been so large a part. The years 1922–1926 had been devoted to the five volumes of *The World Crisis;* the years 1945–1953 were devoted to the six volumes of new war memoirs, *The Second World War.*

The Second World War is an essential historical document. Some critics maintain that, in comparison with *The World Crisis,* it is too much of a document: its documentation sometimes impedes the text. But this fault, if it is a fault, is implicit in its virtues. In World War I, Churchill had not been in command. He had been a partisan indeed—after 1915, a defeated and rejected partisan—and his advocacy in *The World Crisis,* for all its magnanimous objectivity, is advocacy still. In World War II there were—thanks to far abler, more generous leadership—no internecine issues, and Churchill himself, in Hopkins's words, was "the government in every sense of the word." Such controversies as there were, were debates among allies: they were never feuds within a government; and therefore the second war memoirs are far less personal than the first, far more of an official history.

Nevertheless, the personality constantly breaks through—more especially in the first volume, which deals with the whole period from the Treaty of Versailles in 1919 to Churchill's accession to power in May 1940. And of course there is the style, which is the same as ever: clear and direct in purpose, magnificent in sweep, with the great purple passages which sometimes tremble on the verge of fustian, only to be saved, just in time, by the unfailing Churchillian virtues of humanity, humor, and irony. Altogether, *The Second World War* is a work worthy of its subject: the personal, and yet objective account of the greatest war ever fought, by the man whose courage, statesmanship, and strategy turned defeat into victory.

The writing of *The Second World War* did not exclude other activities during the years of the Labor government. Churchill was leader of the opposition, and active in public affairs. It was in those years, in particular, that he delivered two famous speeches which show him as great a prophet in peace as in war. The first was delivered in America, at Fulton, Missouri, and warned the American people, then enjoying a honeymoon period of Russophilia, that Stalin was building up in eastern Europe and Asia a power no less ominous and threatening than Hitler's power in Central Europe had been. This speech was very ill-received at the time. Had it been better understood, the American people would perhaps not have yielded to such panic measures when Russian aggression in Korea, four years later, taught the same lesson in a more forcible manner.

The second famous speech was delivered soon afterward at Zurich. It was a plea for union of the old states of Europe in the face of the great continental power which overshadowed them in the east. This plea has since been heard and accepted—in part.

The period as leader of the opposition ended in 1951. In that year the Labor government in Britain was defeated and Churchill became, for the second time, Prime Minister. After four years he retired and was succeeded by Sir Anthony Eden. He was now in his eightieth year, and it seemed time to retire, at least from politics.

But not from literature. Before laying down his pen Churchill had one old ambition to fulfill. Himself half-American, and convinced that the future of the world depended on cooperation between Britain and America, he had planned to follow up his work on Marlborough with a complete history, not of Britain only, but of "the English-speaking peoples." Munich and its terrible consequences naturally suspended that project; but twenty years later, when war and war memoirs alike were victoriously completed, a fresh period of leisure enabled him to resume the half-completed task. And he resumed it with all the old energy. Between 1956 and 1958, there appeared the four successive volumes of *The History of the English Speaking Peoples*.

The History of the English Speaking Peoples, like all Churchill's historical writing, is accurate, even professional, in its standards. As always, professional assistance was called in, and the most carping critic would find it difficult to discover errors of fact. The criticism that can be leveled is of another kind. Historical science, in professional hands, has changed since the days of Macaulay and Michelet. New forces have been explored, and new dimensions given to it. Economics, sociology, anthropology are now called in to illustrate and explain the progress and decline of nations, the rise of ideologies, the crises of structure. Those who seek such explanations will not find them in Churchill's writing. On the other hand, these modern historians seldom present their new discoveries in very readable form. Having turned history into a science, they have, too often, buried it in scientific jargon. They have forgotten that, if history is a science, historiography is an art.

Churchill's historiography is always a work of art, and in this last work, which sets out frankly to tell a story—and a success story at that—the old methods are revived with all the old virtues. Here is the history of England, of Britain, of the English and British colonies, and of their common development from the be-

ginning to 1900, told by a romantic statesman as an eloquent, but also accurate story. It is not a story of economic growth or social change but a story of kings and statesmen, battles and crises. And as such it is second to none; and it will doubtless be read long after the more pioneering, more technical writings of his professional rivals are forgotten.

The Life of Lord Randolph Churchill, The World Crisis, My Early Life, Great Contemporaries, Marlborough, the great war speeches from 1938 to 1945, *The Second World War*, and perhaps *The History of the English Speaking Peoples*, these are the great literary works of Winston Churchill. There are other lesser works too, which I have not mentioned: political pamphlets on emergent topics; miscellaneous parliamentary speeches; casual studies—sometimes charming studies such as his little book on his own private hobby of painting. And there are also the Apocrypha: books which are often wrongly ascribed to him, such as the works of the other Winston Churchill. For there was another Winston Churchill, an American novelist whose works—*The Crisis, The Crossing, Richard Carvel*—were popular in America at the time when the English Winston Churchill was beginning his career. Fortunately, the English Churchill soon discovered the existence of his namesake and to avoid confusion, undertook always to sign himself "Winston S. Churchill": this signature, and only this signature, is the guarantee of authenticity. But it is by these great works that he will always be remembered as a man of letters. They are enough to make any literary reputation, and a great reputation too. It takes an effort to believe that they are the spare-time production of the greatest statesman of our time.

Hugh Trevor-Roper, a prominent English writer on current affairs and a specialist on World War II, is professor of history at Oxford University.

THE 1953 PRIZE

By KJELL STRÖMBERG

ON OCCASION, the Swedish Academy has surprised everyone by its choice of Nobel laureates. It happened in 1953, when after awards for literature to Per Lagerkvist and François Mauriac in the preceding two years, the Academy chose Sir Winston Churchill. Whatever may have been the literary merits of this extraordinary laureate, it is certain that for most people throughout the world he was chiefly, if not exclusively, the great statesman who had been the architect of victory in the greatest of all wars. Another point was that, after six years out of power, Churchill had become once again Prime Minister of Great Britain in 1951, and it was generally believed that the Swedish Academy had assumed a tacit obligation not to crown any writer who was either holding a government position or playing a political role of first rank in his country at the time his candidacy might be presented.

This time the Academy ignored such considerations. Churchill had been proposed for the Nobel Prize for Literature —and probably for the peace prize as well—as early as 1946, after having been forced out of power by the Labor party in the 1945 elections. The Nobel Committee had had plenty of time in which to crown him during this period when he was only a member of Parliament and leader of His Britannic Majesty's loyal

opposition and decidedly a writer by profession. His six years of involuntary leisure had been devoted to composing six powerful volumes of notes and memoirs on the Second World War, of which the last was published in 1953. Perhaps the Swedish Academy had decided to wait until this full stop had been put to an entire life's work (almost half a century) as historian and writer of memoirs before awarding him a Nobel Prize.

Churchill's name was first thought of in connection with the Prize by the Swedish. In later years, this candidacy, which quickly became popular, was proposed again and again, almost exclusively by Swedish writers and historians. Several of these were members of the Academy, and they were quick to settle on this name, which by midcentury was illustrious above all others. Even so, it was passed through a fine critical sieve by two reporting Academicians.

The first report on the candidate, written by the aged Per Hallström, former permanent secretary of the Academy, was rather negative in its conclusions. He found no literary merit whatever in the little adventure novel entitled *Savrola,* which a youthful Lieutenant Churchill had written to relieve the boredom of garrison life in India when there was no enemy to fight. Although his first attempt at autobiography, a self-portrait based on childhood memories (*My Early Life*), is not entirely lacking in charm, or in artistic quality, in Hallström's opinion, only the four-volume biography of his great ancestor Marlborough, the conqueror of Louis XIV, can serve as a basis for a judgment of Churchill as a historian. He dismissed *The World Crisis,* Churchill's highly praised account of the First World War, as history. Recalling that only Theodor Mommsen had been judged worthy of a Nobel Prize for his work as a historian, the reporter asked the historians among his Academy colleagues whether the award of such a distinction based on only the Marlborough biography could really be defended.

Two years later, in 1948, Professor Nils Ahnlund of the Swedish Academy answered his venerable colleague in preparing a second report, which was not limited to his own opinions of Churchill's historical works. First of all he referred to Professor George Trevelyan of Cambridge University, an eminent authority on English history in Marlborough's period. A great admirer of Churchill's work, Trevelyan was himself to propose Churchill for the Nobel Prize in spite of the violent abuse which Churchill had heaped upon the celebrated historian Macaulay who was Trevelyan's great-uncle and the first biographer of Marlborough.

Unlike Hallström, Ahnlund stressed the great documentary value of Churchill's magnificent work on World War I. At no place in the exceptionally rich historical literature on that war, he observed, was the true pulse of the age to be sensed so well or the direct breath of the great events to be felt so clearly. To create such impressions called above all for outstanding literary and artistic qualities, and in Ahnlund's opinion Churchill was the incomparable painter of the history of our time. And yet, he concluded,

perhaps his historical work could not, by itself, justify the award of the Nobel Prize. But if his literary reputation were to be reinforced by his activity as an orator, there would be no doubt that he would fulfill the conditions of the Prize, for Churchill was an orator without a peer in his century. "No man has better known how to awaken such an echo by his eloquence, or to reach so vast a public," Ahnlund commented. "It is, then, basically for his oratory that Churchill deserves the Prize; but his art as an orator is well framed by the rest of his production."

In spite of this extremely favorable second report, the Academy eventually waited another five years before yielding to the appeals which came with ever greater urgency from all corners of the globe. In 1953, Churchill not only received the Nobel Prize, but also, at the time of the Queen's coronation, was awarded knighthood in the Order of the Garter.

Competition for the Nobel Prize that year was not particularly fierce. The Swedish Pen Club, under its very active president Prince William, had had good luck with its choices in previous years, but for the moment it confined itself to backing once again the choice of its British counterpart—E. M. Forster. Included among the twenty-five remaining contenders were the American Ernest Hemingway, the Icelandic writer Halldór Laxness, and the Spaniard Juan Ramón Jiménez; all three were successively to win the Prize in the following years. At any rate, they did not offer a serious threat to Churchill's candidacy. On October 15, the Prize was voted to him "for his mastery of historical and biographical descriptions as well as for brilliant oratory in defending exalted human values."

Because of the particular position of the new laureate, the Academy gave a flexible interpretation to its rule, always scrupulously respected before, concerning the secrecy of the vote until the final count. Thus Churchill was approached through diplomatic channels several days before the final count to learn whether he would be disposed to accept the Prize. The Prime Minister replied without hesitation that he would be deeply honored. He told the Swedish Ambassador to London, Gunnar Hägglöf, when the latter went to No. 10 Downing Street to confirm the Academy's decision, that he especially appreciated such an award for his literary work. He would be delighted to go to Stockholm to thank the Committee personally, to present his respects to "the illustrious and learned Swedish Academy," and to admire the beauties of the city—the only European capital which, to his regret, he had never visited. Then he added that being almost eighty, he was obliged to ration his strength and to limit his participation in the Nobel Prize festivities—no public address, except for a few words of thanks at the banquet following the distribution of the Prizes, and no press conferences. He would of course attend the traditional dinner given by the King, whose guest he was to be during his entire stay in Stockholm, and he hoped to do considerable sightseeing.

Unfortunately, even this limited program could not be carried out. Much to the disappointment of everyone in Sweden, the great statesman was held up by an international conference in the Bermuda Islands, where President Eisenhower had summoned English and French leaders to discuss certain questions regarding the mutual defense of Europe following the death of Stalin and the first experiences of atomic warfare. Instead, Lady Clementine Churchill went to Sweden with her youngest daughter, Mrs. Mary Soames, to represent her illustrious husband at the Nobel Prize festivities.

Lady Churchill and Mrs. Soames were guests of the King. During the banquet at the Stockholm Town Hall, following the ceremony of the distribution of the Prizes, she read her husband's acceptance speech—a charming address in which Churchill's delightful humor counterpointed his graver statements, which were often moving. The speech was heard in a deep silence by a gathering of nearly a thousand and greeted with a veritable thunder of applause.

Translated by Dale McAdoo.